NAVAL
SHIPHANDLING

Operational requirements put a premium on skillful shiphandling as USS Hooper *and* USS Chemung *maneuver in heavy weather.*

NAVAL
SHIPHANDLING

Third Edition

By Captain R. S. Crenshaw, Jr., USN

United States Naval Institute
Annapolis, Maryland

PRINTED IN UNITED STATES OF AMERICA

BY GEORGE BANTA COMPANY, INC., MENASHA, WISCONSIN

INTRODUCTION

FROM THE EARLIEST DAYS of our Navy it has been recognized that, among other desirable qualifications for a great ship commander, the following requisites are paramount: he must first of all be a fighting leader of men, and then, to a very high degree, an exceptional tactician, an able gunnery officer, and last but not least, an expert shiphandler.

In the days of sail and John Paul Jones it was the most skillful shiphandler who placed his ship in the most advantageous fighting position in relation to his opponent. The weather gage and the raking position, combined with superior gunnery and the will to fight, usually determined the victor in single-ship duels—as they did also in fleet actions, as was so convincingly demonstrated by Nelson at the Nile and Trafalgar. Our own Paul Jones gave an excellent illustration of how a determined and skillful captain could win victory although his BONHOMME RICHARD was inferior in most respects to the SERAPIS, and Dewey was equally successful at Manila.

Knowledge of the sea in all its moods is a prime requirement of the successful commander. Such knowledge and experience can be acquired only by going to sea in all kinds of ships. Many of our great naval captains began their seagoing in merchant ships. Paul Jones, Hull, and David Porter were experienced mariners before they served in naval vessels. They learned at an early age that the sea is an unrelenting taskmaster who speedily eliminates the weak and inefficient but richly rewards the skilled and daring mariners. The transition from sail to steam made little change in the courage and skills required. On the contrary, the great advances in speeds and tonnages of varied types of vessels imposed even higher qualifications on successful commanders. The skillful commander will bring his ship unscathed through all kinds of weather and sea conditions, fit to fight without the necessity for "voyage repairs." Good shiphandling includes the exercise of good judgment in preventing damage due to adverse sea conditions or inept handling in harbors and around docks.

Notwithstanding the fact that skill in shiphandling cannot be acquired from books alone, it is none the less important that there be assembled for the beginner all available and pertinent information relating to this subject. This the Naval Institute has endeavored to do in NAVAL SHIPHANDLING, which represents the efforts and experience of many officers over a long period of years. It will be of value and interest not only to the naval profession, but to the Coast Guard and Merchant Marine as well, particularly as these great organizations work so closely with the Navy in time of war, and have contributed so much in experience to the preparation of this book. Credit is also due to our master pilots and to the smallboat sailors of the U.S. Power Squadrons of America, and to numerous amateur yachtsmen who are all specialists in handling small craft under every condition.

NAVAL SHIPHANDLING cannot fail to benefit all seamen everywhere, just as the knowledge and experience of seamen everywhere have contributed to the preparation of this book.

Fleet Admiral, U.S. Navy

FOREWORD

IN THE VAST COMPLEXITY of the Navy today, the practice of shiphandling has suffered because so much of the effort of the individual officer has been called to other duties. To the traditional fields of Navigation, Seamanship, Gunnery, and Engineering have been added the expanding fields of Operations, Communications, Missiles, Electronics, Amphibious, Air, and Submarine Operations, and a host of others, until it is all one can do to keep a minimum acquaintance with all the fields of Naval Science. Although the field of Seamanship has expanded as steadily, if not as spectacularly, as the other fields to meet the increased scope of activity of the Fleet today, the Seamanship experience of the individual officer is less than in former years.

In the "good old days" an officer learned his shiphandling by serving under and observing the "masters of the art." All officers at sea were engaged in deck duties, and the measure of an officer's ability was largely a measure of his ability at shiphandling. There were relatively few officers even on large ships, so all officers had a good opportunity to become expert in the fascinating art.

This book has been prepared to present the fundamentals of shiphandling as required in today's complex operations. In it the author has attempted to review the principles of shiphandling and to offer sound techniques for the solutions of the problems normally encountered. He has tried to offer a "why" along with each explanation of "how." The author's intention is to arm the reader with the principles involved and to prepare him for employing them intelligently, rather than to offer specific solutions to certain problems and then leave it to the reader to deduce the principles.

It is obviously impossible to assemble in one book all that is known on the subject of shiphandling. It was intended that the book cover the field adequately, yet care had to be taken to insure that it would not be bogged down by the sheer mass of information presented. Consequently, for each evolution there is usually presented only one method of solving the problem. One of the first things an officer learns at sea is that there are usually several adequate solutions to each problem. In each case in this book the author has selected for presentation that solution which he prefers. In some cases the superiority of the method presented is believed to be absolute and clear-cut, but in many cases the author freely admits that there are other methods equally as good. In all cases the method presented in this book has been tried and found to be sound.

Since the Captain and the Officer of the Deck have to meet the same problems when they have the conn, this book has been written as though the author and the reader were standing together on the bridge of the ship under discussion and are exploring the problem of the conning officer. It is hoped thereby that the book will meet the needs of officers of all grades and extent of experience.

Finally, this work is dedicated to the thesis that shiphandling is the mastering of physical objects by the use of physical forces; that it is a science that can be mastered by the application of an alert mind to the principles involved and is not an occult art requiring an inborn talent for its mastery.

Inasmuch as physical principles embodying physical forces are technical in nature, it is impossible to treat them without certain technical terms and approaches. Therefore an understanding of the material in Chapter II—"Forces Affecting the Ship"—is absolutely necessary for anyone who aspires to be a competent shiphandler. However, every effort has been made to use such simple terms and explanations, with liberal diagrams, that any layman can read with ready comprehension. A more detailed technical explanation is available in the Appendix for those further advanced who wish to know more of the physics involved.

There is no good reason why any officer who will apply himself to the examination of the objects and forces involved, and who will take the time to study and master the principles, can not become a competent shiphandler. Experience is a necessary ingredient in producing a competent shiphandler, but no amount of experience can substitute for a thorough understanding of the problem.

UNITED STATES NAVAL INSTITUTE

PREFACE TO THE THIRD EDITION

THE PRINCIPAL CHANGES in this edition reflect requirements of the 1960 Revision of the International Rules of the Road, which became effective on 1 September 1965. In addition, considerable up-dating has been done, generally as a result of my experience in command of USS *Springfield* (CLG-7). The assistance of my Navigator, Lieutenant Commander G. W. Stanley, USN, and my Gunnery Officer, Commander Dwight Wadsworth, USN, in this respect, has been especially appreciated.

For the revision of Chapter XX, "Rules of the Road," valuable assistance was found in the analysis of recent changes prepared by Lieutenant Commander Otto W. Will, III, USN, for his book, *Simplified Rules of the Nautical Road*. Additional reference material on this subject was furnished by the Rules of the Road Section, U. S. Coast Guard Headquarters.

To name all those who have contributed to previous editions would, at this point, require listing every major command in the fleet, as well as most flag officers, many present commanding officers, and innumerable offices throughout the Navy Department. Without a great deal of comment and criticism, both specific and unsolicited, the preparation of this work would have been very nearly beyond the ability of any one person. The widespread interest in the work and in its continued effectiveness indicates the high professional pride in the fine art of shiphandling which is traditional in the United States Navy.

R. S. CRENSHAW, JR.
Captain, U. S. Navy

TABLE OF CONTENTS

xiii

LIST OF ILLUSTRATIONS

All photographs are official Navy Department releases unless otherwise noted.

CHAPTER I

SEAMAN'S EYE

THE DESTROYER rounds the buoy and stands smartly up the harbor. She is lean and graceful as her powerful engines drive her along, and her clean lines seem to speak of her capacity to meet any task assigned her and to do it well. The men on deck are quick and alert as they complete their preparations for mooring, and the Captain on the bridge has the easy confidence of a man who has been tried and proven.

She slows as she arrives at the congested part of the harbor, and then in one broad sweep she approaches the nest which is to be her berth for the night. Gently she is brought to a stop exactly abreast her nestmate, the lines go over smartly, she moves in broadside until she is moored securely, and in minutes the Captain's absentee pennant is fluttering from the yardarm, signifying his day's work is done.

The entire evolution was carried out smoothly without a faltering step. The wind and current were judged exactly; every engine and rudder order was timed perfectly to bring the ship in to the desired position. The 180° swing was so graceful that the casual observer hardly noticed the obstacles which lined the path; the shoal water to port, the two mooring buoys in mid-channel, or the nest of destroyers which nearly blocked the approach. The timing and sense of position was so deft that one hardly noticed how extensively her nestmate had been yawing just before she came alongside. The destroyer skipper's excellent shiphandling had made an easy job of a difficult maneuver.

How did he do it? What inner sense told him when to shift his rudder, when to stop his engines? How did he judge his distances, how could he tell his speed?

Seafaring men have long had a name for it. They call it "Seaman's eye."

Before we dismiss this term as connoting some extrasensory ability on the part of real deepwater seamen, let's take a look at it. What is "Seaman's eye" and how does one go about acquiring it?

The expression has a much broader meaning than that of attributing a certain visual ability to a person. Actually, the human eye is at its worst at sea. In the vast expanse of water the distance to objects cannot be determined by the relation to known objects because of the general lack of the latter. At sea the range can be judged by the dip below the horizon, but even experienced mariners make large errors in estimating ranges at sea. Unaided, the eye of even the most experienced seaman is often erratic.

1

"Seaman's eye" is rather an expression of competence at sea. It is an expression connoting judgment and understanding. The Captain with a reputation for "Seaman's Eye" is one who can marshal all the information on the situation available to him, combine it with his intimate knowledge of his ship and her characteristics, and take his course of action with the judgment of the Master Mariner. This judgment is made up of intelligence, knowledge of ships and the sea, and an understanding of the physics of shiphandling.

Regardless of the special qualifications of a Line officer, the real source of his reputation is his ability to command at sea. One can be the most able engineer in the Fleet or the most successful gunner, but when the tales of great officers are swapped in the wardroom the most telling mark of the admired officer is his reputation as a shiphandler. A skipper might have many shortcomings, but if he is really the master of his ship, he is a success in the hearts of his officers and his men. Shiphandling ability is the common denominator of all real naval officers. It is the ultimate measure of expertness in seamanship, and it is the universal figure of merit in establishing an officer's ability as a mariner.

The ship itself derives her reputation largely from the skill with which she is handled. The ship may excel in spirit, she may break all the records in gunnery, she may be the best in the Fleet in CIC, or she may be a marvel of engineering efficiency, but these achievements might be known only to those few on the staff who keep the records or by the limited few who are aware of the relative standings of the ships of the Fleet. Just how USS TUSCARORA made her landing at the fuel dock yesterday is common knowledge in the harbor. A ship famed for excellent maneuvers will draw a crowd of admiring critics each time she makes a landing or snatches a buoy, and her skipper is the unofficial hero of the port. A ship noted for careless seamanship or indifferent handling will deserve the scorn of the crews of her nestmates. She will be greeted by cries of "Clear the side!" or "Watch out, George, she's coming around again!" Her sailors will have to defend the dubious reputation of an inept Captain. Her Captain must endure the indifference accorded one of little ability. Good seamanship is the hallmark of Naval ability, and good shiphandling is the means available to the officer to demonstrate his ability in this field.

Acquiring Seaman's Eye

If ability at shiphandling is so important to a naval officer, how then does one acquire it? How can the junior officer prepare himself for his opportunity at command? Can he learn shiphandling from books, or is it an undefined art that can only be acquired through long years of association?

In the first place, a ship is a physical body that responds in a normal way to the forces brought to bear upon it. If we study the manner in which the ship responds to a certain type of force, and we study the source and characteristics of the force, we will be able to predict when the force will be present and what effect it will have on the ship. When we have acquired a complete understanding of the forces that come to bear on our ship and have explored the reaction of our ship to all of the different forces, we will be prepared to anticipate her movement under any set of conditions. A firm understanding of physical principles is the foundation upon which excellence in ship-handling must be based.

Consideration and study of the physical forces is not enough; the ship-handler must be familiar with the environment of the sea and he must have experience in handling ships if he is to acquire the judgment to correctly evaluate the conditions. How can the novice estimate the effect of the wind in approaching a buoy? How can he be expected to comprehend the world of relative motion into which he is suddenly thrust as his ship joins a complex formation? It takes years of experience on the bridge of an operating ship before an officer becomes accustomed to all of the situations in which his ship might be placed.

If such long experience is necessary to form the basis for the judgment needed by the shiphandler, perhaps one can only learn from experience. Perhaps this is a field in which only a long apprenticeship can properly prepare the aspirant. Perhaps the only solution is to observe the masters at their work and learn to follow their example.

Shiphandling, however, is one skill that cannot be mastered by imitation. One could watch a Master Mariner make a hundred perfect landings at a pier, but unless he understood the principles being employed, he could not go out and repeat the performance. No two evolutions are the same. There is always a difference of wind, current, or in the execution of a command; and the shiphandler must be able to evaluate when these changes occur and must be ready to make the necessary correction.

Shiphandling cannot be taught by example alone. Though it is highly interesting to learn how some other shiphandler solved his problem under a certain set of conditions, we might search forever to find an identical situation. The simple explanation of "what" was done is not useful in preparing us for our problems unless we have a clear understanding of "why" the action was taken.

The best preparation for handling the ship, then, is a combination of a study of the principles involved and sufficient experience at sea to be able to evaluate the situation. Neither extensive experience nor theoretical understanding can stand alone. The competent shiphandler must have both.

Preparing for Command

There is a difference between having spent time on a ship at sea and having acquired experience at shiphandling. Officers should seize every opportunity presented to actually maneuver the ship. Commanding officers should insure that all officers are given a chance to acquire the necessary basic experience. No matter what the evolution, having had the conn and maneuvered the ship for a few minutes is a valuable piece of experience.

Not only should all opportunities for shiphandling by junior officers be seized, they should be created. The wise skipper is the one who schedules ample time for "box drill" so that all officers have the opportunity of making practice landings. Occasionally when operations permit, a period should be set aside for maneuvering close alongside another ship or making approaches on a buoy. A morning spent allowing officers to make practice landings at a pier will pay big dividends, not only in shiphandling ability but also in enthusiasm for the task. No matter how much an officer has considered "how he would do the job" and observed others actually doing it, there is nothing so instructive as actually doing it himself.

Another aspect of the necessity of preparing young officers to become competent shiphandlers is that, as an officer becomes more senior, it is automatically assumed that he has this ability until proved otherwise. He is assigned duties in accordance with his seniority and not necessarily in accordance with his qualifications. It is assumed that at a given seniority he is a competent shiphandler, and if this is not so, serious consequences can ensue. An officer who was denied the opportunity for experience in shiphandling during his junior years may suddenly find himself placed in command of a ship on a difficult mission. His inadequacy may have serious consequences. It is of the utmost importance that every opportunity be seized to train all officers in this most important phase of their duties.

A System of Shiphandling

Having recognized the importance of shiphandling and considered the means through which this skill is acquired, we should explore the methods by which one arrives at a satisfactory solution to a shiphandling problem. If we understand the steps necessary in the solution of our problem, we can solve it in an orderly and efficient manner.

The first input to our solution is a study of the forces which affect our ship. We must understand their characteristics and magnitudes, and be able to predict which ones will come into play in a given set of circumstances. The second input to our solution is a thorough study of our ship and her particular handling characteristics. We should be familiar with her hull form, her propellers, and her rudders to be able to predict their interaction. We should know her equipment and its uses, and we should be familiar with her major dimensions. The last basic input in preparing to solve shiphandling problems is to calibrate our ship. We must experimentally determine what we can expect from a given engine or rudder order. We must know how far and how fast our ship will move in a given situation.

Having studied the forces, studied the ship, and calibrated her reaction to given controls, we are ready to meet specific shiphandling problems. To solve any particular problem we must carry out the following three basic steps:

1. *Measure the Situation*. Measure the ranges and bearings important to the maneuver. Measure the ship's speed, the depth of water, the velocity of the wind.

2. *Calculate the Maneuver*. Calculate the ranges at which to turn, the bearings at which the speed should be changed, the time to maintain a course.

3. *Check and Correct*. As the maneuver progresses, continual revaluation of the situation is required. At each opportunity the accuracy of the maneuver should be checked and corrections made as required. There are too many variables to expect the initial solution to hold good throughout an extended maneuver.

If the shiphandler follows these basic steps in facing his problem, he can perform an accurate maneuver with confidence in its success. Measurement by use of the instruments with which our ship is equipped, calculation by means of easily employed approximations and thumb rules, and checks by the same means will allow any officer to perform excellent maneuvers.

An air of mystery has often cloaked the good shiphandler. Many have avoided trying to explain why certain results are obtained because they felt the causes must be too complex to understand. Many very excellent shiphandlers seem to have no system of maneuver; they handle the ship by intuitive feel, and are at a loss to explain how they decide when to give a certain command. Most discussion on the subject merely outlines the results without exploring the causes.

The following chapters will examine the principles involved in handling a ship. We will examine the forces, the ships, and the situations, and will evolve a system of maneuver to fit each demand. We will rely on measurements rather than intuition, and we will present a method that is useful to all officers. Above all we will attempt to explore the subject in such a manner that the reader is provided with a sound foundation for meeting the problems he will face when he stands on the bridge of his ship.

CHAPTER II

FORCES AFFECTING THE SHIP

IN ORDER TO PREDICT the movement of our ship accurately, we must thoroughly understand the nature and magnitude of the forces which affect her. There are six general sources of forces which can be brought to bear on our ship independent of any other vessel. They are the propellers, the rudders, the mooring lines, the ground tackle, the wind, and finally the current. The first four are controllable from the ship itself. The wind and the current (and this includes tidal currents), though not controllable, can be utilized to serve our aims if properly handled. Each of these forces can produce important effects, as indicated in Figure 1, so it is worth while to take the time to study and understand each of them. Let's remember from the beginning, however, that these are *forces* only, and that *motion* results only after *inertia* has played its part.

A modern ship may have a distributed mass of many thousand tons and may be several hundred feet long. Such a body not only has tremendous inertia to resist linear acceleration, but it also has a tremendous *moment of inertia* to resist rotational accelerations. The ship is resting in a fluid (water) covered by another fluid (air), both of which will offer a resistance to relative motion. Thus, when we apply a single force to the ship, we can expect an acceleration until the fluid resistance produced by the motion balances out the original force. This will apply to angular motion produced by an off-center force as well as by force applied through the center of gravity. Thus, when we apply any force to the ship, we can expect motion to gradually build up until a state of equilibrium is reached, at which time the velocity of the motion will become constant.

Basic Principles

Forces in water manifest themselves as pressure differences. Water is incompressible, but by applying force to it we can build up a higher pressure in one area as compared to surrounding areas, and this difference in pressure will cause the water to flow from the area of higher pressure to the surrounding area of lower pressure. When we pull an oar through the water, for instance, we build up high pressure on the face of the blade toward which the blade is moving, and we create a low pressure on the face which is moving away from the water. During the motion, water flows from the high pressure region to the low pressure region. The greater the immersed

6

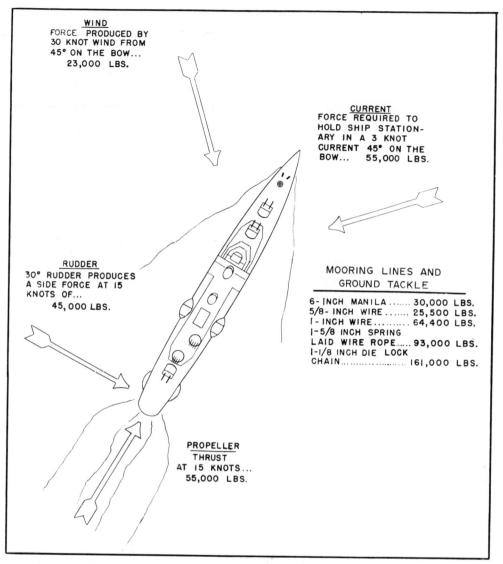

Figure 1. Forces which can bear on a ship (figures for a 2,200-ton DD).

area of the blade, the greater the area upon which the pressure can act. The greater the force applied to the oar, the greater the pressure difference. The average difference of pressure between the two sides, multiplied by the immersed area of the blade, is a measure of the force we are exerting on the water. Since the inertia of the water resists the force being applied by the blade end of the oar, this resistance, working through the oar, applies a force to the boat in the opposite direction. Resistance to the oar exists only when the particles of water are being set in motion by the movement of the oar. Without the force we apply to the oar, there would be no motion.

no pressure difference, and no resistance. Thus we see that force, resistance, and motion are irrevocably interlocked when dealing in a fluid medium.

The above discussion illustrates the fact that all forces in water manifest themselves as pressure differences. If we are going to apply force on a waterborne object, such as our ship, we can do it only by creating a pressure difference across a part of the ship's structure. And if at any time our ship moves in any way, we know that some force is acting somewhere on our ship's structure—and we can locate that force by looking for the pressure difference that causes it.

In any large body of water, there are always two components of pressure present at any point: one is the static pressure due to depth, or sheer weight of the water above the point; the other is the dynamic pressure caused by motion in the surrounding water. In the sea the static pressure does not cause motion, because it is the same everywhere at any given depth level, and hence balances out as far as we are concerned. But in restricted waters, such as rivers and harbors, static pressure or "water head" is caused by differences of elevation; these differences in static pressure head cause the water to flow from the point of higher elevation toward points of lower elevation. In addition to "pressure head" caused by differences in ground elevation, in tidewater there will be a pressure head difference set up by the difference in water level caused by the height of the tide.

Hence it can be generally stated that currents in a body of water are caused by pressure differences. If a current increases in velocity between one point and another, we know there has been a drop in pressure between the first point and the second; if the velocity decreases, we know there has been a pressure rise between the two points. In a steady flow, the pressure differences are evidenced by differences in the height of the surface or "water level."

A last general characteristic of water that is important in our study is its continuity; it tends to exist as a continuous body, without gaps or holes except as caused by extraordinary forces. If a volume of water is moved away so quickly, by a propeller blade, for instance, that the pressure differences there are insufficient to accelerate water *in* as fast as it is being moved *away,* then a gap would occur on the back side of the propeller blade. This gap is known as *separation.*

A companion phenomenon occurs when, in a high velocity stream, the velocity gets so high and the pressure so low that the pressure in the stream drops to the vaporization point of water. In this case drops of water become vaporized in the area described, in a manner similar to boiling. This phenomenon is known as *cavitation.*

Separation and cavitation are of interest to the shiphandler, because, when they occur, they upset the pattern of streamlines and change the resulting forces. These phenomena are likely to occur around abrupt changes in the underwater body of a ship moving at high speed, or about the blade of a propeller that is being rotated rapidly.

A flat plate placed at an angle in a stream of water, as indicated in Figure 2 (a), causes the water to accelerate to move out of the way on the leading side and to accelerate to move in behind the trailing side. This creates a high pressure on the leading side and a low pressure on the trailing side. This difference of pressure exerts a force on the plate as indicated in the figure. With smooth flow, this force is proportional to the angle of inclination, the square of the velocity of the current, and the area of the plate. Since an abrupt change of flow is required at Point A, separation could exist at such a point, and could alter the pressure distribution over the surface of the plate. If the plate is shaped as indicated in Figure 2(b), however, the acceleration of the water will be gradual and separation will be avoided.

Before proceeding further with a discussion of the hydrodynamic effects, it is necessary to set down certain definitions to assist the reader in following the explanation. The following definitions are used throughout the book:

Hydrofoil. Any relatively thin, plate-like member, such as a propeller blade or rudder, designed to obtain a lift force when inclined to the flow of the water.

Angle of Attack. The angle at which a hydrofoil is inclined to the relative free stream flow.

Lift. That component of the reaction force on a hydrofoil which lies in a direction perpendicular to the relative free stream flow of the water.

Drag. That component of the reaction force on a hydrofoil which lies in a direction parallel to the relative free stream flow of the water.

Pitch. As applied to a propeller, pitch is defined by the helix angle. It is normally expressed in feet-per-revolution, indicating the distance per revolution the propeller would travel when turning ideally (with no slip) in still water.

Slip. The amount the actual speed of the propeller through the water falls short of the ideal speed. (Ideal speed is defined as the product of the pitch multiplied by the RPM, or Revolutions per Minute.)

The Propeller

One of the most important sources of force on a ship is her own propeller. One would expect, since the propeller is designed to propel the ship, that turning the propeller AHEAD would cause the ship to move *straight ahead,*

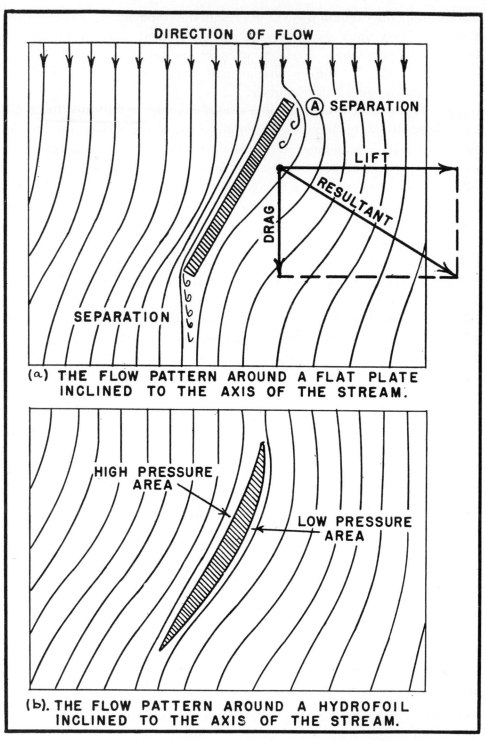

Figure 2. Flow patterns about an inclined plane.

and that turning the propeller ASTERN would cause the ship to move *straight astern*. This is not necessarily the case, however, and the shiphandler must study the action of a propeller in order to be able to predict its action on his ship.

The objective in designing a propeller is to produce the maximum thrust along the line of the shaft from a given rotational force or torque applied to the shaft itself. A fixed blade propeller is designed for optimum performance at one particular speed of the ship, usually the maximum speed, but it can be depended upon to operate efficiently at all normal speeds. The actual speed of the ship through the water is less than the ideal speed (pitch × RPM) because the blade of the propeller must be inclined to the direction of the water flow relative to the blade in order for the water to exert force on the blade and drive the ship. The cross-section of the blade is shaped to provide the greatest *lift* and the required strength, but at the same time to reduce separation and cavitation to a minimum.

To operate at another speed than design speed, the rotational speed of the propeller is simply changed to the RPM corresponding to the new speed. With a well-designed propeller the speed varies nearly linearly with shaft RPM. This relation holds true until a speed is reached where separation and cavitation become pronounced.

The water exerts force on the propeller by the differential pressure on the opposing faces of the blade. Therefore this force must be perpendicular to the mean face of the blade. Since the blades are inclined, this force is inclined to the propeller shaft rather than along its axis. However, since there is normally more than one blade on any propeller, and since the blades are disposed symmetrically around the axis, all of the radial components cancel out and the remaining thrust is along the axis of the shaft. It is because of the necessity for exact balancing of the radial components of force that the blade alignment of a propeller is so important. Though the propeller and shaft are well supported to withstand large forces along the axis of the shaft, the length of external shafting and the small number of relatively weak supports (the struts) form a structure poorly designed to withstand large radial forces at the propeller. A seemingly unimportant nick or dent in a single blade can alter the balance of the radial forces significantly, even though the useful thrust obtainable from the propeller is not significantly affected. It is because of the upsetting of the radial forces that a damaged propeller causes so much vibration or pounding.

A propeller is designed for a given ahead speed, but it works quite well turning astern also. The pitch of the propeller is the same going astern as it is going ahead, the major difference being that the blade cross-section

is now reversed from that best suited for preventing cavitation and turbulence. When operating astern, a given propeller is less efficient than when
going ahead. This means that more power will be required for a given shaft
RPM astern than for the same RPM ahead, but approximately the same
thrust will result from a given RPM whether turning ahead or astern.

Though the propeller is designed to force water through itself parallel to
the shaft, the actual flow is somewhat different, as indicated in Figure 3. The
character of the flow is due to the acceleration of the stream as it passes
through the propeller, and to the rotation imparted by the propeller. The
amount of disturbance of the parallel flow varies with the difference in

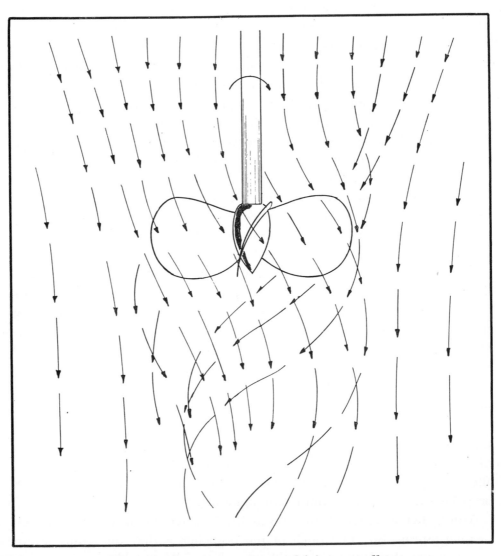

Figure 3. Flow pattern about a driving propeller.

velocity between the mean flow through the propeller and the mean current of the surrounding water. Thus a minimum disturbance of the parallel flow through the propeller occurs when the propeller is doing the least work. A great deal of disturbance occurs, however, when the ship is at a standstill and the propellers are being turned rapidly. And the maximum disturbance is created when the ship is moving in one direction and the propellers are being turned with maximum power in the other direction.

There is also a tangential component of motion imparted to the water by the propeller. Since the force from the propeller blades is nearly perpendicular to the blade surfaces, the initial acceleration of the water must be in line with this force. Thus the propeller, as it rotates, imparts a rotational motion as well as a backward motion to the water. This effect is evident in the spiral discharge from a propeller, as indicated in Figure 3.

The flow pattern about the propeller is of great interest in determining the forces on the ship. Although the direct effect of rotating the propeller is obtained as thrust along the propeller shaft, the secondary effects of the current flow are often just as important in handling the ship. It is often the adroit use of the secondary effects of the propeller's rotation that allows us to accomplish intricate maneuvers.

SINGLE-SCREW SHIPS

Side Force on a Propeller

As mentioned above, in addition to a *thrust* along the propeller shaft, we obtain a *side force* which affects the maneuvering of the ship. In our discussion of the propeller, we were considering an isolated screw turning in an unlimited body of water. In an actual ship, the propeller is not isolated, but is in close proximity to the hull and the necessary supporting structure for the propeller itself. Hence, the water cannot flow parallel to the propeller shaft, but always flows into the propeller at some inclination to the propeller's axis. In the upper part of the propeller disc, the blades are near the surface, and "churning" and "air drawing" are experienced under certain circumstances. Finally, the helical discharge from the propeller can produce unusual effects. All of these conditions contribute to producing a resultant side force which can be of sufficient magnitude to have an important effect in the movement of the ship.

The physical causes of the resultant side force are somewhat subtle and a discussion has been prepared in Appendix I for the reader who is interested in the origin of the force. It is sufficient for the purposes of the shiphandler to consider that, as a result of rotating the propeller, a force is created tending to move the stern of his ship to one side or the other. The *magnitude* of this force will vary with the type of ship and the character of the under-water structure in the vicinity of the propeller, but the *direction* of this force depends on the *direction of rotation* of the propeller only, and will be as though the lower blades of the propeller were bearing on the bottom and pushing the stern to the side as the shaft rotates. A propeller turning to the *right,* or clockwise, as seen from astern, will tend to force the stern to the right as shown in Figure 4. A propeller turning to the *left,* or counter-clockwise as seen from astern, will tend to force the stern to the left. When the direction of rotation is reversed, the direction of the side force is reversed.

When moving ahead at a steady speed in a single-screw ship, the side force on the propeller is not large. In order to insure good propulsive efficiency, such a ship is carefully designed to minimize the side force (and the amount of rudder required to overcome it). When backing or maneuvering with little way, the side force may be much larger.

When a single-screw ship backs, the helical discharge from the screw is thrown directly into the ship's structure, and the side force experienced is usually the strongest encountered under any circumstances. For this reason, it is difficult to prevent the stern moving to port when backing a single-screw ship with a righthand screw.

When maneuvering with little way on, the propeller may be driving at a high speed while the ship is moving relatively slowly. With this high "slip" condition, separation and turbulance may cause an unusually powerful side force to be felt.

Thus, regardless of the motion of the ship, a side force is experienced as a result of the rotation of the propeller, and this force must enter into the calculations of the conning officer in estimating the motion of his ship.

The Rudder, in a Single-Screw Ship

Having considered the action of the single-screw ship with the rudder amidships, let us now consider the action of the rudder. The rudder, like any other hydrofoil, experiences a lift force when it is inclined to the flow of the water in which it is submerged. This force is proportional to the area of the rudder, its angle of attack, and the square of the velocity of flow. If we can estimate the actual flow at the rudder resulting from the combination of the ship's motion and the screw current, we can predict the effectiveness we will obtain from the rudder. Since the force on the rudder varies as the square of the velocity of flow, if we can double the velocity of flow past the rudder, we can *quadruple* the force obtained from a given rudder angle.

In a single-screw ship, since the rudder is placed directly astern of the

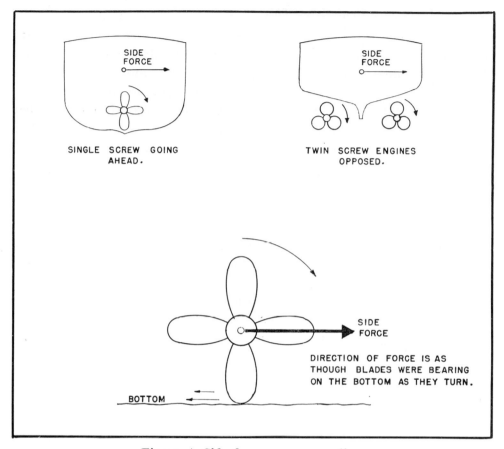

Figure 4. Side force on a propeller.

propeller, the screw current is usually the dominant factor in determining the effectiveness of the rudder. When the screw is going ahead, the velocity of flow past the rudder is almost exactly the discharge current of the screw, regardless of the ship's motion. Under these circumstances very large side force can be supplied by the rudder independent of the ship's speed through the water. So long as the screw is going ahead, we can depend on good rudder effectiveness.

When the propeller is turning astern, however, the strong discharge current is not directed against the rudder, and the relatively unconcentrated suction current has little effect on the rudder. Consequently, such a ship must rely nearly entirely on sternward velocity to provide the flow necessary to produce strong rudder forces. For this reason a single-screw ship must build up considerable speed astern before she responds well to her rudder. If *strong* rudder forces are desired, the propeller must be turning *ahead*.

Resultant Force on a Single-Screw Ship

Though we have considered the thrust, the side force, and the rudder action separately, it is the resultant of all three that determines the motion of a ship. We must combine the separate components into a single resultant force if we are to be able to predict their combined reaction of the ship.

If we define as *screw thrust* the component of propeller action that acts in line with the propeller shaft, we can lump all other components of propeller action in the horizontal plane into a single athwartships component which we can call *side force*. Since the force on a rudder inclined to the flow is nearly perpendicular to the faces of the rudder, we can define the *rudder force* as a force perpendicular to the faces of the rudder. Since all of these forces act at nearly the same place near the stern of the ship, we can for all practical purposes consider their combined effect as a *single resultant force* acting at the propeller. We control the ship by controlling this resultant force.

In addition to the active forces mentioned above, there is the drag of the hull as it moves through the water. This drag force depends upon the speed of the ship through the water, and it can be considered to act at the center of gravity in a direction opposite to the movement of the ship through the water. If the force we apply at the stern is exactly equal to the drag force, and if the line of action of the applied force passes through the center of gravity, a steady state is achieved and the ship will proceed at a steady speed with no tendency to turn.

If, on the other hand, the line of action of the resultant force at the stern does *not* pass through the center of gravity of the ship, there will be a torque on the ship and the ship will turn. The amount of this torque will be equal to the force on the stern multiplied by its effective lever arm with respect to the center of gravity of the ship. For all practical purposes, the center of gravity of a ship can be considered to lie on the centerline.

Since we control the ship by controlling the force on the stern, it is useful to set up a system for determining this force. If we can consider all of the forces on the stern to be acting at one place, we can construct a vector diagram to determine the resultant force on the ship. The drag force can be viewed as a reaction force, as can the resistance torque which opposes the rotation of the ship in the water, and thus they can be omitted from the resolution of active control forces on the stern.

Figure 5 illustrates the range of variation of the force on the stern obtainable by the use of the rudder while the ship is being driven ahead at a constant speed. It will be noticed that the side force allows more transverse force to be applied to starboard than to port. Thus the ship can turn more rapidly to port than to starboard. Figure 6 illustrates the effects of the screw and the rudder while the ship is dead in the water. The side force is shown greater than when the ship is moving ahead, which is the normal experience in single-screw ships. When the screw is turning astern, the side force completely overshadows the rudder force available while the ship is dead in the water, and the resultant force is always to port. Thus, though it is possible to twist the ship to the right with the screw turning ahead, she twists much better to the left. With the screw turning astern while dead in the water, the stern goes to port regardless of the rudder.

In Figure 7 we construct the vector diagrams for the engine driving astern while the ship also is moving astern. In this condition the rudder is once again effective, and a condition is selected where the rudder is able to overcome the side force and produce a resultant with a component to starboard. It is evident from the figure that much greater forces can be applied to port than to starboard.

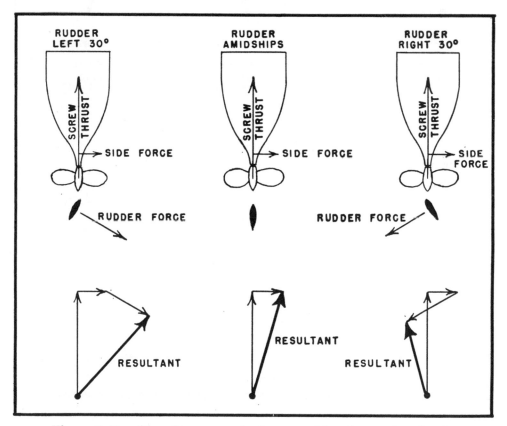

Figure 5. Resultant force on a single-screw ship when going ahead.

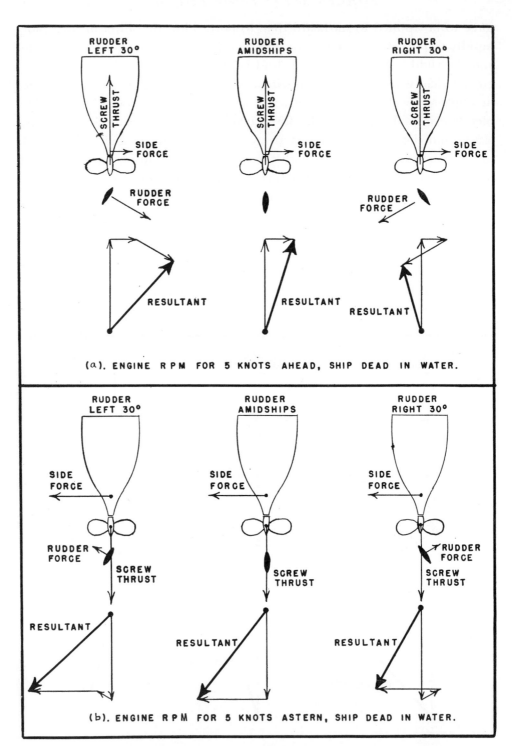

Figure 6. Resultant force on a single-screw ship with no way on.

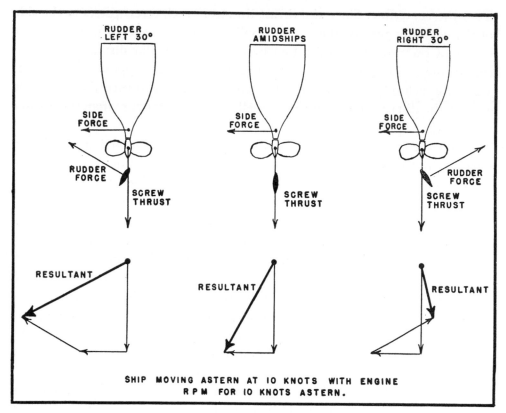

Figure 7. Resultant force on a single-screw ship when going astern.

TWIN-SCREW SHIPS

Most Navy ships have twin propellers, and some of the largest have four. Normally, when driving ahead, the propellers turn outboard, the starboard propeller turning clockwise and the port propeller turning counter-clockwise, as seen from astern. Providing a ship with an even number of opposed propellers eliminates many of the troubles found in single-screw ships. As long as the propellers are driving together, the side forces (which depend on the direction of rotation) are cancelled out, whether the screws are turning ahead or astern. On the other hand, if the propellers are *opposed*, one turning ahead and the other astern, the side forces then augment each other. Thus, with two or four screws, we have an ideal situation where the side forces cancel out if we are proceeding steadily ahead or astern, yet we can obtain an augmented side force by *opposing* the screws when we so desire.

In addition to the augmented side force with the screws opposed, we obtain a torque or twisting effect on the ship, because the shafts are displaced from the centerline. Since the thrust line from each screw passes to the side of the center of gravity, the torque applied by each propeller is equal to the thrust of the propeller multiplied by the perpendicular distance from this thrust line to the center of gravity. Since the screws are opposed, the torques augment each other and the resulting moment tends to turn the ship. The greater the distance between the propellers (with parallel shafts), the greater will be this effect.

When the screws on opposite sides of the ship are opposed, a circulating current in the horizontal plane is created by the suction and discharge streams of the propellers, as indicated in Figure 8. When this current impinges on a part of the ship's underwater structure, it produces a force. Forward of the screws there are many obstructions to this flow, and a strong athwartships force is experienced. Abaft the screws, only the rudder(s) are encountered, and if these are turned to conform to the flow, little force results. Consequently, the effect of the circulating current can be considered to be a side force on the structure forward of the propellers.

All of the effects mentioned in the above paragraphs resulting from opposing the engines of a twin-screw ship, with outward turning screws, act in the same direction. In combination they can produce a strong resultant side force which can play an important part in maneuvering the ship.

When the twin-screw ship is going ahead on one screw only, there is a tendency to veer to the side opposite from the screw in use. This tendency is, of course, caused by the side force and the offset position of the driving screw. At low speeds, the tendency is quite marked, but at higher speeds this tendency can be overcome by the use of a moderate amount of rudder.

When backing with only one screw, a stronger turning effect is noticed. In this case we have not only the normal side force and torque due to the offsetting of the propeller, but also a strong additional side force caused by the helical discharge current. When backing, the propeller throws a strong helical current into the struts, which are above the shaft, causing a strong athwartship force. This causes a much stronger side force than when the screw is turning ahead.

Following the above observations we can draw a diagram as indicated in Figure 9, showing the direction of the force that we can apply to the stern of a twin-screw ship by turning each screw individually. The average direction of the resultant force from using a screw in a given direction is indicated in the figure, and if the length of the vector is made proportional to the RPM of the shaft, we can combine the vectors to determine the resultant force on the stern of the ship from the two propellers. It is useful to keep Figure 9 in mind when maneuvering with the engines.

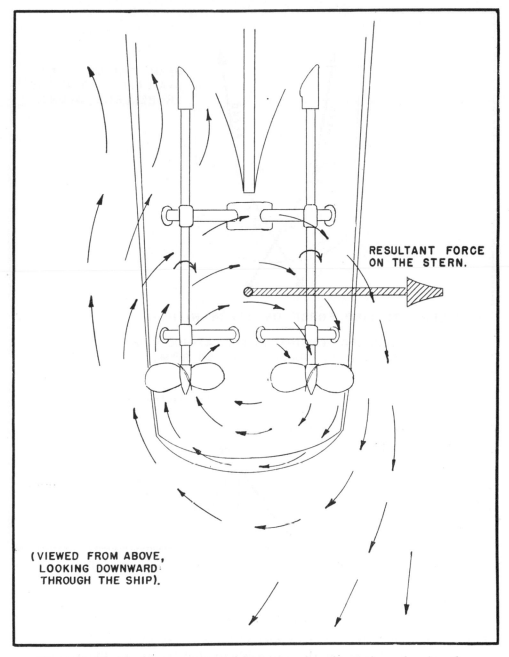

RESULTANT FORCE
ON THE STERN.

(VIEWED FROM ABOVE,
LOOKING DOWNWARD
THROUGH THE SHIP).

Figure 8. Circulating current caused by opposing the engines, showing the
resultant force on a destroyer's typical underwater structure.

The Rudder, with Twin Screws

The rudder of a twin-screw, single-rudder ship is mounted on the centerline just abaft the screws. As indicated in Figure 10, it does not feel the dis-

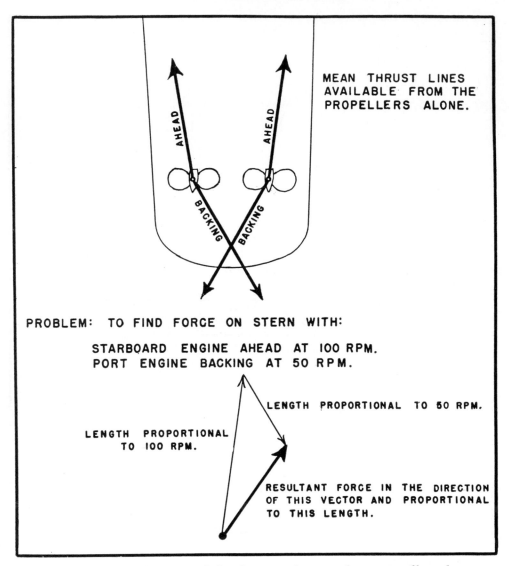

Figure 9. Diagram for determining force on the stern from propellers alone.

charge current from the propellers when it is positioned "amidships." Consequently, when using small rudder angles, only the *forward motion of the ship* through the water has any appreciable effect on the velocity of flow past the rudder and hence on the force obtainable by use of the rudder. At larger rudder angles, however (usually about 15° or more, depending on the type of ship), the after edge of the rudder enters the discharge current from the propeller on the side to which it is turned. Thus, at large rudder angles an augmented effect is obtained if the screw on the side to which the rudder is deflected is turning ahead.

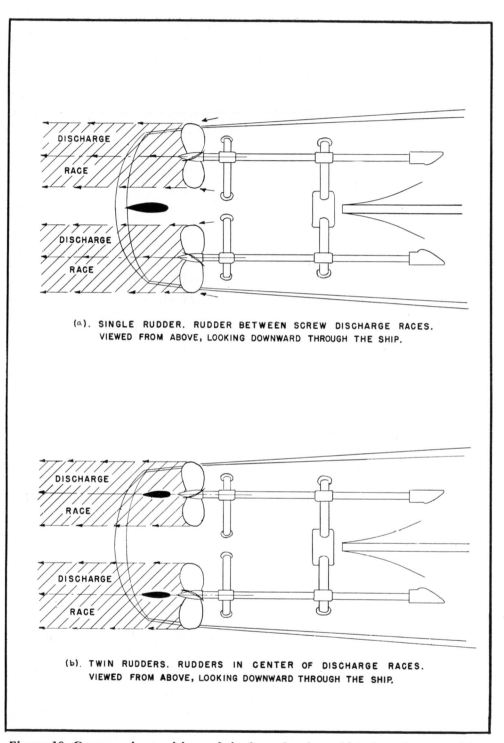

(a). SINGLE RUDDER. RUDDER BETWEEN SCREW DISCHARGE RACES. VIEWED FROM ABOVE, LOOKING DOWNWARD THROUGH THE SHIP.

(b). TWIN RUDDERS. RUDDERS IN CENTER OF DISCHARGE RACES. VIEWED FROM ABOVE, LOOKING DOWNWARD THROUGH THE SHIP.

Figure 10. Comparative positions of single and twin rudders in twin-screw ships.

Many modern types of vessels are equipped with twin rudders. In this design the rudders are mounted directly astern of the propellers, as shown in Figure 10, and their effectiveness is increased by the screw current impinging directly on the rudders. Since the screw discharge can produce a high velocity current at the rudder regardless of the ship's motion, it is this screw discharge that is the controlling factor in rudder effectiveness. If the screws are opposed, the one going ahead will have the greatest effect on the rudder action for this reason. In fact, with a twin-screw, twin-rudder ship, we can quite easily twist in our own water, with no way on, by opposing the engines equally and using full rudder in the direction we desire to turn. The side force from the rudder astern of the propeller which is driving ahead more than overcomes the weak opposing force of the other rudder.

Resultant Force on a Twin-Screw Ship

To construct the complete vector diagram for the forces on the stern, we must first resolve the off-center effect of the screws by replacing the resultant couple by an equivalent side force acting at the screws. Having done this, we can consider that all the forces act at the centerline between the screws, and thus can resolve the single resulting force by a vector polygon. This, of course, overlooks the longitudinal distance from the screws to the rudders, but this discrepancy produces only a minor inaccuracy. Figure 11 is an example of the vector solution for the force on the stern of a twin-screw, twin-rudder ship.

By using the various combinations available with a twin-screw ship, we can create a force in any desired direction at the stern. Our speed through the water will vary the amount of side force that we can apply, and, generally speaking, the amount of side force we can produce will be much less than the fore-and-aft force that is at our command. Nevertheless, by proper selection of the engine and rudder combination with a twin-screw ship, we can create a force at the stern in any direction we desire. Figure 12 indicates the engine and rudder combination required for producing force in each of the relative octants. A twin-rudder vessel is indicated because this type is the most versatile type. The figure assumes that the ship has no way on, and it will be noted that the rudders are positioned to achieve a maximum effect from that rudder which is astern of the screw that is going ahead.

In handling a ship it is very difficult at times to judge correctly what is the actual current in the vicinity of the screws and the rudder. Even the most experienced shiphandler will misjudge the direction of the flow during an intricate maneuver, and will put his rudder over the wrong way. When in doubt as to the combined effect of the engines and rudder, watch the surface

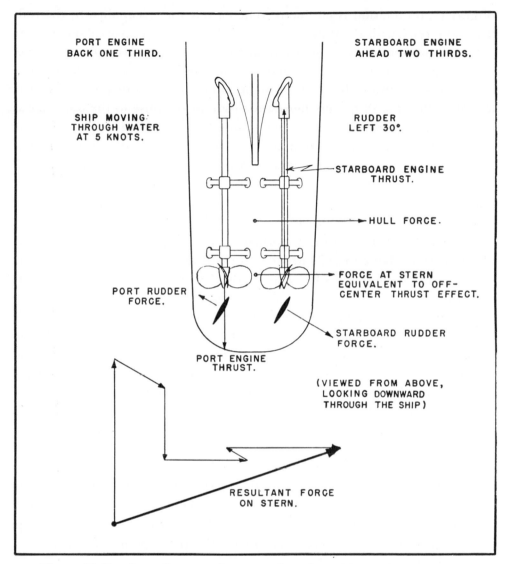

PORT ENGINE
BACK ONE THIRD.

STARBOARD ENGINE
AHEAD TWO THIRDS.

SHIP MOVING
THROUGH WATER
AT 5 KNOTS.

RUDDER
LEFT 30°.

STARBOARD ENGINE
THRUST.

HULL FORCE.

FORCE AT STERN
EQUIVALENT TO OFF-
CENTER THRUST EFFECT.

PORT RUDDER
FORCE.

STARBOARD RUDDER
FORCE.

PORT ENGINE
THRUST.

(VIEWED FROM ABOVE,
LOOKING DOWNWARD
THROUGH THE SHIP)

RESULTANT FORCE
ON STERN.

Figure 11. Resultant force on the stern of a twin-rudder, twin-screw ship.

of the water in the vicinity of the stern. Since the water is accelerated in the direction *opposite* to that of the force on the stern, the mean resultant flow from the stern will indicate the *direction* of the force we are obtaining. The *magnitude* of the force can be estimated by the *strength* of the flow.

Turning

We have discussed the rudder and the screw forces that act at the stern of the ship, but we have not explored *how the ship reacts* to the application of these forces. So long as the resultant force vector passes through the center of gravity, no rotation is produced. When a side force is applied by the rudder and screws, with the ship dead in the water, the ship pivots about a point about 30 per cent of the distance from the bow to the stern. One might expect the ship to spin about its midpoint—and thus it should, from the application of a pure torque—but in the case of an unbalanced side force applied at the propeller, the ship must move broadside in response to the unbalanced directional force, as well as rotate in response to the resulting torque. Thus the combination of the side motion and the rotation causes the ship to appear to rotate about a point considerably forward of the midpoint. Figure 13 illustrates how a ship turns about its *pivot point* when twisting with no way on.

When under way and proceeding ahead, the pivot point moves forward as the speed increases, until, at normal operating speeds, the pivot point is abaft the stem about 15 to 20 per cent of the length of the ship. This shifting of the pivot point is caused by the hydrodynamic effects of the flow past the hull.

When under way, the only means we have of controlling the ship is through her engines and rudder, and both of these act near the stern of the ship. Thus we can consider that we *steer* the ship by *forcing the stern* from side to side. To make a turn we force the stern to the side *opposite* to the direction in which we wish to turn, and this has two effects. First, the hull of the ship is inclined to the initial direction of motion, and this produces a large force pushing the ship in the direction of the turn; and second, the thrust from the screws is now inclined to the initial direction of motion, and this also forces the ship off its former course in the direction of the turn. This is a continuous process, and as the ship proceeds around in its turn, the centerline of the ship is inclined toward the center of the turn. The stern rides to the outside and the bow to the inside of the mean path of the ship. The ship as a whole proceeds as though the pivot point were making a smooth turn.

It is a useful concept to consider that we are maneuvering the pivot point through the water when we handle the ship. We can always *twist about* the pivot point to correct our alignment, but we can't *move* the pivot point *sideways* with the engines and rudder.

Control Commands

Though we have discussed the use of the engines and propellers in general terms, it is apparent that we must have precise control of the propellers if we are going to handle the ship skillfully. To do this we must define our engine commands, and this is not as simple as it might appear.

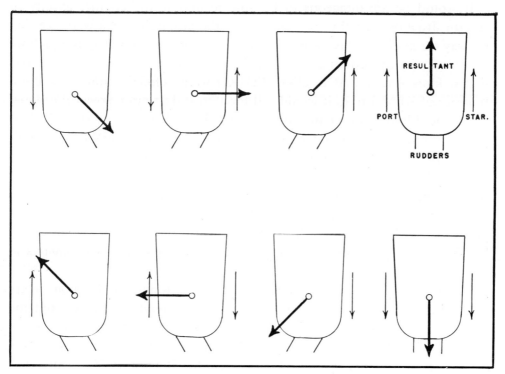

Figure 12. Resultant force with various screw and rudder combinations.

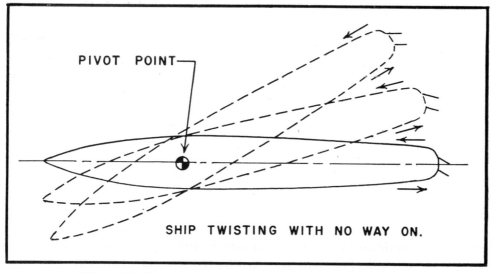

Figure 13. Pivot point of a ship twisting with no way on.

It would be advantageous to be able to oppose the engines exactly in certain situations and thus be able to twist the ship in her own water, getting no way on in either direction. Since the pitch of the propellers is equal, we could do this by ordering equal RPM in opposite directions on the two shafts. However, if BACK ONE THIRD were defined simply as a given number of RPM astern, it would call for a great deal more power if ordered while the ship was proceeding at full speed ahead than if ordered while dead in the water. In fact, in a destroyer an eager throttleman might drag off all the steam from a boiler in trying to produce 100 RPM astern quickly for a BACK TWO THIRDS bell if the initial speed ahead were high. Because the amount of steam required to produce a certain RPM varies with the speed through the water, many ships define their backing speeds as steam pressures on the turbines. This system avoids the trouble described above, but it sacrifices the precision possible when using the shaft tachometers to produce exact RPM.

The order STOP is not as simple as it appears. Remembering that we are delivering force with the engine, we would like the engine to cease supplying force when we give the order STOP. If we meant to have the shaft stop rotating, we might have to apply a great deal of power to keep the shaft from rotating merely from the effect of the current flowing past it. Most ships have adopted the definition of STOP which calls for all throttles closed and the propeller idling. The command STOP SHAFTS is an emergency order meaning to stop the shafts from rotating while passing an obstruction.

The exact definitions used in a given ship will depend upon a number of factors, but under any circumstances it is essential that all hands have a clear and accurate understanding of all of the orders used. Whether on the bridge or in the engineering spaces, the engine orders must have the same meaning. The definitions in Figure 14 were set up for a destroyer and have been found to be very useful. They are adequate to meet the most stringent demands. This system capitalizes on the advantages of both the *steam pressure* and the *RPM systems* of defining backing bells, since the steam pressure is used until the RPM is reached, and the RPM thereafter.

In Navy ships the orders are given to the engines by means of the engine order telegraphs, which order the direction and general magnitude of the speed desired, and by the revolution indicator, which specifies the RPM desired. The telegraphs can be read in all of the engineering spaces, but the revolution indicator is normally installed only in the engine-rooms. The system of multiple rings indicated in Figure 14 is provided to keep the fire-rooms informed of changes of speed beyond the range of the telegraphs.

On the standard engine order telegraph, in addition to the STOP position there are five positions for AHEAD speeds, but only three positions are used for BACK speeds. Because of the symmetry of construction of the actual Navy units, this leaves two unused positions in the BACK arc on all of the transmitters and indicators. By simply lettering in the proper labels, we can utilize these two spare segments for STOP SHAFT and BACK EMERGENCY. Thus by the expedient of more completely using the equipment provided, we obtain means of ordering these very useful commands.

The prior discussion has dealt with engine telegraph orders exclusively, but the revolution indicator is also a very important link in our engine command system. It is an essential aid in precise shiphandling when engine changes less than five knots are desired. Quite often when exact control is required at a speed intermediate between the increments of the telegraphs, the revolution order becomes the controlling means of command. Under these circumstances it is the normal practice to keep the engine telegraphs set on

---

ENGINE ORDERS

AHEAD ONE-THIRD ....RPM for 5 Knots Ahead

AHEAD TWO-THIRDS ....RPM for 10 Knots Ahead

AHEAD STANDARD ....RPM for 15 Knots Ahead

AHEAD FULL ....RPM for 20 Knots Ahead

AHEAD FLANK ....RPM for 25 Knots Ahead

FLANK RUNG TWICE ....RPM for 30 Knots Ahead

FLANK RUNG THREE TIMES ....RPM for 35 Knots Ahead

STOP ....All Throttles Closed

BACK ONE-THIRD ....60 Lbs. Pressure on Astern Turbine Until 50 RPM Reached. Then RPM Astern for 5 Knots

BACK TWO-THIRDS ....120 Lbs. Pressure on Astern Turbine Until 100 RPM Reached. Then RPM Astern for 10 Knots

BACK FULL ....200 Lbs. Pressure on Astern Turbine

BACK EMERGENCY ....Backing Throttle Open Completely, Except Steam Pressure at Throttle Not Allowed to Fall Below 500 Lbs.

STOP SHAFT ....Apply Sufficient Steam to Stop All Rotation of Shaft

---

Figure 14. Table of Engine Orders (for a destroyer with a
600 psi propulsion plant).

the increment nearest to the speed actually desired. We must remember, how-ever, that moving the telegraphs will signal a speed change of at least five knots to those stations not equipped with both a telegraph receiver and a revolution indicator, and all stations will take action. If the telegraphs are being moved simply to match the revolutions, and if a large incremental change is not desired, the conning officer must be careful that the engineers are notified of his desires. If this is not done, an inefficient and smoky opera-tion will result as the firerooms prepare for the change that never comes to pass and then have to change their firing rate drastically to compensate for their undesired forehandedness.

Since two instruments are used to give commands to the engines, it is essential that a system be worked out which specifies *which* shall be followed in case they give conflicting orders. Most ships adopt the rule that the *latest command* holds, regardless of the instrument upon which received. Thus, if we are steaming at 18 knots with the telegraphs set at STANDARD, and we wish to correct the situation, we must set the telegraphs at FULL and then ring off and ring back the appropriate turns for 18 knots. If this were not done, the engine-rooms would follow the command FULL calling for 20 knots, because it was the latest command.

The revolution indicator can be used with the engines opposed if this condition has been adequately defined. In this case, the engine-rooms answer the telegraphs for *direction* and the indicators for *amount*. Obviously this system cannot be used when it is desired to oppose the engines at different powers. Under circumstances where it is desired to use unequal power, the increments of the telegraphs are normally quite adequate.

Since there is a problem of the interaction of the engine telegraphs and the revolution indicator, it is convenient to set up a system to eliminate the revolution indicator when it is not needed. This is the normal case in a harbor, and it is useful to define MANEUVERING BELLS as the system where the engine order telegraphs are used exclusively and the revolution indicator is ignored. Conversely, the normal system using both the tele-graphs and the revolution indicators is defined as STEAMING BELLS. It is convenient to order MANEUVERING BELLS by setting the revo-lution indicator on a certain number *beyond* the range of the engines, such as 777 RPM. The return to STEAMING BELLS is ordered simply by ring-ing up the desired number of turns.

For the same reasons that engine orders need exact definitions, rudder orders must be precisely defined. The order STANDARD RUDDER can no longer be used, because ships are now required to turn to specific tactical diameters depending on the composition of the Force and regardless of speed.

The amount of rudder to produce even a single tactical diameter will vary with the speed. Since the helmsman reads his rudder angle indicator in degrees and the conning officer checks it on the open bridge on a repeater graduated in degrees, it is most desirable that all rudder angles be ordered in degrees. The command should be "RIGHT, EIGHTEEN DEGREES RUD-DER," or "LEFT, THIRTY-FIVE DEGREES RUDDER," instead of "RIGHT, STANDARD," or "LEFT, HARD RUDDER." The slight difference in number of words is more than compensated by the resulting certainty that the order can't be misinterpreted.

The conning officer should school himself in giving his orders clearly and properly. Orders to the engines should invariably be given in the sequence: *engine, direction, amount.* Thus the proper command would be "STAR-BOARD ENGINE, AHEAD, TWO-THIRDS," or "PORT ENGINE, BACK, FULL." In the same manner, rudder orders should be given in the sequence: *direction, amount.* Since there is only one control for the rudders regardless of how many are installed, the word "rudder" is normally left until the end of the order.

All orders should be given in a clear, loud voice. Although the man to execute the order may be standing next to the conning officer, it is important that all hands in the conning station hear the order so as to keep them abreast of the situation and functioning at maximum efficiency.

Wind

Having discussed at length the use and effects of the engine and the rudder, we can now consider the next important source of force on the ship, the wind. This force warrants thorough study because it is not only outside the control of the shiphandler but is quite changeable. Though the wind is often a hazard to the shiphandler, it can also be a very useful aid. By carefully playing the effect of the wind on the ship we can do things that would have been impossible through the use of the engines and rudders alone.

The wind normally acts to force the ship bodily *downwind.* The force it exerts is proportional to the square of the velocity of the wind, the cross-sectional area presented normal to the flow of air, and the form of the super-structure in the air flow. If we double the velocity of the relative wind, we quadruple the force on the ship from this source. If we turn the ship so that a larger cross-section is presented normal to the wind, the resultant force is increased. If the superstructure of the ship is irregular and presents many flat surfaces to the wind, the force of the wind will be larger than if the super-structure presents a smooth, streamlined form.

It is relatively easy to predict the reaction of the wind on a given ship. If the ship has high freeboard and is of shallow draft, the force from the wind will be large, the resistance to motion from the water will be small, and the ship will respond quite readily to the wind. If the ship is of deep draft and presents a small streamlined body to the wind, the wind effect will be a minimum. This also applies to the sections of the ship. With a given ship, if the bow is high, the stern low, and the ship trimmed down by the stern, the wind will tend to carry the bow *downwind*. Generally speaking, a ship lightly loaded is more sensitive to the wind than one heavy laden.

If we remember that the propellers and rudders give us means to apply force to the stern only, it is apparent that to force the ship to turn into a beam wind, it is necessary to overcome the wind force tending to blow the bow downwind. We must move the *stern* downwind faster than the wind is moving the *bow* downwind. If the bow presents a much larger "sail" area than the stern, the side force needed at the stern might be quite large. Since the side forces available from the engines alone are relatively small, it is often necessary to gain considerable headway before the additional force from the rudder is sufficient to overcome the wind.

Current

The last general force to be considered is the force due to current. The resistance of the underwater body of the ship to the flow of water is very similar to the resistance of the superstructure to the wind; however, the force resulting is much larger for a given velocity because the density of the medium is much greater. The streamlining of the hull is most important, and the top speed of a given ship is that speed at which the total resistance of the hull exactly balances the maximum force that can be delivered by the propellers.

The resistance of the underwater body to the flow of current is proportional to the square of the velocity of the current and the cross-sectional area presented to the flow, and is inversely dependent upon the streamlining of the body with respect to the direction of the flow. Obviously the resistance of the hull to a given current from ahead would be much smaller than the resistance to the same current from abeam.

Since the current is by definition the movement of the water, the ship is normally carried along with this movement. If we handle our ship as though there were no current and the stationary objects were moving at the speed of the current but in the opposite direction, we would have little trouble predicting the behavior of the ship. This simple solution is satisfactory for a steady current, but unfortunately the current is not steady in the vicinity of stationary objects. However, the special problems of current in the vicinity of docks and buoys will be covered later.

Actually, it is impossible to have a current relative to the ship other than from ahead or astern except by the application of forces external to the ship. If the flow of current relative to the ship is to be other than parallel to the axis of the keel, there must be some restraining force provided by mooring lines or ground tackle.

The shiphandler must always consider the current in maneuvering his ship near stationary objects. He must add the current vector to the vector of his own ship's motion through the water to determine his true movement relative to the ground. As he changes his speed through the water he must remember that the current velocity remains generally constant, and he must compensate for it. Finally, as he handles his ship broadside to the current, he must expect to be swept along with the current unless he uses external means to restrain the ship, and in that case the forces required will be relatively large.

SUMMARY

We have now examined the forces that come to bear on a ship due to the environment in which it operates and the manner in which it is propelled and controlled. We have considered the reasons why these forces exist, and we have prepared ourselves to be ready to estimate these forces for a given ship in a given situation.

The shiphandler must always be alert for evidences of conditions which will affect the handling of his ship. He must watch his bunting and rigging to determine the relative wind, and he must watch the surface of the water for signs of the true wind and current. If he is completely aware of the forces playing on his ship, he can compensate for the undesired effects and make use of the helpful effects.

A thorough understanding of all of the forces which can act upon the ship is the cornerstone of ability at shiphandling. Unless the shiphandler thoroughly understands the forces that come to play on his ship, how they act, and how they can be controlled, he cannot hope to handle his ship efficiently.

CHAPTER III

THE DESTROYER

THOUGH we can discuss the forces on a ship and the environment of the sea from a generalized point of view, as soon as we begin to examine specific problems which confront the shiphandler our solution will depend to a large extent upon the type of ship we are considering. Each type of ship has peculiarities which set it off from other types, and these must be taken into account when deciding upon a solution for a particular problem. If each evolution were discussed for all types at the outset, the discussion might become so involved that the reader would miss the principles. Consequently, it is best to cover the entire field of shiphandling from the point of view of a single type, and then later point out where other types require different treatment.

The **Destroyer** has been selected as the type with which to first explore the problems which face the shiphandler. The destroyer was selected because she embodies the characteristics of even the most complex type while possessing the capacity to solve most of the problems which will face her. She was also selected because of the traditional excellence of destroyer handling in the Fleet, and because of the fierce pride that destroyer officers have in this phase of their work.

Most officers feel that the peak of their careers is reached with the command of a destroyer. Although many have assignments of more prestige and achieve a rank much senior to that of a destroyer skipper, in their hearts the most satisfying tour of duty is that in command of a fine destroyer. Much of that satisfaction comes from the pleasure and sense of accomplishment that comes from having handled her well.

Within her sleek sides the destroyer possesses the greatest capacity for maneuvering of all ships. She is the fastest and most maneuverable major ship in the Navy. Though the battleship is immensely larger, mounts a vastly superior battery, and can steam as many weeks as the destroyer can steam days, she is treated like an invalid in port. A battleship is given only the safest berths, she never moves except on the most favorable tide, and she is usually attended by a bevy of tugs. Handling the destroyer is like driving a sports car: commanding a capital ship is like being mayor of a city.

Actually the destroyer is the largest ship in the fleet that is habitually handled without assistance. Displacing 4,000 tons or more, the modern destroyer is not a small ship. She is long and she is heavy, but her powerful engines give her the greatest horsepower-per-ton ratio of any major type of ship. In the hands of a competent shiphandler she can be made to do almost anything that any other ship can do, and she handles with a grace beautiful to behold.

Another reason why the destroyer has been selected as the ship with which to explore the field of shiphandling is that she is called upon for the greatest variety of duty. She is active in every phase of Fleet operations from Anti-Submarine Warfare to Amphibious Support. She is found in the screen of every major naval force, and she is an integral part of carrier air operations. In fact, except for the submerged operation of the submarine or the beaching of a landing ship, the destroyer participates in every phase of Fleet activity. She is therefore the ideal example for discussion.

The Fleet Destroyer

Counted as Destroyer Types today we have ships with displacements of from 1,500 tons to 9,050 tons, lengths from 306 ft. to 540 ft., and many combinations of screws and rudders. With such variation in size and characteristics it would seem impossible to consider destroyers as a single category, and indeed there are important differences among the various classes of destroyers. However, all of these ships are of similar hull form and possess very powerful engines in comparison to their displacement, and to the shiphandler the differences between the classes are generally in degree, not in principle.

The newer twin-screw, twin-rudder ships are now the most numerous and they are also the easiest to handle. Among these we find many of the Frigates, the DDG's, the DD 931- and DD 692-class ships, and the World War II DE's. Almost equally numerous are the twin-screw, single-rudder ships which include two large classes of DLG's, the DD 445-class, and most of the new DE's. An exception to the above groups is the DEALEY-class of DE's with a single screw and twin rudders.

Besides the differences in engines and rudders, the major factor of difference between the various types is the relative distribution of sail area. In a crosswind, one of the frigates or a late FORREST SHERMAN with its very high bow is much more difficult to handle than, for example, a GEARING with her lower and more evenly distributed sail area. However, with the notable

Figure 15. USS FORREST SHERMAN (DD-931), a typical modern destroyer.

Figure 16. USS BAINBRIDGE (DLGN-25), world's first
nuclear-powered guided missile frigate

exception of the DEALEY-class, all of the types have sufficient engine and rudder power to be handled safely except under extraordinary circumstances.

As the example for our discussion of the handling of a destroyer, we shall normally use FORREST SHERMAN unless otherwise indicated, since she is one of the most modern examples of the most numerous group. In the few cases where the difference between a single rudder and twin rudders is important, reference will be made to the technique applicable to the FLETCHER, but in most cases all classes should be handled similarly.

Figure 15 shows FORREST SHERMAN at sea. She has the following characteristics:

Length	418 ft.
Beam	45 ft.
Draft	20 ft.
Displacement	
Full Load	3,890 tons
Total Shaft Horsepower	70,000
Maximum Speed	34 knots
Crew (War Complement)	18 Officers
	325 Enlisted

Figure 17 shows the arrangement of the screws and rudders on a twin-screw, twin-rudder destroyer, GEARING in this case. The large propellers extend even beyond the sides of the hull, necessitating the installation of screw guards, and the rudders are installed directly in line with the screws. The reader will note the relative flatness of the hull under the stern, a feature typical of high speed ships which also adds to the directional maneuverability of the ship.

Mooring Lines

A sound knowledge of the mooring lines and associated deck equipment is vital to the shiphandler. In Chapter II we discussed the forces which come to play upon the ship in open water, but our study would not be complete unless we also discussed the means we use to adjust and secure the ship in her berth. Many a beautiful approach has been wasted by the inept use of the mooring lines.

Ships are moored to piers by a system of mooring lines which may vary according to the size and character of the ship. In all of the systems the various

Figure 17. Stern view of a 2,400-ton destroyer

lines are classified in accordance with their employment as *breast lines* or as *spring lines*. A breast line leads nearly perpendicular to the keel of the ship and controls the distance of that part of the ship from the pier. A spring line leads obliquely but nearly parallel to the keel and controls the fore-and aft position of the ship with respect to her berth. "Springing" is a term applied to the use of spring lines to move the ship in toward the pier by surging forward or aft against a line which leads obliquely to the pier.

A destroyer is normally moored with six mooring lines, and the lines are identified by number, from forward aft, in the order in which they are run out from the ship as shown in Figure 19. Numbers one and six are breast lines and should be led out as nearly directly abeam as possible to hold the ship against the pier with the minimum strain. Numbers two through five are spring lines and should be led nearly fore and aft. Two and four lead aft and prevent the ship from riding forward, and three and five lead forward and prevent the ship from riding aft.

The separation of the functions of the lines greatly assists in handling the ship alongside. If care is taken that one and six are actually placed on the pier so that they act as breast lines and the other lines as spring lines, the conning

Figure 18. A destroyer moored to a pier.

officer can accurately predict the result he will obtain by working a certain line. When destroyers are nested with ships of the same class, there is no danger of leading out the bow and stern lines as anything but breasts, because there is no other place to lead them; but alongside a pier there is a tendency to lead them out too far forward and aft so that they actually serve as springs. At a crowded pier, insuring that the bow and stern lines are led out directly abeam will prevent interference with the mooring lines of other ships.

When the ship is secured, the mooring lines are normally "doubled up," which means that an extra bight of line is passed to the pier or other ship, giving three parts of line instead of only one part. Often skippers believe they are doubled when in fact only one part of the line is taking the strain. To insure that the three parts take equal strain, only a simple turn should be taken on the ship's bitts before the bight goes over to the pier.

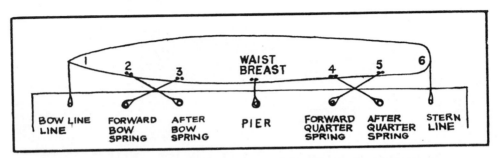

Figure 19. Proper positions for mooring lines of a destroyer.

Figure 20 shows a correctly secured mooring line, and Figure 21 shows a method of holding the strain with a "stopper" while the bight is being passed to the pier.

Normally, as we come alongside, it is desirable to get numbers one and six over as soon as possible, because it is with these lines that we work ourselves in against the face of the pier. The spring lines come into play later as we are adjusting our final position. Consequently it is desirable that the bow and stern lines be as long as practical. Since manila line comes in 100-fathom coils, 60-fathom lines for one and six, and 40-fathom lines for the spring lines work out very nicely.

It will be found useful to have one really strong mooring line on board. Wire is not desirable because it is awkward to handle and has so little spring. A Nylon line, though very strong, has too much spring and a very large manila line is difficult to procure and difficult to stow. Spring laid wire rope, a combination wire and hemp line is a good compromise. A 1⅝-inch "spring lay" is more than three times as strong as best grade 6-inch manila line. It can be handled almost as easily as manila, it can be stowed in less

Figure 20. Correctly doubled mooring line.

Figure 21. Method of holding strain while doubling lines.

space, and it will outlast manila in normal usage by a good margin. It is a comforting thing to watch such a "strong line" take the strain when the safety of the ship depends upon that line holding.

In giving orders to the line-handling stations, it is mandatory that the order have the same meaning on the forecastle as was intended by the Conning Officer. The following examples and definitions are in common use in the Fleet and can form the basis for all orders to lines:

Order	*Meaning*
SEND THE LINES OVER	Pass the lines to the pier, place the eye over the appropriate bollard, but *take no strain*.
TAKE A STRAIN ON ONE	Put line number one under tension.
SLACK ONE	Take all tension off of line number one and let it hang slack.
EASE ONE	Let number one line out until it is under less tension, but not slacked.
TAKE NUMBER TWO TO THE CAPSTAN	Lead the end of line number two to the capstan, take the slack out of the line, but *take no strain*.
HEAVE AROUND ON THREE	Apply tension on number three line with the capstan.
AVAST HEAVING	Stop the capstan.
HOLD WHAT YOU'VE GOT	Hold the line as it is.
HOLD FIVE	Do not allow any more line to go out on number five. (Caution—this risks parting the line).
CHECK FIVE	Hold heavy tension on line number five but render it as necessary to prevent parting the line.
SURGE FIVE	Hold moderate tension on number five line, but render it enough to permit movement of the ship (used when moving along the pier to adjust position).
DOUBLE UP	Pass an additional bight on all mooring lines so that there are three parts of each line to the pier.
SINGLE UP	Take in all bights and extra lines so there remains only a single part of each of the normal mooring lines.

TAKE IN ALL LINES   Used when secured with your *own* lines, and it
                                means to have the ends of all lines cast off from
                                the pier and brought on board.

CAST OFF ALL LINES   Used when secured with *another* ship's lines in a
                                nest, and it means to cast off the ends of the lines
                                and allow the other ship to retrieve her lines.

Fenders

The fenders that are ready topside are a matter of concern to the conning officer. The most important item among fenders is the "big" fender—normally a pneumatic fender about four feet long and three feet in diameter. It should be lowered to just clear the water at the extreme beam amidships. We normally ride against this fender alone when alongside another ship, and the perfect maneuver culminates in a gentle "One Point" landing on this fender.

In addition to the fender amidships, we should have four more cylindrical fenders ready: two on the forecastle and two on the fantail. These can be smaller pneumatic fenders or "home made" manila fenders, about four feet long and a foot in diameter. It is normally desirable to place one of these with its top about one foot above the deck edge just forward of the forecastle windbreak and another similarly placed abreast the after end of the deckhouse. The remaining two cylindrical fenders are kept "in hand" ready for use to protect the forecastle and the propeller guards respectively.

Finally, several ball fenders should be ready to be placed at the point of contact when the side of the ship comes into contact with the pier or the other ship. These are not as dependable as the cylindrical fenders because they are more easily squeezed out from between the ships, but they are easier to handle and can be put in place quickly as the situation develops.

Ground Tackle

The capabilities of the ground tackle and the anchor windlass should be appreciated by the conning officer. All destroyer officers should be able to handle the anchors and ground tackle without any help. If any officer has not actually worked the gear, he should take time out to get the experience. It will pay good dividends in appreciating the problems of the forecastle and developing the patience so desirable on the part of the bridge personnel.

The anchor windlass is driven by a hydraulic motor which has an electric motor as the prime mover. In case the windlass is overloaded, instead of stripping gears the safety valve lifts and no permanent harm is done. Through suitable gearing this hydraulic motor is connected permanently to the capstan, which always turns when the motor is turning. On the capstan shaft is the wildcat, a sprocket for taking the anchor chain which can be locked to the capstan shaft when desired. The wildcat is "connected up" when it is locked to the capstan shaft, and it is "disconnected" when unlocked. Also there is a brake which acts upon the wildcat and is rugged enough to hold the wildcat under almost any conditions.

Our destroyer is equipped with two anchors and two chains. The longer chain is 120 fathoms, and the shorter 105 fathoms, and in addition there is a 5-fathom "bending shot" on each of the anchors. The conning officer should know which anchor on his ship has the longer chain. Should the need ever arise, one chain could be shackled to the end of the other and more than 225 fathoms provided, but we must make sure that the anchor windlass is powerful enough to recover the longer scope in deep water. (The windlass has to lift, in addition to the anchor, the weight of the chain necessary to reach the bottom.)

Although there are two anchors and chains, there is only one wildcat, so only one anchor can be worked at a time. However, there is a compressor on each chainpipe which can be used to restrain the chain. Whenever it is desired to shift from one anchor to the other, it is necessary to walk out sufficient chain from the chain locker, set the compressor to keep the chain from running back into the chain locker, disengage the chain from the wildcat, lift the chain over and clear of the anchor windlass, then rouse out sufficient chain on the other anchor, lift it over the windlass, and finally engage it in the wildcat. All of this takes time, and the "Bridge" must learn to allow for it.

The anchor windlass is conveniently designed so that the maximum peripheral force that can be applied by the capstan is 30,000 lbs; the breakage strength of a top grade 6-inch manila line. Thus, if using this size line, the windlass can apply all of the tension the line can stand. If one were to try to get more effect from the line by springing in, he would probably only succeed in parting the line.

Springing

The subject of springing is often misunderstood. There is a popular misconception that there are immense latent forces available from this technique which greatly exceed any other forces which we can apply to the ship. Springing is a very useful practice, but the adequate capstan forward and the precise control of the engines of today have resulted in springing being employed quite infrequently.

In analyzing the action of springing, we can first define it as obtaining a sidewise force on the ship by moving forward or aft against a line led out obliquely to the pier, thus providing an athwartships component of force as well as a restraining component parallel to the keel. Obviously the maximum force that can be applied by a single line can be no greater than the breaking strength of that line, and any component of a force can never be greater than the whole force. Thus the maximum springing force available from a single line can be no greater than can be obtained by the capstan.

It will be readily seen that to obtain maximum force from springing, the line should lead almost abeam. On the other hand, to allow maximum side motion with minimum fore-and-aft motion, the line should lead nearly fore and aft. Normally we spring with the line at an oblique angle different from the theoretical optimum because of line slippage and elasticity.

To obtain the absolute maximum side force on the ship, we must use *all* of the forces at our disposal. This is occasionally necessary when "crabbing" up to a berth against a very strong wind or current. We spring on as many lines as possible in addition to using the capstan on number one, employing the waist breast, and twisting the stern in with maximum practical engine power. Under these conditions it is usually best to lead all lines directly to the pier (i.e., not crossing the springs), and surging forward and aft by unbalancing the engines. With this arrangement all lines can be used for springing at the same time whether surging forward or astern. Have all line-handlers alert to "take in" the slack whenever they can get it, and to hold (but not part) the lines whenever they tend to take a strain. The ship can be worked in to the pier under very severe conditions when using all of the forces available.

Heaving Lines

Heaving lines and line-throwing guns play an important part when going alongside. The Captain should encourage his line-throwers to practice to obtain maximum distance and accuracy, because the speed with which the lines can be sent to the pier is often decisive. It is best to have at least four line-throwers ready both fore and aft when making the approach. The men must not bend their heaving lines to the mooring lines until the "monkey fist" is on the pier. When a successful throw has been achieved, this heaving line can then be bent to the mooring line that is needed first—usually number one—regardless of which line-thrower makes the successful heave. Under difficult conditions it is best to bend the heaving lines for the additional mooring lines to the first line that goes over, instead of making further attempts to heave them over.

In addition to normal heaving lines it is very useful to have "Bolo" lines ready both fore and aft. These latter are a relatively recent development in the fleet and are not yet standardized. They usually consist of a lead weight or weighted "monkey fist" attached to the end of a Nylon shot line with a throwing toggle about two feet from the weight. With a "Bolo" a skillful sailor can reach to fully twice the distance achievable with a normal heaving line, and because of the relative heaviness of the weight as compared to the line, a "Bolo" is much more effective in the wind than is a normal heaving line.

The line-throwing gun should be used without hesitation whenever its use will assist the maneuver. We must guard against the crew becoming careless of safety when using the gun, and we must insist on having the men on the pier or on the other ship take cover when we are firing. The timely use of the line-throwing gun often speeds up the operation and occasionally allows the successful completion of a maneuver which otherwise would have required a second approach. Some shiphandlers pride themselves on never using a line-throwing gun, but they usually pay for their pride by sweating out precarious moments that the timely use of the gun would have avoided. It is more cause for pride to employ skillfully all the tools at our disposal than to demonstrate that we could get along with less.

Deck Experience

It is invaluable training for a shiphandler to have had a tour of duty as First Lieutenant. The handling of the lines and fenders is an art that is of vital importance to good shiphandling. An officer who has not had the benefit of experience in Deck Seamanship should spend as much time as possible with the Deck Force while they are handling the deck gear, so that he can understand the capabilities of the equipment and the problems of its employment. An officer must be a competent seaman before he can be a competent captain.

CHAPTER IV

MEASURING THE SITUATION

IF WE ARE to maneuver with precision, it is necessary that we measure the situation exactly and frequently to know where we stand and to judge what to do next. If we have calibrated our ship so that we know what she will do when a certain order is given, and if we have accurately measured the range and bearing to our destination, we can maneuver with confidence to our destination, providing of course that we have gauged the wind and current accurately. The secret to understanding the situation is to have all the available information at our fingertips and to use it all.

Calibration

The first step in accurate shiphandling is to calibrate the ship so that we know what she will do. Test the ship with the engines opposed equally to insure that we actually do not get any way on ahead or astern while twisting. Note the turning rate when twisting at ONE THIRD and when twisting at TWO THIRDS. It will probably be found that it is necessary to twist at TWO THIRDS to achieve a good turning rate.

The distance required to come to a stop when going ahead at various speeds while using various backing powers is vital information for the conning officer. For instance the distance the ship moves ahead before stopping when BACK ONE THIRD is ordered while going ahead at five knots should be kept in mind because it is very useful when going alongside or making a buoy. And the distance the ship moves ahead before coming to rest when BACK TWO THIRDS is ordered at 15 knots is vitally important knowledge when recovering torpedoes or picking up a downed aviator. When taking over a ship, the new captain should take his ship out and measure these values for himself. A conning officer should familiarize himself with these values to be sure he is ready for emergencies. It will pay dividends later in accurate shiphandling.

The amount the ship "surges" during a speed increase or decrease should be remembered. Perhaps the best way to explain the meaning of "surge" is to give a typical example. Suppose our ship is making 20 knots and is coming up from behind to join a column which is proceeding at only 10 knots. We accordingly drop our own speed to 10 knots. But by the time our ship slows down from 20 knots to 10 knots, we will have closed up on the ship ahead of us in column by perhaps 350 yards. In other words, in slowing from 20 knots to 10 knots we have closed by 350 yards, or 35 yards per knot of speed change. We call this ratio the surge, and the example given is about typical of the average destroyer.

The turning data also should be known and certain key values committed to memory. The minimum turning diameters at 10, 20, and 30 knots should be remembered and the turning diameters for 10, 20, and 30 degrees rudder should be memorized for a speed of 15 knots. The *rate* of turn in degrees per second using 30 degrees rudder at 20 knots is useful for solving maneuvering board problems when the turning circle has to be taken into account.

Measuring Distance

Distance is a primary factor in shiphandling, and it is certainly the most difficult factor to estimate. There are many methods of measuring distance, and all of them are useful at times. Radar, though excellent for tactical maneuvers, is less useful for shiphandling, where the ranges of interest are 1000 yards or less. The stadimeter is still the most useful all-around range measuring device for close shiphandling, and the 7×50 binocular is good for darkened ship steaming if our radar is not effective at short ranges.

The stadimeter can be used in the conventional way and will give excellent ranges from 250 to 3,000 yards if used properly. However, it is often necessary to make an approach on an object floating in the water or on a ship the masthead height of which is not known. Using the stadimeter in the Inverted Method is very useful in such cases. To do this, the bridge height-of-eye for our own bridge is set on the stadimeter as "masthead height," and the horizon is brought down to the waterline of the object. The geometry of the situation is indicated in Figure 22. In actual practice, since the minimum height on the scale of a standard Navy stadimeter is 50 feet, and since the bridge height of eye on our destroyers is about 35 feet, double the height of eye can be set and the true range then found by dividing the scale reading by two. This has the advantage of allowing us to obtain ranges on objects as close as 125 yards, even though the lowest figure on the stadimeter is 250 yards.

The standard 7×50 binocular is very useful for judging the distance to a known ship (See Figure 23). The full field of a 7×50 is 7° 10′, or 125 mils. At 300 yards a destroyer, from the waterline at the stern to the top of the highest antenna, will just fill the field of view vertically. Therefore, if the destroyer fills one-half of the field, she is about 600 yards away; one-third, about 900 yards, etc. An aircraft carrier fills the field at approximately 430 yards, and a cruiser at about 375 yards. This is a rough method of measuring

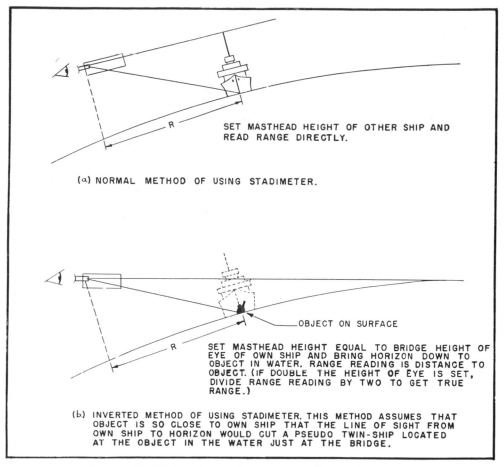

SET MASTHEAD HEIGHT OF OTHER SHIP AND
READ RANGE DIRECTLY.

(a) NORMAL METHOD OF USING STADIMETER.

OBJECT ON SURFACE

SET MASTHEAD HEIGHT EQUAL TO BRIDGE HEIGHT OF
EYE OF OWN SHIP AND BRING HORIZON DOWN TO
OBJECT IN WATER. RANGE READING IS DISTANCE TO
OBJECT. (IF DOUBLE THE HEIGHT OF EYE IS SET,
DIVIDE RANGE READING BY TWO TO GET TRUE
RANGE.)

(b) INVERTED METHOD OF USING STADIMETER. THIS METHOD ASSUMES THAT
OBJECT IS SO CLOSE TO OWN SHIP THAT THE LINE OF SIGHT FROM
OWN SHIP TO HORIZON WOULD CUT A PSEUDO TWIN-SHIP LOCATED
AT THE OBJECT IN THE WATER JUST AT THE BRIDGE.

Figure 22. Using the stadimeter to measure distances.

distance, but it will be found very useful when no other method is available.

The jackstaff and bullnose are convenient range marks when we are approaching something dead ahead. Some skippers mark 500, 200, and 100 yard marks on their jackstaffs so that when they are standing on their normal conning station their line of sight past these marks hits the surface of the water 500, 200, and 100 yards ahead of the bow respectively. The accuracy of this system depends upon ship's speed and trim, but if the horizon mark is also indicated on the jackstaff as a reference, accurate ranges can be obtained.

Radian Rule

Knowing the range to an object, the Radian rule or the "One in Sixty" rule comes into play. This is one of the most useful rules available to the

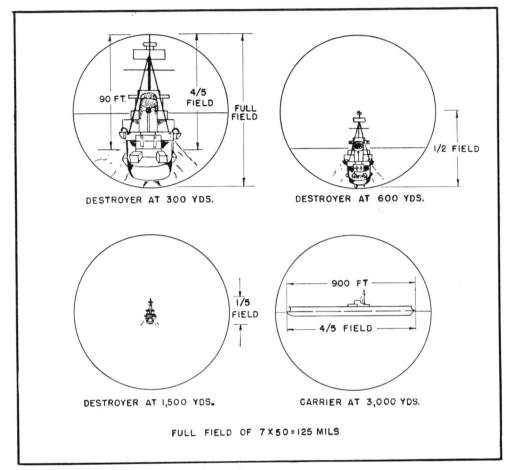

Figure 23. Using 7 × 50 binoculars to measure distances.

shiphandler. It is based on the fact that since the radian subtends 57.3°, it is approximately correct that the perpendicular distance subtended by 1° is 1/60th of the range. Thus if a 300-foot vessel "beam-on" subtends an arc of 1° at the observer, it is 6,000 yards away. At 6,000 yards a boat at the same range as a buoy but separated from it by $4\frac{1}{2}$° is 450 yards from the buoy. If you wish to pass a ship 500 yards abeam when coming up from astern and the range is 3,000 yards, you divide 3,000 by 60, which gives 50 yards; since 50 goes into 500 ten times, then the spot 500 yards abeam of the ship ahead is 10° to one side of her. When using this rule, check points are selected at ranges easily divisible by 60.

Speed, Time, and Distance

Another important piece of shiphandling information is the exact relation between speed, time, and distance. The following equivalents and approximations should be memorized:

   1 knot = 2,000 yards per hour, or 100 yards in 3 minutes
15 knots = 500 yards per minute
   1 knot =   33 yards per minute
   1 knot = ½ yard per second
   1 knot = 10 turns on the Revolution Indicator

These values are very useful tools in shiphandling. For instance, if we are fueling at sea and we drop back ten yards on the oiler in two minutes, this is five yards per minute or about 1/6 of a knot; hence, adding two turns should check our motion, and adding four turns should put us back on station in two minutes. If we are 125 yards behind station in column, we can be back on station in two minutes by adding two knots.

Approximate Mathematics

The Radian rule and the speed equivalents are constantly useful in maneuvering at sea. Suppose that with speed at 15 knots, we are on the beam of the guide at 3,000 yards and we wish to move in to 2,000 yards. Using the rules we see that a 4° course change will move us *in* at 1 knot, or 33 yards per minute. If we desire to complete the maneuver in 10 minutes we must have a closing rate of 100 yards per minute, or three knots. This would require us to change our course toward the guide by 12° and add a few turns to keep our bearing constant.

It may seem that this is too much mental mathematics for an officer who is busy conning a ship. Actually, after a little practice the calculations become second nature, and they assist in achieving real excellence in shiphandling. The really efficient conning officer is constantly measuring, checking, and calculating as he handles his ship. Don't "guesstimate" the situation; *measure* it. Having measured it, compute your course of action by use of the thumb rules and "approximate mathematics" as illustrated above. The habit of precision is invaluable at sea.

CHAPTER V

HANDLING ALONGSIDE

ONE OF THE MOST interesting and enjoyable phases of shiphandling is that of handling alongside. In discussing this phase we shall cover the problems of going alongside and getting clear of both piers and ships. The interesting situations and special problems are so numerous that they cannot be covered here, so we shall deal only with general principles. If the principles are understood, the solution to any particular problem will be readily apparent.

The guiding principle in handling alongside should be SAFETY. It is simply poor seamanship and bad shiphandling if any damage is done to our ship or the ship or pier we are alongside. There are extremes of weather and cases of emergency when even the most able shiphandlers will bend a stanchion, but under normal circumstances it is positive evidence of bad judgment if any damage is done. In every case where damage has resulted, the conning officer concerned should analyze his actions to see where the mistake was made. Dash and smartness are traditional in destroyer officers, but it is neither smart nor dashing to damage your own or someone else's ship.

Going Alongside

The most common error among inexperienced shiphandlers is to make the approach too *close* to the ship or pier they are approaching. They are afraid of not making the landing and have heard too many stories about legendary skippers making "one bell" landings and handing the lines over "doubled up." With a modern ship the shiphandler has no reason for lying closer than 10 yards from another ship or dock under normal conditions until he has all six lines over and he is ready to move in. A safety margin smaller than this is not sufficient to allow for a quirk of wind or a momentary unbalance between the engines.

The normal procedure for going alongside (See Figure 24) should be as follows:

We approach on a converging course about 10° to 20° from the heading of our berth for a position so that our engaged side will be 20 yards out from the pier when we are opposite our berth; as we come opposite the berth, we swing parallel and stop the ship, get the lines over to the pier, and finally when all lies are set, "walk" the ship in broadside, using the capstan on number one line and twisting the stern in with the engines. We take plenty of time moving in, and are careful to keep the ship exactly broadside. Our de-

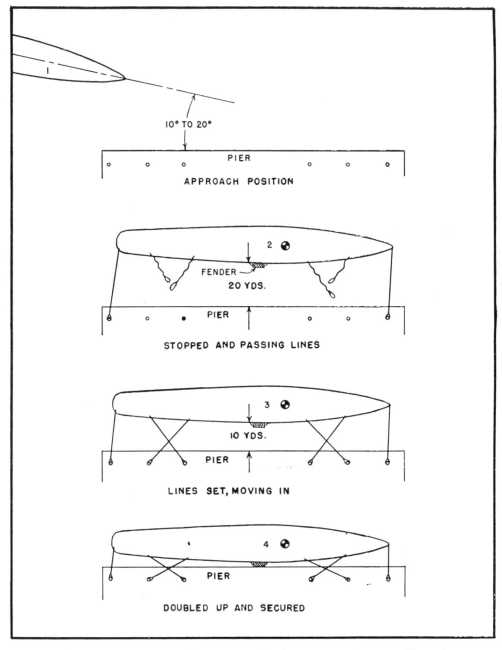

Figure 24. Sequence of maneuvers during a normal uncomplicated
landing at a pier.

stroyers today are long and covered with gear at the deck edge, and the
slightest inclination as the ship touches the pier face may cause damage.

The reason for the recommended initial inclination is to keep the stern

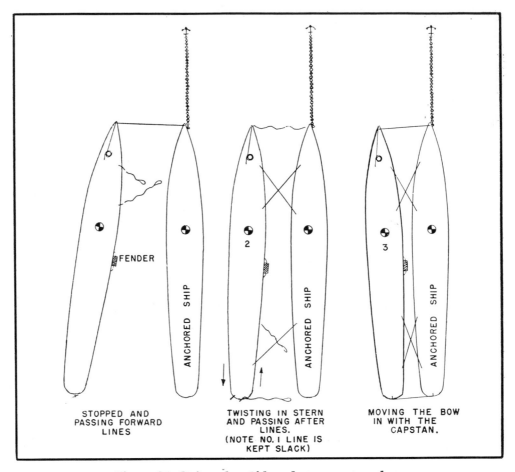

FENDER

ANCHORED SHIP

2

ANCHORED SHIP

3

ANCHORED SHIP

STOPPED AND
PASSING FORWARD
LINES

TWISTING IN STERN
AND PASSING AFTER
LINES.
(NOTE NO. I LINE IS
KEPT SLACK)

MOVING THE BOW
IN WITH THE
CAPSTAN.

Figure 25. Going alongside a destroyer at anchor.

free for swinging as long as possible and also to be ready to back clear should anything go wrong. It will be noted that the above procedure envisions moving in broadside instead of sliding in against the pier. Rubbing against the pier should be avoided if at all possible. Frequently projections on the pier or ship will catch and cause damage, and under any circumstances such action will rub the side paint off our beautiful ship.

When going alongside another ship in the stream (See Figure 25), the same principles hold as for the pier except that the conning officer must be doubly careful. If the ship being approached is at a single buoy or is anchored, she may be yawing and hence the problem is further complicated. In this case the original approach inclination should be at least 20°, and the approach should be made a little wider to provide against a sudden swing of the other ship towards us. Because of these extra safety precautions it may be necessary to get the forward lines over first and then twist the stern *in* until the after lines can be gotten over. When twisting in this case, the forward lines, especially number one, should be left slack to keep from spinning the other ship. Remember that she is essentially floating free, and if we pull her bow toward us, her stern will move away. It is not an uncommon sight to see a ship twist nearly 90° trying to move her stern *in* because the forward lines were not slacked. Because of the tendency of the other ship to spin and the lack of a capstan aft, it is often necessary to "see-saw" the ship in, slacking the forward lines when moving the stern in with the engines, then holding the after lines as we breast in the bow with the capstan. Actually the "see-saw" is imperceptible if the ship is properly handled, because the conning officer will adjust his forces so that the movement is continuous.

Wind, When Going Alongside a Pier

Wind, of course, complicates the problem of going alongside. When the wind is blowing *off* the pier where we are to tie up, it is necessary to approach faster and closer in order to get the lines over before the wind has blown our ship away from the pier. But we must not let this lure us into approaching too fast and too close. If we conn from the engaged wing pelorus, and sight over a bearing circle set at the course we have ordered, we can see exactly where the engaged side of our ship is headed. Except for extreme circumstances, all courses ordered during the final approach should be such that if the engines did not respond exactly as ordered, our ship will still pass clear of everything.

The procedure when the wind is blowing *off* (See Figure 26) is to get our "strong line" over forward as quickly as possible to hold the ship while we get the other lines over. As soon as the bow is secured to the pier, we can hold our stern up into the wind by the engines. If the bow is secure, the stern can be twisted up to the dock under almost any conditions.

If the wind is so strong that there is doubt that the bow can be managed quickly enough with the lines, then we approach rapidly, and when the bow is close to the pier and opposite its eventual position, we let go the engaged anchor. This anchor, snubbed up, will hold the bow up while we get the forward lines set, and it can be picked up later when we are in our berth.

When the wind is blowing *onto* the pier, in most cases the problem is simpler, because the wind is helping the maneuver, even though often it is boisterous with its help. The secret of this type of landing is to approach wide enough so that the ship is not blown down on the pier until we are ready. Don't be afraid to make it too wide, because the wind will eventually blow us down onto the pier if we are too far out in the beginning. Care must be taken to keep the ship parallel to the pier as we come into the berth. The

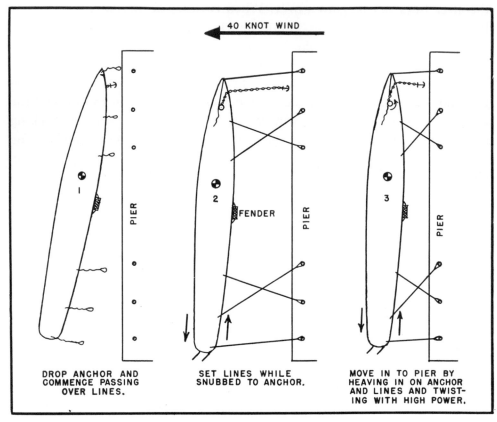

Figure 26. Making a landing when being blown off by a strong wind.

wind will tend to blow the bow down on the pier and this will have to be counteracted by moving the stern in with the engines. The best solution is to touch the pier face exactly parallel, and not swinging. There is a temptation to touch with the bow *in* to keep the propeller guards from being damaged; but actually, if the bow hits first, it is far more likely to cause the ship to pivot and thus swing the propeller guards hard against the pier.

If the wind is blowing hard (over 20 knots) onto the pier, even though we keep the ship parallel as we move in, the speed broadsides may be too great for safety. In this case we should approach to a position opposite the berth, but 50 yards out, and let go the windward anchor (See Figure 27). This anchor will hold the bow up into the wind, and it will also give something to work against while keeping the stern off the pier with the engines. With these arrangements we can get our lines over in an orderly manner and move in to the berth as slowly as we desire. This procedure is especially necessary if we are going alongside another ship at the pier. After getting alongside, the anchor chain of the anchor we have dropped should be slacked to the bottom to keep it clear of passing ships. The anchor can be picked up upon leaving the berth, and it may actually be very useful for getting clear, espe-cially if the wind is still blowing onto the pier.

Wind, When Going Alongside in the Stream

Going alongside a ship at anchor or at a buoy, with the wind blowing, is a different problem because the other ship will head into the wind and usually will yaw considerably. This yaw can be reduced if the other ship shortens the scope of her chain, but in a strong wind the swing becomes quite large. Many shiphandlers recommend studying the swing and seizing the opportunity to approach quickly from downwind while the moored ship has swung clear, but this will occasionally require backing clear because of an error in timing.

A ship anchored or moored to a buoy does not simply swing back and forth around her bow. Actually the ship becomes inclined to the wind and sails

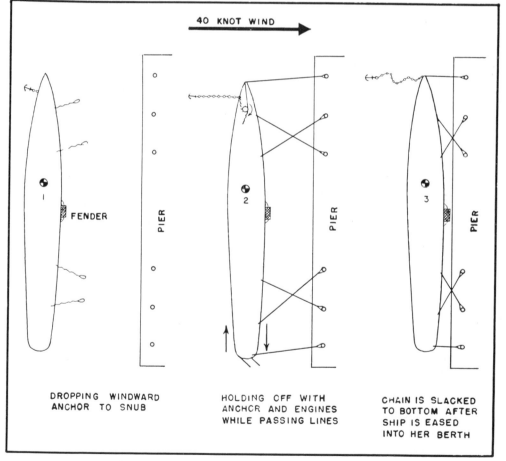

Figure 27. Making a landing when being blown on by a strong wind.

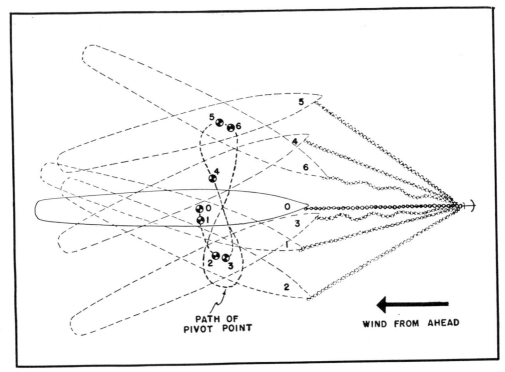

Figure 28. Manner in which a ship swings
in the wind when at anchor.

crosswind until restrained by her anchor chain. This spins the ship, present-
ing the other bow to the wind, and the ship then sails back on the other tack.
This action is illustrated in Figure 28. The trouble with approaching from
downwind is that the moored ship is actually *sailing toward us* when she presents a clear side.

A safer method (See Figure 29) is to approach to a point abreast the ship
but beyond her extreme swing, and then "sail" in broadside by inclining our
ship about 10° to the wind and keeping her at this angle with the engines.
The moment to get the lines over is as the other ship's bow reaches its extreme swing towards us. If our timing is off while using this method, we can
bring our ship parallel to the wind and wait for the other ship to swing
properly. We should get the forward lines over as rapidly as possible because
it may be necessary to take a strain on these lines to prevent the other ship's
stern from swinging into our stern.

The problem of going alongside another ship at a buoy when the wind is
blowing onto a nearby shoal (Figure 30), is a difficult one, but one frequently
encountered. In this case a steering casualty or a momentary loss of power
could spell disaster, so we must be careful to stay well clear of the shoal.

Twisting in safe water, maneuvering to a point slightly ahead of the moored ship's beam but clear of her swing, and then sailing in as before, is a good solution to this problem. But we must have an anchor ready in case our swing is retarded!

Clearing from Alongside

Getting clear from alongside is often more difficult than coming alongside, because, except for wind and current. there is no *direct* way to get our bow out from the other ship or the pier. The general procedure for backing out is to get the stern well clear and then back out rapidly, using *in* rudder initially to swing the bow out. There is a distinct tendency for the bow to suck in to

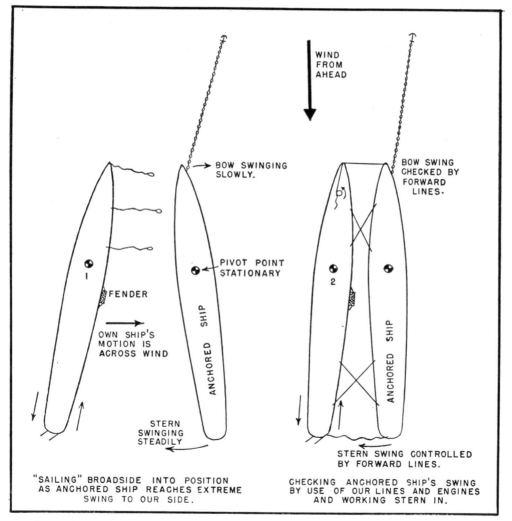

Figure 29. Going alongside an anchored ship that is swinging to her anchor.

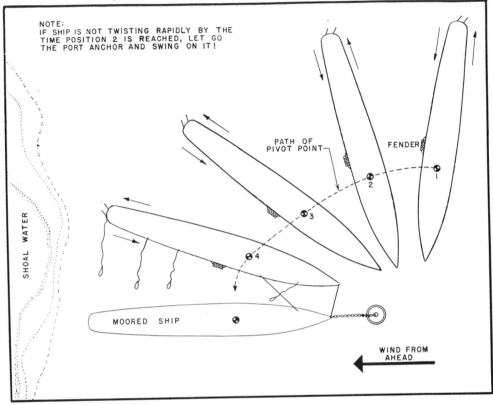

NOTE:
IF SHIP IS NOT TWISTING RAPIDLY BY THE
TIME POSITION 2 IS REACHED, LET GO
THE PORT ANCHOR AND SWING ON IT!

SHOAL WATER

PATH OF
PIVOT POINT

FENDER

2

3

4

MOORED   SHIP

WIND FROM
AHEAD

**Figure 30. Going alongside a destroyer whose stern is
being blown toward shoal water.**

the other ship as we back clear, and we must be careful that our engaged
anchor does not rake the other ship.

The stern can normally be gotten out quite handily by taking in all after
lines, taking all of the slack out of the forward lines, and twisting the stern
out with the engines. This should be done quite slowly, with careful attention to the forward fenders, until the engaged bow is resting securely against
the pier or ship alongside. The stern can then be twisted out handily as desired. When the stern is out sufficiently, stop all engines and slack the forward
lines. The bow will normally bounce out a little as the pressure of twisting
is released, and we can take in all lines and back straight out. If the bow does
not come out, we can twist the bow *out* and the stern *in* momentarily before
backing, since the above procedure has moved our pivot point away from
the pier. Often it is useful to back with the outboard engine only, and use *in*
rudder after having gotten the stern well out initially.

Another and gentler method of getting the stern out is to snub in the bow, using number one line and the capstan. This is slower, and there is less chance of an unexpected surge causing damage, but we cannot get our stern out as far with this method, and we cannot disengage as quickly as when using the engines.

With a very strong wind blowing us onto the pier, it may be advisable to twist the stern out until the ship is nearly perpendicular to the face of the pier before backing out. Under such circumstances we will need extra fenders forward to keep the bow from damaging the pier, because the entire wind load on the ship will come to bear on the point of contact between the bow and the pier. If we can twist the stern out the first 10°, with a wind blowing directly against the pier, we will have no difficulty twisting the remaining 80°, since the wind force becomes less effective in opposing the motion as our ship comes more into line with the wind.

Having moved the stern upwind, it is often advisable to capitalize further on the ship's tendency to back into the wind. As we clear, we can back directly into the wind to gain sea room before "squaring away" on our new course. Utilizing the ship's tendency to back into the wind can also be helpful when clawing away from a lee shore. Why go ahead and fight the tendency for the bow to go down wind, when the ship will readily back into the wind?

Whatever the method used when clearing from alongside a pier, the secret to success is to get the stern far enough out from the pier so that we can back clear with no danger of fouling obstructions. The stern is far enough out, under a given set of conditions, if the ship will pull completely clear of contact with the pier as soon as she starts moving astern.

Occasionally circumstances demand that we back straight out. Such a situation exists when we are one of the inner ships in a nest, but must go out first. In this case we are forced to accept the rubbing of our sides, but normally this won't be serious. The first step is to insure that we have no projections which can catch on the other ships. When we are sure of this, BACK both engines TWO THIRDS or FULL until the ship begins to move astern, and then slow, if desired, to ONE THIRD. This will give a surge of screw current on both sides which will tend to force the ships apart and open a way for us to back clear. This surge of screw current is very useful when backing clear of solid piers or other ships. The more powerful the surge, the more effective it is in pushing us out from a pier or in separating the ships. But bear in mind that if the two engines don't answer together, the unbalance might cause the ship to twist rapidly.

Another method which is useful when clearing from the inside of a nest is to slack all the after lines or take them in, and BACK momentarily against number three lines, port and starboard. This will open out the sterns of the adjacent ships, and we can cast off and get on our way while the nest is open.

Flow Effects

The effect of current between two ships or between a ship and a comparatively solid pier is interesting. If a steady current flows between two ships that are near each other and parallel, the *venturi effect* will exert a force tending to force the ships together. This force will be dependent on the proximity of the two bodies and the character of the restricted channel between them. The force experienced will be proportional to the difference between the square of the velocity of the flow *between* the bodies and the square of the velocity of the flow *on the outer sides* of the ships. On the other hand, if a surge of current suddenly is forced between the ships, it will tend to force them apart. It is as though water were quickly piled up between the ships, and as it flows out from the pile it forces the ships apart. Finally, the entire problem is often complicated by the fact that one ship is moving during the critical period.

As we back clear of another ship with which we were nested, there is always a force which sucks our bow in towards her stern and frequently moves her stern towards us. In spite of what we do, our bow does not pass the other ship's stern by as wide a margin as we would have expected from the original situation.

This effect is present because the water which our ship displaced while lying alongside must be replaced as we back clear. On our engaged side the water cannot be replaced easily because of the presence of our ship and the other ship, so the flow of water is from the outside, tending to force the ships together. This effect can be observed as we back clear from alongside. The distance between the ships at the closest point tends to remain constant as we back clear! Thus, the flat of our bow will be about the same distance out from the other ship's quarter as our bow passes her propeller guard, as it was from her side when it passed amidships. This effect is illustrated in Figure 31.

This displacement effect also works in reverse and is probably the reason why there are so many "close" situations with relatively few accidents. As two ships come close together sideways, the water between the two hulls acts as a cushion and prevents the ships from actually touching.

Going Out Ahead

The above discussion has dealt with *backing* out from a mooring only. Often it is more convenient to go out *ahead,* but there are several factors which must be considered when using this method to clear a mooring. Going out ahead violates the basic rule of "Keep your stern away from danger." When we back out from a mooring, our stern is the first part of the ship to reach open water and we are soon free to maneuver the stern of our ship at will. If we go out ahead we cannot swing our stern towards the ship or pier that we are leaving until we are completely clear. This means that during the clearing operation we can only turn *toward* the ship or pier. Because this is often completely unacceptable, we find ourselves restricted to not maneuvering at all as we go out ahead.

Though one must be careful when going out ahead, it is still a useful and safe maneuver if done properly. Since we have no other means of moving the bow of our ship away from the pier, we must have wind or current for this maneuver unless we go out parallel. Going out parallel is usually very

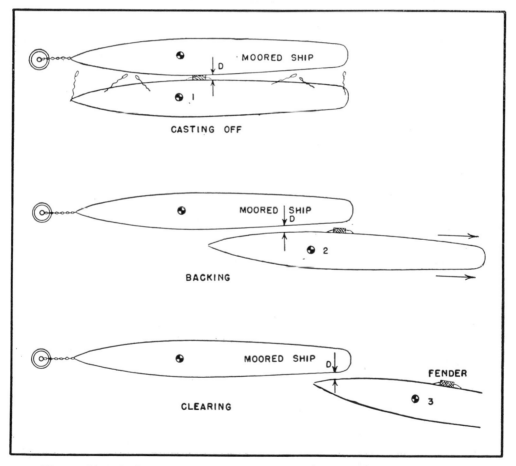

Figure 31. Displacement effect when clearing the side of another ship. The distance (D) tends to remain constant.

unsatisfactory, because we will scrape along the whole length of the pier before we finally clear. In order to go out ahead safely, we must first have our bow well out from the ship or pier that we are clearing, and this requires a wind or current from ahead or from the engaged side.

When going out ahead with such a wind or current, we slack the forward lines until the bow drifts out and the ship assumes the desired inclination. While doing this we must watch our stern to make sure that it does not bear in too hard against the pier we are leaving. As soon as we are ready, we cast off all lines and kick ahead on the outboard screw using inboard rudder. As soon as the stern comes clear, we can use both engines and move out expeditiously.

Going out ahead is seldom used from piers because we normally go into them ahead and we must usually back away to clear them. On the other hand, when moored to a ship that is swinging to its anchor or to a buoy, it is very often desirable and at times necessary to clear ahead. Normally the nest will swing so that the wind or current is ahead or slightly from the side of the ship that is anchored or moored to the buoy. It is therefore perfectly oriented for getting our bow out. Actually, if there is a good wind or current, it is safer to go out ahead than to back out. If we hold number five as we slack the forward lines, as shown in Figure 32, the bow will come out nicely. Then we can hold the forward lines, after the ship has reached the proper inclination, and the stern will move out from the ship. The secret to moving the bow out, but, at the same time keeping the stern clear of the other ship, is to ease the lines slowly. This prevents the ship from pivoting and throwing the stern into the other ship. If we are using a current to get the bow out, we can use the rudder to help hold the stern away from the other ship.

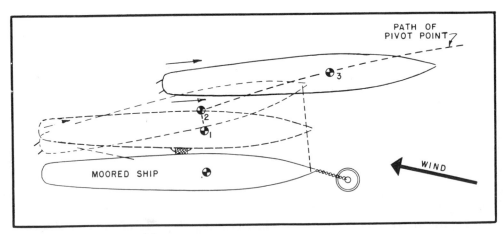

Figure 32. Going out ahead, using the wind to get the bow well out before starting.

If the nest that we are clearing is swinging, we must be careful that the wind does not catch our outboard bow after we have gotten the bow well out. Should this happen, the bow would be blown in rapidly, and we would have to commence the operation again, even if no damage were done. If we observe the swing carefully, we can get the bow out and be ready to clear as the nest reaches the extremity of its swing towards our ship. We must be ready to move away from the other ship rapidly, because it will be remembered that the stern of a ship yawing with the wind continues to swing *outboard* as the ship passes the limit of its excursion and starts on the opposite tack.

In the case where it is necessary to go out ahead, and there is no wind or current, we must go out "around the bow," as illustrated in Figure 33. In this case it is well to have the moored ship snub up to its anchor or to the buoy to insure that its anchor chain is held in as close to its stem as possible. We must work our lines so that the bow is inclined outward as much as possible, and, when ready, cast off all lines and go ahead, using plenty of power. As soon as our pivot point is abreast the moored ship's bow, we can put the rudder over FULL towards the other ship. This will start moving our stern out from the other ship's side at the earliest safe opportunity. We must continue this turn around the moored ship's bow until our stern is well clear of the mooring. Since this maneuver is required only in the absence of wind and current, the conditions are ideal and little trouble will be experienced.

Steerageway

When handling a ship alongside, the controllability of the ship is of major concern to the shiphandler at all times. Because the ship is being brought to a stop, those controls which depend on the ship's motion become less effective as the ship slows. Obviously, when dead in the water, the rudder is ineffective unless the discharge current of a propeller is playing upon it.

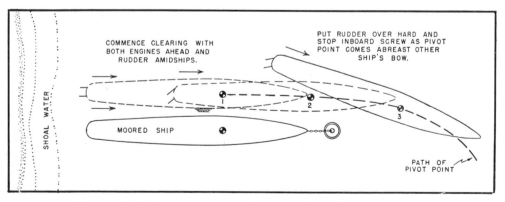

Figure 33. Going out around the bow when there is no wind or tide to help get the bow out.

A ship is said to have "steerageway" as long as she can be controlled by her rudder. The usual test is that the ship can still be held on a steady course by use of the rudder alone, and a ship is said to have "lost steerageway" when the bow wanders from the desired heading in spite of the rudder.

The rudder will exert *some* control force on the ship as long as there is *any* flow past it. The amount of force required to hold the ship on course will depend upon the magnitude of the forces tending to move her off course. These forces are caused by wind, current, or by unsymmetrical flow past the hull, and the magnitude of the resultant force will depend upon the conditions. The speed at which the rudder can no longer overcome them, then, changes as the conditions change. Consequently we must recognize that there is no definite speed at which a ship loses steerageway.

Loss of steerageway is not so serious with a twin-screw ship, because the necessary control force can be supplied by opposing the screws. As we go alongside, then, we should not be overly concerned about the loss of rudder effectiveness since we can take over with the screws. In the normal approach, the rudder and the screws are worked together, and the more the rudder loses its effect, the more the screws are used to maintain or change the ship's heading. With a twin-rudder ship, working ahead, the term "steerageway" loses its meaning, because ample rudder forces can be obtained regardless of the ship's speed.

Steering While Moving Astern

When moving astern, the steering of the ship is more difficult than when going ahead. There is no discharge current available for increasing the effect of the rudders when the engines are backing, and, despite the propeller side forces, the ship handles awkwardly. More has happened than just the reversal of the direction of motion.

The hull of a ship is designed for optimum stability when moving ahead. The sharp bow and general hull shape are selected for optimum performance when moving ahead. If the ship becomes inclined to the direction of flow, there is a restoring moment that tends to force the hull to line up with its direction of motion through the water. In the absence of a force such as a rudder force to hold her at an inclination, the well-designed hull, moving ahead, will straighten out and proceed on a steady course.

Moving astern is a different situation. The ideal hull form is now reversed, and the ship is proceeding with her blunt stern first, followed by the long tapered bow. Moving astern, the stability of the hull is much reduced, and on some ships the hull is actually unstable when moving astern; that is, when the ship becomes inclined to the flow, the resultant moment tends to increase the inclination. Such a ship, when backing, will tend to veer off to one side or the other, and it will take strong forces to bring her out of the turn.

If a ship is barely moving astern, the unstable hull forces mentioned above can easily be overcome by the side forces obtainable from the screws. At a bit higher speed, however, these forces may become larger than those obtainable by the screws, and in that case the ship will continue in a turn, once she starts, despite the action of the screws. At a still higher speed, the rudder effectiveness becomes high enough to force the stern around despite the divergent tendency, and the ship is once more controllable. Thus, if we wish to be able to control the ship's heading while moving astern, we should either move very slowly and control with the engines, or else move at a sufficient speed to insure the rudder effectiveness.

A destroyer drifting slowly astern can be handled quite effectively with the engines. When backing steadily at ONE THIRD on both engines, FULL RUDDER is required to swing the stern, and the ship is apt to veer unexpectedly. Backing steadily at TWO THIRDS is required to obtain effective control with the rudder alone—and very large rudder angles are required even then to reverse her swing, once she starts turning.

Because of the difficulty of maintaining the ship's heading while going astern, it is wise not to attempt to back into tight places. Not only are we leading with our most vulnerable part, the stern, but we don't have the nice control that is available when moving ahead.

Dipping the Engaged Anchor

If there is any doubt about the engaged anchor clearing when handling alongside, we should insure that it won't catch on anything by moving it out of the way. It is very easy to "dip" the engaged anchor, and this will prevent damage by removing a major source. When miscalculations bring two ships together, it is usually the engaged anchor of the ship making the move that does the damage.

The troublesome anchor can quickly be swung clear by suspending it under the bullnose as indicated in Figure 34. A suitable wire is run out of the bullnose, back up the hawsepipe, and secured to the jew's harp of the anchor. When ready to dip the anchor, we walk out the anchor until it clears the hawsepipe; next, we take the slack out of the wire and secure the end on deck, and then we walk out the anchor until it hangs suspended beneath the bullnose. In this position it is well inside the edge of the deck, and, should anything brush against it, it will simply swing around the stem to the unengaged side. This precaution with the anchor takes only a moment, but it will prevent damage by removing one of its most common sources.

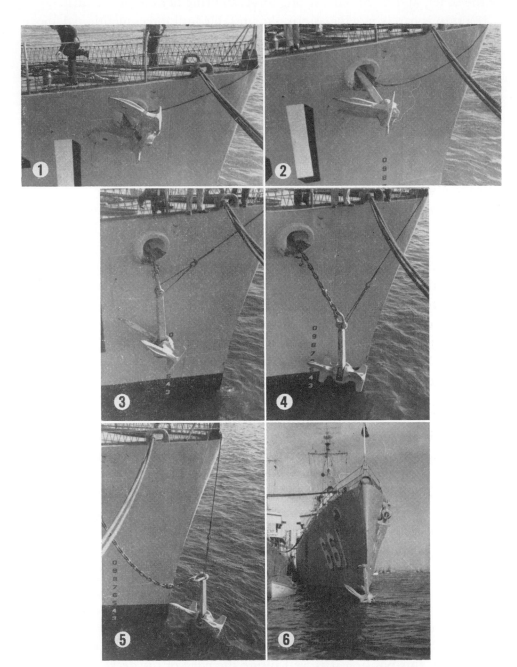

Figure 34. Sequence of actions in dipping the anchor.

Evaluating the Situation

Handling alongside when there is both wind and current is a more complex problem. It is often not clear which of the two will have the predominant effect, and it is difficult to judge the combined effect of the two forces when they are not parallel. It is best to study the situation carefully, make an estimate of the effect on our ship at the various stages of the maneuver, and then be alert to modify our plan quickly if the actual effect is different from that expected.

It is very useful to *test* a confusing condition by slacking the lines for a moment to see what the *actual* movement of the ship is going to be. It is surprising how often the result of this test will demonstrate that the resultant force will carry the ship clear very nicely. One must remember, however, that this test indicates the effect which will be experienced only *at the start* of the maneuver. For instance, our ship might temporarily be shielded from the wind, but after a few yards of travel the wind might have an entirely different effect. In open water it is easier to predict the action of the wind and current on the ship, and as we move away from our moorings, we are normally moving towards open water. Thus the "slack lines" test will give us the initial condition, and our judgment can usually predict the open water condition. The remaining problem lies in predicting the transition from one situation to the other.

CHAPTER VI

ANCHORING

THE ART OF ANCHORING and the use of the anchor tends to be neglected in the United States Navy. Foreign men-o'-war and merchant ships use their anchors a great deal more than our Navy ships, and often our shiphandlers deny themselves the use of this very important tool. It should always be remembered that the anchor represents the only means at our disposal to work directly upon the bow of our ship unless we are using mooring lines. If one doubts the utility of the anchor as a shiphandling aid, he should watch a capable Master maneuver his single-screw, lightly-loaded merchantman in a confined harbor without tugs. With the anchor "snubbing" the bow and resisting forward motion, high engine power can be used with resultant high side forces which facilitate the maneuver.

The Anchor and Its Action

Though the anchor itself is usually formidable in size and weight, it is still amazing that a 3-ton anchor can hold a 4,000-ton vessel in her berth. If we depended upon the friction of the anchor against the bottom to hold us, the anchor would have to be many times heavier than the ones we use. Obviously we must have something more certain to hold us than the friction of the anchor against the bottom.

Navyships carry either "Stockless" or "Light-weight type" (LWT) anchors or both. These anchors are designed to dig into the bottom and bury themselves so deeply that they can resist tremendous forces. If the bottom is too hard for the flukes to dig in, they are designed to catch on any suitable projection and to hold by this method.

When an anchor first strikes the bottom, it lies flat, as indicated in Figure 35. As soon as the ship begins to drag the anchor along the bottom, the flukes rotate and begin to dig into the bottom. The more the ship pulls on the anchor, the deeper the anchor digs in, and eventually the anchor buries itself. It can be seen that it is most desirable that the chain exerts its pull as nearly parallel to the bottom as possible. Otherwise the anchor will not have as favorable an opportunity to bite into the bottom.

If, while digging in, the pull of the chain on the anchor varies from side to side, it may cause the anchor to capsize and reverse its action. This may also be caused by striking a rock as indicated in Figure 36. If the anchor turns completely over, further strain on the chain will cause the anchor to

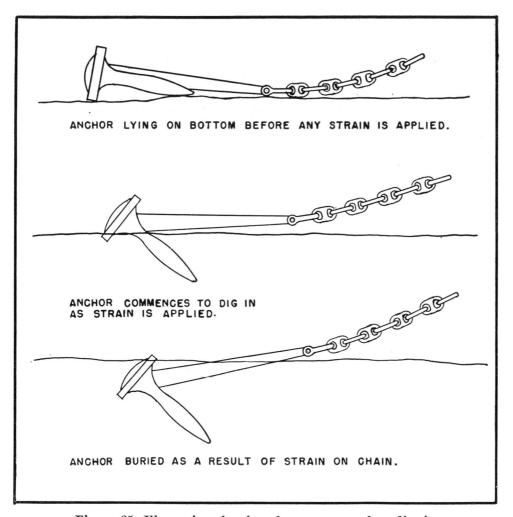

ANCHOR LYING ON BOTTOM BEFORE ANY STRAIN IS APPLIED.

ANCHOR COMMENCES TO DIG IN
AS STRAIN IS APPLIED.

ANCHOR BURIED AS A RESULT OF STRAIN ON CHAIN.

Figure 35. Illustration showing the way an anchor digs in.

dig itself out of the bottom. It is for this reason that it is most desirable that the pull on the chain be steady and in one direction while the anchor is digging in.

If the anchor does not hold, it may drag in a number of ways. First, if the bottom is too hard for the flukes to bite in, the anchor will drag with an intermittent, jerky motion as it catches on successive protrusions from the bottom. If, on the other hand, the bottom is soft enough but of uneven consistency, the anchor may begin to dig in, then capsize and come out, and then go on and repeat this process. In any event, dragging is evidenced by the chain alternately getting taut and going slack as the ship tries to take a strain.

Since the anchor completely buries itself and is capable of holding against tremendous forces exerted by the ship, one might ask how we ever get it back

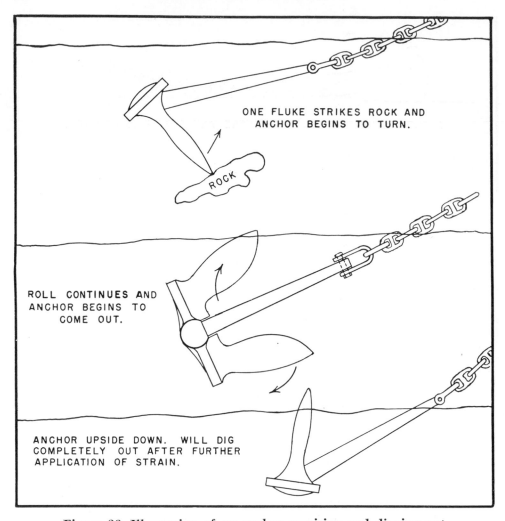

ONE FLUKE STRIKES ROCK AND
ANCHOR BEGINS TO TURN.

ROCK

ROLL CONTINUES AND
ANCHOR BEGINS TO
COME OUT.

ANCHOR UPSIDE DOWN. WILL DIG
COMPLETELY OUT AFTER FURTHER
APPLICATION OF STRAIN.

Figure 36. Illustration of an anchor capsizing and digging out.

up. When we weigh anchor, we heave in on the chain until the chain leads nearly straight up to the hawsepipe of the ship. This rotates the anchor, as indicated in Figure 37, and further pulling on the chain will allow the anchor to dig out. The trick of breaking the anchor out of the bottom is to exert the pull *vertically* instead of horizontally. Conversely, the secret to digging in the anchor is to insure that the pull of the chain on the anchor is *horizontal*.

If the anchor is held at short stay so that the chain tends near the vertical, as indicated in Figure 38, the anchor will not dig into the bottom because the flukes are above the horizontal. The shorter the scope of chain, the less the anchor digs in. When it is desired that the anchor not hold but merely act as a drag on the bow, we can keep it at short stay and it will not dig itself into the bottom. An anchor at short stay is often very useful for holding the bow against the wind while twisting in a harbor, and at times it can be used to control the bow when going alongside to moor.

Therefore, if we wish to anchor securely—and this is the reason for anchoring—we should insure that no appreciable strain is put on the chain until sufficient chain is out to insure that the pull on the anchor is horizontal. We must be sure that the pull is steady so that the anchor buries iself, and, once the anchor is dug in, we should avoid excessive yawing. To set the anchor securely it is worthwhile to lay out the chain and dig in the anchor by use of the ship's engines. This must be done smoothly and without too much power or the anchor is likely to capsize and come out of the bottom. If the

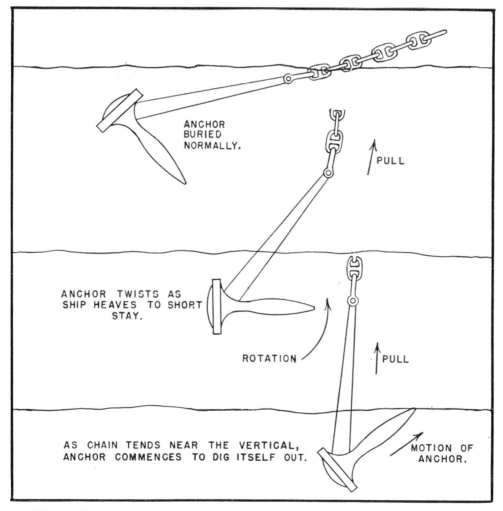

Figure 37. Digging out when weighing. (The anchor digs itself out as the ship heaves in on the anchor chain.)

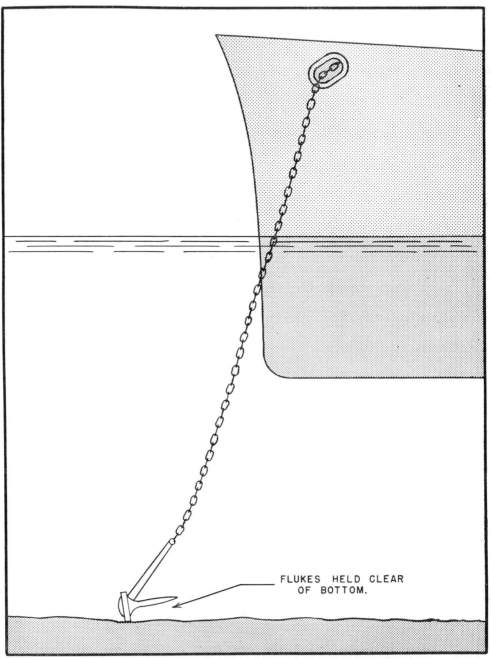

FLUKES HELD CLEAR
OF BOTTOM.

Figure 38. The anchor at short stay. (In this position it cannot dig in.)

ship is yawing considerably and the anchor is tending to drag, it is often very useful to drop a second anchor at short stay under the forefoot so as to snub the excursions of the bow and thus insure that the pull on the holding anchor will be from a nearly constant direction.

Another consideration in anchoring is to use the proper scope of chain. When at anchor, the bow of the ship moves considerably owing to wave motion, yawing, gusts of wind, and current eddies. As a result of this motion the ship tends to come up against the end of the chain with a jerk; and if jerks thus created were applied directly to the anchor, it would soon break free from the bottom. If, however, we use sufficient chain, the weight of the catenary applies an increasing force on the ship as it pulls the chain taut, and this smoothes out the jerks that would otherwise tend to disturb the anchor. Thus, in addition to having enough chain out to insure that the pull on the anchor is horizontal, we must have a sufficient weight of chain out to smooth out the jerks caused by the motion of the ship.

Anchoring

Having considered the general action of the anchor, let's look into the use of this tool by the shiphandler.

Whenever we use the anchor in a destroyer, we must remember the sonar gear. This vital equipment is easily damaged, and if the anchor chain ever gets under the keel and against this gear, it will probably mean dry-docking to repair the damage. It is normally quite easy to maneuver so that this danger is eliminated, but, the general rule is, "Don't drop an anchor while moving ahead." If there is little wind and current, this problem is solved by surging slightly past the anchorage and then dropping the anchor while backing through the "Let Go" bearing. If the rule is followed to anchor only when moving astern, the chain will always be payed out clear of the ship, and it will thus be laid out nicely on the bottom without fouling the anchor. Backing down upon anchoring will also expedite digging in the anchor firmly when the desired scope has been payed out.

It is difficult at times to determine when the ship ceases to move ahead and begins to move astern. Often the landmarks being used to fix the ship's position are so far away that small movements of the ship have no measurable effect on the bearing. If the forecastle has been provided with some small pieces of wood, these can be thrown into the water and the ship's movement readily determined by observing her motion with respect to the "chips." We must remember that our movement over the bottom can differ from our movement with respect to the surface of the water by the amount of the current, but "throwing a chip over" is very useful in determining the ship's motion through the water at low speeds.

Occasionally, because of wind and current or because of restricted maneuvering room, it is desirable to drop the anchor while moving ahead. In a small or congested harbor it is often necessary to approach the anchorage going down wind or current. In this case, since the ship will be carried down by the wind or current, the chain could tend back under the ship before she

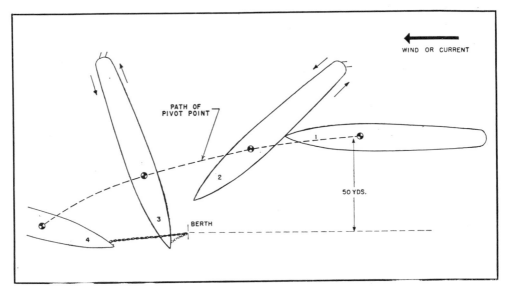

Figure 39. Anchoring downwind or down-current.

swings. The situation should be studied and the anchor used on that side which will insure that the wind and current will carry the ship *away* from the anchor, and that the chain will pay out clear of the ship. If we are approaching our anchorage directly down current, it is very useful to head for a point about 50 yards to one side of the center of the berth as shown in Figure 39, and, as we arrive at the berth, twist the bow towards the berth with the engines and the rudders. If this maneuver is done correctly, the ship will have considerable inclination to the current as the bow passes over the center of the berth. Once this position is reached, the anchor can be safely dropped and the chain will pay out directly up current and clear of the ship.

When anchoring in a cross wind, it is often impractical to pass through and then back across the center of the berth because the wind may carry us off course during the period when we are dead in the water. In this case, since the wind will tend to move us broadside away from the anchor, the only precaution necessary is to use the upwind anchor and have as little headway as possible when we "let go." The same is true when anchoring in a cross-current.

If the situation gets out of control and the chain tends back under the ship or under the bow, we should keep the chain slack and back clear with our engines. Remember that we have at least 105 fathoms (210 yards) of chain available before the "bitter end," and if we keep it slack it will lie on the bottom and clear of the underwater projections. A lot of maneuvering can be done within the 210 yard radius of our shortest anchor chain.

The question of whether to let the anchor go from the hawsepipe or to "walk" it out with the anchor windlass often arises. Certainly, if an anchor were dropped repeatedly from a great height onto rocks or coral heads, it could damage the anchor, and in any case the weight and momentum of a long scope of chain running out is a factor to be considered. On the other hand, walking the anchor out takes time, and the anchor might catch on something as we move about the harbor. A compromise can be reached by making it a rule to drop the anchor only the last 10 fathoms. Thus, if we are going to anchor in 25 fathoms of water, we would walk the anchor out 15 fathoms, disconnect the wildcat from the windlass, leaving the chain held by the brake or by a stopper, then drop the anchor for the last 10 fathoms. This is a relatively safe system because the charted depth should be sufficiently accurate to keep the anchor well clear of the bottom, and it is quite safe to drop an anchor 10 fathoms. We must not forget the "bending shot," and we must be sure that all concerned know the point from which the chain is being measured. It is very convenient to measure the length of chain "at the hawse" since this can be checked visually from the bridge.

The question now arises, "How much chain should we use?" In addition to the considerations mentioned above, we must take into account the size of the berth, the character of the bottom, and the expected weather. In any case the longer the scope of chain, the less likely the ship is to drag. The following amounts of chain have been found to be quite satisfactory for a destroyer under normal conditions:

Depth of water up to 7 fathoms . . . . 30 fathoms of chain
Depth of water 7 to 12 fathoms . . . . 45 fathoms of chain
Depth of water 12 to 20 fathoms . . . . 60 fathoms of chain
Over 20 fathoms of water . . . . Three times the depth

In bad weather it may be necessary to veer to a very long scope of chain to prevent the chain from becoming taut and applying jerks to the anchor.

Weighing anchor is normally a simple evolution if certain basic rules are followed. First, we must handle the ship so that the anchor chain does not get under the keel. The ship can be maneuvered at low power, if necessary, to back away from the anchor and straighten the chain out forward. Due to wind and current it may be necessary to spin the ship on her anchor before weighing, but we should not do this until we have heaved short. A long scope of chain can be deceiving. Finally, we must be careful not to get way on the ship until the anchor is in sight and we have received the report, "Clear anchor." For, until we actually sight the anchor, it is impossible to tell what it may have hooked onto.

The Approach

Anchoring precisely is often important, yet at times precision is difficult to achieve. Generally speaking, a destroyer shiphandler should be able to place his anchor within 25 yards of the designated anchorage. If the anchor misses by more than 40 yards, he should weigh and try again. Remember the Golden Rule here, for there is nothing more annoying than having to worry about a ship that has anchored haphazardly in an adjacent berth.

The secret to accurate anchoring is careful planning ahead of time. Once the anchorage has been assigned, the conning officer should study the anchorage carefully to select the most advantageous approach course and the most useful landmarks. Generally speaking, a straight run for the last 1,000 yards is very convenient, and if this can be made directly towards a known landmark, the problem is greatly simplified. A prominent landmark on the beam should be selected upon which to "let go" when we arrive at the anchorage. The selection of bearings on both a landmark ahead and one on the beam can establish the desired "let go" position of the ship, and the conning officer's job is simplified to conning until these bearings are reached.

The Navigator should lay out distance back along the track on the chart so that all during the approach he can rapidly report the remaining distance to the anchorage. Marks at 1,000, 500, 300, 200, and 100 yards are especially desired, and it will often be useful to establish bearings for these points ahead of time. It is almost customary for a destroyer's gyro to act up just as the anchorage is approached. Since a few erratic fixes are usual before the navigating team begins to function properly, thorough advance preparations are very comforting.

When making a normal approach to anchor with a destroyer, the following system has been found very useful:

Yards to Berth	Action
500	Be making 5 knots through the water
200	STOP
100	BACK ONE THIRD

This should allow us to surge slowly through the "let go" bearing and the anchor can be dropped as we back through the bearing the second time.

As in all other maneuvers, however, each Skipper must calibrate his own ship and modify the above figures to suit his own situation.

Often it is not possible to make a steady 1,000-yard approach because of the shape and size of the harbor and the presence of other ships at anchor. If a short approach must be made as a result of congestion, it is usually feasible to establish the location of the assigned anchorage by eye with respect to the other ships or to landmarks. Having identified the location, the conning officer should keep his eye on this spot and maneuver the ship so that the anchor is over the spot selected. In this type of approach, we should approach slowly and check our estimate with fixes before dropping the anchor. In a naval anchorage it is relatively easy to locate one's berth because the other warships can normally be depended upon to anchor with precision. On the other hand, the average merchantman exerts little effort to anchor in the center of his berth, and his position can be considered to be only approximate.

Emergency Use of the Anchor

In addition to the above considerations on its use, the anchor should be looked upon as the "emergency brake" of the ship. When maneuvering in shoal water or in a harbor, the anchor should be ready for use on a moment's notice. In case of an engine casualty or a steering casualty, it can stop and hold the ship to keep her from running aground. While a ship is proceeding at normal speed she is normally quite controllable, regardless of the state of the weather, but when she is required to lie to for any reason, she is largely at the mercy of the elements. If something prevents proceeding to our destination in a harbor, and we are forced to stop, the anchor is the only means through which we can secure the ship and prevent her drifting with the wind and current.

General

As the shiphandler learns to use his anchors he will learn that they are more than portable moorings. For instance, he will save time and effort by spinning on his anchor instead of laboriously twisting with the engines. He will use his anchor to control his approach when making a downwind landing, and he will leave an anchor out in the stream when he thinks it may be useful later. The anchor of a good shiphandler spends a lot of time on the bottom serving a useful purpose, rather than just rusting in the hawsepipe.

CHAPTER VII

MOORING

AT MOST NAVAL BASES the destroyers are moored to buoys. These buoys are firmly anchored with multiple anchors, and the chain leading up from the anchors to the mooring ring is very large and strong. The actual buoy is simply a float to hold the end of this mooring chain above the surface so that a ship can be secured to it. Mooring to a buoy is safer than anchoring because the ship is thereby secured to heavier and better anchors. The berths can be smaller in a harbor where buoys are used, because a buoy, having both up-stream and downstream anchors, is practically stationary, and ships (moored with a short scope of chain) swing in a circle of smaller diameter.

A destroyer normally moors to a buoy with her anchor chain, and it is this practice that makes "picking up" or "snatching" the buoy somewhat difficult. The anchor chain is so heavy that a man can scarcely displace the lower end of the chain as it hangs from the bow. Heavy manila line can be run fifty yards to the buoy if necessary, because it nearly floats as the water bears most of its weight, and even relatively heavy wire can be run several yards. But from a practical point of view, we should consider that the end of an anchor chain cannot be moved by hand. Consequently, the end of the anchor chain *must be placed* directly on the buoy when mooring.

There are many methods of snatching a buoy, but all of them require that men be placed on the buoy to handle the lines and to shackle the bitter end of the chain to the buoy. It is occasionally possible to put the bullnose directly over the buoy, lower the men and the chain to the buoy from the ship, and secure directly to the buoy. This, needless to say, is a precision maneuver, and it is very difficult if there is any wind or current. It is safer, if less spec-tacular, to use our boat to get the men on the buoy and to use another method to get the chain to the buoy.

The first step in any good method of snatching the buoy is to secure the bow to the buoy by some temporary means, such as a "hook rope," to hold the ship and to give us time to get the chain to the buoy. A 6-inch manila mooring line is not strong enough to withstand the strain as the ship is snubbed in to the buoy, and a heavy wire is very difficult to run for any distance. In a strong wind or current we have only seconds to get our hook rope secured to the buoy before our bow is carried out of range. This is where the spring laid wire rope mentioned earlier is again worth its weight in gold. It is strong enough to hold the bow under almost any wind condition,

80

and it is relatively easy to handle. Once a destroyer is secured to a buoy with a 1⅝-inch "spring lay," only the most drastic abuse will cause the line to part.

Thorough knowledge by the conning officer of the details of the mooring arrangements is essential to a successful evolution. The bridge, forecastle, and engine-room must work together as a team more during this operation than during almost any other. The conning officer must know beforehand where the First Lieutenant will want the buoy with respect to the bow at any given time, and the throttle-man must have a feel for the delicacy of the maneuver.

Rigging for the Trolley Method

The "trolley method" of sending the chain to the buoy will be described because it is the quickest and surest method in use in the Fleet today. This method uses a minimum of lines and men, and has a maximum safety factor at all times. As in most seamanship evolutions, the secret of success is thorough preparation.

In rigging for the trolley method of snatching a buoy (see Figure 40), we first break the anchor chain, connect the buoy shackle to it, and lead the chain to the bullnose. Then we pass the buoy line out through the bullnose and back to the lifeline on the side on which the boat is to be lowered. Next, using relatively large shackles (1-inch are good for this), place them over the buoy line and secure them to the chain a few feet above the big buoy shackle and at intervals of about 6 feet along the chain. These shackles act as trolleys for running the chain down the buoy line. Finally "21-thread" handling lines on the buoy shackle and a short messenger on the buoy line will be found useful. When all has been rigged, pass the end of the chain out the bullnose and rouse out enough chain so that the buoy shackle just clears the water. Make sure that the buoy line runs free through the trolley shackles.

Approach and Mooring

Now we are ready to approach the buoy (See Figure 41). When about 500 yards from the buoy and making about 5 knots, put the buoy party in the boat, lower it, and have it come up under the bow. The boat can be put in the water safely by a competent crew at speeds up to 10 knots, but since the boat can make only about 6 knots, we must proceed slowly enough to allow the boat to gain its position on the bow and ahead.

At 200 yards, stop the engines, pass the buoy line and messenger to the boat, and send the boat out ahead with the buoy line. Our boat should reach the buoy about 50 yards ahead of the ship, and the men can be on the buoy

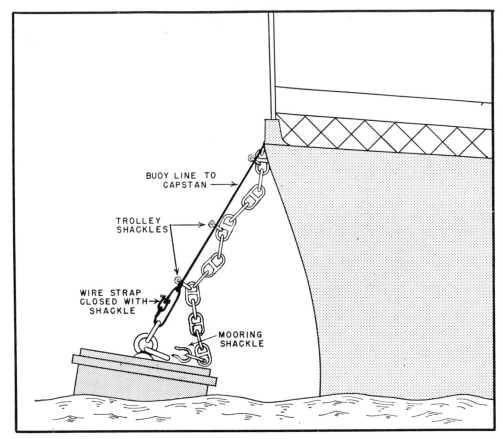

Figure 40. Trolley method of snatching a buoy.

securing the buoy line by the time we bring the ship gently to a stop.

A strong wire strap and shackle is excellent for securing the buoy line to the buoy since it will fit any size or combination of rings and links. This is especially important when mooring to an unfamiliar buoy which might have an oddsize ring. Do not use a buoy hook for securing the buoy line. Not only are these hooks large and unwieldy, but they have been known to straighten out and fail just when they are needed most.

The ideal buoy approach puts our bullnose *abreast* the buoy, about 10 yards to one side, with the ship heading into the wind or current so that she can be maintained in this position while the buoy line is being secured to the buoy. As soon as the buoy line is secured to the buoy, we should heave in until the buoy is close to the bow.

By keeping the buoy abreast the bullnose instead of dead ahead, the conning officer can see the buoy at all times and thus can handle the situation more adroitly. Once the line has been secured to the buoy, it is usually advisable not to use the engines again until the chain has been securely shackled to the buoy, as the bow can generally be heaved to the buoy with the anchor windlass alone. There are times, of course, when the engines must be used to keep the bow close to the buoy, but the use of the engines should be kept to a minimum.

Throughout the maneuvering the ship must be handled with great care. It takes two seamen to handle the line and the mooring shackle at the buoy, and while these men are on the buoy the ship must not be allowed to surge against the buoy line or to brush against the buoy. It is surprising to see how readily a ship can pull a buoy under. It takes only a slight brush to spin the buoy and endanger the men on it.

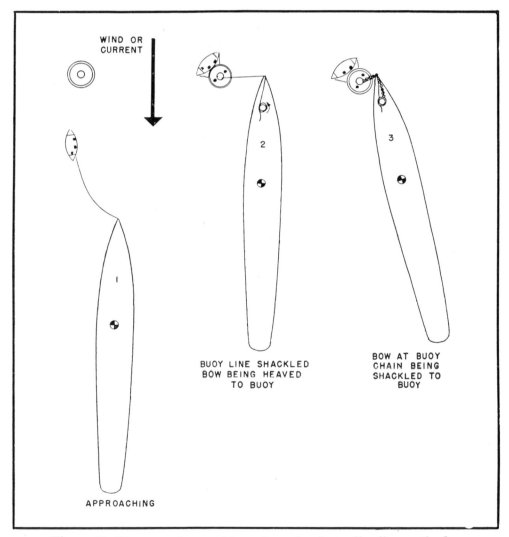

Figure 41. Maneuver in snatching a buoy by the trolley line method.

Never allow the boat to get *between* the buoy and the ship. A sudden surge or a parting line here could spell tragedy. *Always* remove the men from the buoy before taking any considerable strain. Under normal conditions the ship's bow will be drifting gently in toward the buoy while the buoy line is being secured, and so can be easily brought to the buoy with the men on the buoy. If more than a light strain is needed to work the bow to the buoy, get the men off first before taking the strain, and then put them back on when the bow is snubbed up to the buoy and the chain is ready for shackling.

When making a buoy downwind or down-current it is usually feasible to hold the stern up into the wind or current with the engines until we are secured to the buoy, and then to let the ship swing, keeping the buoy out from the bow by use of the engines.

Making a buoy crosswind or cross-current is the most difficult way to make it. Under such circumstances we should, if possible, approach to the position described above with the wind or current dead ahead; but if this is impossible, it will be necessary to make a "flying snatch." The speed of the men on the buoy is the key to this maneuver. Approach so as to put the bow well upwind and slightly short of the buoy (to insure that it will pass clear of the buoy as the ship is blown downwind). Use the engines and helm to twist the bow upwind throughout the operation. This will keep the bow as near the buoy as possible as the stern is swept downwind, and will give the men on the buoy a maximum opportunity to get the buoy line secured. Once the buoy line is secured, we can swing to it and eventually heave the bow up to the buoy. We must be careful while swinging, because a parted buoy line at this time will require another approach at the very least.

Mooring to Two Buoys

Making both bow and stern buoys offers certain new problems to the conning officer. Generally, the problem is readily solved by concentrating on making one buoy at a time and simply avoiding the other buoy until we are secured to the first one. Normally, in an uncomplicated situation, make the bow buoy as described above. If two boats are available, the stern wire can be run to the other buoy while the bow is being secured, but no strain should be taken aft until all is secured forward. When all is ready, walk out the chain forward and move the stern towards its buoy with the engines until the stern wire can be heaved in to the desired scope. When the stern wire is secured at the desired length, tauten the moor by heaving in on the chain, forward, to the desired tautness.

Making two buoys when heading downwind or down-current requires securing to the stern buoy first. In this case we should avoid getting the stern

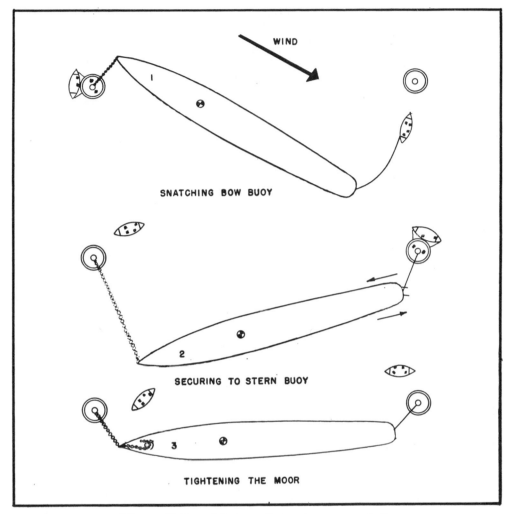

WIND

SNATCHING BOW BUOY

SECURING TO STERN BUOY

TIGHTENING THE MOOR

Figure 42. Snatching two buoys in a crosswind.

buoy dead astern until the stern wire has been run and then secured at the desired scope. A buoy dead astern cannot be seen from the bridge, whereas one slightly on the quarter can easily be seen. Running out the chain forward is relatively simple except that, in this case, the chain probably will not slide down the buoy line because of the long scope of the buoy line out forward, and it will be necessary to pass a messenger through the forward buoy mooring ring and back to the capstan to haul the chain out to the buoy.

Mooring fore and aft to buoys in a crosswind or cross-current is a problem frequently encountered (See Figure 42). As before, the solution is to moor to one buoy at a time. Once the ship is secured to the forward buoy, we can walk the stern up to the stern buoy with the engines. This can be done in all but

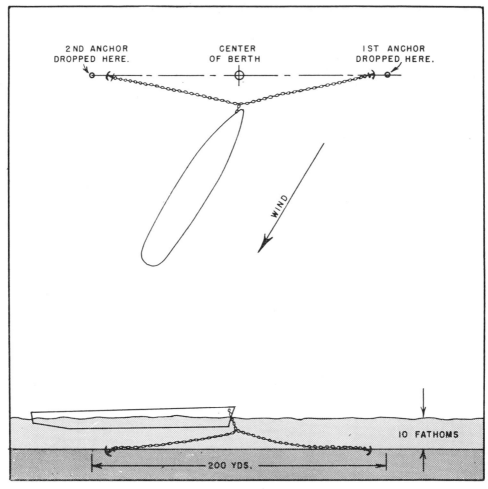

Figure 43. Mooring to two anchors in 10 fathoms of water,
wind across the moor.

the strongest winds, but since it puts considerable strain on the forward buoy,
we must not attempt it until the chain has been secured to the buoy forward.

Mooring to Two Anchors

Though seldom seen today in the United States Navy, the practice of mooring to two anchors is very useful and merits the consideration of the accomplished mariner. A classical moor is to drop two anchors a substantial distance
apart and then adjust the scope of chain to each until the ship's bow is held securely midway between the two anchors. If the ship may be moored for a
considerable time and may swing around her moor with the change of tide,
it is normal with naval ships to insert a mooring swivel in the rig to prevent
the chains from fouling. Most merchant mariners, however, don't bother

with a swivel, feeling that it takes no longer to clear the chains before getting underway than it does to rig and unrig the swivel.

The advantage of mooring in this manner is that the bow of the ship is snubbed to one place. When assigned to a small anchorage, if the ship is moored so that her mooring swivel is over the center of her berth, she can swing with the tide and wind and her stern will never extend much more than a shiplength from the center of the berth. She might require twice this radius of clearance were she to anchor normally.

More important than the capability to ride within a small radius of the center of the berth is the increased security of the moor versus normal anchoring. As pointed out in Figure 28, a ship riding to a single anchor tends to yaw; the stronger the wind, the greater the yaw. The frequent change in the direction of the pull on the anchor combined with the jerks on the anchor when the ship "comes about" while yawing is the most frequent cause of dragging anchor. If a ship has her anchor dug in, has adequate chain out, and does not yaw, there is little danger of dragging. Mooring to two anchors very nearly assures such safety.

In the average situation, while moored as indicated in Figure 43, the pull of the ship is divided between the two anchors in accordance with the geometry of the moor, *but* the pull on each anchor is always along the line from the anchor to the mooring swivel, which direction never varies more than a few degrees from that from the anchor to the center of the berth. This is in sharp contrast to the situation when anchored to a single anchor where the pull on the anchor changes with the direction of the wind and current. Furthermore, under a given combination of wind and current, a moored ship is very stable. Since the two anchor arrangement provides restraints to keep the bow from moving to the side, the ship does not yaw and the pull on each of the anchors is constant.

When the ship swings in line with the two anchors, however, the restraining side forces do not come into play until the bow has moved appreciably to one side. In this case, the two anchor moor does not eliminate yawing, but it does tend to reduce the amount of yaw considerably. In a situation where maximum security of the mooring is the prime objective, the line between the two anchors should be appreciably different from the direction in which the ship is expected to head in response to the combination of the wind and current.

One should not conclude, however, that mooring with the anchors in line with a reversing tidal current, for example, is a useless evolution. On the contrary, in addition to reducing the diameter of the berth by an amount equal to twice the scope of chain which would have been used, the alteration in the direction of pull on the anchors is avoided. As the direction of the tide shifts, the ship shifts from riding to one anchor to riding to the other, and the pull on each anchor is always in the same direction, i.e., towards the center of the berth. If the ship is moored during several changes of tide, the anchors dig in more and more securely instead of being uprooted and replanted at each change of the direction of current.

The operation of the forecastle when mooring and unmooring is one of the grand evolutions of deck seamanship. The details of mooring a battleship by the "Eldridge method" or the "O'Neil method" are adequately covered in *Knight's Seamanship* and need not be dealt with here, but we should understand the problem and principles involved. In mooring to two anchors, if we wish to use a mooring swivel (and the major difficulties in mooring surround the rigging and unrigging of this swivel), we must arrange that the chains to the two anchors meet at a place where the chains can be broken, that we can hold the chains securely while attaching the swivel, and that, after the chains are attached, the swivel can be eased out of the hawse and the two chains run clear. The essential difference between the Eldridge and the O'Neil methods is that in the former both chains are run out of the same hawsepipe *before* the anchors are dropped, and in the latter the anchors are each dropped from their own hawse, and, after the ship has been adjusted to the center of the berth, the chains are re-rigged so their ends enter the same hawse for rigging the swivel. In a destroyer, the O'Neil method, modified to suit the particular forecastle installation, is probably the more practical.

The conning officer's problem in mooring is to place the two anchors correctly and maneuver the ship as necessary while adjusting to the center of the berth. Obviously, the easiest method of placing the anchors is to pass through the center of the berth heading into the existing combination of wind and current, dropping one anchor the desired distance short of the center and the other the desired distance past the center of the berth. If the conning officer drops his first anchor before passing through the center and carries on to drop the second, the evolution is known as a "flying moor." If, on the other hand, he passes through the center and drops the upstream or "riding" anchor and then eases back through the berth to drop the downstream or "lee" anchor, the maneuver is called an "ordinary moor" Since a destroyer has only one anchor windlass and must drop one of her anchors from a chain compressor (and thus cannot heave in on this anchor without re-rigging the chains), she should always drop the anchor connected to the wildcat first, pass through the center of the berth, drop the second anchor from its compressor, and then heave back to the center of the berth with the chain to the wildcat while gradually paying out chain from the compressor.

This procedure dictates the use of the ordinary moor except when there is so little wind or current that there would be no concern about riding to a chain held only by the compressor.

Let's consider the problem of mooring a destroyer in 10 fathoms of water with a mud bottom. Because of the depth of the water we would like to have 45 fathoms of chain to a single anchor, so we might decide to insert the mooring swivel at the 45-fathom shackle in each of our chains. Taking into account the five-fathom, bending shots this will give us 50 fathoms or 100 yards of chain from the mooring swivel to each of the anchors. Since the swivel will be about two fathoms below the surface, this amount of chain will give a scope-to-depth-of-water ratio of greater than six to one.

In 10 fathoms of water, our hawsepipes are about 14 fathoms from the bottom and simple triangulation indicates that each anchor should end up 96 yards from the center of the berth with the chains taut. The chains, however, will never be completely straight and about four fathoms of slack in one chain is necessary for dipping around the bow and connecting to the swivel, so we will have about as taut a moor as possible if the anchors actually end up each 90 yards from the center of the berth. On the other hand, we wish to be sure the anchors are well dug in in their final position, so we should allow about 10 yards of movement for each anchor for this purpose. In summary then, our calculations show that we should drop the anchors 200 yards apart and then heave them in until the two 45-fathom shackles are on deck (with chains through the same hawsepipe) so the mooring swivel can be inserted.

In approaching such a moor, we should have both anchors ready for letting go, one from the wildcat and the other from its compressor. Heading into the wind and current, we should pass through the center of the berth and drop the anchor from the wildcat exactly 100 yards beyond the center of the berth. We should then back through the center of the berth, veering chain as we go, and when 100 yards back from the center, let go the other anchor from its compressor. We can use the first anchor chain to measure the distance between the anchors, letting go the second anchor when we have veered to 100 fathoms on the first one (the movement of the anchor in digging-in will just about cancel the sag in the chain). We can then heave ourselves to the center of the berth with the riding chain and go through the evolution of connecting the shackle.

The above procedure is for achieving a very taut moor for riding in a small berth in a tideway, for example. Under such conditions the tighter the moor the better, and the moor is properly made heading into the existing current. On the other hand, if the ship is being moored to be more secure in the face of strong winds, it is not desirable to have the anchors in line with the expected wind, and it is neither desirable nor possible to keep as taut a moor. In such a case, the line between the anchors should be at right angles to the direction of the wind, and the anchors should be dropped about 80 yards to each side of the center of the berth. In any case, the strain on the chains as the wind picks up will cause the anchors to dig in further and will cause the geometry of the moor to adjust to the wind condition. Under severe conditions the anchors might drag until they are sharp on either bow, but as long as the ship is prevented from yawing, the shiphandler can feel sure he is getting about as much holding power as possible out of the two anchors.

Mooring is neither difficult nor extraordinarily time consuming. The added security of a two-anchor mooring especially in light of the frequent mishaps caused by dragged anchors, should be very appealing to the careful mariner. It is much wiser to put that second anchor on the bottom in a manner planned to produce maximum security for the ship, than to leave it resting in its hawsepipe. When the first anchor has already started dragging, it is usually too late to do a good job with the second.

The Hammerlock Moor

Riding out a very severe storm or hurricane at anchor requires the utmost skill on the part of the shiphandler, and he must extract the last measure of safety from his preparations. A planned mooring is much better than the haphazard dropping of two anchors, but even a well planned normal moor can be improved upon for a heavy blow. The "Hammerlock moor" was discovered by skillful accident by the skipper of an AKA riding out a hurricane in Chesapeake Bay, but it is equally applicable to any type ship equipped with two anchors.

A normal moor using a mooring swivel has several disadvantages for use during a severe storm. First, if even a short scope of chain is allowed between the hawse and the mooring swivel, the bow is not held rigidly and the ship may commence to yaw. Second, the entire strain is placed upon a single length of chain, the parting of which would cost the ship all capability of anchoring. Last, the anchors cannot be worked individually or weighed without disconnecting the mooring swivel, and this may be nearly impossible during a really bad storm. The Hammerlock avoids these disadvantages.

The Hammerlock moor can be executed by dropping the first anchor, veering to the desired scope of chain, and then maneuvering towards the side from which the anchor was dropped until the chain is hard around the bow and laid out directly across the direction of the wind. The second anchor is then dropped and, as chain is veered to this second anchor, the ship will move back to an intermediate position with an anchor broad on each bow and the chains tightly crossed on her stem. In this position her bow will be fixed, she will not yaw, and the full holding power of both anchors will be utilized in securing the ship. Either anchor can be worked at will to adjust the moor, and the only disadvantage, besides a bit of paint scraped from the bow by the chains, is that we must be careful to weigh our anchors in the correct order to avoid fouling them.

The advantage of crossing the chains on the stem instead of using each anchor to its own bow is that the foremost point on the ship, the stem, is firmly fixed by the action of the two anchors and the tendency to yaw is thus minimized. If the two chains lead normally off their respective bows from their hawsepipes, the point at which their lines of action crossed, which determines the point about which the ship would tend to pivot, would be farther aft than the stem, the amount depending upon the physical location of the hawsepipes. In a normal warship the hawsepipes are so far forward and so close together that there is probably little practical gain in crossing the chains and the chains would be least likely to fail because of chafe when leading directly from their own hawsepipes. Consequently, if the hawsepipes are well forward and close together, the chains should not be crossed.

In a hurricane the wind veers as the center of the storm passes, and the direction to which it will veer is usually known in advance. If wind shifts can be predicted, the moor can be kept properly oriented to the wind by riding to a shorter scope of chain on the anchor towards which the wind is expected to veer. As the direction of the wind changes, a larger share of the load will fall on this "weaker" anchor; it will consequently drag until its share of the load diminishes, and the whole mooring will be reoriented to meet the new direction of the wind.

Using the Engines to Ease the Strain

It would seem that in any case when the ship is being forced back against her moorings by the wind or the current that the engines could be used to ease the strain. This theory is true in principle, of course, but if a ship is yawing severely, it is very difficult to put it into practice. The use of engine power when yawing often accentuates the yaw and worsens the situation instead of easing it. The amount of wind force exerted on the ship increases as the ship becomes inclined to the direction of the wind, and as the ship yaws her inclination to the wind varies constantly. The engine power which might ease

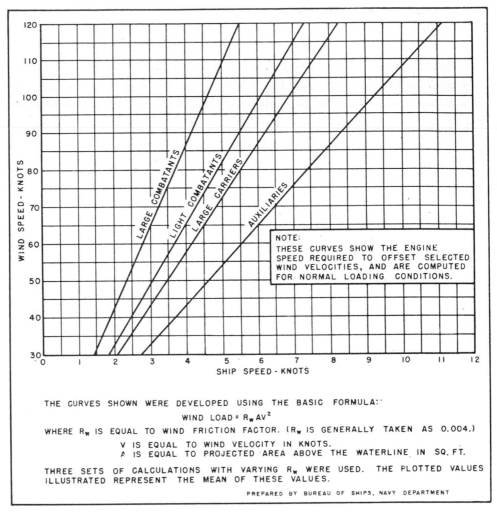

Figure 44. Engine speed vs. wind velocity for offsetting force of wind.

the strain at one moment might cause the ship to surge ahead and slacken the moor a few moments later.

If the bow of the ship is held steady by a normal moor or a Hammerlock, on the other hand, the use of the engines to reduce the strain is simple and straightforward. We should use a little less power than that required to overcome the effect of the wind on the ship, thus the ship will ride back nicely against her moorings but without excess strain. Figure 44 is a chart indicating the engine speed required to offset the effect of the wind for various types of ships in the Navy. If, in using this chart, we select an engine speed of two knots less than that required to offset the wind being experienced, the strain on the mooring will be the same as though we were moored on a calm day in a current of two knots. This, of course, is a very acceptable situation, but we must watch the velocity of the wind and adjust the engine speed as necessary to keep the strain on the moorings constant.

Mediterranean Moor

The "Mediterranean moor" is a method that destroyers are nowadays being required to use frequently. Mooring with the stern to the mole or pier allows more ships to be moored within a given amount of dock space, and furthermore allows each ship to have her own brow to the mole. It is an excellent way to moor in small, well-protected harbors where space is at a premium, and many of the troubles experienced in nesting are eliminated. The European navies use this method extensively.

Essentially the "Med moor" is mooring one end of the ship to a mole or pier and anchoring the other end. Since the ship can't swing to the anchor, it is necessary to put two anchors out, one on each bow, so that the bow can be held in place with a wind from either beam. If the anchors are well separated, the chains will tend sufficiently out to the side to hold the bow even in a strong wind. Actually, an optimum arrangement for security of the moor would be to have the chains tending 60° out from each bow, but the harbor situation seldom allows such separation. In case the congestion of the harbor does not allow good separation, the method outlined for cruisers in Chapter XII should be used.

In preparing to make the Mediterranean moor we must decide how far out from the mole to drop the anchors. It is advantageous, when clearing, to have the anchors well out from the mole, because, since we have but one capstan, we must work the anchors one at a time, and it is more comfortable to accomplish this time-consuming task as far out in the stream as feasible. Since our shortest anchor chain is 105 fathoms, we might pick 75 fathoms as a good scope of chain and thus allow a 30 fathom margin for error.

As indicated in Figure 45, for a GEARING-class destroyer, with 75 fathoms of chain, a 390-foot ship, and our stern close to the mole when secured, we should drop our anchors 280 yards out from the face of the mole. In order to accomplish this and to separate our anchors adequately, an approach parallel to the face of the mole is advantageous. We drop our first anchor when the hawse is about 50 yards short of a position abreast our berth, and then we drop the second anchor when the bow is about 50 yards past the berth. By putting the rudder over full and twisting the engines as we let go the first anchor, we can keep the chain from getting under the ship. The anchor which will be upwind as we BACK into our berth should be handled on the wildcat, and the other can be handled from its compressor.

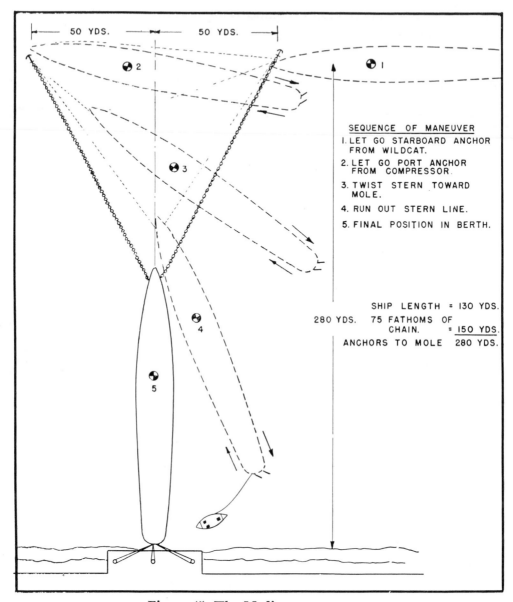

SEQUENCE OF MANEUVER
1. LET GO STARBOARD ANCHOR FROM WILDCAT.
2. LET GO PORT ANCHOR FROM COMPRESSOR.
3. TWIST STERN TOWARD MOLE.
4. RUN OUT STERN LINE.
5. FINAL POSITION IN BERTH.

SHIP LENGTH = 130 YDS.
75 FATHOMS OF CHAIN. = 150 YDS.
ANCHORS TO MOLE 280 YDS.

50 YDS.   50 YDS.

280 YDS.

Figure 45. The Mediterranean moor.

When both anchors are down, we commence twisting the ship and backing her into her berth, veering out chain proportionately as we proceed. As soon as possible we should run our stern line to the mole. As the stern approaches the mole it is advisable to shift the conn to the fantail where the situation can be seen firsthand. The stern is ultimately moved into place by backing slowly and gradually easing the chains. If the anchor on the wildcat has been dug in firmly, the motion can be controlled by slowly walking out the chain while backing steadily at a low power.

The stern is secured to the mole with a stern line and two quarter lines. Crossing the quarter lines under the stern, as indicated in Figure 44, insures a more secure moor, but on some ships this is difficult due to obstructions on the stern. It is wise to use our "strong mooring line" or even the towing hawser for the stern line.

After the stern has been secured, the moor is tautened by heaving in and equalizing the anchor chains. When the ship is finally secure, the anchor chains should both be taking a moderate strain and standing well out of the water. Remember that we have not allowed any margin astern in case of a wind from ahead, so there must be *no* slack in the chains.

CHAPTER VIII

HANDLING AT SEA

WHEN WE LEAVE the calm but congested environment of the harbor and head for the open sea, we must readjust our thinking. At the harbor entrance, as our bows first rise to the swells of the open sea, we shift to an environment where 2,000 yards is a short distance and speeds up to 30 knots are the normal operating speeds. Our ability to estimate distance and to judge motion is greatly reduced as the familiar checkpoints of the harbor slip behind us. We must be ready to meet the extremes of weather and sea condition in a world where the environment can shift from a distant passing situation to an urgent collision situation in an extremely short time.

We clear the harbor and normally move into our place in a tactical formation. As we join the forming, reorienting, turning, wheeling, and all of the other intricate maneuvers of a complex formation, we begin to see the need for a system of maneuver to apply to our individual ship.

Superheat

One of the most irritating problems which face those handling the older classes of destroyers (1,600, 2,100, 2,200, and 2,400 tonners) is the problem of superheat. In the newer classes with their 1,200 psi steam systems, the designers have gone back to the pre-World War II arrangement of boilers with integral superheaters that are always in use. In the FORREST SHERMAN and the frigates, superheated steam is used for all purposes, so adequate steam flow is always assured and the conning officer need not be concerned about the "superheat problem." In such a ship the conning officer can ring up maximum speed for the boilers on the line or he can ring up STOP without any great preparation or warning. For recovering an object in the water, the ship can approach at maximum speed, back to a stop, and then stop all engines and lie to with no hazard to the engineering plant. This is not so in the older classes, and close coordination must be maintained between the bridge and the engineers to prevent damage to the boilers.

Because of thermal stress we must not change the temperature in a boiler rapidly. The boilers of the older destroyers are designed for 650 lbs. per sq. in. pressure and 850°F maximum superheat. Saturated steam at this pressure is at a temperature of about 600°F, so to change from saturated to full superheat, we must increase the temperature of the steam 250°F. This requires an even greater temperature change in the structure of the boiler, and good operating practice limits the maximum rate at which the temperature of the superheat may be changed to 50° every five minutes, or 10° per minute. This means that it will take us 25 minutes to reduce the temperature of a boiler at full superheat to that of saturated steam at the same pressure!

In the World War II type boilers the steam is heated to this high temperature in a separate part of the boiler from the main furnace, and the burners for this part must be lighted off and controlled separately. However, both parts of the boilers use the same flues, and if the superheater casing is opened (as when inserting a torch to light the burners), the gases from the main furnace can blow back through the opening. Because of this, superheaters cannot be lighted off while the boiler is steaming at a high rate, and it is the normal practice never to attempt to light off superheaters when steaming faster than 17 knots.

Superheated steam cannot be mixed with saturated steam, because of the thermal stresses and changes in flow caused by the difference in temperature. When two of these older boilers are being connected to the same steam line, then, it is the practice to lower both boilers to saturated steam, cross-connect them, and then raise them together to the desired superheat.

Finally, when using the superheaters in these boilers, one must insure that the steam is actually flowing through the superheaters at all times. If the flow of steam ceases, and thus the carrying away of the heat is stopped, the superheater tubes will burn out in a matter of moments. Even though the burners were cut out, the radiation from the furnace of a heat-soaked boiler is enough to burn out the tubes or cause them to twist and sag.

Thus, though adding to power and efficiency, the provision of boilers with separately fired superheaters adds a distinct complication in the operation of the ship.

Without superheat in such a ship, the maximum speed with a given number of boilers on the line is quite limited, but one can steam at any speed he may desire from zero to this maximum without any complication. *With* superheat, maximum power is available, but a certain minimum speed must be maintained to insure sufficient steam flow through the superheaters to prevent damage. To ring up STOP with superheat on is inviting disaster.

From an operational point of view in the older destroyers then, we can consider that we have the choice of the following steaming conditions:

Boilers in Use	Speed Range with Saturated Steam	Speed Range with 850°F Superheat
1	0 to 17 knots	8 to 20 knots
2	0 to 22 knots	10 to 27 knots
4	0 to 29 knots	15 to 35 knots

Having selected one of these speed ranges, it takes time to shift to another. If we wish to increase the number of boilers in use, the temperature of the steam in the steaming boilers must be lowered to "saturated" to permit the new boilers to be cut in. If we wish to be able to stop quickly from a high speed, we must steam with saturated steam and more boilers may be required than for the same speed using superheat.

A typical example of the problem of handling superheat presents itself when a World War II destroyer with full superheat on two boilers, finds she can't keep up with the carrier she is plane-guarding. To steam at a higher speed, she must first reduce the superheat on her steaming boilers (while preparing the new boilers for being cut in); then cut in the new boilers when the proper temperatures have been reached, light off all superheaters once again, and finally commence building up for high speed. It will take 25 minutes to reduce the superheat (and she will have to be reducing her speed as she loses superheat); she will have to slow to 17 knots momentarily for cutting in the new boilers and lighting off the superheaters; and it will take 25 minutes to build back up to 850°F superheat again. Thus, it will be over 50 minutes before she can be steaming at her maximum speed. For this reason the alert shiphandler tries to predict his speed requirements well ahead, and allows a safe margin when there is any doubt.

As with most rules, the above rules can be occasionally violated if the shiphandler understands the limitations. The principal danger lies in slowing down rapidly and stopping the flow of steam through the superheater tubes.

The conning officer should immediately notify the engine-room as soon as it becomes apparent that he will be required to slow drastically or stop. The engineers can commence lowering superheat immediately and prepare emergency measures for maintaining the required steam flow. Lifting the superheater safeties by hand can always allow the required flow.

Rather than ring up STOP with superheat on, it is better to "rock" the engines back and forth from AHEAD ONE-THIRD to BACK ONE-THIRD to maintain the flow. This can be done frequently enough so that no appreciable way will be gotten on the ship. If the engineers have been notified promptly, they can reduce the superheat and maintain the flow so the ship can be safely stopped after a few minutes.

To meet the normal operational requirements and also largely to remove the necessity of special orders concerning superheat in the older destroyers, the following system has been found useful:

1. The Captain designates how many boilers shall be in use and whether they shall be steamed "with" or "without" superheat.

2. If "with superheat," and the speed is sufficient, the boilers are brought up to 700°F without further orders.

3. If the ordered speed requires it, the superheat is raised without order; but as soon as the requirement is removed, the superheat is again lowered to 700°F.

4. If the speed is lowered too low to maintain the necessary flow, superheat will be reduced or cut out as necessary without order; but when the speed is raised again, superheaters will be lighted and the superheat raised to 700°F without further order.

5. Should the conning officer be required to stop without sufficient notice, he will "rock" the engines instead of ringing up STOP, until the engine-room reports that the superheat has been lowered to saturated.

The above procedures offer a satisfactory system which will meet the normal operational requirements of a destroyer. The moderate superheat can be quickly lowered with little chance of damage to the boilers, yet the superheaters are lighted and the ship has the ability of building up to the maximum speed for the boilers in use without having to slow even momentarily.

The Destroyer's Role

In a destroyer we are always required to perform the most difficult maneuvers. When the large ships change course by simple turn, we must reorient through the entire arc of the turn. If the turn is large, we must countermarch or split the screen and reorient. When the course is fully set, the signal flags flutter again and we are shifted from a circular to a bent line screen, but as soon as an air attack threatens we are called back. These formation maneuvers are laced with a liberal dose of plane guarding, mail passing, fueling at sea, and general messenger work. A destroyer spends a large part of each day and night skirting around the edges or knifing through the center of the formation, and she must do it smartly and precisely or the most serious consequences can occur.

Because of the power and maneuverability of the destroyer (and the normal courtesy to seniors), it has become accepted that the destroyer will keep out of the way of heavy ships. Although the rules of the road apply in a naval formation as well as upon the high seas, the destroyer conning officer is considered to have blundered if he allows his ship to get into a position where a heavy ship is forced to maneuver to avoid him.

This subordinate position of the destroyer occasionally leads to awkward situations with heavy ships. At times, destroyers have literally to flee for their lives because an Officer of the Deck on a large ship has too liberally evaluated the destroyer's ability to keep out of the way. Nevertheless, it has always been a point of pride among destroyer officers that they could always accord the heavy ships the privilege of right of way and still maneuver with them effectively.

Maneuvering Through a Formation

The trick of maneuvering through a formation is to handle the ship so that not only will we pass clear of the other ships in the formation, but also we will convince the OODs of these ships that we are doing so. This requires that we make our intentions clear to everyone at the earliest possible moment. In a crossing situation, a course which points our ship 30° ahead of the other ship's beam may actually be sufficient to carry us astern of him, but if we alter course sufficiently so that we are actually *pointing* astern of him, the conning officer of the other ship knows at a glance that we will clear him. So we should make it a rule to change course boldly enough so that our intention is clear from the first moment.

In keeping clear of other ships, the question naturally arises, "How much is *clear?*" Certainly if a collision does not occur, the ship has cleared. On the other hand the record of a carrier skipper's blood pressure while a destroyer cuts under his bow might be a better measure of the "closeness." Actually it is well to draw an imaginary "keep out" boundary 2,000 yards ahead, 1,000 yards abeam, and 500 yards astern of each heavy ship, as shown in Figure 46, and stay well outside of it. If we are approaching on an opposite course, we should push the forward boundary out further ahead, or if we are on a parallel course, we can shave the boundaries a little. These arbitrary boundaries have proved very satisfactory in practice, and if we stay clear of this "Keep Out" area there will be no cause for criticism of our actions.

A very useful rule for safe maneuvering when close to another vessel and heading towards her is to keep our bow on the same side of the line-of-sight between us as the other ship's stern, as illustrated in Figure 47. This will insure that we will pass astern of her, if she continues her present course. In the case where she unexpectedly turns toward us, it also allows us to clear by turning in the direction we had originally offset our bow from the line-of-sight. In this case we have a head start in the turn, and, by holding our turn, can insure that a collision will not occur.

Another cardinal rule for safe maneuvering is, "Always Turn *Away*." This rule means to keep our bow pointed out from the formation toward clear water as much as possible during a maneuver, and under no circumstances to get caught on the *inside* of a turn. When beginning a maneuver calling for an

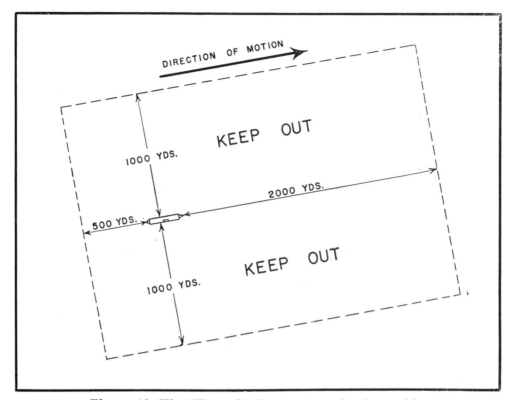

DIRECTION OF MOTION

KEEP OUT

1000 YDS.

2000 YDS.

500 YDS.

KEEP OUT

1000 YDS.

Figure 46. The "Keep Out" area around a large ship.

initial radical turn, we should make the turn to the side *away* from the formation. If we are on the wing of a bent line screen, this may require a turn of nearly 270° to come to the first course, as shown in Figure 47, but it will pay dividends in undamaged nerves. If the maneuver requires a terminal radical turn, we should make it outboard also. When approaching from ahead, if this would require passing too close to some other ship, we should first pass at a safe distance from the other ship, then turn outboard to come up abreast of the station, and finally ease in to the correct station on a course nearly parallel to that of the formation.

The beauty of the Turn Away is not always immediately apparent to the uninitiated. However, it is only necessary to sweat out one shuddering turn with one's mind undecided between BACK EMERGENCY or AHEAD FLANK (because we miscalculated the situation) to make one appreciate this rule.

Station Keeping and Maneuvering in Formation

Destroyers are expected to maneuver smartly at all times. In many cases they must commence their maneuver the moment the signal is understood,

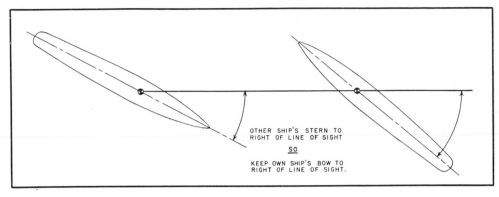

Safety rule when maneuvering in vicinity of other ships.

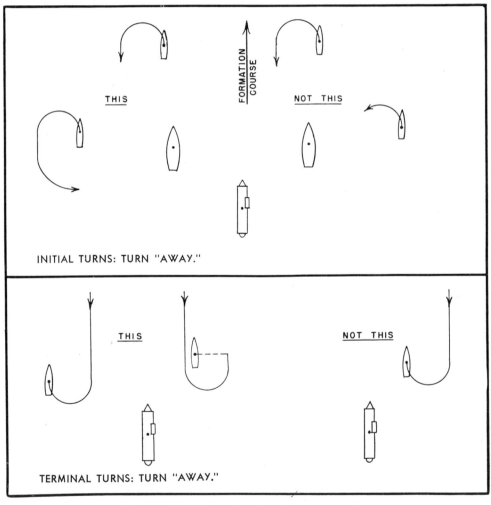

Figure 47. Principles of safe maneuvering

and under any circumstances they are expected to "get up and go" the minute the signal is executed. FLANK SPEED should be used unless another maneuvering speed has been specified, and 30° RUDDER should be used for all turns unless executing a precision turn with the formation. The amount gained by using plenty of rudder for the initial turn may put us on our new station minutes ahead of time.

The exactness of station keeping is a good measure of the smartness of the ship. It is a good rule to define "on station" as being within 100 yards of the assigned station. The OOD should initiate corrective action at any time the ship exceeds this limit. On some ships, basic station tolerances are defined as a definite range tolerance and a certain bearing tolerance. This is not a very good system, because it requires different excellence in station keeping at different ranges. Modern equipment allows very accurate measurement, and it is relatively simple to convert a distance tolerance to bearing limits when on station.

To produce really good station keeping on a given station, the relationship between range and bearing and own ship's course and speed should be known. The fore-and-aft and athwartship components of incremental changes of course and speed should be determined. For instance, if the formation speed is 18 knots (600 yards per minute), a 5° course change will give a 50 yard per minute athwartship component of motion, whereas it will take a 15 RPM change in speed to produce the equivalent fore-and-aft component. Thus, if our station is 45° on the bow of the guide and we wish to decrease the range while keeping the bearing constant, we can accomplish this by dropping our speed 15 turns and changing our course 5° toward the guide as shown in Figure 48(a).

If we are 70° on the bow of the guide and wish to decrease his bearing while keeping the range constant, we can solve our problem by visualizing a 70-20 right triangle. By the Radian rule, the leg opposite the 20° angle is $\frac{1}{3}$ the length of the leg adjacent to this angle, so we see that we must keep our athwartships component one-third of the fore-and-aft component if we are to change the only bearing. As Figure 48(b) shows, an increase in speed of 45 turns while steering *in* 5° will do the trick.

If the conning officer will analyze each correction he makes in order to know exactly what motion to expect, he will soon acquire the habit of exact station keeping. He will be able to adjust more rapidly in a new station and quickly calibrate the performance of the guide. As soon as the mystery of relative motion has disappeared, he will be able to accurately forecast the effect of incremental changes of course and speed.

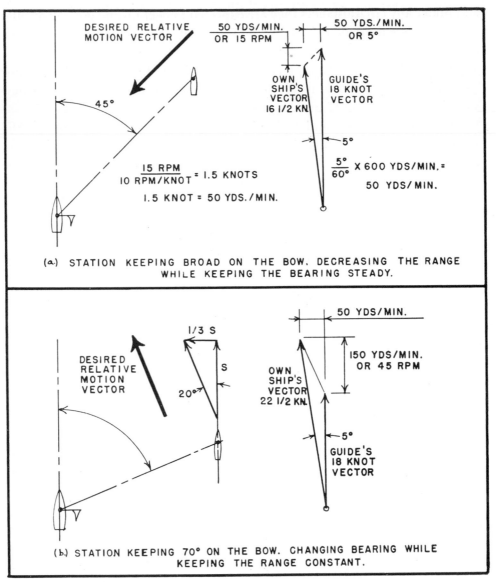

DESIRED RELATIVE MOTION VECTOR

50 YDS/MIN. OR 15 RPM

50 YDS./MIN. OR 5°

OWN SHIP'S VECTOR 16 1/2 KN

GUIDE'S 18 KNOT VECTOR

45°

5°

$$\frac{15 \text{ RPM}}{10 \text{ RPM/KNOT}} = 1.5 \text{ KNOTS}$$

1.5 KNOT = 50 YDS./MIN.

$$\frac{5°}{60°} \times 600 \text{ YDS/MIN.} = 50 \text{ YDS/MIN.}$$

(a) STATION KEEPING BROAD ON THE BOW. DECREASING THE RANGE WHILE KEEPING THE BEARING STEADY.

1/3 S

S

DESIRED RELATIVE MOTION VECTOR

20°

OWN SHIP'S VECTOR 22 1/2 KN.

50 YDS/MIN.

150 YDS/MIN. OR 45 RPM

5°

GUIDE'S 18 KNOT VECTOR

(b) STATION KEEPING 70° ON THE BOW. CHANGING BEARING WHILE KEEPING THE RANGE CONSTANT.

Figure 48. Keeping station by approximating the relative motion.

The reputation of a ship in a formation is rapidly acquired and is hard to change, once acquired. There are good ships and bad ships. The good ships are dependable and predictable; the bad ones must be kept under surveillance to avoid a catastrophe. It is not necessarily a measure of the Captain's ship-handling ability, but rather a measure of the reputation of the whole regime of the Skipper and his OODs. If a ship can be depended upon to "get up and go" when the signal hits the air, if she is maneuvered with decision and prudence at any hour of the day or night, and if she can take her station rapidly and maintain it with accuracy, the ship will always be marked as a *smart* destroyer.

Heavy Weather

The above discussion has dealt with operating at sea in company with other ships, and with maneuvering in formations. Though the complex evolutions of modern naval formations pose difficult problems, the sea itself presents the gravest and most trying test of the shiphandler's ability. The annals of the sea are full of moving tales of the seaman's fight against the elements as he dares the mighty ocean in his relatively frail craft. As the wind changes the sea from a pleasant calm to a refreshing swell, to a troublesome chop, to a pounding sea, and finally to the brutal crushing fury of a full gale, the shiphandler's attention shifts from the niceties of perfect maneuvers to the problem of simple survival. There is no more awe inspiring sight than to see a tremendous wave towering above our bridge, combing and curling as it crashes toward us. There is no greater moment of incredulous relief than the moment we perceive that the ship is being borne up and over the menacing mountain of water instead of being buried beneath its immensity. If we are to be able to cope with the sea in its ugliest moods, we must study the mechanism of waves and see how they act upon the ship.

The Formation of Waves

We will not investigate the causes and peculiarities of the different types of storms because the meteorological aspects are adequately covered in the literature on weather. Rather than probing into the reasons why the storm came into being, we will consider *what to do about it* once it is upon us. We will look into the character of the wind and the waves and find out how to handle the ship safely in spite of them.

When the wind blows, the friction of the air against the surface of the water tends to drag the water along with it. When the air stream begins to play upon the surface of the water, it accelerates the particles on the surface; but as these particles of water begin to move, they "pile up" in certain areas ahead because the particles in these areas have not been accelerated as much. The individual particles soon find their motion opposed by a "piled up" mass of water, and the motion of the individual particle is reversed as the gravitational result of the piling-up overcomes the wind action. Then, after the initial pile of water particles has moved on, the motion of the individual particle is reversed a second time by the front slope of the following pile. The piles of water particles, or waves, formed by the action of the wind move along quite rapidly across the surface of the water. The movement of the individual particles in the pile is oscillatory due to the action of gravity as they are alternately on the front slope and the back slope of the wave. There is also the unidirectional average movement called the surface current, resulting from the drag of the wind. In a typical situation the wind might be blowing at 30 knots, the waves moving in the direction of the wind at 20 knots, the individual particles of water on the surface surging forward and backwards a total of 5 feet, and an average surface current due to the wind of 2 knots.

Normally, the stronger the wind, the higher the waves will be. The higher the waves, the faster they will move, because the particles on the leading face are carried higher and will reach a higher velocity as a result of the greater distance to accelerate. Also, the higher the waves, the greater will be the distance between crests. Thus, as the wind increases we can expect the waves to grow larger, to move faster, and to have a greater distance between crest and crest.

It takes an appreciable time for a wave system to be set up, and, because of the movement of the waves, it also takes a considerable distance. The highest waves for a given wind velocity are found where the wind has been blowing steadily for days across hundreds of miles of deep, unobstructed sea. Under these circumstances a 40-knot wind might produce waves averaging 20 feet in height from trough to crest, and 30-foot waves would be encountered frequently. Under more severe conditions much higher waves are occasionally encountered, but it is quite difficult to judge the height of waves from a ship because of the severe plunging and rolling encountered in such seas. For a complete discussion of the formation and character of waves, refer to Hydrographic Office Publication No. 602—*Wind, Waves at Sea: Breakers and Surf,* by H. B. Bigelow and W. T. Edmonson.

Handling the Ship in Rough Seas

We can thus consider that in rough weather the surface of the water is a series of troughs and crests moving along at some mean velocity, but that except for a small surface current, the surface of the water is not moving along with the wind. The force that a moving fluid can exert at a given velocity is proportional to its density, and since water is so much denser than air, the combined effect of the wind and the waves on the ship is almost solely that due to the waves. The wind becomes an important effect in the survival of the ship only at hurricane velocities where the wind is so strong that it can cause a ship to carry a large list to leeward.

Each type of ship reacts differently to the action of the waves. According to its mass distribution and righting characteristics, each ship has a natural frequency in roll and pitch. This is the frequency at which the ship would tend to roll in calm water if she were listed slightly to one side and then released. A ship will tend to roll at this frequency under all conditions of wave motion, and the most severe rolling will occur when the frequency of the wave motion approximates the natural frequency of the ship. Actually, this frequency is usually measured by its period (the time required to go from even keel to extreme right, to extreme left, and back to even keel), and a ship's natural period of roll is a matter of interest to the shiphandler. The normal period of roll for a destroyer is about 9 seconds.

The greater the righting moment for a given inclination (the moment tending to return the ship to an even keel when inclined), the shorter will be the period of roll. If a ship is losing its righting moment due to the free surface effect or a change in its mass distribution due to flooding, its period of roll will increase. If a ship's period of roll increases, it is losing its stability. Each officer of a ship should know the natural period of roll for the ship so that he will be quick to notice any change in this important characteristic.

The first action of the ship which should be examined is simple rolling. When heading into or running with a sea, destroyers frequently roll 20° to a side. This is considerably increased when heading diagonally across the seas, and the maximum rolling normally occurs when the sea is on the beam or the ship is "in the trough" of the waves. If the period of the waves approximates the natural period of the ship, a resonant condition exists and the ship will roll severely with deep, steady rolls. The list caused by a turn at high speed, coupled with the normal wave motion, can produce an augmented roll which can be quite large. There are few destroyers which have not experienced a roll of 50° at some time during their service.

Obviously, rolling of the magnitude mentioned above is of concern to the conning officer of the ship. If the ship were to take a single roll of 30° unexpectedly during a meal, great damage could easily be done in broken crockery and glassware alone. The damage to spare parts and stores mounts with each roll unless such gear has been stowed perfectly. The damage to office machines, furniture, instruments, etc., is always great during severe rolling as these objects get away from the grip of the user. When a ship rolls deeply, she dips her side under the water, and a destroyer will occasionally submerge her lifeboat at the davit head. Such rolling is not only uncomfortable and fatiguing to the crew, but it is dangerous to life and limb, and it is almost always accompanied by material damage to the ship and her equipment. The good shiphandler is always alert to minimize the ship's roll, and he makes sure to warn all hands ahead of time to make preparations for rolling when it cannot be avoided.

Usually the best way to minimize the roll is to run with the sea at a few knots faster or slower than the waves. This means we will have a low, but steady, relative motion with respect to the waves, and thus will avoid the unsteady motion experienced when going at about the same speed as the waves. When traveling about the wave speed, we are alternately accelerated by the front slope of the wave and retarded by the rear slope. Since the water at the crest of a wave is momentarily travelling at about the velocity of the wave, we will have less rudder effectiveness due to the low relative velocity at the rudder when our stern is on the crest. This combined with the tendency to "skid" as we hang on the crest of the wave, makes it desirable to go at a speed different from that of the waves.

Heading directly into the waves also minimizes the roll, but this usually makes the pitch a maximum. This is not quite as good a solution as running before the sea, because the general action of the waves on the ship is more violent. The momentum of the waves is opposed to the motion of the ship in this case.

The more the sea is brought to the beam, the more the ship will roll. The athwartships inclination of the surface of the water is greatest in this orientation, so the amplitude of the force which is initiating the roll is at a maximum. The period of the initiating force is also important, and if the period of the waves is nearly the natural period of the ship, maximum rolling will be experienced. On the other hand, if the period of the waves is much longer than the natural period of the ship, the ship may ride quite comfortably parallel to the trough as she rides up and over the waves with little inclination.

The most severe pitching is experienced when headed directly into the seas. In this case the bow is carried up by the oncoming wave, and then the ship plunges into the trough as the wave passes. The resonant period of the ship in pitch is often matched by the waves, and, from the point of view of possible damage, pitching is equally as important as roll. When a ship buries her bow under tons of water while bucking into a rough sea, there is a tremendous stress on her hull.

In rough weather, severe damage can be done to our ship by the action of the waves. In addition to damage simply from the violent motion of the ship, deck equipment can be bent and torn loose by the impact of the water as the waves sweep over the deck. Plates are sprung and warped, and whenever a leak occurs, water damage follows. The more our ship is punished by the seas, the less efficient she is. The crew, though veterans of the stormiest weather, become fatigued by the struggle to exist, because they must continually hold on to keep from being thrown from their feet and hence can get no real relaxation, day or night.

Obviously, we must learn to operate in rough weather or our ship will be useless in a storm. On the other hand the ship will be of no service to anyone if she is lost because her crew did not take sufficient precaution. How rough can the weather be without severely damaging our ship? Where is the point at which we must cease thinking of the operations and take steps to protect the ship from the storm? These are important questions that must always be borne in mind.

These are certainly matters of degree, and the point of decision must change with the operation. The risk taken must be justified by the importance of the mission. It is imperative, however, that the shiphandler know when his ship is in danger, and it is vital that he know what to do about it.

Simple rolling up to 30° to the side is acceptable as one of the normal problems found at sea. As long as the gear which has been stowed in the proper manner in the proper place is still secure, we must recognize that any damage caused by loose gear is caused by improper securing. On the other hand, when gear is breaking loose from its regular stowage, when lifeboats are dipping, and when the decks are being swept by combers, it is time to search for means of reducing the effect of the weather. Heading into the sea or away from it will normally reduce the roll to an acceptable level, and changing speed will often alter the rolling by changing the frequency with which we are cutting the waves.

Destroyers can be driven into the seas until their keels come clear of the water all the way back to the bridge, and they can disappear in their own spray as they bury themselves into the waves. They can do this occasionally with little apparent damage, but abuse such as this will eventually cause extensive damage in buckled bulkheads, lost deck gear, cracked plates, etc. Any weakness on the forecastle will be searched out as the waves cave in the gun mount, rip off the fire plugs, and sweep away the hose and line reels.

There are two good indications when the ship is being driven into the sea too severely. The first is the pounding experienced when the bow comes clear of the water and crashes into the next wave. This produces a shock that can be felt throughout the ship and is an indication of the severity of the force of the waves. The second effect is a vertical vibration of low frequency which is set up as the whole ship bends longitudinally under the weight of water picked up by the forecastle as the ship plows under the waves. Unless there is an overbearing operational need to do otherwise, the course and speed should be set so that neither this pounding nor vibration is encountered.

In selecting the course and speed for the easiest riding, it is usually necessary to try a few experiments before a completely satisfactory combination is found. Generally, downwind courses are much more comfortable courses than those into the wind. Avoid courses near the trough, unless the seas are long and steady. If pitching is the problem, try courses inclined to the direction of the seas; this will make the wave fronts appear less abrupt. In most cases, when heading into the seas, the ship will ride better at a low speed. A difference of only two knots may be the difference between severe pounding and acceptable pitching.

Survival in Mountainous Seas

We have discussed means of making the ship ride more easily in a rough sea, and we have discussed how to avoid the relatively minor damage caused by rolling and pitching. However, when the ocean goes wild during a hurricane, these relatively minor factors are set aside and we are faced with stark survival. A full gale in the North Atlantic or a typhoon in the South China Sea can toss the mightiest ship about as though she were a toy boat. The waves lose their normal form as their tops are sliced off by the howling wind, and the air is a mixture of rain and spray. Visibility drops with the barometer. The waves dwarf a destroyer, and they seem intent on the destruction of everything living.

If we are to survive these extreme storms, we must have the principles of heavy-weather shiphandling foremost in our minds. If we lose electrical or propulsive power, we lose our ability to control the ship and then we are at the mercy of the seas. A ship without her engines and rudder will soon broach and expose her vulnerable sides to the onslaught of the waves. The seas will find her weaknesses as they cascade over her helpless form, and she will soon begin to take on water. Finally, with her stability reduced by the free surface of the water in her hull, she will succumb to a mighty wave, will capsize, and be lost to the storm. Sea anchors and oil bags still have their place in modern seamanship under specialized circumstances, but by the time it is apparent that the ship is *in extremis,* the weather is usually much too severe for men to work on the decks streaming gear of any kind.

The guiding principles of survival in a severe storm are: *maintain power, maintain buoyancy,* and *maintain stability.*

To preserve these vital properties we must make certain of the watertight integrity of the ship. At the first sign of a severe storm the ship should be secured for heavy weather. All topside gear should be secured with extra lashings, inboard lifelines should be rigged, and all watertight hatches should be battened down and checked. The most common cause of loss of power is the "grounding" of the main switchboards when salt water gets to them.

We must make sure that all hatches or ventilation ducts in the vicinity of the generators or switchboards are firmly secured.

The buoyancy and stability of the ship go hand in hand. To keep the center-of-gravity down, the ship should be properly ballasted. Free surface should be avoided wherever possible, and all tanks should be either completely full or completely empty. All compartments which should be dry must be kept that way. Bilges should be pumped, and if water leaks into any normally dry compartment, it should be pumped out immediately. If we are properly ballasted, if we have kept the free surface to a minimum, and if we have maintained our buoyancy, we should come through any storm with flying colors.

The trick of controlling the ship in a typhoon is to keep out of the trough. As indicated in Figure 49, if the ship is proceeding at an angle to the seas,

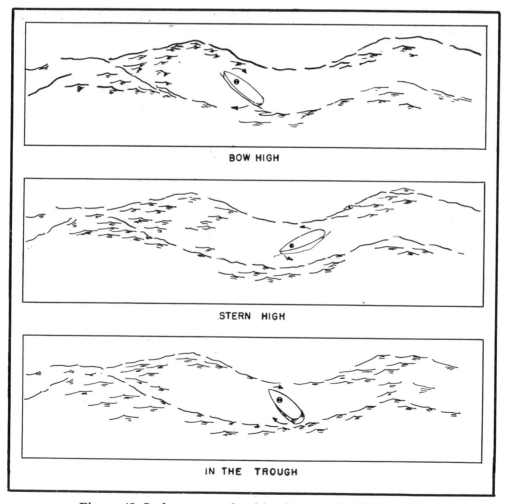

BOW HIGH

STERN HIGH

IN THE TROUGH

Figure 49. In heavy seas the ship always seeks the trough.

there is a tendency to force her to align herself parallel to the trough as she crosses the wave fronts. When she goes up the forward face of a wave, gravity tends to force her bow down into the trough. As she goes down the trailing face of the wave, gravity again tries to twist her into the trough by skidding her stern down the face of the wave.

If our ship gets caught in the trough, the waves will crash into her broadside and she will roll wildly. Once in the trough, it is very difficult to get out, because any control we can exert on the ship is overwhelmed by the action of the waves. The side forces available from the engines and rudder are small compared to the force of the sea. Our best chance lies in going ahead at maximum speed to insure maximum rudder force and in seizing any opportunity to turn out of the trough. In most cases it is advisable to turn *downwind,* because this allows us the greatest interval before being struck by the next succeeding wave.

Once we are heading nearly parallel to the wind and seas, it is possible to maintain our heading if the helm is handled skillfully. The choice whether to head into or away from the wind is an important one. Our ship is built to take the most severe waves from ahead. The bow is shaped for it, and, generally speaking, the rest of the forward structure is designed to take heavy seas. On the other hand, if we head into the wind, we add our own velocity to that of the sea, and the resulting impact is greater. We must maintain an adequate speed ahead to insure that we can steer or else we will lose control of our heading and broach, so we cannot slow below a certain minimum.

If we head downwind, on the other hand, we reduce the relative velocity of the waves by the amount of our speed, but we are exposing our stern to the wave fronts and it is neither shaped nor reinforced to resist the direct action of the waves. However, if we can maintain a speed so that the relative velocity of the waves is low, the stern will be able to stand up under the reduced action of the waves. As long as the waves do not crash down upon our fantail and "poop" our ship, running before the wind is the most gentle method of riding out a severe storm.

The choice of whether to head into the seas or to run with them will also depend upon the location of the center of the storm. In a cyclonic storm the wind blows nearly toward the center of the storm except in the vicinity of the "eye," where it blows tangentially, and our selection of the direction in which to ride out the storm must be modified by our desire to get out of the storm as soon as possible. A less advantageous inclination to the seas can be accepted if it will carry us out of the path of the storm and away from the most intense portion.

As in most phases of shiphandling, safety in a severe storm depends upon forehandedness. The ship that is properly ballasted and carefully secured for the storm will have a minimum of trouble riding out the most severe storm. The skipper who has studied his ship and is alert to the signs of the sea will be able to handle his craft in spite of the weather. A sound ship handled on sound principles of shiphandling can weather any storm. The shiphandling skill of the officer at the conn is the keystone to safety at sea.

The Do-Nothing Theory

It was stated in an article, "Typhoon Doctrine—All Engines Stopped," by E. W. Malanot, *U. S. Naval Institute* Proceedings, July 1955 that the best way to ride out a typhoon is to stop all engines and let nature take its course. This radically unusual approach has been used with proven success in the case of ships of the merchant type, and it is suggested that it might be utilized by all classes of ships when facing the fury of a typhoon. There has been sufficient discussion in naval circles of this method of riding out a hurricane to warrant a careful evaluation of its merits.

Actually the central thesis of the proposal is this: "at the center of a hurricane or typhoon the seas come from any and all directions and under such confused conditions the best thing to do is to stop the engines and let the ship drift with the forces." Certainly any action we might take with the engines and rudders should be aimed at minimizing the action of the seas or the wind. Obviously such action should be planned to counter a certain direction of the wind and sea, but if there is no fixed direction of the wind and seas, how can one logically select a course and speed? At the center of the storm, therefore, where the seas are confused and the wind has died down or is variable, the recommendation to stop the engines and let the ship drift seems completely sound.

The extension of the proposal, however, calls for stopping the engines and letting the ship drift throughout the duration of the storm. The theory seems to be that if the ship can ride through the "eye" of the storm (which is the worst part), in this manner, she can ride out the whole storm with her engines stopped. This was actually demonstrated on several occasions by merchant type ships.

This last is a dangerous suggestion. What may be safe in a large bluff merchant hull with high freeboard and great metacentric height, might be the greatest folly in a low, sleek destroyer. Destroyers, especially the newer ones with their deck houses extending nearly to the sides, are very vulnerable to beam seas, and the prudent conning officer will do well to do all within his power to avoid taking hurricane seas on the beam. Of the four modern destroyers that were lost in such storms in World War II, all available information indicates that the ships got into the trough of the seas and were unable to extricate themselves. The severe rolling and force of the waves on their sides caused material failures, and in a very short time the ships were capsized by the action of the wind and the waves. Though lack of proper ballasting and other factors played their parts, the fact remains that once in the trough, though the ships had taken relatively little water aboard, the wind and seas literally bowled them over.

No, the Do-Nothing Theory is not advisable for a destroyer and should be attempted with caution in any type ship. At the center of the storm (or at any other time when a situation is confused and there is no logical basis for selecting a course and speed) it is reasonable to stop the engines and wait for the situation to change. But under the normal conditions outside of the "eye," where the direction of the wind and the seas is all too definite, the shiphandler should use his engines and rudders to keep his ship oriented so that the impact of the forces of the storm are minimized. This ordinarily calls for the conning officer to head his ship into the approaching seas and to hold her there with whatever power is required. A hurricane is the most savage of storms and one should not risk the damage of being pooped by a hurricane sea. The ship is constructed to withstand more safely the force of the waves from ahead, so the ship should be conned to keep her bow into the seas, but with as little headway as possible, since the energy of such forward motion would just be added to that of the onrushing waves.

Practicing for Heavy Weather

It is one thing to pass the word, "Secure ship for heavy weather," and another to actually have it done effectively. A wise skipper will have a thorough inspection made each time the ship is prepared for a storm. Hatches, lifelines, storerooms, and engineering spaces should get special attention. The more effort spent in preparing for heavy weather, the less damage can be caused by the storm.

As the opportunity permits during bad but not dangerous weather, experiments should be made to determine the best courses and speeds for the ship during very rough weather. The average and extreme rolls of the ship during similar periods on courses into and with the seas should be compared and any tendency to pitch severely or to pound should be noted. The skipper and the crew should prove to themselves the capabilities and limitations of their ship so when they are actually faced with a hurricane they can have confidence in their ability to cope with it. Having determined the storm characteristics of his ship by experiment, the skipper should firmly decide the best method of handling his particular ship in a hurricane and make sure that all conning officers are acquainted with his decision.

CHAPTER IX

RADAR, SONAR, AND CIC

THE DEVELOPMENTS of modern science have increased the scope of the ship-handler to allow him to handle his ship under conditions which otherwise would have been impossible. He can maneuver his ship safely at night and in low visibility in cases previously beyond his ability. Instead of anchoring until the fog lifts, the modern shiphandler, aided by his radar and his improved sonar, can maneuver with certainty. Instead of depending solely upon the meager glimpses he might catch of shadowy landmarks, and following the advice of a Navigator whose plot is a mixture of rainwater, witchcraft, and hope, the conning officer of today is supported by a specially trained and well equipped crew who are applying all of the powerful tools of modern electronics in guiding the ship safely when the elements blind the senses of man.

It is not sufficient, however, that the conning officer follow the advice of his supporting team blindly. For each of the important gifts that the recent developments have brought us, we have an increased problem of interpretation of the electronic innuendoes. The old sea dog's eyes are wrinkled from scanning the horizon for the dangers that might threaten his vessel, and it takes years of experience to learn to evaluate what the eye can perceive. It would be foolhardy to think that the interpretation of a radar scope is any less demanding. The radar scans the same area that is viewed by the mariner from his bridge, and though the scene is neatly presented on a relatively small cathode ray tube, it contains even more information of tactical interest than can be obtained by eye. The conning officer, therefore, must be an expert at handling his radar and interpreting its presentation. He must at all times apply his experience and his direct contact with the visible elements of the situation to monitor the activity of his Combat Information Center (CIC) and other supporting groups.

A good Officer of the Deck would not tolerate a set of binoculars which are out of focus, so why should he tolerate a remote radar scope that is out of focus? He would not be on the bridge if he had to ask the quartermaster to focus his glasses for him, and the same should be true if he had to call for an electronics technician to make the manual adjustments to his radar scope. An OOD should be relieved if he spends his time looking close aboard when he should be scanning the horizon, and he should also be relieved if at night, when cruising alone, he were to have his PPI on short scale when it should be set for long range search. The radar on a ship is only as valuable as the information which is derived from it. If the conning officer cannot utilize the radar competently, he is not ready to do a competent job of conning a modern ship.

If the throttleman did not notice a drop in the oil pressure to his main bearing, he would be dealt with most harshly and he would not be allowed to continue in his position of responsibility. If a radarman does not notice and report a new contact that is showing on his scope, he is failing in his duty just as much as the throttleman. Neither the throttleman nor the radarman will produce peak performance until they know that their ability is being evaluated and their product is being utilized. As in all segments of a ship's operation, the motivation originates from the bridge. The Officer of the Deck should require the same quality of performance from his CIC as he requires from his look-outs or his helmsman. Though the CIC is in an advisory position, most of the other watch stations on the ship are also, and they all should be required to make excellence their habit.

CIC

On the bridge it is occasionally difficult to utilize a radar scope because of the lighting conditions and conflicting activities. The CIC, on the other hand, is arranged for ideal utilization of this instrument and sacrifices all else to this end. Thus the CIC should be able to obtain the maximum results from the radar at all times, and should keep the bridge informed of all developments.

In CIC there is space and equipment for plotting and tabulating any information desired. All applicable publications are there and ready for reference. The conning officer should therefore look upon his CIC as his source of up-to-the-minute information on the tactical situation and as a ready source for interpretation of the situation.

The conning officer should recognize that he can gain more from a single glance at his own scope than the CIC evaluator can tell him in several minutes. Though he should demand sufficient information from CIC to insure it is keeping abreast of the situation, he should use his CIC to *augment* what he can derive directly from his equipment. As a matter of practice he should acquire the habit of looking at the bridge PPI when discussing the radar information with CIC.

The capabilities and limitations of the radar and CIC must be known by the shiphandler. If he expects more than the installation is capable of producing, he may take the ship into danger without knowing it. If he demands less than the equipment can provide, he is unnecessarily limiting his ship.

CIC performs one of its most useful functions in detecting other ships and keeping track of them. From its plots CIC can inform the bridge of the location and movement of any ship on the radar screen at any time. The plot should yield the range, bearing, course, speed, and closest point of approach (CPA) of any ship in radar range.

The surface summary plot is the most useful plot in CIC for the ship-handler, and it must be kept up to the minute. The conning officer should frequently check the accuracy of this plot from his own observations.

Such a plot cannot be kept by simply glancing at a radar scope occasionally and sketching in the picture on another plot. The surface summary plot must accurately identify and locate each contact regardless of the complexity of the situation. Though a fixed formation steaming steadily can be sketched by eye with reasonable accuracy, the picture becomes confused as soon as the formation begins a maneuver. As the contacts merge and their tracks cross on the scope, the sketched plot loses its value, and a better method of summary plotting must be found.

An adequate summary plot must be maintained by frequent and accurate plotting of the complete presentation on the radar. Though this can be done with limited success by measuring and plotting the coordinates of all contacts, a large number of contacts cannot be handled in this way.

If the ship is equipped with any of the more modern radar repeaters, the summary plot can be kept right on the scope itself. Such repeaters are equipped with plotting heads so that all identification marks and tracks appear directly on the face of the scope. With a summary plot controller keeping the overall picture directly on his radar scope, but backed up by a more precise plotting board for measuring exact CPA's and solving maneuvering problems, CIC can maintain an accurate and useful summary of the surface situation and be a real help to the conning officer.

In addition to keeping track of the situation as presented by the radar, CIC should be ready to recommend courses and speeds during maneuvers. As soon as the signal for a maneuver is received, CIC should apply itself to solving the maneuvering problem presented. CIC should advise the bridge of the direction of the course change, and the initial course and speed, and should continually monitor the maneuver to recommend corrections if needed during the evolution.

Although the CIC is prepared to solve the maneuvering problem, it is not practical to leave this problem to them alone. Because the personnel in CIC are separated from visual contact with the situation, they frequently make mistakes that would be obvious from the bridge. Though CIC is charged with the responsibility of providing recommendations for courses and speeds during a maneuver, the maneuver should also be solved by maneuvering board on the bridge so that the conning officer has a ready picture of the maneuver. Though an experienced destroyer officer can estimate the initial course to his new station within narrow limits, he should be backed up immediately with an accurate maneuvering board solution. The CIC solution and the bridge solution will provide a check against one another.

Formation Maneuvering Board

In problems involving the maneuvers of a complex formation composed of many ships, the simple maneuvering board is not adequate. Rotations of the axis and reorientation of the screen require replotting *all* of the ships in the formation, and since modern formations and screens are often irregular, this is a major undertaking. The conning officer cannot wait for the entire formation to be replotted to find his new station and begin his maneuver. We must therefore find a method which will allow the reorientation of the formation to be handled quickly and smoothly.

A circular formation is made up of two groups of ships: the *main body,* and the *screen.* Whereas a rotation of the formation axis must be ordered to rotate the main body about the formation center, the screen might have to reorient each time the base course of the formation is changed. If we can devise a system that permits the axis of the formation to be rotated without replotting the formation, and that also allows us to rotate the screen independently of the main body, we will have provided a system which greatly simplifies setting up the maneuvering board solutions of a complex formation.

The formation maneuvering board illustrated in Figure 50 is recommended for use in a complex formation. Essentially it consists of a pair of standard maneuvering boards placed side by side and covered with plexiglass. Bottom lighting is provided for use at night. The right-hand board is constructed to accommodate the maneuvers of a circular formation, and the other board is simply an auxiliary board available to augment its more elaborate partner. A small drafting machine is a useful addition, especially when transferring bearings from one board to the other.

The plexiglass top has a circular hole centered over the right-hand board and of slightly larger diameter than the largest circle of the board. This hole can accommodate two thin plexiglass discs, one on top of the other, and, when inserted, these discs can be turned to any orientation desired. A plexiglass cover is provided over the assembly of discs to allow plotting without disturbing the markings on the discs.

In use, the main body of the formation is plotted on the lower disc, and

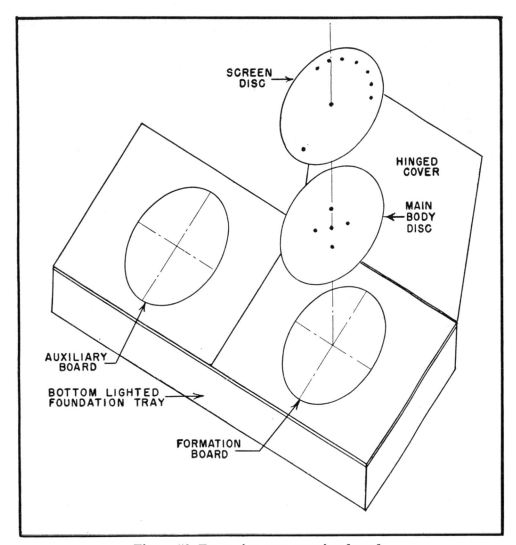

Figure 50. Formation maneuvering board.

this disc is then rotated to the formation axis. The screen is then plotted on the second disc and this, in turn, is inserted and rotated to the screen axis. The cover is lowered, our own ship's position is then plotted on the cover (presumably directly over our assigned station as indicated by one of the lower discs), and we are ready for changes in the formation.

If the formation and screen axes are changed together, we rotate both discs to the new orientation, and we have the new stations located. If the screen is reoriented with no change in formation axis, we rotate only the screen disc. If we are using several different formations and shifting from one to another frequently enough to warrant it, we can have several sets of discs with the formations and screens already plotted and ready for use. A formation maneuvering board is a valuable aid both on the bridge and in CIC. It is well worth the trouble to construct one if the ship does not already have one.

Advanced Maneuvering

Destroyer officers should be the best maneuvering board operators in the Fleet because their ships are required to maneuver more frequently than any others. Since it is often highly important in their maneuvering, they should be prepared to take the ship's turning circle into account. This technique is not normally covered in publications on the use of maneuvering boards, but unless it is mastered, many maneuvers will have to be made by "cut and try," since the conventional solution is inadequate.

When allowing for turns in using the maneuvering board, it is not feasible to solve the relative motion during the turn. The easiest method is to approximate the motion of our own ship and the guide during the turn, and estimate the relative position upon completion of the turn. For a maneuver requiring an initial turn to the maneuvering course and a terminal turn upon arriving on station, it is the course and speed to use between these turns that we hope to get from the maneuvering board. The following example illustrates this method of taking the turning circle into account:

PROBLEM

To change station from 5030 to 3090 at 25 knots while guide is steady on 000°T at 15 knots.

Simple Solution (Figure 51)

For simple relative motion from A to B: *Steer 170°T at 25 knots.*

Advanced Solution (See Figure 52)

A quick glance at the problem shows we will have to make a turn of approximately 180° to the right at the start and complete the maneuver with a turn of about 180° to the left. Since we will be speeding up during the first turn and slowing down during the second, we can assume that we average 20 knots during the turns.

At 20 knots, with 30° rudder, our calibration shows that we turn 2° per second with a 600 yard diameter. Therefore, during our first 180° turn, we will move 600 yards to the side and complete the turn in 90 seconds. During this time the guide advances 750 yards (1½ minutes at 15 knots), so our position relative to the guide upon completion of the initial turn is not A

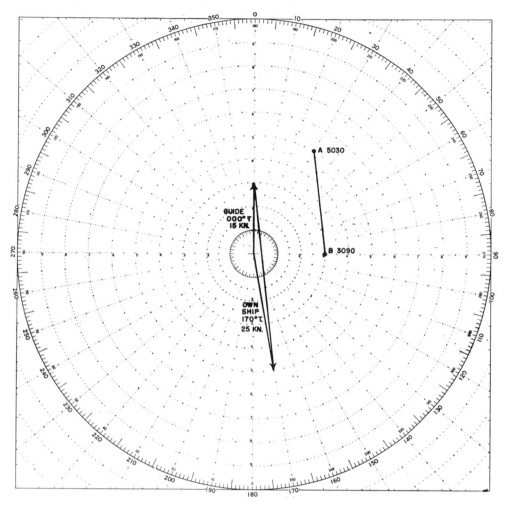

Figure 51. Simple maneuvering board solution.

but (a) as shown in the figure. Similarly, upon arriving in the vicinity of our new station, we must execute another 180° turn to resume the formation course, and again we will translate 600 yards to the side while the Guide advances 750 yards. To allow for this, we should maneuver to arrive at point (b) instead of B. Solving the relative motion problem for the move from (a) to (b), we find we must proceed on course 203°T at 25 knots. This we see is much different from the simple solution which did not take our turns into account. We also perceive that we have located a very important point, (b), the spot where we must put the rudder over and shift the engine order telegraphs to AHEAD STANDARD.

Obviously our solution is not exact because we assumed turns of 180° when in fact our initial turn is 203°. However, we are 33° closer to the cor-

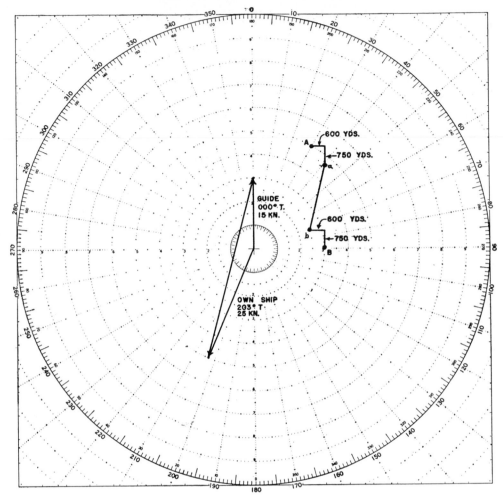

Figure 52. Advanced maneuvering board solution.

rect course than we would have been had we used only the simple solution. As we complete our initial turn to 203°T we can recalculate our course for point (b). If we maneuver to pass through point (b) on course 180°T, we can complete our maneuver accurately and end up exactly at point B upon completion of our terminal turn.

Radar

When on soundings or within radar range of land, CIC should be required to keep a navigational plot. By proper use of the radar and visual information, CIC can keep the ship's location very accurately, and if this plot is maintained on the dead reckoning tracer (DRT) the instantaneous location of the ship is always available. This is especially valuable in an emergency when the ship's location must be known immediately. There is a tendency in some CICs to use radar information exclusively because it would be "peeking" to use visual bearings. Although our CIC team must be prepared to navigate on radar information alone during reduced visibility, they must be impressed with the idea that they are engaged in deadly serious business and not playing a game.

We have spoken of the capabilities and limitations of the radar, and we have mentioned the necessity of the bridge stimulating the radar operators to better performance, but we have not defined our terms. As most mariners can testify, the excellence of the radar performance is dependent upon the standard demanded from the bridge. If the bridge does not require peak performance at all times, it is not likely to receive it. If the Captain is easily satisfied and considers frequent radar failures an acceptable level of performance, such frequent failures will become the habit in his ship. If, on the other hand, the Captain has an acute interest in the performance of his radars and accepts only high reliability, the excellence of his radars will be assured. The radars reflect the interest and effort of the men who service and operate them. If the Command inspires these men to exert their best efforts, it will be rewarded by improved radar performance.

Though the radar is capable of detecting objects at very long ranges, and of indicating the range and bearing to them with amazing accuracy, it is discouraging to observe the low level of performance actually obtained unless the conning officer pays particular attention to the adjustment and operation of the radars. The surface search radars in current use in the Fleet can detect a target as soon as a substantial part of its superstructure appears above the horizon visible from the height of eye of the antenna. If the radar is properly adjusted, it should give the correct range within 50 yards and the correct bearing within 1°. If the surface search radar is not producing this level of performance, it should be adjusted until it does produce these results.

In order to be able to depend upon his radar information, the conning officer must check his radars frequently. The detection range can be checked by noting the maximum range at which targets are acquired. The radar should always detect a target before it can be sighted from the bridge, and one soon learns to judge the maximum range at which a ship of a given type should be detected. If the conning officer knows that a given type ship has at one time been detected by his radar at a certain range, he should accept nothing less than this range subsequently. Although there are unusual weather conditions that allow extreme ranges to be obtained with radar, these are infrequent. The conning officer can feel confident that his demands remain within the realm of the possible if he is requiring the repetition of performance obtained previously with the same equipment. If radar ranges less than this acceptable level are experienced, the radar should be checked for failure and retuned.

To determine the accuracy of the ranges being obtained, the radar's performance should be checked against other radars, and frequent "double echo" checks should be made. Though the range accuracy possible is within 50 yards of the true range, it is surprising to note how often the radar can be so badly out of calibration that the ranges reported are in error by several hundred yards. This inaccuracy will be due in part to maladjustments of the radar and in part to the improper reading of the information. Whatever the cause, it is susceptible to correction if the conning officer requires the appropriate level of performance. Ranges from all of the radars on the ship should be compared frequently and adjustments made until any radar on the ship can be depended upon to produce accuracy commensurate with the capabilities of the equipment.

The bearing accuracy of the radars is easily checked. Simply select a target at sufficient range so that it subtends a small arc, and check then the radar bearing against the visual bearing measured from the bridge pelorus. Normally the radar bearing should be within 1° of the visual bearing, but the accuracy will depend on the type of radar installed and the method used in measuring the bearing. If the radar is inherently poor in bearing discrimination, a series of bearings might fall in a small area about the correct bearing, but the average of these bearings should be very near the correct bearing. If there is any constant error, this should be eliminated by alignment of the radar.

The inherent capability of a modern radar is immense. If the conning officer does not demand high standards of performance, he will not realize this capability. Continual interest in the radar and frequent checking of its performance will go a long way toward insuring that the ship will have this tool available when needed.

Fathometer and Sonar

Though the radar is the right arm of the shiphandler, the Fathometer is also an important aid. The character of the bottom of the ocean and its tributaries is as distinctive as the shoreline. The dependability and accuracy of the Fathometer makes this instrument invaluable to the mariner when he is in shoal water. The Fathometer should be used whenever the depth is of interest to the conning officer.

Most Fathometers measure the depth from the bottom of the ship, and thus measure the true distance from the keel to the floor of the ocean. The Fathom eter can measure the depth with great accuracy from one fathom to a thousand fathoms or more; but to insure this accuracy, it should be calibrated in port and frequently checked against a lead line. If care is taken with the Fathometer it is better than the lead line when the ship is moving. Even in the hands of an expert quartermaster, the lead line readings are of questionable accuracy if the ship is moving at appreciable speed and if the interval between soundings is quite long. On the other hand, the accuracy of the Fathometer is not affected by the speed of the ship, and the soundings come so rapidly that they can be considered to be continuous.

The sonar of today is of great value in a channel and when close to other ships. At short ranges older type radars become difficult to use. Sonar, on the other hand, is at its best at short ranges, and it can do much to fill in the gap. In dangerous situations where neither visual nor radar information is available, sonar can show us all of the shoals and ships in our vicinity. It is the danger close at hand that must be avoided, and sonar gives us eyes under the water that are especially perceptive to things close aboard.

Fog

The real test of the shiphandler's ability to utilize the new electronic aids at his command comes when entering a harbor in a dense fog. Normally, radar and sonar merely assist the shiphandler and provide him with information of greater accuracy than is obtainable by other means; but in restricted waters, with zero visibility, these aids provide the *only* means of moving the ship with safety. Ferryboats may continue to operate in a fog, because their runs are short and never change. Their captains, through years of study, learn every landmark and source of sound or light along the track, and know every habit of the wind and current. "Whistle toot" ranging (timing the interval until the echo returns from the shore after a "toot" of the whistle) can be resorted to if the air is calm and the banks of the harbor are abrupt (such as found in Puget Sound). But except for such special cases, ships without modern electronic equipment are paralyzed by a heavy fog.

When proceeding at low visibility, maximum use must be made of every aid. Special fog lookouts should be posted and instructed to be alert for sounds as well as visual contacts. The best radar and sonar operators should be operating the equipment, and the most skilled CIC team should be on station. The conning officer should place himself where he can make use of all of the information that is available. Ideally, he should take a position where he can have good visibility in case the fog lifts momentarily, but at the same time he should be able to view a radar and a sonar repeater. He should be in contact with the CIC, and he should be receiving the Fathometer reports directly. Above all, it is most important that the navigational plot be available so that he can be continually abreast of the Navigator's best estimate of the ship's position and can have constant reference to the chart. It is a good practice to have a separate chart for the conning officer's exclusive use for identifying landmarks and for correlating the radar and sonar information with the ship's position.

It has been traditional for the conning officer to station himself on the open bridge, trying to pierce the fog by sheer force of will when poking about in low visibility. Though in this location he is well placed to observe the last moments before the collision, he can see nothing at all during the period when effective action could have been taken. Some officers propose that the Captain should be in CIC where the "best" information is available, but such officers do not appreciate the importance of *visual* information in an emergency. Though 95 per cent of all emergencies can be handled by efficient use of the information in the CIC, it is that last 5 per cent that has kept the "Old Man" from being obsolete in this modern electronic world.

The Captain, who normally has the conn during low visibility, should no more concentrate on being a lookout, and thus deny himself access to his other instruments, than he should bury himself in CIC and lose the information he might gain from his eyes and ears. He should study the problem and make sure that he has placed himself where he can best receive and employ all information that might become available. More can be obtained by a glance at the horizon than through a lengthy report from a lookout. More can be derived by studying a radar scope for a moment than can be received by hundreds of words from CIC. And explanations and reports are more quickly understood if the recipient is looking at the radar or sonar picture while receiving the information.

A combination conning position is therefore best, and this can be provided on most of our Navy ships. The conning officer should place himself in front of a bridge radar PPI, next to the Navigator's chart desk, adjacent to the sonar repeater, in communication with CIC and the Fathometer, and in a position with good visibility and in direct communication with the helmsman and the annunciators. If our ship does not have such a position on the open bridge or in the pilot house, we had better get busy requesting alterations, because she is not ready to make full use of the equipment with which she is provided.

Thus, as the ship proceeds in the fog, her position can be plotted from the radar ranges and bearings on the relatively long range landmarks, and this position can be verified by comparing the plotted position on the chart with the picture on the radar scope.

The most difficult part of "zero visibility" shiphandling is the detection and avoiding of other craft moving about in the harbor. The smaller the craft, the less easy she is to detect. However, through alert use of the radar and sonar information, we can detect even the smallest vessels. With some practice, the approximate size and speed of unseen vessels can be predicted by their propeller noise on the sonar.

Radar and sonar have made it possible for the ship to be maneuvered with safety under conditions which previously would have denied operations. If we understand our equipment and are skillful in its utilization, we can proceed, regardless of the weather or visibility. On the other hand, if we blindly accept the indications of this new equipment without understanding its vagaries and limitations, we are headed for disaster. As with other technical equipment, radar and sonar are effective only in the hands of skilled men.

CHAPTER X

SPECIAL MANEUVERS AT SEA

ALTHOUGH the most satisfying shiphandling is usually done in restricted waters where the ship must be positioned with precision in the vicinity of a number of obstacles, there are many very demanding and delicate evolutions required at sea. The more the Fleet becomes self sustaining at sea, the more often ships are required to go alongside one another (See Figure 53). Fueling and provisioning at sea have long been commonplace on extended cruises, and today deployed fleets are entirely dependent upon transfer at sea.

Replenishment at Sea

Replenishing of fuel, stores and communication at sea is an evolution frequently performed, and at times conducted even under adverse weather conditions (See Figure 54), though potentially dangerous since the ships must steam very close to one another for a long time and a steering casualty, a momentary engine breakdown, or a misunderstood order could cause a collision. The techniques are so well developed that accidents are very infrequent.

When approaching alongside another vessel, it is best to control the ship's heading by giving the "course to steer" to the helmsman. Select the best helmsman on board, and limit his task to keeping the ship's head on the course ordered. It is generally unsatisfactory to try to give rudder angles to the helmsman while maneuvering alongside, because not only would that be attempting to do the helmsman's job for him, but, depending upon the fore-and-aft position with respect to the other ship, as much as 15° right or left rudder may be required just to keep the ship's head steady.

When commencing an approach to go alongside it is desirable to start from between 500 and 1,000 yards astern, and, if the situation allows, to take a few minutes to check the other ship's course and speed. Usually we will find it necessary to steer a few degrees from the signalled course, and to steam at perhaps 5 turns from the signalled speed. These are not large differences, but knowing exactly what the other ship is doing allows us to make a more accurate approach.

Our intention is to arrive abreast the supply ship on a parallel course at exactly her speed at a convenient but safe distance from her side, and to do so in a minimum of time. A practical way to arrive abreast at the desired distance is to make the approach parallel to the other ship's wake at the

Figure 53. USS ENTERPRISE (CVAN-65) and USS SHASTA (AF-6)
take replenishment stations.

Figure 54. USS MASSEY refueling from USS LEYTE in heavy weather.

desired distance to the proper side and have the opportunity to check the accuracy of the chosen course continually during the approach. This parallel approach from astern is not absolutely necessary and a safe approach can be made by a skilled shiphandler with little or no parallel run, but if the operations permit the luxury, it is convenient to make the last 500 to 1,000 yards of the approach on a steady course parallel to that of the supply ship.

What is the desired distance between ships when we complete the approach? Some shiphandlers consider it daring to approach very close to the supply ship to facilitate the passing of lines and rigs, and they like to stay "in close" to shorten the transfer time. Such daring may be satisfying to the ego, but it seldom actually has any beneficial effect on the time required for the evolution, and it is rather foolish to get close unnecessarily since the only *serious* mistake one can make when replenishing is to get so close to the supply ship that a collision results.

When all is ready, the conning officer, on the engaged wing of the bridge, increases speed and begins the approach (See Figure 55), so as to put the side of his ship about 90 feet from the supply ship. From the engaged pelorus we sight along the course we have ordered to see where the engaged wing of the bridge is heading. When our ship is at the proper distance to the side, sighting along the same bearing as the other ship's course should intersect a spot in the water 90 feet from her side.

Another useful check when making the approach is to compare the wake with that of the supply ship. When in the correct position to the side during the approach, there should be about 5 yards of blue water between the white foam of the wakes of the two ships.

As we approach, we commence using the Radian Rule. At 600 yards astern, the supply ship's side should bear 3° from the course if we are approaching correctly. At 300 yards, its side should bear 6° from the course. By checking the bearing continually, we can adjust our final distance from her side on the approach.

Using the "coast in" method, the engines should be slowed to replenishment speed when the ship reaches a point 175 yards astern of the abreast position (5 knots at 35 yards per knot surge). Using the "back down" method at 25 knots, the engines should be ordered BACK TWO-THIRDS when about 100 yards astern of the desired position and shifted to AHEAD TWO-THIRDS and to replenishment revolutions just before the ship has actually slowed to the speed of the supply ship. If one is *behind* position, shift the engines *ahead* while still a few knots above replenishment speed; if *ahead*, *back* to a few knots below replenishment speed before shifting the engines ahead.

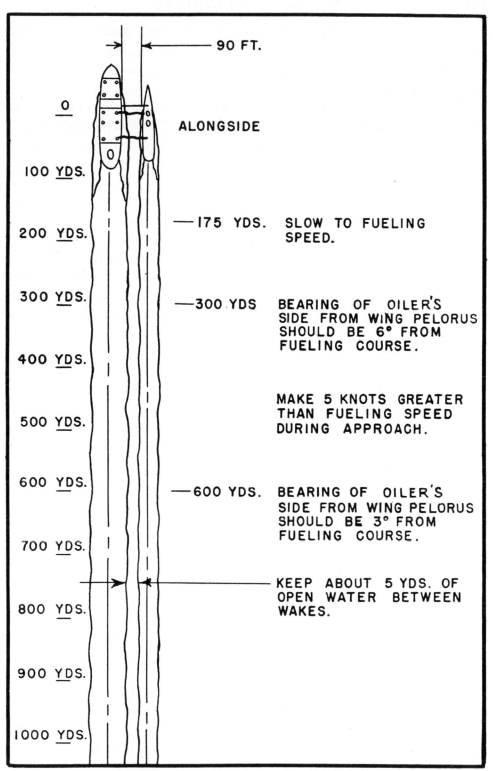

Figure 55. "Coast in" approach for fueling.

Throughout the deceleration it is very useful to have someone in position to read the speed by pitometer log. As a result of the major speed change and possible corrections, it may be difficult to predict the actual speed through the water, but the "pit log" will give the true speed.

The best position to ride alongside is a matter of debate. Most publications on the subject speak of distances from 60 to 100 feet, but all agree that it may be necessary to adjust these distances. The basic thought that should be borne in mind is that danger of collision lies on the side *toward* the oiler, and only the embarrassment of parting the hoses lies away from the oiler. The riding position should be selected not only to provide the margin necessary for the anticipated conning errors, but also to take into account the possibility of a steering or engine casualty.

Using the span wire or other modern rigs, the receiving ship can sheer out to as much as 300 feet before parting the hoses, so there is no necessity to ride in too close. An average position between 100 and 120 feet has been found comfortable for a destroyer and there is plenty of margin outside of these limits for correction before damage to the rig or the ships becomes imminent. For a destroyer an initial position with 90 feet between ships for passing lines and a mean distance of 110 feet while replenishing has been found safe and efficient.

In rough weather or with a short approach run it is safer to approach wide. We can come always up to a point abreast our fueling station and then move in to the desired distance. This is particularly recommended if the supply ship is yawing badly.

One of the sharpest debates among modern mariners is that concerning the proper approach speed when going alongside another ship. The "conservative" school recommends approaching at 5 knots greater than the supply ship's speed, slowing to the replenishment speed at the proper distance and "coasting" into position abreast the supply ship. The "radical" school recommends approaching at 25 knots and backing the engines to reduce speed at the required moment. The "conservatives" speak darkly of engines backing unevenly, causing a veer to one side and they are concerned about possible damage to boilers and machinery resulting from such "rough" use; the "radicals" speak of simplicity, efficiency and smartness.

The author has been converted from "conservative" to "radical." Experiments with both FORREST SHERMAN and SPRINGFIELD showed that no combination of engine power (including such as STARBOARD, BACK FULL with PORT, AHEAD ONE-THIRD) had any significant effect on the helmsman's ability to steer a precise course when backing from 25 knots, as long as the ship was making 8 knots or more through the water. Since replenishment speeds are normally 10 knots or greater and the approaching ship never slows much below replenishment speed, concern for the effect of uneven engine response can be dismissed. (It is suggested, however, that any shiphandler with lingering doubts on this point take time to test his ship to observe her behavior under such conditions.) As for damage to the engineering plant caused by backing at high speeds, the plants are designed for such power changes and there is little in the history of the many ships which have used the "back down" approach for years to support such fears.

To deny oneself the use of backing power while going along side another ship at sea would be similar to denying himself backing power when making a pier in port. Certainly such a landing can be made, but it is so much easier to use the engines to bring the ship to a stop. The same is true underway: it is much easier to reduce the ship's speed quickly to the replenishment speed when close to the desired position by the use of backing power than it is to estimate the moment to reduce the engine revolutions to replenishment speed and depend on water resistance to slow her.

As for the approach speed, any speed greater than the replenishment speed can be used, but obviously the higher the speed the more quickly one arrives alongside. Replenishment speed plus 5 knots is recommended when using the "coast in" method, and 20 or 25 knots is normal when using the "backdown" approach: 20 knots when first getting used to the system or for night approaches, 25 knots for most normal daylight approaches.

While riding alongside, it is often convenient to divide the station-keeping duties between two officers. By giving one officer control of the ship's course—that is, the distance from the supply ship—and the other officer control of the ship's speed—that is, the fore-and-aft position—we can control the ship very nicely. These two factors are almost completely independent when a ship is alongside, and each officer has only one factor to consider.

Following course and speed changes by the supply ship while we are alongside is not as difficult as it might seem. As long as the changes are made gradually and with complete exchange of information, it is only slightly more difficult to maintain station alongside during a maneuver than while steaming steadily. For course changes, it is usually advisable to change course in 10° to 20° increments, with the oiler using a small amount of rudder. We can follow the turn by ordering successive courses-to-steer to the helmsman.

At the completion of each increment, a slight pause should be made to allow the destroyer to catch up, and at the end of each 45°, a couple of minutes should be allowed to let the destroyer settle down again. The only difficulty in making a large course change in one steady movement is that once the destroyer conning becomes erratic, it is apt to become more so by over-correction. Stopping momentarily at each 15° gives a series of check points, and the pause at 45° allows complete steadying.

Speed changes while alongside are relatively simple, because supply ships accelerate very slowly. Again, incremental changes and complete exchange of information are essential. In this case, changes of a knot at a time are easily followed.

Plane Guard

Plane guarding is a duty frequently assigned a destroyer. In this role, as rescue destroyer she not only stands by to assist in case of an accident, but also serves as a marker pylon upon which the pilots gauge their turns. For this reason, when plane guarding, the destroyer conning officer must keep his station accurately.

The primary rescue destroyer station is the one astern of the carrier (usually 165° relative, 1,000 yards). This distance was selected to allow the destroyer ample room to stop before running past any crash occurring near the carrier. The station is slightly on the quarter to allow the destroyer's bridge personnel to see across the bow of the carrier in case a plane "goes in" over the bow. This also moves the plane guard out of the "landing pattern," which is to port of the carrier.

Other rescue destroyer stations may be assigned, especially at night when it is desirable to establish a visual horizon for the pilots by using the truck-lights of the rescue destroyer to provide this reference. When a number of rescue destroyers are assigned, the group is handled as a small Task Group, with complete signals for the stationing and maneuvering desired. When a single rescue destroyer is assigned, she is expected to assume her station and maneuver properly with little or no further instruction. The conning officer of a rescue destroyer is expected to anticipate and follow whatever move the carrier may make.

Obviously the proper position for the rescue destroyer during flight operations is 165° from the true wind, so upon being ordered to assume her station, she should proceed to a station 1,000 yards from the carrier, with the true wind on the proper bearing. Once on station, she should parallel the carrier and follow her movements by simple turns. The problem has been further simplified by the current fleet practice of predicting the flight course well beforehand and allowing the rescue destroyer ample time to get on station. Difficulty arises, however, when the wind is light and the carrier does not desire to use the predicted course for her actual operations.

Should the carrier commence to turn unexpectedly, we should head for her wake to insure that we will be able to follow astern as she maneuvers. Our objective is to gain our proper station as quickly as possible once she settles on a course, and from 1,000 yards dead astern we can slide out to our proper station very quickly. We must not make the mistake, though, of assuming too early that the carrier is on course or we will end up on the inside of the turn and have to sheer away for safety's sake. In very calm weather carriers often turn radically when searching for the almost non-existent breeze.

If we are on station on the quarter, and the carrier makes a change of course, it is a useful practice to change course approximately an equal amount but in the *opposite* direction until the bearing has been corrected, and then swing parallel to her, as shown in Figure 56. For example, if the carrier changes her course 10° to the right, we should change our course 10° to the left until the bearing to the carrier has changed the required 10°, and then we should come 20° to the right to parallel her. For left turns, we might turn right a smaller amount than the carrier turned (or even hold our course), but for small adjustments of course it is a useful rule.

Plane Crash

If a plane crashes, head directly for at best speed, as shown in Figure 57. The coming officer must station men on the pelorus and on a stadimeter (used as described in Chapter IV) to obtain ranges and bearings to the scene of the crash. It is a good rule to drop our speed at the last minute so as to be making 15 knots through the water at 500 yards from the crash, and with 450 yards to go, BACK TWO-THIRDS. This should bring the ship dead in the water abreast the crash, but we still have BACK FULL or BACK ONE-THIRD should we need adjustment. When about 100 yards from the downed pilot, we should change course slightly to *windward* to bring the pilot along the *lee* side. When the ship is dead in the water it will

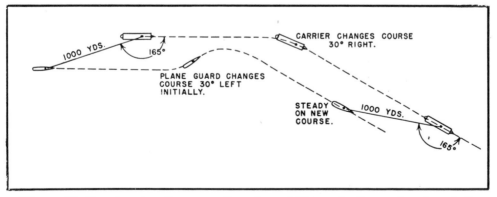

Figure 56. Keeping on plane guard station while carrier hunts for the wind.

drift with the wind, while a man in the water is practically unaffected by the wind; therefore, from a windward position, the ship will drift *down on* the pilot. Once the ship has been brought to a stop with the man close aboard, it is easy to work him to the survivor's net or rescue basket with lines and swimmers.

Don't be afraid of running the man down as we approach. In the first place, the chance of being able to actually hit him with the stem is quite remote, and, even if we did, our speed through the water is so low that it probably wouldn't hurt him. It is an unfortunate fact that in crashes of carrier-type planes at sea, the occupants are either in good shape or they don't survive, so we can expect that if the pilot is afloat, he can paddle around a bit and will avoid the stem. The biggest trouble we will experience will be that the fliers swim away from the ship because of lurid tales they have heard about being "sucked into the screws." The effect of the screws on a man on the surface is usually overrated, and in case the man in the water should get close to the screws, we can order STOP SHAFT until he is clear.

The reader might be wondering about the 15 knots and 450 yards mentioned above. These figures were derived by calibrating a 2,100-ton destroyer in calm weather with no wind. A slight adjustment is necessary in case of wind, but the figures work out remarkably well. Backing TWO-THIRDS at 600 yards for an approach speed of 20 knots worked out very well also, but each skipper should calibrate his own ship. Approach speeds greater than 20 knots need not be figured, because the speed can be knocked down to 15 or 20 knots rapidly just before the final approach is made.

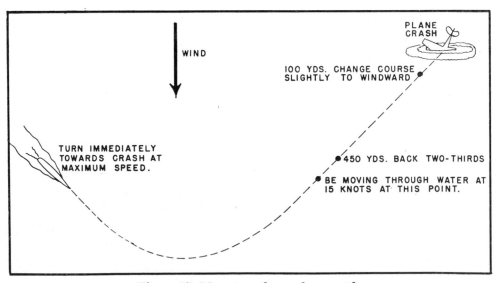

Figure 57. Maneuver for a plane crash.

Survivor Rescue

The rescue basket mentioned above and illustrated in Figure 58 is a relatively new development in survivor rescue, and one of great value. The problem of getting an exhausted or injured flier aboard in a rough sea has always been difficult, but the rescue basket offers a real solution. Essentially it is a shallow net about six feet across that can be lowered into the water so the survivor can climb or be pushed into it for hoisting aboard. It is swung from a small davit amidships, and when used in conjunction with a couple of good swimmers on safety lines it should offer the solution under almost any conditions.

A boat is not normally used in the rescue operation unless the approach is so poor that we have completely missed the man in the water, or unless there are so many men in the water that it would be advisable. Of course we would use the boat at any time it would offer a speedier or safer method of rescue, but in practice the ship itself has become the primary rescue vessel. However,

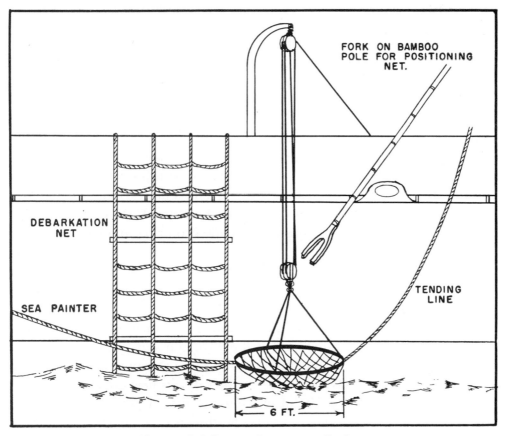

Figure 58. The survivor rescue basket.

the boat is normally maintained manned and ready at the rail to be lowered when needed.

The helicopter, which is so extensively used for plane guarding today, presents an additional problem to the destroyer. As the helicopter hovers over the wreck trying to pick up survivors, it blocks the destroyer's approach, and it must clear before the destroyer can safely move in. It is a command function of the carrier to call off the helicopter or to direct the destroyer to keep clear, but since the destroyer must initiate his clearing action several hundred yards before he arrives at the scene, late instructions can cause an awkward situation. If no orders have been received by the time we are about 500 yards from the crash, it is best to sheer out to the side, stop abreast of the scene, and send our boat to the survivors. A whaleboat and a helicopter can work together with no undue danger.

Man Overboard

Maneuvering for a man overboard is similar to the situation at plane crash, except that it is assumed that the man in the water is initially just astern of the ship. If the situation allows, the stern should be swung away from the man in the water and the screw on that side stopped, but normally the bridge is not aware of the man in the water until too late for such action. The initial turn is usually made *toward* the side to which the man fell, in hopes that a turn in that direction will help clear him by moving the stern *away* from him.

A good approach for recovering the man in the water can be made with a continuous full rudder turn in one direction, as shown in Figure 59, until the bow is pointed at the man. The speed should be adjusted to 15 knots during the last half of the turn, and the engines should be ordered BACK TWO-THIRDS when 450 yards from the man in the water. If the man is in sight, this continuous turn in one direction promises to bring him back on board in the shortest time.

If the man is not in sight, or if conditions are such that it would be difficult to find him should we lose contact, a "Williamson turn" may be a better approach. As indicated in Figure 60, this calls for continuing the initial full rudder turn until 60° from the initial heading, and then *ordering* the helm shifted and reversing the direction of the turn. Our ship's heading will normally just reach 90° from the initial heading as she commences to swing in the opposite direction. We continue turning in this new direction until we can steady up on the opposite of our initial course. Upon completion of a Williamson turn, we will find ourselves heading back along our initial track and about one turning diameter from the point at which we commenced the turn. This allows us to search carefully back along our former track until we locate our man in the water.

Locating the man in the water is often the most difficult part of the operation. The life buoy watch should be equipped and instructed to throw over a package of marker dye and a float light (which gives off both flame and dense smoke) as close to the man in the water as possible. Even though he

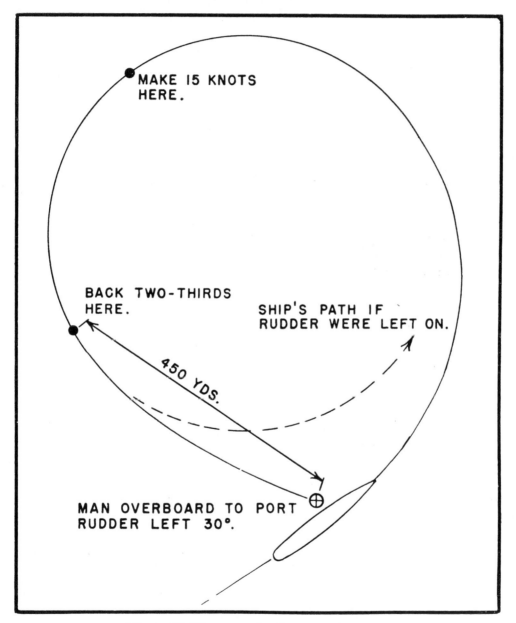

Figure 59. Maneuver for "man overboard."

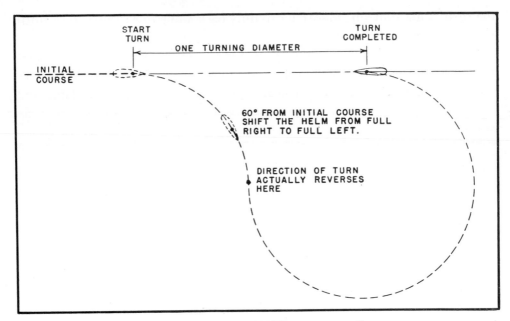

Figure 60. The "Williamson turn."

does not see the man, the life buoy watch should throw these markers over to assist in establishing the ship's former track for reference, in order to return to the exact area after completing the turn.

CIC can be of great assistance during "man overboard." If a mark is made on the plot at the moment that "man overboard" is reported, CIC, by use of the dead reckoning tracer, can always report the bearing and distance to this spot and can advise in maneuvering the ship back to the place where the man fell over. If he is still in sight during the first part of the maneuver, CIC should be kept informed of the actual ranges and bearings to the man in the water, so that they can correct their plot and have better information in case contact is later lost.

Handling Boats at Sea

Though we have pointed out that it has become the practice in the Fleet to use the ship itself to perform most of the functions required, there are times when it is necessary to lower a boat at sea. Rescuing large numbers of people from the water and recovering torpedoes are typical evolutions in which a boat is used. The problem in employing a boat at sea is getting it *into* and *out of* the water safely.

Lowering a boat is relatively easy, even when using the older crescent davits, because the falls can be lowered rapidly; and the boat, once waterborne, can be quickly disconnected by using the quick-release feature of the hooks. We must, of course, be sure that the stern hook is released first and that the falls are pulled clear of the boat quickly, but these are relatively simple matters. It is hooking on and hoisting a boat at sea that is difficult. The heavy lower block of the standard whaleboat falls is nearly unmanageable if the boat is bobbing up and down and the ship is rolling. One moment the lower block is resting in the boat with the slack of the falls draped over the bowhook's shoulders as he struggles to engage the hook, and the next moment it is jerked high above the heads of the boat's crew as the ship rolls away from the boat. This lower block is a man-killer. Because it has inflicted so many injuries on boat crews over the years, skippers are reluctant to lower a boat at sea unless absolutely necessary.

The constant tension modification to the Welin-type gravity davits in

Figure 61. USS FORREST SHERMAN modification of
Welin-type Gravity Davits.

FORREST SHERMAN eliminates to a large extent the difficulty and hazard of lowering and hoisting boats at sea. As illustrated in Figure 61, a freely rotating arm is added to each davit which holds a weighted sheave on the bight of the wire just inboard of the head sheave. The downward weight on the bight is selected in relation to the weight of the hook on the end of the fall so that there is a net pull of about 20 pounds tending to pull the hook upwards. The free rotation of the arm between its stops is sufficient to allow a total pull-out of about 10 feet with this slight upward pull. In operation, when the boat is lowered into the water, this upward force keeps the falls taut and the hook engaged while the boat can bob freely through a range of up to 10 feet without coming up hard against the falls or having the falls go slack. To unhook the boat, the crew needs only to pull down with a force of a little more than 20 pounds, trip the hook, and let go—the tension feature will pull the hook up and clear smartly. For hooking on, the falls are lowered until the hooks are about 5 feet above the mean level of the boat, the men in the boat reach up and pull the hooks down against the tension until they can be hooked into the hoisting rings, and in a few seconds the boat is ready for hoisting. With this rig, even in difficult weather, the lowering and hoisting of boats at sea becomes a safe evolution which can be accomplished both quickly and efficiently.

Regardless of the type davit being used, the fundamental difficulty in handling boats at sea is caused by the rapid changing of the distance from the davit head to the surface of the water alongside the ship. The most capable boatswain's mate in the world can't control this as he struggles to hoist his boat; it is the shiphandler only who has this under any control.

To assist the deck force in their task of lowering and hoisting the boat, the conning officer should select a course to provide a minimum roll and the slowest changing of the level of the water alongside. Running downwind at the speed of the waves would provide a perfect solution, but unfortunately the boat cannot make such a speed and thus could not come under the falls. Consequently, since the ship's speed through the water is limited to the maximum speed that the boat can make, our ship's speed must be not more than five knots when handling a standard motor whaleboat. The best solution with this limitation is to take a downwind course at a low speed in order to minimize the ship's roll and to reduce the relative velocity of the waves as much as possible. If it does not increase the roll, a course which brings the wind to the quarter on the opposite side from the falls will assist further by making a lee in the vicinity of the falls.

When handling a boat while running with the seas, we must be careful that the boat does not broach as she runs down the face of a following wave. The

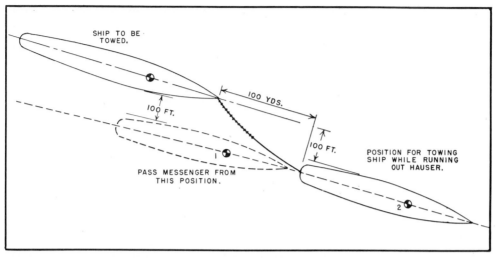

SHIP TO BE TOWED.

100 FT.

100 YDS.

100 FT.

POSITION FOR TOWING SHIP WHILE RUNNING OUT HAUSER.

PASS MESSENGER FROM THIS POSITION.

Figure 62. The approach for towing.

higher the speed at which we are conducting the operation and the more the tension on the sea painter, the less trouble we will have with the boat. In very high seas it may be advisable to pass a stern line led well aft on the ship to hold the boat in her fore-and-aft position in spite of the overtaking waves.

If the wind and the sea are not from the same direction, a compromise course may be required. Usually, however, it will be the direction of the wave motion that dictates our course. The hazards of lowering and hoisting boats at sea are minimized if we have minimized our roll and have reduce the relative motion of the waves as much as possible. The longer the interval between wave crests, the longer is our opportunity to hook on and hoist away.

Towing

Towing another vessel at sea is a maneuver that has been made difficult by too much planning and discussion. Actually it is a relatively simple evolution under good sea conditions, and in no case is it any more difficult than fueling at sea. Fundamentally, the ship to be towed is lying dead in the water; the towing ship passes close and sends over the messenger for the towing hawser. The towing ship then stops and maintains her position sufficiently close to allow the hawser to be run, and finally, after the hawser has been secured and the towed ship's chain has been run out the towing ship slowly sets taut and commences towing.

In the first place, much of the complicated preparation which is normal practice is not necessary. There is no reason for running the messenger up to the forward part of the ship. Since the stern is going to follow along after the bow, we can shoot our "shot line" or heave our heaving line just as well from the stern as from the bow. Next, draping the towing hawser in bights about the stern is inviting trouble. It can easily get out of hand, and it has been known to foul a screw. On a destroyer the towing hawser can be stopped down on deck and run out of the stern chock very handily. An "easing out lizard" can be used for easing out successive bights, and this same lizard will be useful in retrieving the hawser later.

We should make the approach nearly parallel to the ship to be towed as shown in Figure 62, so as to pass about 100 feet to windward of her forecastle; next, send over the messenger, and then bring the ship to a position where our stern will be about 100 yards ahead and 100 feet abeam of the other ship's stem. This position allows us a clear view of the situation from the bridge and insures safety in case the other ship should surge ahead or we should surge astern.

The secret in passing the towing hawser is to maintain the proper distance from our stern to her forecastle. If we send a junior officer to the fantail with a stadimeter set for ten times the height of the other ship's bullnose by dividing his reading by ten the JO can send us the exact distance from our stern to the other ship's stem. This is most important during the time the other ship is shackling her chain to our hawser, because if we open the distance too much, the hawser may be lost and the whole operation must be started again.

As soon as the hawser has been run and the other ship's chain run out, we can begin the delicate operation of "taking the strain." If our towing hawser is 100 fathoms long, and if the towed ship has 80 fathoms of chain out at her bullnose, our stern will be 360 yards from the other ship's bullnose when the hawser is straightened out. The stadimeter on the fantail will be of great help during this part of the evolution, but we must remember that accuracy of the ranges depends upon accurately setting for the other ship's bullnose height. By nudging our ship with the engines, we can slowly open until the hawser begins to tend *aft* instead of up and down. From this time on we must watch the distance carefully and allow it to open only gradually. Until the strain has been taken and is steady, there is a real danger of parting the hawser, because an almost undiscernible forward motion will end in a severe jerk. As the hawser begins to straighten out, the towed ship will begin to move until finally a state of equilibrium is reached, with the hawser taking a steady strain.

Once the tow has been gotten underway and the first "steady strain" condition reached, the difficult part of taking a ship in tow has been completed. From this point on, the speed can be gradually increased in one knot increments until we are towing at about 10 knots. This speed represents about the maximum that a destroyer can tow another ship with the conventional rig. Higher speeds could probably be made in deep water by leaving an anchor rigged at the end of the towed ship's chain, where it is shackled to the towing hawser, to give more weight to the catenary. This would provide greater cushioning action and allow greater stresses before the towing hawser is straightened out.

When towing for an extended period, the scope of the tow may have to be adjusted to suit the sea conditions. If the towing ship is being *slowed* by the front face of an oncoming wave at the same time that the towed ship is *accelerating* down the back slope of a wave that has passed, the towed hawser will go slack. As the situation reverses and the towing ship *increases speed* down the back face of a wave and the towed ship *slows* on the front face of a wave, the towing hawser will be pulled taut with a jerk. Such a situation can part the tow even under mild sea conditions.

The ideal situation is to adjust the length of the tow so that the two ships are experiencing the same wave action at the same time. This will be the case when the distance between bridges is equal to the distance between wave crests, or a multiple of this distance. The scope of the tow can be adjusted most easily by having the towed ship vary the amount of chain she has out. If the towed ship has no power, it may be necessary to change course until the two ships are "in step."

When ready to cast off, we must reduce speed gradually so that the towed ship will not run up on the towing ship. We must remember that the weight of the catenary is always pulling on the towed ship, so, until we have cast off, the towed ship will continue to move ahead slowly. We can keep out of the way by maintaining a constant distance, such as 100 yards, between the ships during the disconnecting.

Plan Ahead

The special maneuvers required at sea can all be made simple by having a pre-selected plan of action and knowing the calibration of our ship. Though a special situation may require a departure from our plan, we will have a firm basis from which to proceed to meet the requirements of a particular case. The conning officer should insure that he has a complete plan for meeting *all of the normal emergencies* encountered at sea. For the scheduled evolutions, such as fueling or towing, he can make more elaborate preparations. Forehandedness includes solving as much of the problem ahead of time as the situation permits.

CHAPTER XI

RESTRICTED WATERS

WHEN OUR SHIP is under way within the confines of the harbor, we are faced with different problems from those we have faced in the open seas. The channel narrows until at times it is scarcely wider than the ship itself. The depth of water decreases until the bottom is only a few feet from our keel. Landmarks are so plentiful that any single one tends to be lost in the multitude. Even the buoys and beacons appear to have been scattered haphazardly as the various channels meet and intertwine.

When moving about in such waters our first concern is to make certain we know our position and to insure that the course we are following is in safe water. This sounds like a statement of the Navigator's duty, but the conning officer also has a share in this task. In a restricted harbor, the Navigator has his hands full just keeping track of the ship's location. With a well trained team, he can plot the ship's position accurately about once each minute. Thus he can tell us where we *have* been a few moments after we have been there, and he can lay out the major segments of our track ahead and tell us when to turn. But when we begin threading the buoys in a narrow channel, when we are required to maneuver to pass other shipping, or when we are making complex turns using the engines, the ability of the Navigator to keep abreast of the situation is strained. He can no longer keep the position accurately plotted and lay out the maneuver of the moment, and still advise the conning officer in sufficient time for this officer to depend entirely on the Navigator's advice.

In a busy harbor we must leave the realm of formal navigation to a certain extent and enter the realm of visual piloting. Consequently, the conning officer in the harbor must at all times navigate by eye. He should do this not only to guard against the possibility of a Navigator's mistake, but also to be ready to meet the situation when the scene moves too fast for the plotting team.

Conning Chart

To keep track of the ship's position, identify buoys and landmarks, and check the charted depth of the channel, the conning officer must have access to a harbor chart. It often interferes with the navigational plot if the conning officer must use the Navigator's chart for information. This officer has enough on his hands without being required to step aside every few moments to let someone have another look at the chart.

It is a minor extravagance that will pay big dividends if we provide an extra harbor chart for the exclusive use of the conning officer. This chart should be up to date, with the latest recommended track for passing through the harbor; and, if the ship's berth is known ahead of time, the Navigator's recommended courses and speeds should be laid down on it.

Some officers like to have this chart mounted on a convenient desk or surface immediately in front of their conning position so they can check off the ship's progress as she moves to her berth. Others prefer to have the chart mounted on a thin board or else simply folded conveniently so that they can orient the chart to the ship's heading and sight across the chart when identifying landmarks. The first system has the advantage of having the conning chart oriented to true north (as is normal when using charts), and thus minimizes the chance of ordering an incorrect true course. The second system has the advantage of maintaining the relative picture oriented correctly with the ship's head. Either system provides the conning officer with immediate access to a harbor chart without interfering with the navigating team.

Preparation for Handling in Port

Before any officer conns a ship in a restricted harbor, he should carefully study the chart. He should trace the intended course with the Navigator to insure that he is aware of all of the dangers he might encounter. He should check the charted depth of water throughout the track to make sure that he has not overlooked any shallow spots. He should select his turning points and plan his speed while he has ample time to study the situation. He should make note of any dangerous spots, and should select "danger bearings" on prominent objects to mark the separation between danger and safety. The safety with which he handles the ship in the harbor is dependent to a large measure in the thoroughness with which he has studied the harbor chart.

It is not sufficient to study the chart by itself, because important features might thus be overlooked. The chart should be studied with the help of the applicable *Coast Pilot* to make sure that all of the important points are ferreted out. The *Coast Pilot* gives not only the salient features of the harbor but also the recommended routes that should be followed. The *Coast Pilot* describes the tide and current conditions which will be encountered in the harbor, and if these are significant, the conning officer should insure that he is provided with complete and accurate data from the appropriate *Tide* and *Current Tables*.

Navigating by Eye

Having completed our study of the harbor and having provided ourselves with a conning chart, we are ready to commence handling our ship in these restricted waters. As mentioned above, our first task is to determine the ship's location on the chart.

Navigating by eye is neither as difficult nor as inexact as one might think. Because of the extreme care taken in Navy ships in the matter of navigation, there is a tendency to depend upon the Navigator's chart to the exclusion of all else. Actually, in a well marked harbor, the ship can be moved in and out of port by visual piloting without referring to the Navigator and his carefully marked chart. This does not lessen the need for the Navigator, for he must be at all times ready to take us through the unmarked sections of the harbor, but it does indicate the capability of visual piloting in handling the ship in the harbor.

We make our first rough location of the ship's position by identifying enough landmarks to decide the general area in which the ship is located. Then by checking bearings, estimating ranges, and utilizing pairs of landmarks as they come into line and establish a range, we refine our position until we are confident that it is correct within relatively narrow limits. As we approach the more restricted part of the harbor, our estimating becomes more exact, because we are getting nearer to the navigation markers upon which we are fixing our position. We can frequently check our position as we pass buoys close aboard, leave headlands abeam, or steer for known objects ahead.

For the simple entry into or departure from a harbor we usually have the assistance of the *harbor ranges*. There is normally a series of ranges marking the center of the main channel, and we simply shift from one range to the next as we proceed through the harbor. It is quite simple to steer so as to keep the range markers in line and thus proceed accurately along the track marked by the ranges. If the ship is exactly on the range, we have a very good fix each time we pass a channel buoy.

In the absence of a harbor range, we can establish a similar piloting aid by selecting courses that head directly for prominent objects in the harbor. We can easily follow the track thus selected by adjusting the ship's head so that the bearing to the selected object remains constant and equal to the course of the selected track. In this manner we obtain the equivalent of a range by substituting a single landmark and the ship's gyro compass for the two landmarks of a range.

Gauging the Set

Whether steering the harbor range or following a constant bearing to a fixed object ahead, we have a good check on the cross-channel *set*. This may be due to wind or cross-current, and it is helpful to have an estimate of how much of each we are feeling. This information may come in handy later, since the wind effect is usually felt to about the same extent all over the harbor, but the current at any point is dependent upon the channels in the vicinity.

The set we are experiencing *parallel* to the ship's head is more difficult to estimate. However, since the effect of wind from dead ahead or dead astern is usually negligible except when handling alongside, we can attribute all fore-and-aft set to current without being far wrong. This can be found by comparing our speed through the water, measured by pitometer log or RPM, against the speed actually being made good over the ground as reported by the navigator.

Though we can measure the set we are actually experiencing, we must also be able to *anticipate* the current we are going to encounter. The most obvious means of determining the current in the channel is to observe the current wake at a buoy or past some pilings. A one-knot current causes a definite ripple, a three-knot current will cause swirls and eddies for several yards, and a five-knot current will cause a boiling wake to stretch out downstream for fifty yards.

The angle of lean of the harbor buoys is also a good indication of the direction and strength of the current. Spar buoys are designed to assist in estimating the current, but one must be careful in using them to estimate the strength of the current. Some are so delicately balanced that they lean heavily to the side even in very light currents. It is a good habit to make a mental note of the current indicated at each channel buoy as we proceed along our way.

Following the Channel

In a tortuous channel it is often impractical to mark the channel with ranges, so the edges of the channel are marked with channel buoys. These are usually placed in pairs on opposite sides of the channel, so the channel can be followed by simply steering for the midpoint between the next pair of buoys. Along difficult sections of the channel the buoys are placed more frequently and they clearly outline the edges of safety.

As the channel widens into the open sections of the harbor, the need for paired channel buoys no longer exists. Here only the shoal water and submerged dangers are marked, and only an occasional *fairway* buoy is added to indicate the recommended channel. Under these conditions the pattern is not so easy to follow, and it is necessary to take extra care in identifying each buoy.

When only one side of the channel is extensively marked, or when following one side of a wide channel, we are faced with the problem of adjusting

our course to markers *on one side only*. We must follow the channel by keeping an appropriate distance out from the line of buoys marking the side. As
the channel winds, we must adjust our course to the new line of buoys.

It is usually safe to proceed directly from one channel buoy to the next if
we insure that we remain *inboard* of the line connecting the two buoys. If
we lay down a track parallel to the line connecting successive buoys and at a
convenient distance, such as 50 yards, inboard of the buoys, it will be an
ideal track to follow. Between buoys we can check our position by fixes and
can catch our drift readily by watching the bearing on the next buoy ahead.
This buoy is nearly dead ahead and should draw to the *off-channel* side as we
approach it. If the bearing draws to the *channel* side, we are being set out of
the channel and must take corrective action.

The only difficulty in following a channel marked on one side only is to
make the turns correctly. We know the new course in advance as we turn
into a new leg of our track, because it is the line connecting the next successive buoys. Our problem, therefore, is one of deciding how much rudder to
use and when to order it.

Turn Diagram

To make our turns accurately we can prepare a *turn diagram,* as shown
in Figure 63, from the ship's turning data. This turn diagram is a plot of
the ship's track when making 10 knots through the water and turning with
10, 15, 20, and 30 degrees of rudder. It is assumed that the ship was proceeding steadily on course 000° at 10 knots and that the rudder was ordered
over as the pivot point passed through the center of the plot. The numbers
along each track show the points at which the ship's heading changes each
successive ten degrees from the original heading. Though this diagram is
exact only for 10 knots, small differences in speed do not make any appreciable difference in the track of the ship, so the diagram is usable throughout
the range of speeds normally used in the harbor.

To use the diagram, we measure the amount we are about to change our
course and then locate this change in ship's head along the curve for the
amount of rudder we intend to use. This locates the *range* and *bearing* to
the point at which our course change will be completed from the point
at which we order rudder. If we then select the point on the navigating
chart at which we wish the turn to be completed, we can plot back from
this point to determine *when* to order the rudder. If we wish to reference our
turn to any other point, we can plot such a point on the diagram in the
same manner in which point A was plotted in the figure.

Another use of the diagram is to select the *rudder angle* to be used for a certain turn. If we are running 100 yards inboard of a line of buoys, and the next leg of our track is 80° toward the buoys from our present course, we can locate the position of the turning buoy on the turn diagram by the

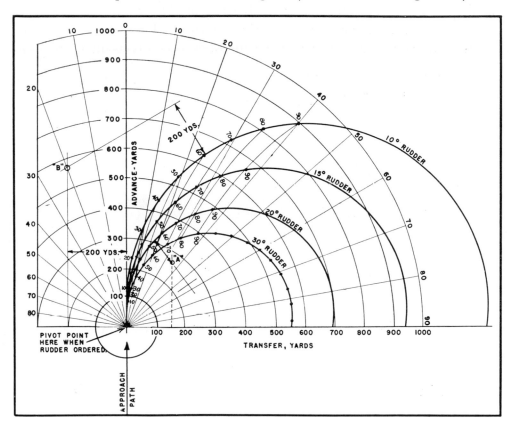

Figure 63. Turn diagram for speed of 10 knots. (Indicating points at which ship's heading has changed the indicated number of degrees from the initial approach course.)

Example of Use:

PROBLEM

To determine how to approach and when to order rudder to pass 100 yards abeam of a Buoy "A" on a course 55° from present course, using 20° rudder.

SOLUTION

From 55° point on 20° rudder curve, lay off Point "A" 100 yards 145° (90° from a track of 55°).

This indicates that we should approach on a track which would pass 160 yards abeam of Buoy "A," and we should put the rudder over when the buoy bears 35° from our approach course and is 270 yards away.

(Note: This diagram is for illustration only and is not accurate for any certain ship).

intersection of the lines 100 yards on our beam before and after the turn, as indicated for points A, B, and C of Figure 64. From Figure 64 it is seen that 10° rudder will put us outside of the channel, and 20° rudder will put us quite close to the buoy, so we had better use 30° rudder for the turn. It is apparent that in any case of turning *toward* the buoy, the more rudder we use, the farther we will pass from the buoy. The disadvantage of using

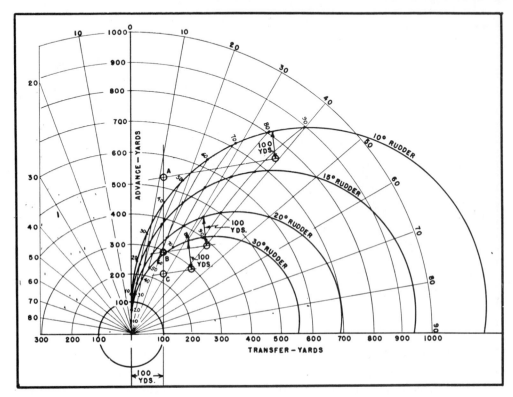

Figure 64. Using the turn diagram for selecting rudder for a turn around a buoy.

PROBLEM

We are running 100 yards inboard of a line of buoys and desire to continue to do so. The next turn is 80° toward the line of buoys. How much rudder should we use, and when should we order it?

SOLUTION

Plot the lines 100 yards on our beam before and after the turn for 10°, 20°, and 30° rudder, giving intersections A, B, and C. A is outside of 10° track, B is too close to 20° track. We should therefore use 30° rudder and order the helm over when the buoy is bearing 28° from approach course, distance 220 yards.

large rudder angles is that a steering error or casualty may cause us to over-shoot and cross the line of buoys.

When the turn is to the side *away* from the line of buoys, we can use any amount of rudder we desire if the channel is wide enough to accommodate a slow, easy turn. The easier our turn, when turning *away,* the farther we will pass from the buoy. To determine the point at which to order helm, we plot the offset lines on the turn diagram as before, but in this case they will be *outside* of the turn circle. The range and bearing to the buoy when we should order the rudder over are indicated by the intersection of the offset lines. Point "B" in Figure 63 is such an intersection for a 10° rudder turn in the case where we are running 200 yards from the buoys and our turn is 60° *away* from the buoys.

When time or circumstance does not allow the careful plotting of the turn as indicated above, we can make our turn by eye. If we can be on the new course when the buoy is the desired distance on our beam, we will have accomplished the turn satisfactorily. To achieve this, the conning officer can estimate this beam position by eye, and can steer to put his pivot point through this point just as the ship swings to the new course. This is not as difficult as it sounds, because, having mentally selected his objective as a point in the water at the beginning of the turn, the conning officer can take corrective action as necessary as he approaches this point.

A typical track for following one side of the channel is indicated in Figure 65. The points at which to put the rudder over were selected by using the turn diagram. Good target points for making the turns by eye are indicated, and it will be noted that they are slightly advanced along the track from the actual beam points to allow an easier turn. Care should be taken not to come too close (closer than 30 yards) to the buoys when making sharp turns.

Squatting

As a ship increases speed, she sinks appreciably with respect to the mean surface of the water. Both her bow and stern ride lower in the water as her velocity is increased (See Figure 66), and the water level alongside, amidships, is lower than that of the surrounding water. There is a distinct bow wave and a distinct stern wave, and the water between the two is depressed. This is caused in part by the increase in relative velocity of the water as it flows under the ship, and in part by the interaction of the bow and stern wave systems. As the ship travels along, she rides in a depression created by her own passage.

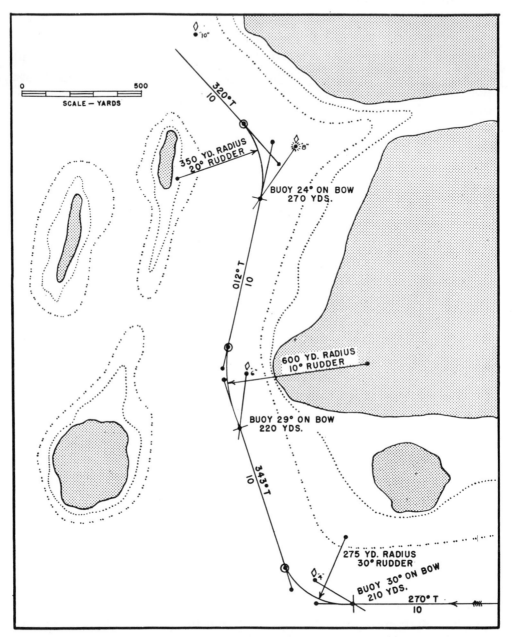

Figure 65. Following a channel marked on one side only. (Running 100 yards abeam of buoys, using the turn diagram for making turns. Target points for making turns by eye are indicated by dotted circle.)

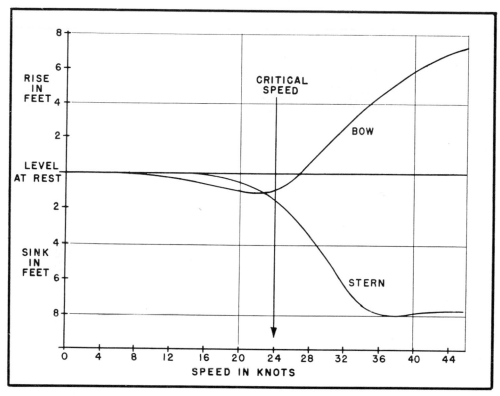

Figure 66. Change in level of bow and stern as ship increases speed. (For 400-foot, high-speed ship. Drawn from Figure 157, "Speed and Power of Ships," by Rear Admiral David W. Taylor CC, USN [Ret.].)

If the speed is further increased past the "critical speed,"* the bow begins to rise abruptly and the stern sinks more rapidly, as indicated in the figure. This phenomenon is known as "Squatting," and has a distinct effect on the resistance to the ship's motion and the speed resulting from a given power.

The wave system, known as a Kelvin Wave Group (see Figure 67), caused by the passage of a ship consists of curved waves that spread out sideways, nearly parallel to the sides of the bow, and transverse waves, nearly perpendicular to the direction of the motion of the ship, which follow astern at approximately the speed of the ship. It is these transverse waves that play an important part in the squatting of a ship. As the speed is increased, the crest of the bow wave moves back along the ship, and the bow tends to ride up on its own bow wave. At the same time, if the stern is riding in a depres-

---

* For further information on critical speed, see Appendix II.

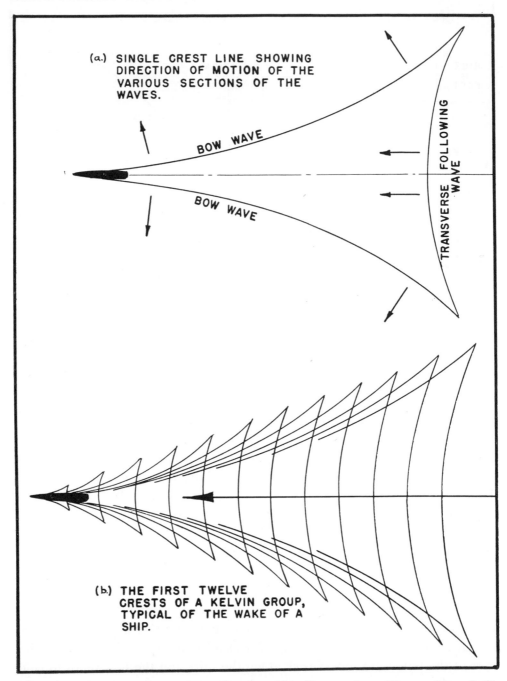

Figure 67. Wave system in the wake of a ship. (Drawn from Figures 36 and 37, "Speed and Power of Ships," by Rear Admiral David W. Taylor CC, USN [Ret.].)

sion of the transverse wave system, the stern will sink. If the first depression of the transverse wave system is at the stern, the ship can be considered to be riding on the back of its own bow wave as indicated in Figure 68. It is the coincidence of this first depression with the stern (and its wave system) that determines the "critical speed."

Both sinking and squatting are increased in shallow water. The proximity of the bottom causes increased relative velocity as the water flows under the ship, and the waves of the wake are more pronounced. Squatting can become a serious problem in shallow water, both from its effect on the propulsion of the ship and from the danger of the resultant wake.

In a typical situation of attempting to make high speed in shallow water, a destroyer making turns for 30 knots in 30 feet of water might only be making 22 knots over the ground. The squat would be so severe that the stern would be riding about 8 feet *lower* than normal, while the bow might be 4 feet *above* the normal level. With our ship drawing 19 feet at the propellers, this would mean that at the bottom of their travel the blade tips would be only *3 feet* from the bottom. Severe pounding would most probably be felt at the propellers as the blades passed through the area of

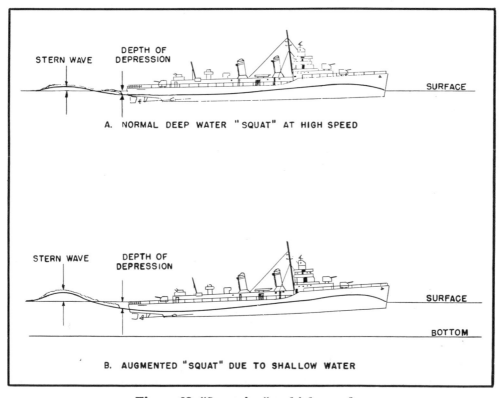

Figure 68. "Squatting" at high speeds.

varying velocities and eddies between the bottom of the ship and the bottom of the channel.

The severe squatting experienced in shallow water is attended by a huge stern wave that towers over the fantail of the ship. If we stand on the fantail of a destroyer while attempting high speed in shallow water, the crests of the outward moving bow waves abreast the stern would be nearly at eye level, and the transverse stern wave would stand menacingly 15 feet higher than the level of the deck at the stern.

The danger from these waves is not to our ship but to the other ships in the harbor, and to the docks and other structures at the water's edge. It is as though the ship were racing about the harbor towing a train of tidal waves astern. Such waves can lift large ships bodily and cause them to roll heavily. Such waves can sever moorings, break up nests, and throw ships against their docks. Such waves can cause damage to beach structures as far away as 1,000 yards from the ship's track.

Consequently, though we should steam at sufficient speed to keep good control of the ship, we should limit our speed in the harbor to that which will cause no damage. Most shallow harbors have definite speed restrictions, and vessels are not allowed to proceed at more than 10 or 12 knots. Except in the deepest and most open harbors it is not wise to exceed 15 knots.

Meeting Other Ships

When steaming about the harbor we usually meet other vessels and are often required to pass very close to them. In order to do so safely, we must be able to ascertain the other ship's intentions before we are so close that we cannot accommodate our movements to an alteration of his course. The system of passing signals set out in the *Rules of the Road* is for this purpose, and the whistle is the main instrument for exchanging such intelligence.

Most naval officers, however, look upon the whistle as an emergency signal only, and save it for such use. Thus, they proceed with incomplete information about the intentions of the vessel they are meeting, when adequate means has been provided to easily obtain this information.

The whistle signals should be used whenever it is desirable to determine the intentions of another ship. An exchange of signals definitely establishes that the other ship is aware of our presence and agrees to passing in a certain manner. If additional use of the whistle will assist the safe and efficient transit of the harbor, the whistle should not be spared. It is certainly not smart shiphandling to proceed on incomplete information.

Four or more blasts on the whistle means "I do not understand your intentions," as well as being the danger signal. It should be used as soon as there is serious doubt as to the intentions of the other vessel. It is not intended that we wait until a situation has become dangerous before we use this signal.

Though there are only four whistle signals, it is remarkable how many problems can be solved in this four-word "language." We should recognize its limitations, though, and be alert for those times when an understanding has not been reached. At such times it is wise to sound four blasts early in the game and let everyone know that there is doubt in our minds.

A particular passing problem which is often troublesome is the encounter with a small craft not equipped with a whistle. The fishing boat, yacht, or launch may be on a collision course, but we cannot exchange signals. We may also remember that a whistle signal is not complete until it is *answered* by an identical signal from the other vessel. What should we do?

In this case, we should indicate our intentions to the small vessel by appropriate whistle signal, and then proceed accordingly. Though we have not sealed a mutual pact by a complete exchange, we have helped things by drawing his attention to us and indicating our intentions. If he does not respond correctly to the one-sided signals, we still have the four-blast signal at our command.

Actually in most situations where the danger of collision with a small craft becomes evident, the situation is caused by inattention on the part of the crew of the small vessel, or, because of the nimbleness of his craft, the skipper of the smaller vessel hasn't yet considered the problem pressing. Small vessels usually go to great pains to avoid embarrassing larger ships, and if their attention is drawn by a whistle signal, they will quickly take steps to avoid the larger ship. The four-blast signal is very handy for calling the attention of the smaller vessel to the fact that the conning officer of the larger ship considers the situation acute.

Handling the Ship in a Canal

Occasionally our ship must make a passage through a canal, and we must be prepared for the problems of such waterways. Because a canal is a man-made channel, it is only as wide as absolutely necessary for its purpose. We therefore find ourselves in a waterway much narrower than is our normal experience, and we seem to be in danger of going aground on both sides of the channel at the same time.

In addition to the obvious limitations to maneuvering in a canal, there are several unexpected effects which we encounter in these narrow channels. (This subject is covered in Report 601 of the David Taylor Model Basin, entitled *The Performance of Model Ships in Restricted Channels in Relation to the Design of a Ship Canal.*) As we attempt to proceed at a higher speed, the ship may appear to sink alarmingly with respect to the banks of the canal. If we stray from the center of the channel, our steering is affected. There is a tendency for the ship to move *bodily toward* the near bank, and there is an opposing tendency to force the *bow away* from the near bank. Although these effects are more noticeable in large ships, it is worthwhile for all shiphandlers to become acquainted with them.

In a restricted channel where the cross-sectional area of the ship becomes an appreciable part of the cross-section of the channel, the sinkage of the ship with speed is much more pronounced than that experienced at sea or even that experienced in shallow water. A large ship, when traveling at 12 knots in a 45-foot channel 500 feet wide, might sink bodily 8 feet *below* its normal level when dead in the water in the channel. Just before reaching critical speed (where the bow commences to rise and the stern to sink), the ship rides in a deep depression in the surface of the water that extends nearly the entire length of the ship. This "sinkage" must be considered in determining whether the channel depth is sufficient to allow the passage of our ship.

This increased sinkage is caused by the increased velocity with which the water, displaced forward, must flow aft about the ship as the ship moves ahead. This increased velocity, and the attendant decrease in pressure, causes the level of water to be lowered all along the midship section. Since the area of the passage between the ship and the boundaries of the canal is decreased, the velocity of the water moving astern must increase to "fill in" behind the ship at a given ship's speed. The action of the propellers in taking their suction from the restricted area increases the sinkage experienced by from 10 per cent to 15 per cent.

As the ship strays from the center of the channel and steams closer to one bank than the other, the passage between her side and the nearer bank becomes even more restricted; the velocity of flow on that side must therefore increase, and the water level between the ship and the near bank is lowered. This tends to force the ship into the near bank, an effect known as "bank suction." If a ship is maintained on a course parallel to the adjacent bank, she will move bodily in to the bank.

As the ship approaches the bank, the bow wave on the *near* side becomes augmented and tends to push the bow *away* from the bank. This is clearly indicated in Figure 69, which is drawn from actual experimental data with models. Thus, in addition to the bank suction tending to draw the ship bodily *in to* the bank, there is the bank effect which applies a twisting movement to the ship and tends to make the ship sheer *away* from the bank.

In practice, a ship can usually steam safely near one bank of a canal, but she must maintain a slight inclination *away* from the near bank to overcome the bank suction, and she will usually require several degrees of rudder

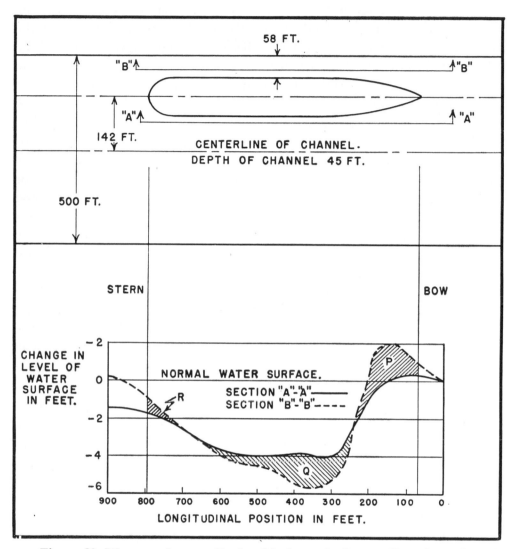

Figure 69. Water surface profile for ship located off centerline of canal.

Bank effect is felt because Area P is larger than Area R.

Bank suction is felt because Area Q is larger than P plus R.

   (Data are from Figure 7.20 of Report 601, of the David Taylor Model Basin, entitled "The Performance of Model Ships in Restricted Channels in Relation to the Design of a Ship Canal." Figures are for a large tanker, 720 feet long, making 11 knots in a 500-foot-wide channel with vertical banks.)

toward the near bank to hold the ship's head steady against the bank effect.

An insidious situation can result while steaming close to the bank of a canal when the ship momentarily gets too close to the side. The bank effect may become too large to be overcome by the rudder, and the bow may be forced away from the near bank. This will cause the stern to swing towards the near bank; the bank suction will then become stronger on the stern, and the sheer will be increased as the stern is drawn toward the near bank. The resulting sheer may be so great that the ship will cross the canal and go aground on the *opposite* bank before she can be gotten under control again.

Another problem when navigating in a canal occurs when passing sections where the bank has been cut out to form docks for mooring ships or for other purposes. The pilots of the Suez Canal, where cutouts are provided to allow large ships to pass one another, have reported a serious tendency for ships to veer *into* the cutouts as they come abreast of them. This has caused passing ships to veer toward and collide with ships waiting in the cutouts when it initially appeared that they were passing with a safe margin.

The tendency to veer into a cutout is caused by the removal of the bank effect as the ship comes abreast the interruption in the canal bank. When the force tending to push the bow *away* from the bank is removed, the rudder used to counteract it commences to turn the ship *toward* the near bank and *into* the cutout! Unless this rudder angle is removed immediately, the ship will turn in response to her rudder. When passing interruptions in the canal bank, the shiphandler must be alert to detect and counteract any changes in the forces on his ship.

The severe sinking, the bank effect, and the bank suction described above are usually troublesome only to very large ships in very restricted canals. A destroyer can maneuver safely quite close to the bank of a canal with little noticeable effect. These effects are dependent on the ship's speed through the water, and, as with most hydrodynamic effects, the strength of the force on the ship varies generally as the square of the ship's speed. *Moderate speed should be the rule when navigating a canal.*

Normally a canal is just as easy a place in which to handle the ship as is a narrow marked channel in the harbor, but the proximity of the banks makes it seem more confined. The canal has one distinct advantage, however, in that the current, if any, flows parallel to the banks, so there is no cross-channel set due to current. Further, canals are very thoroughly marked, and one is seldom in doubt about his position.

The most difficult part of handling a ship in a canal is following sharp turns in the channel when there is considerable current flowing. If we are going up stream and turn late (Figure 70), the current can get on our in-

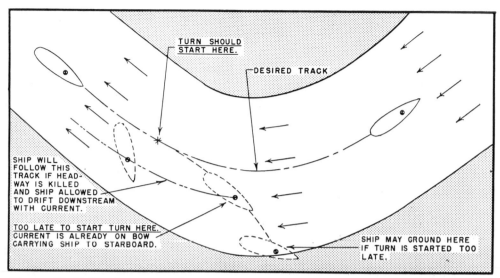

Figure 70. Following a turn in a canal or narrow channel while going upstream.

board bow, retard our turn, and cause us to go into the bank. If we get caught in such a position, the best action is to order **BACK EMERGENCY** to kill the ship's headway, and then drift downstream with the current. If we can kill the ship's way with respect to the water, the ship will be carried downstream at a nearly constant distance from the bank regardless of the orientation of the ship. Once straightened out, we can start ahead again and make our turn in proper fashion.

Making the turn successfully is not difficult. The conning officer should take care to insure that he starts his turn at the correct moment and that he does not get the ship across the current. The proper heading for the ship at any moment during the turn is approximately parallel to the banks at that point in the turn. It is easy to check the correctness of our heading by observing the banks, and, if deviations are detected early, they are readily eliminated by increasing or decreasing the amount of rudder being used.

Making a turn going downstream (Figure 71) presents different problems. The current adds to our ship's speed through the water, so that our speed over the ground is increased. On the other hand the action of the current tends to reduce rather than augment the effect of beginning the turn at the wrong time. Whether we turn too early or too late, the current tends to help our turn and carries us downstream instead of forcing us towards the bank.

Passing Through Restrictions in the Channel

Occasionally in a canal or harbor we must pass through a very narrow restriction, such as the opening in a drawbridge or the entrance through a

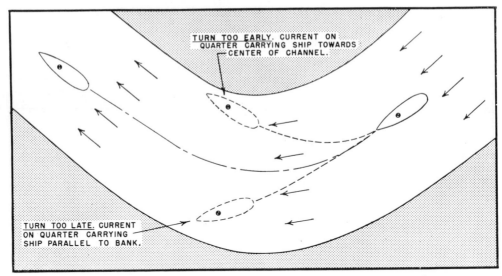

Figure 71. Following a turn in a canal or narrow channel while going downstream.

breakwater. Often there is cross-current or crosswind, and the opening is scarcely larger than the beam of the ship.

In approaching such a restriction, we should maneuver to approach the center of the opening on a constant bearing course. This requires that we alter our ship's head until the bearing on the center of the opening is steady. The difference between the bearing of the center of the opening and the ship's head when the bearing is steady determines the cross-channel angle at which we will pass through the opening. Having thus determined this cross-channel angle, we can project the extremities of the ship at this inclination to estimate whether we can safely pass through the opening. Figure 72 illustrates this projection and shows that with a large cross-channel angle we need a much larger opening than simply the ship's breadth.

If we find that we have too large a cross-channel angle to allow us to pass through the restriction, two courses of action are open. First we can increase our speed. Doubling our speed will halve the cross-channel angle. However, we must also bear in mind that doubling our speed will also quadruple the kinetic energy of the ship and greatly increase the damage should we strike something.

The second course of action, other than waiting for more favorable conditions, is to turn the ship as we go through the restriction (See Figure 73). In this case we swing the ship parallel to the channel just as we arrive in the restriction, and thus we eliminate our cross-channel angle. Of course, as soon as we make this alteration, we will begin to be set across the channel, but before we have moved appreciably across the channel, we will be through the

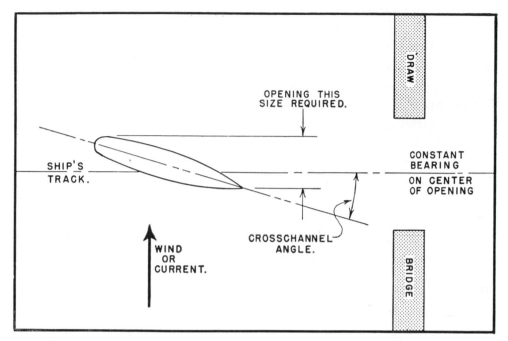

Figure 72. Passing through a restriction while being set cross-channel.

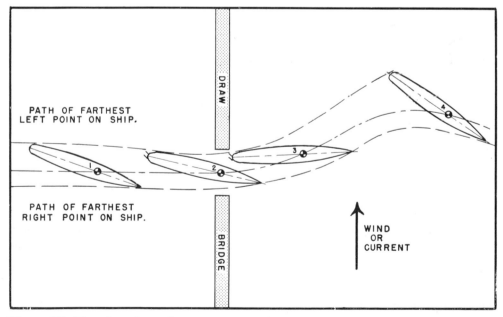

Figure 73. Turning through a narrow restriction with a strong cross-channel set.

restriction. The difference between our heading and our track can be considered to be the same after the turn as before, so we will simply be altering our track over the ground by the amount of the cross-channel angle. It is necessary, of course, that the restriction be short enough and that we have sufficient room on the other side of the restriction to take the attendant excursion to leeward and still return to the center of the channel.

When turning through a restricted gate, it is wise to pass the bow as close to the windward side of the opening as possible. Just as our bow arrives in the restriction, we should kick our stern upwind to keep it clear of the lee side of the gate. While doing this, we allow the bow to fall off downwind as necessary, but as it is already safely through the gate, the present problem is to get the stern through. Hence, as soon as the bow has passed the windward restriction, the conning officer should move to the lee wing of the bridge to have a good vantage point for twisting the stern through.

Handling in Port at Night

Handling a ship in a restricted harbor at night is often required. In this case we are deprived of many of our usual visual aids, and we must depend more thoroughly on navigational aids while moving about the harbor. In preparation for handling the ship at night, the conning officer should memorize beforehand the characteristics of the important navigational lights. He should plan to accomplish his passage utilizing only the lights he has studied, and he should lay out his course accordingly.

Though we are deprived in darkness of certain aids to which we have become accustomed, we still have adequate information to handle the ship safely and efficiently. The harbor ranges are lighted and most of the buoys and beacons are clearly distinguishable, once they have been identified. Though one cannot see as well as in daylight, he can distinguish unlighted objects at surprising distances even on the darkest nights. Finally, other ships are well marked with lights which can be seen clearly at all reasonable distances in the harbor. The most troublesome part of shiphandling at night is the lack of the incidental information one acquires by such actions as observing the surface of the water, checking the commission pennant of a ship at a buoy, or locating a shoal by the color of the water.

It is more difficult to orient oneself in a busy, complex harbor surrounded by a city than in a secluded waterway. In the vicinity of a city, the harbor lights must compete for recognition with the street lights, traffic lights, neon signs, and automobile headlights along the waterfront, whereas in the quiet anchorage the few navigational lights stand out clearly.

One gets an eerie, somewhat detached, feeling steaming about in a harbor at night. Although we can fix our position just as accurately as in the daylight, the familiar surface indications on the water, the buoys, and the shore line are no longer visible. One can't judge distances with any accuracy; he must rely almost completely on the distances reported by the Navigator or from the radar. The conning officer doesn't get a *feel* for his set and drift; he hears the reports and adjusts them mentally, but his ability to doublecheck what is being reported is reduced.

Handling Alongside at Night

The difference between handling the ship at night and handling it in daylight comes most sharply into focus when we are making a landing. As we approach, we find we are less able to judge distances correctly or to grasp the relative orientation of the ship and its surroundings. The dock seems remote and detached, and then, suddenly, we are upon it; we had no *feel* for our approach speed.

The solution for these disadvantages obviously is caution. We should make our approach slowly and sufficiently wide to be sure that we can accommodate ourselves to the unexpected. We should seek our way with patience instead of dashing in rapidly.

The difficulty of making a pier or nest at night can be greatly reduced by the adroit use of lights. If the pier face or the side of the other ship can be illuminated by floodlights, the problem is greatly simplified. Additionally, illuminating our own forecastle and fantail with floodlights is helpful to the conning officer. It helps him keep the picture of the ship's orientation as well as making it easier for the linehandlers. Finally, we can use our searchlights to pinpoint any areas of doubt. An occasional sweep of the water between the ship and the dock tends to complete the picture and gives us a better estimate of the intervening distance.

In the use of lights at night, all hands must take steps to avoid directing the rays of any light into the eyes of the conning officer. A momentary exposure will destroy his night vision for several minutes—and these might be the crucial minutes. All floodlights should be hooded so that no rays shine toward the bridge. Reflecting objects should be kept out of the beam of the searchlight. The deck force must be trained to keep their flashlights pointed away from the bridge. Though the reflected light from the floodlit areas will also affect the conning officer's night vision, this effect is very much less than that caused by direct rays, and we can accept the results in view of the advantage of having these areas illuminated.

Handling the ship in restricted waters is one of the most interesting phases of shiphandling. We are in close proximity with the dangers and difficulties of confined waters, and we are continually facing absorbing problems. Things happen quickly and we must be well prepared for the events as they occur. As the boundaries move in, we must handle our ship more exactly. Restricted waters are not the place for dash and daring; they are the place for *care and precision*. The shiphandler's skill is tested often in the confines of busy harbors and waterways.

CHAPTER XII

CRUISERS AND BATTLESHIPS

THE BO'SUN'S CALL sounded over the amplifying system, followed by, "Now secure the special sea detail." The big man-o'-war lay at rest alongside the pier, her landing completed.

Topsides, the appearance of the men matched the smartness of the ship. They were a proud-looking crew. There were grins on their faces. From heaving line distance, the lines had gone over easily, yet a narrow gap between ship and pier had preserved the sidecleaners' efforts. Below decks, the throttlemen nodded approval as they scanned an orderly series of bells in the bell book. The orders to the engines had been indicative of a conning officer who knew his business.

On the bridge a quartermaster summed it up as he looked toward the back of the conning officer, just disappearing down the ladder: "He handles her like a destroyer."

This finest of shiphandling compliments had more truth in it than the quartermaster realized. What he had meant was obvious. What he did not realize was that the principles employed had been exactly those applicable to a destroyer. For the capital ships of the present day are in fact oversize destroyers.

From time to time the big ships are called the "heavies," but it has been many years since Navy men have thought of them as the "unwieldies" (See Figure 74). Modern cruisers and battleships are called upon to perform most of the feats of shiphandling expected of destroyers.

In replenishment at sea our capital ship must make the same approach as the destroyer on the vessels of the replenishment group. Thanks to a healthy appetite, she must hold alongside for greater periods of time. Tactics and formation steaming also exact a heavy demand. While reorientation of the screen does not involve the capital ship, a change in formation axis finds the destroyers of the circular screen remaining in station while the cruisers and battleships do the maneuvering. The requirement being nearly the same, and the big vessels less easy to handle under some conditions, the cruiser and battleship present a challenge to the conning officer that may be said to be the postgraduate course in shiphandling.

The instructors in this course are well qualified. Our commanding officer is a graduate of the destroyer school, and has probably commanded one or

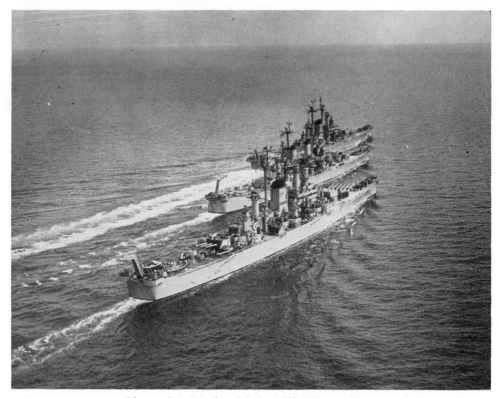

Figure 74. Precise shiphandling in cruisers.

more other types of vessel as well—submarine, amphibious craft, or auxiliary. He is serving his final tour as an individual ship commander and preparing for the important step to flag grade and its responsibility for groups of ships. It is his final performance in shiphandling, and those who attain it are already well schooled in the science. He is an officer who has proved himself in handling vessels of lesser tonnage. We are fortunate in our capital ship to be learning shiphandling under the most competent of instructors.

In addition, our Executive Officer is also an ex-commanding officer. The more senior heads of department have either had a command, or are soon slated for one.

In the midst of this wealth of experience, the officer joining a capital ship might feel that his opportunity to learn shiphandling would be small. Quite the contrary. Farsighted commanding officers do all in their power to pass along their experience and knowledge. They frequently offer the opportunity to their juniors to familiarize themselves with the science of shiphandling through practice as well as instruction and observation.

The fundamentals discussed in the previous chapters are as applicable to cruisers and battleships as they are to destroyers. This chapter will emphasize the variations in execution of these fundamentals which the tonnage, power, and configuration of these big ships require. The physical characteristics of these magnificent vessels will be discussed, and then, following the sequence of the preceding chapters, we will apply the fundamentals to these characteristics. Our battleships are now out of commission, so we will deal principally with cruisers in this chapter. However, to inform the reader of the handling characteristics of these huge ships, a summary section on battleships is included.

CRUISERS

In comparison with destroyers, **Cruisers** are vessels of heavy tonnage and great length. Heavy and light cruisers were so designated because of their gun batteries, not their tonnage. With the advent of guided missiles this designation became less meaningful because all have great striking power and are heavy ships. From the shiphandler's point of view they are all similar, so for purposes of illustration we will use USS COLUMBUS (CG-12), which has the following characteristics:

Length	673 ft.
Beam	71 ft.
Draft	32 ft.

Figure 75. USS COLUMBUS (CG-12).

Displacement	
Standard	13,600 tons
Full Load	17,000 tons
Total Shaft Horsepower	120,000
Maximum Speed	34 knots
Crew	80 Officers and 1,500 men

From the photograph of COLUMBUS, we note the cruisers general characteristics from the shiphandler's point of view. She is long and slim, with a high superstructure nearly equally disributed fore and aft. Her hull form is nearly identical to that of the destroyer. The most notable difference, other than the obvious difference in size, is that she is provided with four propellers instead of two.

The two inboard propellers are mounted just forward of the rudder and are relatively close to the centerline. The outboard propellers are set well forward, and are offset to the side more than a full propeller diameter beyond the inboard shafts. Consequently the discharge and circulating currents of the inboard propellers greatly affect the rudder action, while the currents produced by the outboard propellers are very little felt by the rudder. A cruiser's rudder is large enough so that when turned through only a small angle, it actually enters the discharge race of the inboard screw on that side. On the other hand, though the outboard propellers have little effect on the rudder, they produce a much greater twisting moment when opposed, because of their greater lever arm. For these reasons it is sometimes desirable to handle the shafts on a side independently.

Another important characteristic is the reduced horsepower-per-ton of the cruiser in comparison with the destroyer. Our cruiser has six times the mass of a destroyer but only twice the power! A destroyer has about 19 horsepower per ton, while a cruiser has only about 6.5 horsepower per ton (total shaft horsepower vs. full load tonnage). This means that, neglecting all other factors, the destroyer can accelerate three times as fast as the cruiser.

Although the destroyer has three times the horsepower per ton of a cruiser, the maximum speed of the two types is nearly the same (about 34 knots nominally). The reader may wonder why the smaller vessel requires so much more power in comparison with her tonnage. For those who may wish a more complete discussion of the technical aspects of this problem, a further treatment is presented in Appendix II.

Seaman's Eye

"Seaman's Eye," the expression of a conning officer's competence in shiphandling, is as pertinent to the handling of a cruiser as of a destroyer. In fact, it must be exercised with even greater skill. It has been mentioned earlier that the human eye is at its worst at sea; it is even less capable, in many respects, from a cruiser bridge than from a destroyer bridge. The height of eye from the water lends a remoteness from contact points—distance from bow to bouy, side to pier, stern to obstacle.

Handling a big ship safely requires keen judgment and a full measure of foresight. Decisions must be made early and error is often not susceptible to correction. On the other hand, a cruiser is more stable and can hold her course and speed more precisely than a destroyer, and one finds in her a wealth of talent and equipment.

Consequently the cruiser conning officer, just as his counterpart in the destroyer, must exercise excellent judgment, know his ship intimately, and understand thoroughly the principles of shiphandling. There are actually few evolutions demanded of a destroyer that are not likewise demanded of the modern cruiser.

Handling a destroyer has been likened to driving a sports car. Handling a cruiser is like driving a Rolls Royce. She is called upon for a multitude of duties—anti-aircraft protection in a carrier task force, gunfire support of an amphibious landing, leader of a surface striking force, for example. But the principles learned in the sports car are applicable to driving the Rolls Royce.

Forces Affecting the Ship

The mass of a cruiser is many times that of a destroyer. Her inertia is greater. Consequently her tendency to resist linear acceleration is increased accordingly. Our cruiser is slow to move after the screws begin turning, and slow to come to a halt when the backing turbines have commenced their task. She resists angular acceleration as well, but here the lag over that experienced by a destroyer is less noticeable. Her turning characteristics are more nearly those of a destroyer than are her characteristics of rate of change of speed.

The physical relation between ship and water is more obvious in large ships than in smaller ones. For example, a cruiser in a turn illustrates quite clearly the convergence of the centerline of the ship toward the center of the turn, with the stern riding well outside and the bow inside the mean path as the ship describes the arc. In a ship of such great length it is more apparent that she is rotating about her pivot point during a turn.

The standard orders to the engines discussed in Chapter II apply to our cruiser even though she has four propellers instead of two. On the bridge the engine order telegraph is no different from a destroyer's. Both starboard shafts take their order from the starboard engine telegraph, and both port shafts take theirs from the port engine telegraph. The engines are controlled in pairs. Though there are some situations in which a conning officer may desire to give orders to a single shaft, special signals must first be arranged with the engine room to provide for this.

Wind affects a cruiser much less than a destroyer. The mass of our cruiser creates stiff opposition to the whims of the sea breeze. The long hull riding deep in the water, resists the wind's attempt to move it laterally just as the keel of a racing sloop minimizes leeway.

The distribution of the "sail area" of a cruiser gives her a further advantage with respect to the wind. It provides balance. In backing and filling in restricted waters, the tendency for the bow to work downwind is greatly decreased in a cruiser. Where the destroyer finds it difficult to turn into the wind at low speeds, and even more difficult to back the stern away from the wind, the cruiser has less difficulty. This is because her bow and stern are nearly equal in height and her superstructure is nearly balanced in its fore and aft distribution.

A comparison of the silhouette of the two types makes the difference in wind effect obvious. In proportion, the destroyer bow is seen to be higher, the stern lower than the cruiser's. The destroyer bridge structure is farther forward in relation to the over-all length, and there is a lack of balancing structure aft to match that which the cruiser possesses in her after superstructure.

While the cruiser gains a degree of immunity from the effects of wind, it gains no immunity from current. When lying dead in the water, our cruiser moves identically with the current. It is floating in a fluid that is itself in motion, and is oblivious of the fact that the water which supports it is in turn moving over the ground. The current is recognizable only by a comparison with buoys, piers, or rocks, or by taking navigational "fixes." Were no object in sight and no fixes obtained, the current would be unrecognizable as such.

Current is a term used to express the movement of a mass of water over the bottom in a definite direction. It has a "set" (direction) and "drift" (velocity). A ship which is floating free, with no way on, will be carried with the current. If the current has a set of 250° T and a drift of 4 knots, the ship, dead in the water, will make good 250° T, 4 knots, over the ground. As far as the ship and the water in which it floats are concerned, it makes no difference to the ship whether the water is in motion or not, except that the motion of the water affects the motion of the ship in relation to piers, buoys, shoals, etc. A vessel lying in an 8-knot current would be unaware of any current unless it passed a buoy, or other stationary object. Since the mass of water in which the ship rests is in motion, if the ship wishes to remain stationary in relation to the ground, it must steam into the current at a speed equal to the drift and on a course exactly opposite to the set.

Handling a ship near stationary objects—piers, buoys, etc.—in a current is a problem in relative motion. The water is moving relative to the bottom. The ship can control her motion relative to the water. The motion of the ship with respect to the bottom is then the combination of the two relative movements.

In restricted waters the current at the surface and the current at various depths below the surface are not always the same. At times they differ in velocity; sometimes they actually run in opposite directions. Our cruiser with her greater draft is affected by deeper currents which do not affect a destroyer. The cruiser conning officer knows that he cannot rely on surface current indications alone in predicting the net effect of current on his ship. When he is unfamiliar with the characteristics of the current, he would be prudent to take a pilot and to profit by the pilot's local knowledge.

Lines and Deck Equipment

Our cruiser is secured to her berth or to her buoy in exactly the same manner as the destroyer. The only difference is that she moors with 8-inch manila lines instead of 6-inch. Where a destroyer uses a 5/8-inch wire, we will find a cruiser uses a 1-inch wire. Spring lay wire rope is becoming more popular for use in mooring cruisers.

Though the six-line mooring arrangement is the same, the equipment for handling it is more elaborate. A cruiser has two anchor windlasses on the forecastle and can thus work two lines (or two anchors) at the same time. On her fantail we find a powerful deck winch which can take an 8-inch manila nicely. Even amidships, we may find a small winch which can be utilized for handling lines.

Even with all this equipment and the broad decks for use of the linehandlers, the lines are handled more slowly on a cruiser than on a destroyer. A part of this may be due to a mental attitude, and if so, this should be corrected, but a part of it has valid cause. The lines are heavier, the stresses greater. There is a communication lag as the order is passed down from the bridge through the sound-powered system. More men are required for each task, and their efforts must be coordinated if their numbers are to be effective. The conning officer on the bridge must be aware of this and consider it in his calculations.

The fenders of our cruiser are correspondingly larger than those described earlier for destroyers, and they are more difficult to shift. The conning officer should plan their location carefully and allow ample time for their placement. The long, flat sides of the cruiser's midship section are ideal places for the use of fenders, but at the bow the flare is so pronounced that it is very difficult to place a fender effectively here as the bow moves in against an object.

In general, the conning officer of the cruiser must be just as familiar with the deck equipment of his ship as his counterpart on the destroyer.

Measuring the Situation

As pointed out earlier, the time lag between order and result is greater and the margin for error is less with cruisers than with destroyers. For example, to bring our cruiser to a stop from a given speed, we must BACK for a much longer time than the destroyer, and a greater advance is made in the process. Hence the conning officer must have the characteristics and calibration data of his ship at his finger tips. At the various speeds of approach, he must know the distance required to come to a stop, employing various backing powers; he must know the relative distance required to reduce speed when approaching another ship to replenish or pass mail; and he must know the turning characteristics of his ship. All of this emphasizes the importance of carefully calibrating the ship.

The accuracy required in handling large ships demands that guesswork be kept to a minimum. To make readily available the calibration data of the ship, it has become the practice in large ships to collect these data in a single folder on the bridge known as the *bridge folder*. Turn diagrams, acceleration table, and optimum scopes of chain for anchoring in various depths of water are typical of the items included. The bridge folder is a file of exact tactical data on the ship instantly available to the conning officer and his assistants for use in handling the ship.

One of the most valuable parts of the bridge folder is the acceleration table. This specifies the time rate at which the shaft RPM shall be changed when increasing or decreasing speed. In following the table the throttleman will gradually change the shaft RPM to complete the change in exactly the minutes and seconds specified. By the use of identical acceleration tables, ships can maintain precise station even while changing speed.

Unfortunately there is no universal acceleration table. There is one for each major type, and a ship will ordinarily use the one for her type. In a mixed Task Force, the table to be used must be specified. The conning officer must know what acceleration table is in use, and must insure that this is the one that the engine-room is employing.

In a formation the conning officer frequently wants to predict his "surge" (the distance gained or lost while changing speed). When he approaches a new station at a speed greater than formation speed, he wishes to know when to slow to formation speed. When dropping back into a new station, he wishes to know at what distance ahead of station he should resume formation speed.

We can use an average value of surge as outlined in the previous chapters, and for a limited range it will be quite satisfactory. A surge of *65 yards per knot* is a good average value which applies to a cruiser when operating at about 15 knots. Though this thumb rule applies to a number of cases, we should employ our acceleration data for a more accurate solution.

Actually, the concept of there being a constant surge of a certain number of yards for each knot of the speed change is quite incorrect. A moment's reflection will reveal that, if we decelerate at a constant rate, the amount we will surge varies as the *square* of the speed change, not by a constant amount per knot. For small changes within a limited range, a fixed surge per knot of change will work out, because the time lag (that is, the interval from the time the order is given on the bridge until the speed of the ship actually begins to change) is large and the throttleman actually executes the changes as rapidly as the engines will answer. If we always waited a fixed interval and then changed to the new speed instantaneously, the fixed number of yards per knot would be correct. On the other hand, if we effected all speed changes in exactly the same interval of time, the rule would also be correct. Since we neither make the changes instantaneously nor in a fixed interval of time, especially when following an acceleration curve, we should find a more accurate method of predicting surge.

If we plot our acceleration curve as indicated in Figure 76, it will be a useful addition to the Bridge Folder. A glance at the curve will reveal the change in slope between various sections of the curve, and will indicate the inaccuracy of assuming a constant surge at all speed ranges. At the lower end of the curve the acceleration is 5 knots per minute, but in the vicinity of 25 knots it takes a full minute to change one knot. Obviously the surge is much different in the two ranges.

If, for a specific speed change, we note the elapsed time required to make the change, we can compute the surge by multiplying the speed change by the required time and then dividing by two. In approaching a station, our speed *advantage* over the formation *at the start of the change* is equal to the amount of the change; our speed advantage *at the end of the change* is zero. Therefore our *average speed advantage* throughout the change (assuming constant deceleration) is one half the amount of the change; hence we divide the speed-time product by two.

Referring to Figure 76, if we are making 27 knots and are joining a formation making 20 knots, we will decelerate along the curve from A to B. Our speed change is AC and the time required to accomplish this change is BC. Our surge, then, is equal to the *area* of triangle ABC. To convert this to yards

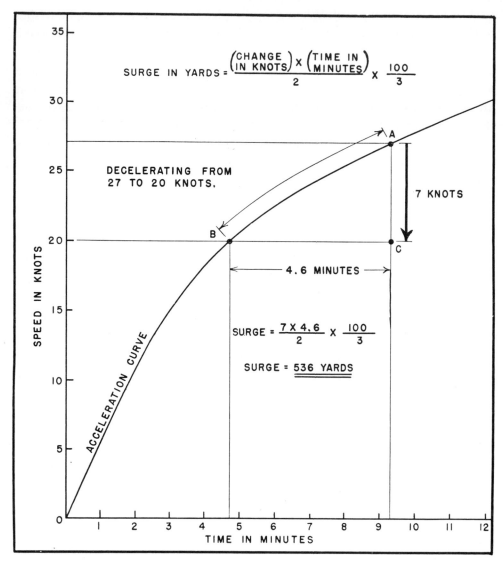

Figure 76. Using the acceleration curve to determine surge. (Note: This curve
is for illustration only and does not apply to any particular ship.)

we multiply this area by 100/3 (100 yards per minute is 3 knots). When
operating at speeds above 15 knots or below 9 knots, this method is much
more accurate than using the thumb-rule constant of 65 yards per knot. The
only inaccuracy involved is the assumption that the ship decelerates along
the chord AB instead of along the curve. The exact solution would include
the small area between the curve and its chord, but the error involved in our
method is inconsequential.

For handy use on the bridge it is useful to pre-compute the surge and to
prepare a surge table (Figure 77) covering the normally encountered speed

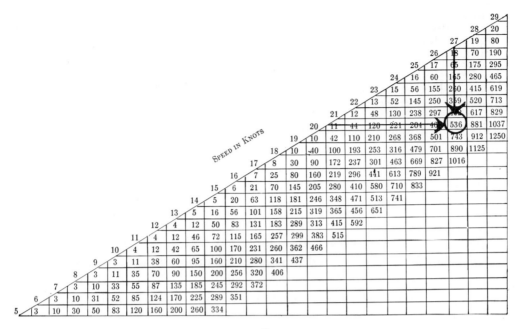

SURGE IN YARDS

Figure 77. Sample surge table for a cruiser. To use, enter table with "initial speed," and read "surge" opposite "final speed." (Note: This table is for illustration purposes only; it does not apply to an actual ship.)

changes. The reader will note that no allowance has been made for time lag in the table. For use aboard ship several entries should be determined by experiment and the table adjusted to include the actual lag.

With the facilities available on a cruiser and the number of officers available to assist in precise shiphandling, the cruiser should be handled to perfection. Habitual use of the Turn Diagram and the Surge Table should be made to take the guesswork out of the maneuver. The advanced maneuvering board solutions taking turning circle and surge into account should be used. Ranges and bearings should be exactly measured, and all maneuvers should be calculated to the limit of the information and time available. The excellence of shiphandling is often based on the care with which the situation is measured.

Handling Alongside

The principles of handling a cruiser alongside a pier are, of course, the same as for handling a destroyer, but there is a temptation to approach too rapidly and overshoot the berth. The big ship glides so smoothly through the water that it seems inconceivable that she will be hard to stop, *but it takes a lot of backing to bring her to a halt.* For this reason we should always approach wide enough so that an overshoot won't get us into trouble.

On the other hand, should we approach to put our bow in position with a 15° inclination, our stern would be too far out to run the mooring lines. With a ship over 200 yards long we must make our final approach more nearly parallel to the pier so that both the forecastle and the fantail can reach with their heaving lines.

Wind causes the cruiser less trouble in mooring than it would a lighter ship. She will take longer to commence being blown downwind, and she will move more slowly when she does respond. On the other hand, once the wind has taken hold and started the ship, greater momentum is involved and the damage which can be done is greater.

Where a fair approach is possible, a landing of our cruiser unassisted by tugs is perfectly feasible. Cruisers can—and frequently do—make landings without assistance. However, in comparison with a destroyer, this landing must be made at a lower speed and more cautiously. Should an error be made with such a heavy ship, severe damage could result. Where navigational hazards or adverse conditions make the evolution difficult, it is prudent to employ tugs.

When restricted maneuvering room dictates leaving the nest by going ahead, the conning officer may approach the situation with confidence. A cruiser can leave a nest by going out ahead just as easily as by backing. Her sides are free from annoying projections, and her slight tumble-home assists in preventing fouling at the main deck level and above. The armor belt provides an ideal bearing surface for the fenders, and her long flat sides assure a clean, smooth getaway.

As in the case of the destroyer when going out ahead, the ship is first opened out laterally by slacking the forward lines and riding to number five as the bow moves out. When the bow has moved out enough, we cast off, kick the engines ahead, and swing the ship parallel to the nest with the rudder (and engines if necessary) to get the stern clear of the other ship. As the ship moves forward, we use the rudder to keep our stern out from the other ship's side, but we must do this cautiously until our pivot point has come abreast the buoy (or anchor chain).

Anchoring

A cruiser, even when fitted with sonar, is not restricted by this cause from anchoring with headway, so long as reasonable precautions are taken to prevent the chain from being snapped taut across the keel. The decision to anchor while moving ahead or astern should be based therefore on the heading on which the ship will lie when she finally rides to her anchor. In order to insure good holding, it is highly desirable that the chain be laid out from the anchor and not dropped upon it. In the latter case a bight of the chain might even foul a fluke and prevent the anchor from "digging in" in the proper manner. Since the ship will swing with the prevailing wind or current, she will ride "downwind" from the point where the anchor is dropped. Thus the ship should be moving (slowly) downwind when we order "Let go." This might require anchoring while moving ahead, while moving astern, or while being carried broadside by the prevailing wind or current. The manner in which the ship is anchored therefore depends upon the prevailing conditions of wind and current and the allowable approach.

In the case where the wind is from ahead as we approach our berth, we should pass through the anchorage slightly and "let go" as we back through the berth. If the prevailing conditions indicate that we will ride on a nearly opposite heading from our approach heading, we should anchor as we pass through the berth going ahead. In this case, however, it is wise to begin swinging the stern to the side opposite the anchor being used as soon as the anchor is released, in order to insure that the chain will not tend under the ship.

When the crosswind approach is used, the ship should be brought to a stop with the hawsepipe slightly to the windward of the "hole." As the wind moves the bow downwind, the anchor should be released as the hawsepipe passes over the center of the berth. The upwind anchor should be used to prevent the chain from riding under the ship or across the bow.

The crosswind approach is more difficult from a navigational point of view than an approach with or into the wind. As the ship loses headway, the leeward set becomes more noticeable. It takes a nice sense of judgment to determine the proper "lead" to place the bow in the desired spot. As the ship slows, the "crabbing" (sidewise motion) becomes more and more severe, and the final approach is usually a constant turn with full rudder as we try to get the bow to the windward of the berth with the little steerageway remaining.

The heavy ground tackle of a cruiser makes it even more desirable to "walk out" the chain so that the anchor is not dropped from too great a height. The momentum of the heavy chain can be difficult to arrest, and, if the anchor is falling rapidly, a certain amount of chain will pile up on top of the anchor before the chain can be stopped. As with a destroyer, the anchor should be walked out until it is within 10 fathoms of the bottom before it is dropped.

The rate at which an anchor chain can be hove in is limited by the speed of the anchor windlass, therefore an adequate time must be allowed by the Officer of the Deck to insure that the anchor can be brought to "short stay" and weighed on schedule. Time must be allowed not only for the designed maximum rate of the anchor windlass but also for delays caused when the wind or current puts excessive strains on the chain and slows the operation, or when a muddy bottom requires more time to clean the chain. On a windy day, with a long scope of chain, it may take a relatively long time to heave in the anchor.

Under severe conditions it may be advisable to assist the anchor windlass by turning over the screws slowly to ease the strain. The chain should only be *eased,* not *slacked,* in doing this. When there is danger of dragging, the chain can be eased in this manner also, but it is important to keep a steady strain on the anchor. To slack the chain and then permit it to come taut with a jerk can initiate dragging.

In our bridge folder, we should have a table of optimum scopes of chain for various depths of water. The table is computed to insure maximum holding while employing the minimum chain required. This table can be made up from Chapter 26 of the *Bureau of Ships Technical Manual.*

It is even more important in a cruiser than in a destroyer that the approach to the anchorage be carefully planned, since corrective action is more difficult to take. As was pointed out in Chapter VI, navigational fixes are always a step behind the ship's actual position, and the conning officer must be ready to bring the ship to her anchorage regardless of what the success of the Navigator may be.

The easiest approach is one made on a constant bearing to a prominent object, with the "distance to go" to anchorage marked by pre-determined bearings of objects near the beam.

Since her backing power is limited, a cruiser should be carefully calibrated to insure she can be stopped accurately when anchoring. Average data from eleven cruisers indicates that the following approach will put the hawsepipe over the center of the berth under no-wind-no-current conditions:

Yards To Berth	Action
1,000	Be making 10 knots through the water
800	STOP all engines
500	BACK ONE-THIRD

If there is appreciable wind or current, an adjustment will be necessary in the above procedure.

If the approach is being made on advice from CIC during reduced visibility, lower speed should be employed. The following is a good system when navigating by radar:

Yards To Berth	Action
2,000	Slow to 5 knots
800	STOP
200	BACK ONE-THIRD

Allowance must be made for the time lag between the order to "Let go" and the time the chain actually starts rattling out the hawsepipe.

Mooring

A cruiser can be moored by the same method as outlined for the destroyer; in fact, the "trolley method" of snatching a buoy was developed in a cruiser. Our cruiser may take a bit longer to moor because of the weight of the gear involved, and is thus subject to the wind and current for a longer period before it can ride secured to the buoy. For this reason, in a heavy wind or strong current, it is desirable to have the assistance of a tug to control the bow.

Under normal conditions the cruiser can be moored to a buoy without assistance just as readily as a destroyer. As with the destroyer, placing the ship so that the buoy is abreast the bow instead of dead ahead will greatly facilitate the approach and initial connections. When ready to shackle the chain, however, the bow will have to be brought nearly directly over the buoy by heaving in on the buoy line in order to permit the men on the buoy to handle the heavier chain.

We must bear in mind the large mass of the ship in proportion to the buoy and the men who are working the moor. A misjudged kick of the engines can work havoc. An imperceptible movement of the ship can result in the buoy being submerged by the strain. The ship must be handled delicately when her bow is at the buoy. Power should be applied with caution.

The men of the mooring party should spend the minimum time on the buoy and be taken off whenever there is danger of the buoy spinning or submerging. Our ship can put a heavy strain on the buoy line, and the buoy may spin under this strain as turns in the buoy moorings are unwound.

When unmooring, the process can be expedited by running a "slip wire" and taking in the heavy chain ahead of time. The slip wire is run from the bow through the mooring ring on the buoy and back on deck. The bitter end is secured on deck with a pelican hook, and the ship rides to the bight of this wire. As soon as the slip wire is taking the strain, the chain can be unshackled and heaved in. Since no buoy party is needed for casting off the slip wire, the boat and buoy party can be hoisted on board. The ship can ride to the slip wire alone for the few minutes until we cast off.

When ready to "slip" the buoy, the pelican hook is simply tripped (this can be done even under heavy strain). The end of the wire is then pulled through the buoy ring and the ship is completely clear of the buoy. In preparing for slipping, care should be taken when running the slip wire to prevent any twisting of the two parts of the bight. If there are any turns as a result of improper running of the wire or spinning of the buoy, these turns will run down to the buoy ring when the bitter end is tripped and will tend to bind the wire and prevent it from being pulled free from the buoy.

When making a Mediterranean moor, the ideal moor is made with the anchors well spread; but with a cruiser this is often impractical because of limited maneuvering and berthing space.

In lieu of spreading the anchors, it is customary to drop both anchors ahead, with the second anchor placed nearly underfoot. The first anchor, with its long scope, provides a good fore-and-aft restraint, and the second anchor quickly restrains any side component when the bow moves to one side in response to wind or current. Figure 78 illustrates this action.

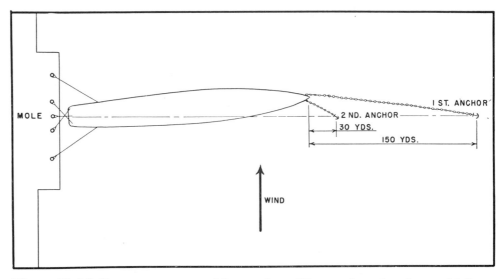

Figure 78. Mediterranean moor with a cruiser. (Note action of anchors with long and short scopes when bow is blown to the side.)

If this method is used, a cruiser can usually make the moor unassisted. She should drop her first anchor at nearly maximum scope to allow ample margin for firmly digging in the anchor. The second anchor should be dropped when the stern is about 60 yards from the mole. Allowing 20 yards for digging in and 10 yards from the stern to the mole, this would leave the second anchor 30 yards ahead of the hawsepipe. At this short scope, the second anchor will begin to provide a side restraint when the bow has moved only a short distance to the side.

If a tug is available and the harbor permits, the anchors can be placed equidistant from the mole and spread by having the tug move the bow first to one side and then to the other while the anchors are being placed. This is not done when ships are moored close together, because if their anchors tend in a direction other than ahead, they can foul the chains of the vessels on either side. In most harbors where the Mediterranean moor is used, extra kedge anchors are provided by the harbor authorities to securely restrain the bows of large ships.

In making a Mediterranean moor with a cruiser, after the anchors are dropped and the first lines run to the mole, it is recommended that the Captain shift aft to the fantail and supervise the completion of the moor from there. From the bridge the stern will appear several yards inland when the moor is completed; the true situation can only be seen from aft.

A danger of backing into the moles does, of course, exist and is met by controlling the sternward movement of the ship with the anchors. As the after lines are heaved in, the anchor chains are carefully eased, allowing the ship to inch backwards toward the mole. Since this is rather an unfair tug-of-war, the engines must usually be used at low power to assist the deck winch aft.

The Captain aft, controlling the maneuver, the OOD on the bridge controlling the engines, the First Lieutenant on the forecastle controlling the anchors, and the Gunnery Officer on the fantail handling the after lines and judging the distance must work as a smooth team in placing the big ship in her berth.

When the ship is finally in place and the stern secured, a good strain is taken on the anchors to prevent the swells or wind from setting the ship against the mole. The chains are heaved in until they provide a nearly flat lead to the anchors. There is no room astern for taking up the slack of a normal catenary.

If heavy weather is expected and several ships are moored stern to the mole in adjacent berths, running normal mooring lines between the ships will add a good measure of security to the moor. The inter-ship mooring lines bind the ships into a nest and prevent them moving relative to one another. When we consider that this nest is secured by several anchors forward and multiple lines aft, we will recognize that this is one of the most secure methods of mooring.

Handling at Sea

Intricate maneuvers in complex formations are not limited to destroyers. Our cruiser has its problems as well. While it is true that a reorientation of the screen has no effect on our cruiser, a change in formation axis often finds the heavier ships maneuvering while the escorts ride undisturbed in their circular screen.

Though destroyers are expected to maneuver so as not to embarrass the heavy ships, it would be foolhardy to depend on this when handling our cruiser in a large formation. Our only safe course is to presume that the converging destroyer will give us no special consideration. We must assume our share of the burden and be guided by the Rules of the Road as we maneuver in the proximity of others.

If bearings are being taken to insure that we are passing clear of another ship, we must take into account the size of our ship and the size of the other ship before concluding that we are passing safely. It is small consolation to have the bow bearing of ENTERPRISE *drawing right* if the bearing on her stern is *drawing left!* Remember that one-third of our ship projects forward of the bridge and two-thirds projects astern. Just getting the bridge safely past the other ship is hardly enough. Take the bearings on the end of the other ship which is to be cleared and be sure to allow ample space to clear it.

A cruiser is a splendid sea vessel and does not suffer from wind and wave to the extent that a destroyer does. She will ride more comfortably on a course with the sea on the quarter or astern than on most other courses, but she rides well under almost any condition. This does not mean that a cruiser doesn't roll and pitch, but she can take almost any sea condition in her stride.

While a cruiser might be riding comfortably into the seas at, say, 18 knots, accompanying destroyers might be nearly submerging as they plow into the waves. A reduction of speed of a few knots could make all the difference to the destroyers without retarding the operation; it could even allow the bridge coffee to be drunk with sugar instead of salt. So our concern when the weather kicks up should be for the escorts. If we are carrying the OTC Officer in Tactical Command (OTC), we should see that he is informed when the destroyers are "taking it green."

A turn at the wheel by the conning officer will give him a better under-standing of the problems of the helmsman and hence make a better ship-handler of him. It is equally worthwhile to take a turn at the throttle and to spend some time in the firerooms during maneuvers in order to become ac-quainted with the particular problems of your vessel's plant.

When maneuvering in formation we should anticipate as much as possible the next maneuver our ship will be called on to perform. Many times there is actual advance warning: the signalled night intentions of the OTC, a shift in the direction of the wind in a carrier task force, etc. We should plan our maneuver, even to the extent of having our maneuvering board solutions ready, so that when the time for execution arrives, the operation will be smooth and correct. In formation, foresight pays dividends.

Should a signal be executed for which we are not prepared, an experienced conning officer can roughly estimate an initial course and speed to head for the new station. We can start on this while a more accurate solution is being worked out. Such an estimate, however, should always be backed up quickly with an accurate maneuvering board solution. A ship equipped and manned as magnificently as our cruiser should be handled with precision at all times.

The use of the answer given by our maneuvering board should be tempered with judgment. The conning officer cannot follow the advice of his supporting team blindly at any time, and his experience and judgment will be most valuable in applying the simple vector solution.

The vector triangle of our maneuvering board makes no allowance for acceleration or deceleration, and it completely ignores our turning circle. It assumes that the ship gains a new speed instantaneously, and that the turning circle can be neglected. In a cruiser, whose acceleration is slower and whose turning diameter is greater, these disadvantages are more pronounced than in a destroyer. The conning officer of a cruiser must be familiar with the advanced maneuvering board techniques described in Chapter IX.

The conning officer's excellence at station keeping and maneuvering is most easily assessed in a column formation. In other formations it may take careful measuring and plotting to check the accuracy of his position, but in a column the success of his maneuver is obvious to the naked eye.

Changing course by "column movement" takes a nice sense of timing, for we must end up in column directly astern of the guide when our course change has been completed.

In this maneuver our best marker for determining when to put the rudder over is the swirl on the inboard side of the turn created when the rudder of the *ship ahead* is put over. As her rudder forces her stern to one side, a reaction current appears on the opposite side. The first surge of this reaction current is plainly visible on the surface of the water as a swirl in the white foam of the wake on the side to which the turn is being made. This swirl, or "rudder kick," plainly marks the spot where *our* rudder kick should appear.

To superimpose our rudder kick on that of the ship ahead (indicating that our turn started in exactly the same spot as his), we must allow for the time it takes our helmsman to put his wheel over and for our rudder to respond. On a cruiser, at 15 knots, the allowance will be about right if we order the rudder over as the other ship's rudder kick comes abreast our bridge. At other speeds we must use other reference points. The time lag between the order and the rudder response is constant at all speeds, so the distance from our rudder forward to the rudder kick of the ship ahead at the moment we should issue our order will be proportional to the speed. For example, at 20 knots the distance should be 4/3 the distance at 15 knots (indicating that the rudder should be ordered over when the swirl of the ship ahead is abreast turret one).

To be exactly in column we should follow directly in the water of the guide, regardless of what the other ships are doing. Thus we should initiate our turn on the rudder kick of the guide. This is usually impractical because the guide's "rudder kick" has usually been obliterated by the wakes of the other ships. Practically our only recourse is to turn in the wake of the ship ahead and trust that she has made her turn properly. Occasionally when the ship ahead makes a very poor turn, it is apparent and we can adjust accordingly.

Once we are in the turn we should check the progress of the turn by noting the position of our jackstaff (or bullnose) with respect to the outer edge of the wake of the ship ahead. This edge of the wake is clearly marked and from it we can make a very good evaluation of our turn. If the edge of the wake moves *down* our jackstaff, it indicates that our ship is working toward the *outside* of the turn. Conversely, if the edge of the wake moves *up* the jackstaff, our ship is working toward the *inside* of the turn. If the edge of the wake is steady, our ship is *following the turn.*

If we are turning outside, tactical instructions and tradition dictate that we hold our rudder and steady up on the new course *out of column* until the ship astern has completed her turn. This rule prevents us tightening our turn and catching the ship astern in a dangerous position if she is turning inside.

Should we find ourselves turning inside, we can correct the situation by easing the rudder. We must be careful not to close the ship ahead when doing this, however, and should slow slightly if necessary. In addition to "cutting corners" when we ease the rudder in a turn, we are decreasing the drag of the rudder and thus increasing our ship's speed.

Should the method outlined above for gauging the time to turn not be working out because of sea conditions or the erratic action of the ships ahead in a long column, we can more accurately accomplish our turns by use of bearings to the guide and the turn diagram. The turn diagram gives us the range and bearing from the point of ordering rudder to the point where the required change of heading has been accomplished. We know what the distance in column to the guide should be, and we can measure it just as the column movement is started. By allowing (by visual estimate from the turn diagram) for the length of the curved path of the turn, we can lay out the maneuver on a maneuvering board (as indicated in Figure 79) and thus derive the bearing to the guide for the moment when our rudder should be ordered over.

Another method for making column movements that is especially useful at night is by stop watch. The conning officer of the guide can be depended upon to order his rudder just as the signal is executed; so if we measure the distance to the guide at "Execute," we can quickly calculate the time until

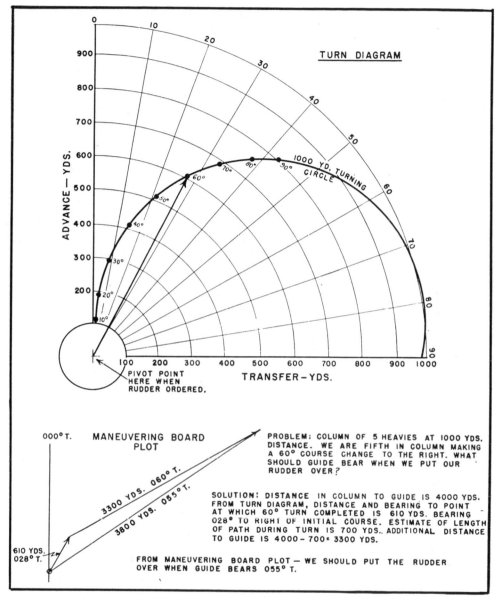

Figure 79. Turn diagram, showing method of turning in
column on bearing to guide.

our rudder should be ordered. We know our speed and we know the distance
to the point where the rudder should be ordered, so it is a simple matter to
compute the time until we should order our rudder. For example, if the
column speed is 15 knots (500 yards per minute) and the distance to guide's
bridge at "Execute" is 1,625 yards, we should order our rudder over exactly
3 minutes and 15 seconds later.

Rules of thumb play their part in conning, and, when properly employed, are sufficiently accurate for most situations. They are a valuable "assist" when the conning officer lacks the opportunity to use more exact methods. For example, let us assume that we are to join a column of ships, taking station astern the last ship presently in column. We are converging on the column from the quarter, and thanks to a correct maneuvering board solution, we are moving directly into our station. When do we put the rudder over to swing into column?

The most accurate solution for the turn would be obtained by referring to the Turn Diagram described in Chapter XI, but the following thumb rule has been found adequate when making such a turn of less than 70°:

TO TURN INTO THE TRACK OF ANOTHER SHIP, PUT THE RUDDER OVER 250 + 5T YARDS BEFORE REACHING THE INTERSECTION OF OUR INITIAL COURSE AND OUR FINAL COURSE. ("T" is the amount of the turn in degrees.)

The derivation of this rule is shown in Figure 80.

This rule, of course, is equally applicable when arriving on any station or when swinging onto any new course.

Before leaving the subject of handling at sea, we should consider our ability to stop our ship in case of emergency. We have discussed our horse-power-per-ton ratio and we recognize that it takes a long time to stop our cruiser. When confronted with a dangerous situation, just how quickly *can* we stop our cruiser?

From a moderate speed, if we order BACK EMERGENCY, we can expect to surge forward slightly less than our advance would be at FULL RUDDER, before we commence moving astern. This means that in an emergency we can stop our ship in about 800 yards. FULL RUDDER and BACK EMERGENCY will combine to produce an advance far less than either action will singly.

In an emergency we should remember that our rudder is also an aid to rapid deceleration. The giant rudder of our cruiser, when it is put over in either direction, has the same effect as dragging a sea anchor. The quickest way to decelerate our ship is to BACK EMERGENCY and use FULL RUDDER. If a particular line of advance must be maintained, the rudder can be "fishtailed" (i.e., shifted from side to side with as great an amplitude as possible).

Replenishment at Sea

Our cruiser is at her best during replenishment at sea. Thanks to her stable characteristics, she holds a steady course with ease. An experienced helmsman

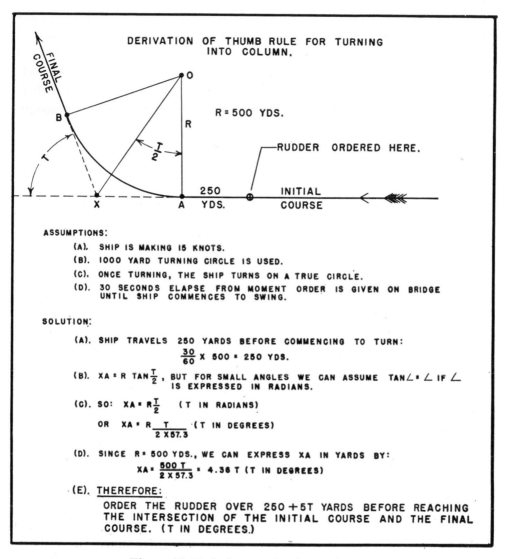

DERIVATION OF THUMB RULE FOR TURNING
INTO COLUMN.

R = 500 YDS.

RUDDER ORDERED HERE.

INITIAL COURSE

250 YDS.

ASSUMPTIONS:

(A). SHIP IS MAKING 15 KNOTS.

(B). 1000 YARD TURNING CIRCLE IS USED.

(C). ONCE TURNING, THE SHIP TURNS ON A TRUE CIRCLE.

(D). 30 SECONDS ELAPSE FROM MOMENT ORDER IS GIVEN ON BRIDGE UNTIL SHIP COMMENCES TO SWING.

SOLUTION:

(A). SHIP TRAVELS 250 YARDS BEFORE COMMENCING TO TURN:
$$\frac{30}{60} \times 500 = 250 \text{ YDS.}$$

(B). $XA = R \tan\frac{T}{2}$, BUT FOR SMALL ANGLES WE CAN ASSUME $\tan\angle = \angle$ IF $\angle$ IS EXPRESSED IN RADIANS.

(C). SO: $XA = R\frac{T}{2}$ (T IN RADIANS)
OR $XA = R\frac{T}{2 \times 57.3}$ (T IN DEGREES)

(D). SINCE R = 500 YDS., WE CAN EXPRESS XA IN YARDS BY:
$$XA = \frac{500 T}{2 \times 57.3} = 4.36 T \text{ (T IN DEGREES)}$$

(E). THEREFORE:
ORDER THE RUDDER OVER 250 + 5T YARDS BEFORE REACHING THE INTERSECTION OF THE INITIAL COURSE AND THE FINAL COURSE. (T IN DEGREES.)

Figure 80. Rule for turning into column.

can steer her to the half degree. Seas which bounce a destroyer about merely cause a gentle lift to her bow.

The general method of going alongside is the same for the cruiser as for the destroyer, but the approach is made slightly wider, and, when alongside, the cruiser should ride slightly farther out. An initial distance of 100 feet between sides is good while handling lines; and after the ship is "connected up," riding at 120 feet will be found to fit the tanker's rig nicely.

The "back down" approach for going alongside another ship works beautifully in cruisers, especially because of their slow deceleration and long surge (65 yards per knot) when no backing power is used. With a 25 knot approach on MISSISSINEWA making 12 knots, SPRINGFIELD should be backed TWO-THIRDS when her jackstaff is abreast the oiler's stack—about 150 yards short of her final position. It is quite useful to have the forecastle give a hand signal as the jackstaff comes abreast the stern of the other ship.

It is better to overshoot slightly than to undershoot the required position. This allows the lines to be passed more quickly and the ship will be settled back into her correct position by the time the gear is ready. An approach that is too short delays the chance to get the shot lines over until the ship is finally brought up to position.

Though there has been much discussion concerning the tendency for ships to pull towards one another when close aboard, cruisers may come as close as 40 feet to ships alongside without experiencing difficulty in opening safely. The good shiphandler, when he finds himself too close, comes out very gradually, using a course not more than two degrees from that which has held him in position. A cruiser is a long ship, and when we open out, the stern swings toward the other vessel. We must come out slowly to prevent the stern from swinging in too far toward the other ship. There is also a tendency to over-correct when we get in too close; this tendency should be guarded against to keep from parting our lines. Correcting in small increments may avoid a series of over-corrections that magnify in amplitude as they compound.

In like manner, if the ship opens to the point where the transfer gear is in danger, only a small course change should be made to close the distance; a larger change might throw the stern out and thus part the after lines.

When handling alongside, it is worthwhile to remember that we can see what the ship is doing more quickly by observing the position and movement of the stern than by watching the bow. Two-thirds of the length of the ship is abaft the pivot point. This means that the stern moves two yards for every yard of bow motion. When the side is used as a reference for parallelism, remember that the "flat of the side" is abaft the bridge.

Changing in small increments applies to speed as well as to course. Add and take off turns sparingly. Allow time for the change to take effect before adding another change. An impatient conning officer will fail to obtain accurate control of speed because he changes his speed order before the throttleman has had a chance to smooth out the adjustment made for the last command. Changing speed only a few turns is a delicate adjustment at the throttle, and it takes a minute or two to actually obtain the new RPM.

If we are fueling from an oiler and a ship comes alongside her opposite side, the oiler will usually slow down slightly. Likewise when a ship clears her opposite side, we can expect the oiler to increase speed a little. We should note when ships approach and clear the opposite side of the replenishment ship, and be ready to compensate for the change.

When clearing the side, the length of our ship must again be considered. The turn-away must be made gradually in order that the stern will not swing into the other ship. A considerate conning officer makes sure that his maneuver will not interfere with the other ship as he clears her side. If he must cross her bow in heading for his new station, he makes sure he is far enough ahead so that he does not embarrass her.

Helicopter Operations

The introduction of the helicopter has created a new conning requirement —that of helicopter operations. The ship must be handled to provide suitable wind conditions in the area where the helicopter will operate.

Though quite versatile, a helicopter is most sensitive to wind gusts and turbulence, and the pilot, when picking up or delivering to our ship, is involved in the most precise flying ever demanded. He needs the smoothest air possible, an unobstructed operating area, and a good reference point clearly visible from the pilot's seat. He must also head into the relative wind while hovering, taking off, or landing, and it is the conning officer's problem to satisfy these conditions in his selection of the ship's course and speed for Flight Operations.

Launching and landing a helicopter on board is normally handled on the fantail, so the wind must not be from ahead because of the turbulence caused by the ship's structure. The wind is usually desired broad on the bow or on the beam, depending on the type of helicopter, and the ship must usually be maneuvered to produce the desired relative wind.

We must keep track of the direction of the true wind and anticipate the maneuver required for helicopter operations. The quickest and most direct method of producing a relative wind from the beam is to turn at right angles to the true wind, and STOP. An alternate solution, if there is some wind blowing, is to put the true wind on the quarter and steam at such a speed that the relative wind is from the bow or beam as desired. A moment's reflection will show us that we can never bring the relative wind exactly on the beam while moving ahead, if the *true* wind is *forward* of the beam.

In addition to limitations on the direction of the wind for helicopter operations, helicopters cannot be started or shut down in high winds because of possible damage to the rotor blades. This limitation is not so severe with modern helicopters, but wind velocity must still be watched carefully. The helicopter bill of most cruisers contains a diagram showing the acceptable velocities and directions of relative wind for helicopter operations—conning officers should discuss these limits with the helicopter pilots to insure a mutual understanding of the requirements.

BATTLESHIPS

The **Battleship** was built to be the ultimate in surface fighting capability, to hit the hardest and to stand the most punishment. To carry her elaborate armament and her massive armor protection she must be big and heavy. She must be powered to keep pace with the top speed of the Fleet, and she must be able to maneuver with the most agile types. Since she must have everything—speed, protection, punch—she is among the largest ships afloat, and is a real challenge to the shiphandler.

Figure 81 shows a scale model of USS MISSOURI (BB 63). It illustrates in detail the elaborate superstructure and the characteristics of the underwater body, but unfortunately it cannot give a sense of the huge size of the ship. In viewing the figure we should bear in mind that her anchor is higher from the surface of the water than a destroyer's bridge, and that she is as long as three football fields placed end to end.

A battleship of this class has the following characteristics:

Length	887 ft.
Beam	108 ft.
Draft	38 ft.
Displacement	
Standard	45,000 tons
Full Load	57,000 tons
Total Shaft Horsepower	212,000
Maximum Speed	32 knots
Crew	115 Officers
	2,200 Enlisted

As the cruiser was to the destroyer, so the battleship is to the cruiser. Instead of the 19 horsepower-per-ton of the destroyer or the 6.5 horsepower-per-ton of the cruiser, the battleship has only 3.7 horsepower-per-ton at full load. Though this power is adequate for steaming steadily at a speed nearly equal to that of any other type, it dictates slow acceleration. The battleship builds up to speed gradually, and the backing turbines must work a long time to bring her to a stop. In a battleship we are dealing with the greatest inertia of

Figure 81. Model of a battleship.

any type, except the super-carriers, with the least proportional power. We have to make our decisions early—and they have to be right.

To give these great ships the maneuverability to operate with the smaller ships of the Fleet, they are provided with twin rudders of optimum design. Figures 82 and 83 show the unusual propeller and rudder arrangement of this class of battleship. They are not only provided with twin rudders, but also with twin skegs to improve the flow in the vicinity of the inboard screws and the rudders. This arrangement gives these ships a rudder effectiveness which allows them to turn with nearly the same diameter as our most maneuverable destroyers.

Shallow Water

At sea the battleship is as easy to handle as the destroyer; sometimes easier, because the wind and sea conditions are seldom severe enough to disturb the heading of so large a ship. It is in port that we find serious difficulties in handling such a ship.

Shallow water has a major effect on the maneuverability of our battleship. When the bottom is close to the keel, she handles sluggishly. She accelerates slowly and she does not respond to her rudder. Our ship which was as lithe as a kitten at sea, is suddenly cranky and unwieldy. Though we have no trouble handling her close to other ships at sea, we must usually rely on tugs for even the simplest operation in port. Why?

The shallow water effect on ships will prove to be of special importance to the battleship conning officer because, since a battleship has the maximum draft of any ship, most of the principal channels of the world were dredged

Figure 82. Stern view of battleship's rudders and propellers. (Model)

with major warships in mind. In ports like New York or Norfolk the battleship's keel may often be within one fathom of the bottom. When alongside a pier, the margin may be so small that mud often enters the main condenser intakes. For this reason these ships usually secure their condensers as much as possible when alongside.

In deep water, the flow about the hull of a ship is three dimensional, and much of the water displaced from ahead of the ship flows down underneath the ship. The streamlines from such flow are clearly shown in Figure 84. If we remember that a ship is turned by inclining it (by use of the rudder) to the direction of motion through the water, and that it is the hydrodynamic reaction on the hull that forces the ship around in the turn, we will realize that it is the displacement of water to the sides (indicated by the horizontal streamlines) which governs the steering of a ship. Thus, in deep water the hull is a very inefficient hydrofoil in the horizontal plane and the rudder can easily produce an inclination to the motion through the water, and so initiate a turn.

In shallow water, on the other hand, the proximity of the bottom prevents the normal flow under the ship, and the water from ahead is displaced to the sides, as indicated in Figure 85. The flow about the hull becomes nearly two-dimensional, and the displacement of the streamlines in the horizontal plane becomes more pronounced. The hull becomes much more efficient as a hydrofoil, and the forces produced are larger.

When a ship is inclined to its direction of motion, not only is the side force mentioned above produced, but, since the resultant force does not pass through the center of gravity, a turning moment is also produced. In a normal, well-designed ship this moment is such that it tends to reduce the angle of inclination and thus return the ship to a straight course. To hold a ship in a steady turn, the rudder must produce a moment which will just balance this reaction moment and thus maintain the ship at a constant inclination to the relative water flow.

In shallow water, as the flow becomes more two-dimensional, the reaction moment for a given inclination becomes larger and larger until it is several

Figure 83. Side view of a battleship's rudders and propellers. (Model)

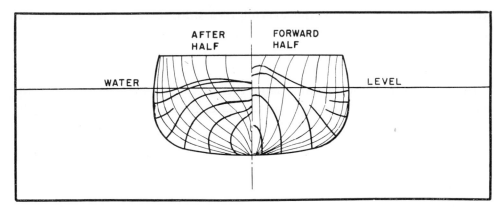

Figure 84. Streamlines about hull as ship moves ahead in deep water. Observe how streamlines go down and under the hull. (Drawn from Figure 28 in "Speed and Power of Ships," by Rear Admiral David W. Taylor CC, USN [Ret.].)

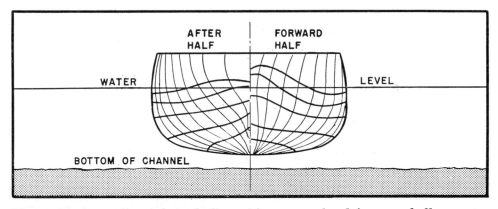

Figure 85. Streamlines about hull as ship moves ahead in very shallow water. Observe how streamlines spread to the side. (Figure 85 is an application of the Shallow Water Effect to Figure 84.)

times that experienced in deep water. Whether in deep or shallow water, the flow about the rudder is essentially two-dimensional (displacement caused by the body of the rudder is in the horizontal plane), so there is little difference in the turning moment produced by the rudder as the depth decreases. Consequently a given rudder angle at a given speed in shallow water is balanced by a smaller inclination of the hull, and less turning effect is achieved. Thus, a battleship with only a fathom of water under her keel responds very sluggishly to her rudder. It is almost always necessary to augment the rudder with the engines when turning in very shallow water.

In addition to its effect on the turning characteristics of our mighty ship, shallow water makes the speed unpredictable. Accompanying the increase in side forces as the flow becomes two-dimensional in shallow water, the hydro-dynamic drag increases. The shallower the water, the greater the drag. This means that our ship accelerates more slowly and slows more rapidly. In a narrow channel, or at high speed, the more complex shallow-water effects discussed in Chapter XI also come into play, but the simple shallow-water effect of increased drag significantly affects shiphandling.

In calculating an approach to a buoy or for anchoring we must take the depth of the water into account. Should the depth vary during the approach, we will have a variation of our deceleration. This necessitates the careful calibration of deceleration at various depths if we are to be able to plan approaches accurately. For a more complete discussion of the shallow-water effects on a ship, the following references will be found interesting: (a) "Maneuvering of Ships in Deep Water, in Shallow Water, and in Canals," by Captain R. Brard (CC, French Navy), printed in the *Transactions of the Society of Naval Architects and Marine Engineers,* Volume 59, 1951; (b) *Speed and Power of Ships,* by David W. Taylor, Rear Admiral, CC, USN (Ret.), Chapter 15.2.

At Sea

In maneuvers at sea, the rules developed for the cruiser are also applicable to the battleship. She handles with equal facility—turning slightly better, accelerating slightly slower—and the general handling characteristics are the same. Because of her greater inertia, a figure of 120 YARDS PER KNOT surge when decelerating is applicable, and the formula for turning into the track of another ship should become 300 + 5T YARDS because the battle-ship commences her swing more slowly.

One significant difference in a battleship is the amount she slows during a turn. The increased drag, caused by the rudder angle and the inclination of the ship relative to the water flow, rapidly overpowers the thrust of her screws. Even though the engine RPM are maintained, a battleship initially making 25 knots will slow to 16 or 17 knots during a 180° turn.

When close alongside another ship, we must consider the wake of a battle-ship. She moves a considerable amount of water aside as she plows through the ocean, and the effect reaches well out. Her bow wave is greater, and the following hollow is deeper. The hollow forward of the screws is also deeper as the water rushes to fill in behind the broad counter.

When we come alongside another ship in a battleship, we must allow more distance than with other types. Should we come alongside at distances accepta-ble with a destroyer, we would seriously disturb the steering of the other ship as our bow wave and the successive crests and hollows of our wake bear upon the other ship's side.

When going alongside a service type for replenishment, it is good practice to come up parallel about 150 feet out, and then ride at from 120 to 150 feet distance while alongside. Approaching wide in this manner eliminates most of the disturbance as the big ship comes alongside. Once we have gotten our bow wave past the other ship's stern, we can ease in a little with no ill effects. It is the initial action of the bow wave that is most disturbing.

An example of the effect of the wake of a battleship on a ship alongside is that the battleship's presence alongside a fleet oiler will cause the oiler to slow one knot while maintaining RPM. This is because the latter's bow is raised by the battleship's bow wave, and at the same time her stern is riding in the depression at the larger ship's quarter. This change of trim of the oiler causes the oiler to require more power to maintain her speed.

Smaller ships coming alongside the battleship must also consider the big ship's wake. The stern waves and the hollow near the battleship's screws make coming alongside her quarter difficult. While this position has the advantage of leaving the destroyer's stern free to swing, it subjects the destroyer to the full force of the battleship's stern wake. Since this increases with speed, a destroyer should be brought alongside abreast the big ship's bridge rather than her quarter, when operating at speeds greater than 12 knots.

In Port

When we bring our big ship into the confines of the harbor and begin to maneuver in making a berth, we should have tugs standing by to assist. The great size of the ship, combined with the shallow-water effects mentioned above, necessitates caution. Though battleships have made landings at piers without assistance, this is the exception and not the rule. Under severe current and wind conditions, as many as eight tugs are sometimes required to handle the great mass of such a ship. Fewer tugs can be used, depending on the conditions, but if the maneuvering room is restricted, it is recommended that at least four tugs be available.

Two tugs, if available, should be used when making a buoy. It takes a long time to shackle the heavy chain to the buoy, and without assistance the bow would most probably be carried away from the buoy before the chain could be secured. Because of the battleship's long forecastle and high, flared bow, it is impossible to see a mooring buoy from the bridge once it is close aboard. As with other ships, the buoy should be kept to one side during the initial operations so that the conning officer can clearly see it, but once the bow is moved close to the buoy to secure the chain, the buoy will invariably disappear from sight from the bridge. Consequently, it is advisable to handle the conning of the ship and the direction of the tugs from the eyes of the ship.

Anchoring is about the only evolution in the harbor that the battleship normally performs unassisted. Under no-wind, no-current conditions in a harbor of such depth that the shallow-water effect is not severe, the following approach has been found satisfactory:

Distance To Berth	Action
2,500 yards	Be making 10 knots through the water
2,000 yards	STOP
1,000 yards	BACK ONE-THIRD

Because we start backing at such a great distance from the berth, and because of the variations caused by the shallow-water effect, it is worthwhile to verify the speed actually being made good at 700, 500, and 300 yards. The speed we should be making can be taken from a series of successful approaches, and we can adjust the backing power accordingly.

Because of the inclination of a battleship's forecastle, and the distance from her wildcats to the hawsepipes, the anchor chain will not run out of its own weight in water of normal depth, once the anchor has hit the bottom. Consequently, it is necessary to anchor with sufficient headway (or sternway) to rouse out the chain.

Different Ships, But Same Principles

Whether our ship is a cruiser, battleship, or one of the several variations that range from 6,000 tons to 60,000 tons, handling one of these major ships of the fleet requires the application of the same principles we explored in discussing the destroyer. Though the time constants are different, the fundamentals are the same. Once accustomed to the new dimensions of the larger ship, we find that the rules we discovered in destroyers apply to her just as well. The mass of the big ship is greater, she occupies greater space, and she often requires more sea room. But the same alert application of the principles of good shiphandling that served us so well in smaller ships will serve us equally well on the big ships.

CHAPTER XIII

CARRIERS

IN ESSENCE the **Aircraft Carrier** (See Figures 86 and 87) is a seagoing air base. She is a ship in which every detail of design is pointed toward accomplishing the prime functions of launching, controlling, recovering, servicing, and stowing combatant aircraft. She must be prepared to operate a maximum number of aircraft of the highest possible performance in playing her part in modern naval warfare.

Like the aircraft which are her reason for being, her body is of low density. The hangar, which provides a protected stowage and servicing area, contributes most to this characteristic.

She is long, because there must be sufficient space on the flight deck for landing and arresting and launching aircraft, since it is most desirable that the ship be able to launch and recover aircraft simultaneously. Even when the launch is by steam catapult and recovery is on the angled deck, this requires a long flight deck.

Since it is extremely difficult to operate aircraft from the deck of a ship which is rolling heavily, the carrier must be designed for a minimum roll. This, combined with the desirability of a wide deck for operating and parking aircraft, calls for a ship of wide beam.

Thus the length and beam requirements dictate that the aircraft carrier be a large ship.

The flight deck must have unobstructed runway with the largest possible area for handling planes, so all interfering structure must be eliminated from the flight-deck area. Control stations, directors, guns, missiles and all other topside equipment are moved to the sides and ends of the ship, and, where possible, they are lowered below the level of the flight deck. The carrier thus acquires a pronounced overhang at the bow and stern, and has many projections from her sides.

The one structure allowed to project above the flight deck is the "Island." This structure normally contains the navigating bridge and conning station and whatever other control and signal stations require all-around vision. These components are usually integrated with the funnel and are surmounted with a maze of radar and radio antennae. To afford maximum clearance for

Figure 86. USS ENTERPRISE (CVAN-65) refuels THE SULLIVANS (DD-537).

the flight operations, the island is placed as far to the side (the starboard side, by convention) as the ship's structure can permit. The island is as narrow as possible because it must present minimum interference to air traffic; and it must cause minimum turbulence of the air flowing over the after portion of the flight deck and astern of the ship.

In the eyes of the shiphandler, then, the aircraft carrier is a large ship of low density. She has an outward flare of the hull at the bow and stern to support a maximum area of flight deck, and her sides are festooned with numerous projections such as gun sponsons, elevators, and flight deck galleries. The navigating bridge is small, and is offset to the starboard edge of the flight deck. On those ships in which the smoke-pipes are included in the island structure, there is an unavoidable obstruction to vision aft. These factors give the conning station a degree of awkwardness which the shiphandler must recognize and include in his calculations.

All is not bad, however in the eccentric conning station of the carrier. The ship control instruments are close at hand, and a good view of the starboard side of the ship is afforded. When it can be arranged to go alongside a pier starboard side to, or to take station to port of the supply ship during an under-way replenishment, the situation is excellent. Since the peculiarity is obvious and well known at sea and in port, provision is normally made for the carrier to do all of her precise shiphandling to starboard.

Shadow Diagram

The extensive obstruction to vision which is caused ahead, to port, and astern by the flight deck may be turned to the advantage of the shiphandler if he constructs a "shadow diagram" for handy reference on the bridge. The shadow diagram is outlined by points where one's line of sight from the normal conning positions on the bridge intersects the surface of the water as the eye sweeps along the edges of the flight deck. A small object floating in the water cannot be seen when it is within the "'shadow," and, conversely, *can* be seen when it is outside of the "shadow." Such a diagram, constructed by reference to the ship's plans, will not only delineate the blind spots from the conning station, but also provide a means for estimating distance.

The shadow diagram is useful in estimating the range to objects close aboard. For instance, if one sees that the waterline of a buoy ahead appears tangent to the forward ramp of the flight deck on a certain relative bearing, reference to the shadow diagram will tell the shiphandler that the buoy is a precise number of yards—for example, 220 yards—from the stem. Thus the flight deck and other obstructions can be used as a sort of built-in stadimeter, an aid to seaman's eye. Large changes in draft, trim, or list, or motion in a seaway will, of course, affect the accuracy of the shadow diagram.

Offset Conning

The conning officer needs always to bear in mind that he is offset to starboard from the centerline about half the beam of the ship. It is useful to post at each pelorus a sign which states, "At this pelorus you are _____ feet to starboard of the centerline." Knowing the distance of our pelorus from the centerline, we realize that our line of sight "dead ahead" (000° Relative) marks a line parallel to the keel of the ship but always displaced to starboard by this distance.

Suppose our carrier is steaming in column astern of a cruiser. A Fleet review is in process, and we wish to be exactly in column. Looking ahead, we admire the symmetry of the cruiser and know that the conning officer on her bridge can stand on the centerline and keep perfect station by keeping the center of the ship ahead on a bearing equal to the formation course. Though we can't stand on the centerline of our carrier when conning, we can achieve the same results by understanding and compensating for our offset.

Suppose our offset is 60 feet and the beam of the cruiser ahead is 80 feet. We can select a point in the water 60 feet to starboard of the centerline of the cruiser by using her beam as a measuring stick. She is 80 feet wide, so a point in the water one-quarter of her beam width to the right of her *starboard side*

Figure 87. Catapults and angled-deck of USS WASP (CVS-18).

will be 60 feet to the right of her keel. If we maneuver our carrier to bring the bearing of this point in the water to exactly equal the formation course, we will be perfectly in column.

We can solve many of the problems created by our offset conning position by applying an equal offset "at the target." Having compensated for the offset "at the target," we can use our bearings in the normal way.

Since we are not on the centerline of the ship, we cannot use the normal centerline objects such as the jackstaff for determining the ship's "head." Though we can establish the ship's heading by sighting through an alidade set on 000° relative, we should provide a quicker reference for use in emergency when time does not permit attention to the alignment of an alidade. Most carriers are equipped with a "steering staff" mounted vertically from the outboard side of the walkway at the forward end of the flight deck. If one stands directly behind the helmsman and looks forward over the steering staff, he is looking "dead ahead." If the ship is steaming steady on course, with no athwartship set, this is also the direction of motion of the ship. This reference, unfortunately, is not always available at sea, because it must be unrigged at flight quarters. One should, therefore, establish other points of reference. The conning officer should locate objects well forward of the bridge which will be on the fore-and-aft line from his normal conning positions. Such points may be stanchions, points on gun sponsons, or distinctive points on the antenna outriggers. But one such mark should be selected for each conning position.

Looking aft, we may find that the plating of the outside of the stack is exactly in a fore-and-aft plane. Thus, sighting along this plane establishes the direction astern which parallels the keel. When situations arise that require immediate action, it is very valuable to have established fore-and-aft "bench marks" beforehand. In such cases the seconds wasted in focussing the eye for careful setting of the bearing circle, and then in re-focussing on the situation ahead or astern, cannot be spared.

Wind Effect on the Carrier

As one would expect, a ship of large volume and low density such as a carrier is more sensitive to the wind than is the normal warship. This is more noticeable in the shallower draft carriers like those of the ESSEX-class than in the deeper-draft carriers of the FORRESTAL- or MIDWAY-classes. But regardless of class, the large, bulky hull and superstructure of the carrier act as a sail, and the force of the wind on the ship is large.

As a typical instance, if the wind is blowing the ship against the face of a pier when getting under way, the effect of the "sail area" of the carrier will be unpleasantly noticeable, for the wind will tend to hold the ship firmly against the face of the pier. Winds of 25 knots or greater can make it very difficult to clear the berth.

Hence, when clearing a pier with a strong wind blowing us on, we must have tugs of sufficient aggregate power to hold the ship broadside in the wind. If we did not have such assistance, we would rub and scrape against the pier as we cleared, and we might cause serious damage. If we do not have enough tugs to hold the entire ship against the wind, then we should place whatever tugs we do have forward to hold the bow off the pier. Under most circumstances we can hold our stern away from the pier with our own engines.

If it becomes necessary to get under way from a pier with a wind setting us on, and there are no tugs available, we can clear under our own power alone if the conditions are not severe. In this case we twist our stern out from the pier and then back out quickly, just as with smaller ships. In doing this we use a camel or float forward as a pivot. With this as a pivot, the stern can be walked out slowly with the engines. But care should be taken to insure that the pressure against this pivot float is steady during the twisting operation. When ready, with all lines clear, the ship should be backed away from her berth with as much power as the circumstances allow, so that the ship will gather way quickly. This minimizes the time the wind has to work on the bow, and gives us the speed necessary for control in a minimum time. Once we are moving at a safe distance out from the face of the pier we can reduce the backing power as may be desirable.

With winds of appreciable velocity, the carrier must be kept a safe distance upwind of obstructions. We should always maintain sufficient way to be able to keep our bow from being set to leeward. Lying to, broadside to the wind, with an obstruction to leeward, is a situation to be avoided.

Because of her large freeboard and unusual superstructure, the carrier yaws markedly with the wind when at anchor. Her motion is similar to that described in Figure 28 for a destroyer, but the effects are more noticeable. When the carrier brings the chain taut as she reaches the extremity of her swing, she may do so with a jerk. If this becomes too severe, it can start the anchor from the ground and cause her to drag.

We can ease the situation by veering chain. The more chain, the heavier the catenary—and the greater the tension before the chain is "straightened out." The tension is, of course, a measure of the force being applied to the ship by the anchor chain, and if we can obtain enough tension to stop the motion of the ship before the chain is "straightened out," there will be no jerk. As link after link is picked up from the bottom, weight is added to the catenary. With enough chain, the ship will usually be brought about from one "tack" to the other steadily, without any jerk.

A large scope of chain also exerts a damping effect on the yawing by its resistance to being dragged sideways across the bottom. This adds to the catenary effect of the weight of the chain, but is more effective in pulling the bow through the wind because it causes the chain to lead more to the side as the ship sails across the wind. If the yaw becomes serious, the situation can be relieved by dropping a second anchor "under foot." This second anchor will be very effective in reducing the sidewise excursions.

Winds on the beam have a marked effect on steering a carrier at sea. The stronger the wind, the more *downwind* rudder must be carried to hold a course. If the helmsman is having difficulty steering the desired course, reminding him of this effect of wind may assist his steering. To obtain smooth control, he should seek an average of downwind rudder, and then apply corrections of a few degrees on either side of this average.

Problems Caused by the Overhang

A characteristic of the carrier which must be considered in handling close aboard is the "overhang." Projections from the side of the ship always complicate handling alongside (See Figure 88) and no type has a greater array of projections than the carrier, especially the FORRESTAL-class.

The many projections from the sides, and the outward flare near the bow

Figure 88. USS FORRESTAL (CVA-59) approaching pier at Norfolk.
(Note large barge alongside pier to the left to hold her off.)

and stern give the carrier a degree of awkwardness from the point of view of the tug master. In working close to the carrier's side, the masts or other top hamper of the tug all too frequently foul on some overhanging appurtenance of the carrier. This can, of course, cause expensive damage to the tug. For this reason a tug may be expected to approach gingerly and to work with her stern as far out from the carrier's side as possible. If, because of current or ship's motion, the tug is swept in parallel to the side, she will often have to cast off and clear the side to keep from suffering damage from the carrier's projecting structure.

A tug master prefers to pull on a hawser rather than push against the side, when working against the flared part of a carrier's hull. When pulling on a line, the tug is well clear of the side and safe from the threatening projections. Also, when the tug comes alongside, she will probably ask for one of our lines instead of using her own, for operational as well as economic reasons. Not only does it save the wear and tear on the tug's gear, but the tug master *knows* that *he* can cast off as rapidly as required—and he is not sure that we will cast him off as quickly as he might desire. By using our line the tug master is sure that he will be carrying all of his own gear with him should he be required to cast off suddenly.

In sending him a line we should remember that, though a line can be cast off from the tug's quick-releasing hook regardless of the strain, a line must be slacked before the "eye" can be cast off from a normal set of bitts or a cleat. Because of the inability to slack a line quickly enough under certain circumstances, an eye over a bitt occasionally must be cut with an axe in order for the tug to get free. For this reason, unless we are certain that the line is going to the tug's towing hook with its quick-release feature, we should send the tug the whipped end of the hawser instead of the eye end.

When it is desirable to place a tug parallel to the ship, as when being moved in a Navy Yard, with no power on the ship, a camel should be placed between the tug and the ship's side to hold the tug clear of the overhang. The tug should make sure that the camel is secured in place (usually by lines to the tug) before the move is begun. Otherwise the camel may become dislodged as way is gotten on the ship.

Overhang is also a consideration when mooring alongside a pier. A camel between the pier face and the ship's side is essential to prevent contact between projections from the ship's side and the pier. The camel must hold the ship far enough off not only to prevent contact at the time of mooring but also to guard against projections being brought down on top of the pier as the tide ebbs. Sufficient clearance must be provided for the full range of the tide.

Since the camels are so important for safe mooring, we must determine that there are sufficient camels of the required size and strength at our berth before we go alongside. At a U. S. Naval facility we will usually find adequate provision of camels and floats, because such a facility is accustomed to handling carriers; but at commercial or foreign facilities, this may not be the case. An otherwise magnificent approach can be completely blighted if the screw wash sweeps away improperly secured camels when we back our engines the final time upon arriving in our berth. If a poorly designed camel up-ends and allows the ship to come in against the camel's narrowest dimension, or if a camel crushes, through structural weakness, we may find ourselves hard against the pier with a damaged side.

Handling Alongside

The shiphandler will find other oddities when handling the carrier alongside. When starboard-side-to the view from the bridge is excellent, but the great length of the ship and the many projections from her side make it very difficult to see the condition of the mooring lines from the bridge. The conning officer cannot observe either the forecastle or the fantail crews as they work the lines, so he must depend upon verbal reports to determine their progress. To keep all stations informed of the situation, it is essential that dependable and accurate communications be maintained between the bridge and the line-handling stations.

A large carrier is normally moored to a pier with many mooring lines as indicated in Figure 89. For handling these mooring lines there are winches of adequate power only on the forecastle and fantail. Line-handling stations elsewhere are usually in cramped spaces and devoid of any adequate winches. Any heavy hauling required should be done with the forward or after lines, because not only are the midship lines not adjacent to winches, but they must be handled from narrow galleries.

The great bulk of the aircraft carrier, and the effect of the wind on that bulk, increases the need to have each mooring line carry its share of the load. If a beam wind drives the carrier directly away from the face of a pier, all of the breast lines should come taut at the same time. Thus each contributes its full strength to holding the moor. But if one comes taut while the others are slack, the load on that one line may exceed its breaking strength and it may part before the other lines have begun to work. Thus the lines may snap in succession, each as its breaking load is exceeded. The whole moor may carry away under conditions which would not have caused failure had each breast line been laid out and tensioned to share the load with the other breast lines. Similarly, if wind or current causes the carrier to surge forward, all after-leading springs should come taut together. If the ship surges aft, all forward-leading springs should come taut together. These principles apply in the mooring of any ship, of course, but they are of particular importance in carriers, where a larger number of mooring lines are used.

Because of the high freeboard of the carrier, the chocks through which mooring lines are led are high up on the side of the ship and frequently are on projecting sponsons. If one tries to lead a breast line out through such chocks, a very steep angle in the mooring line will result. This is obviously inefficient, for, resolving the tension force of the line into the horizontal and vertical directions, one finds that only a small component is applied to holding the ship to the pier, and that most of the force is applied *downward*. Further, such steep, short leads are troublesome as the ship rises and falls with the tide. It is better, therefore, to use such chocks for spring lines, thus obtaining greater force components in the directions desired. Breast lines can be run at locations on the ship farther forward and farther aft where the con-

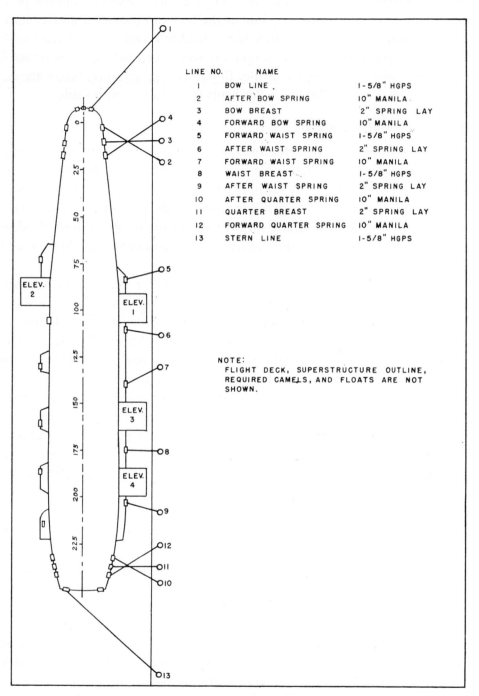

LINE NO.	NAME	
1	BOW LINE	1-5/8" HGPS
2	AFTER BOW SPRING	10" MANILA
3	BOW BREAST	2" SPRING LAY
4	FORWARD BOW SPRING	10" MANILA
5	FORWARD WAIST SPRING	1-5/8" HGPS
6	AFTER WAIST SPRING	2" SPRING LAY
7	FORWARD WAIST SPRING	10" MANILA
8	WAIST BREAST	1-5/8" HGPS
9	AFTER WAIST SPRING	2" SPRING LAY
10	AFTER QUARTER SPRING	10" MANILA
11	QUARTER BREAST	2" SPRING LAY
12	FORWARD QUARTER SPRING	10" MANILA
13	STERN LINE	1-5/8" HGPS

NOTE:
FLIGHT DECK, SUPERSTRUCTURE OUTLINE,
REQUIRED CAMELS, AND FLOATS ARE NOT
SHOWN.

Figure 89. Standard mooring plan for a large carrier.

tours of the ship have carried the chocks to a greater distance from the pier. Leading the lines to the opposite side of the pier can provide a greater horizontal component, but this is often not desirable because it interferes with traffic on the pier. Many of the larger carriers have mooring bitts recessed into the side just above the waterline. If very strong breasting forces are desired, these bitts are available for flat leads from pier to ship's side.

Handling in Restricted Waters

Because of the small size of the bridge on a carrier, the number of instruments and assisting activities immediately accessible from the bridge is reduced to the minimum. Many stations vital to good ship control are remote from the bridge, and the conning officer should endeavor to keep these closely in touch with the progress of the ship. Frequent questions from the bridge, and the supplying of coordinating information, will maintain the interest and teamwork of the remote stations.

First and foremost of these stations is the Combat Information Center. No matter how good the visibility, nor how simple the problem, it is worthwhile to have a complete navigational plot of the ship's track kept in CIC, and to have continual advice from the CIC Officer arriving by telephone on the bridge. This should not be a one-way flow: the bridge should cross-check with CIC. When the ship arrives in the open sea, it is well to have the CIC Officer bring his track chart to the bridge for a check. All points of divergence should be discussed with the Navigator, and the acknowledgement of a job well done is appropriate. Only by continual practice and support can the CIC be developed into an aid upon which we can depend when the visibility is reduced to the point where the CIC facilities are the only means of entering or leaving port safely.

Steering the ship is obviously so important a function that extra precautions should be taken against a possible steering casualty occurring at the worst possible time. It is well, for instance, to have not only an expert helmsman on the bridge, but also a competent and alert crew down below in the steering-gear room itself. The alertness of this crew will be enhanced if it is kept generally posted on what is happening topside. In traversing a long, narrow, or tortuous channel, it may even be prudent to have a qualified deck watch officer in the emergency steering station. If he has a chart and is notified when significant navigational points are passed, he will be in a position to know when periods of particular vigilance are required. The latest order to the helm should be a matter of record in the emergency steering station. The stand-by helmsman should follow continuously what his counterpart on the bridge is doing so that he will know what rudder angles are being used and what is their effect in holding the ship's course.

If the crew in the emergency steering station is both alert and ready, they can take control smoothly and efficiently in the event of a casualty. Steering casualties usually occur through failure of the long electrical control circuit from the bridge. False alarms are often caused by failure of the transmission lines to the rudder indicator on the bridge. In the rare event that the failure is actually in the steering machinery itself, so that the rudder is immobilized, the bridge should be informed immediately so that the conning officer may use the engines to minimize the hazard to the ship.

Other remote stations of particular interest as we maneuver in restricted waters are the control engine-room and the forecastle—the former for accurate and speedy control of the engines; the latter because there must be an anchor ready for letting go so long as the restrictions of maneuvering room require it and the depth of the water permits. Neither station should be slighted in the development of the shiphandling team.

Handling at Sea

When we reach the open sea, the aircraft carrier will devote the major part of her time to the operation of aircraft. This preoccupation requires certain considerations not entirely strange to other types of ship, but differing in degree of emphasis.

In order to understand the basic requirements of the carrier's operation, let us look first at the aircraft which fly from it. The airplane flies because of the flow of air over its wings and control surfaces. This flow is generated by the forward speed of the aircraft through the air. There is a minimum airspeed below which this flow of air becomes inadequate for lift and control. When this minimum airspeed is reached, the aircraft "stalls" and begins falling out of control. When an aircraft is taking off or landing, the airspeed can closely approximate the stalling speed, but there must always remain a small but safe margin above the stalling airspeed if the aircraft is to remain airborne. When a plane is in the air, it is its motion relative to the mass of air in which it is flying that keeps it up. This motion differs from the motion of the aircraft relative to the earth's surface in every case except that in which there is no air mass motion—that is, in a flat calm.

An aircraft at rest on the ground, but headed into the wind, will already have an airspeed equal to the velocity of the wind. Taking advantage of this fact, a take-off run into the wind affords the shortest run, in distance and time, required for the aircraft to become airborne. Likewise, in landing, a direction into the wind is chosen, since the wind thus reduces the velocity of "touchdown" and shortens the landing run. A crosswind landing or take-off not only loses the advantages explained above, but also throws objectionable side loads on the landing gear, since the aircraft, when airborne, takes on the sidewise motion of the air mass itself.

The foregoing basic considerations enter into the operations of launching and recovering aircraft on any aircraft carrier. The conning officer, by combining the ship's speed with the true wind, can create a relative wind down the flight deck—a "wind-over-the-deck"—for maximum effect during the operation.

In launching or recovering aircraft, a relative wind is needed of sufficient intensity to keep within reasonable bounds the energy required of catapults to impart flying velocity to aircraft, or the energy required of the arresting gear to decelerate aircraft in alighting. At the same time the intensity of the relative wind should not be so great as to make overly difficult the towing or taxiing of aircraft as they are moved about the flight deck. Compromising between these considerations, it is usual to employ a relative wind of from 25 to 35 knots.

Ideally, the direction of the relative wind would be that which would permit aircraft to head directly into it when landing or taking off. It is necessary, however, to keep the downwind eddies of the island and the turbulence of the flue gases clear of the landing area; hence, one finds the best direction of the relative wind usually to be from dead ahead to slightly on the port bow.

Modern attack carriers are fitted with an angled deck, inclined 10° to port of the centerline of the ship. This feature provides an unobstructed deck for recovering aircraft regardless of the congestion on the forward part of the axial deck. Launching can be conducted from both the axial and the angled decks simultaneously if desired, and aircraft can be recovered on the angled deck while others are being launched from the axial deck. When only one deck is being used, the relative wind should be along the axis of that deck, i.e., dead ahead for the axial deck and 10° to port for the angled deck. When both decks are being used for launching, the relative wind should be kept between them, i.e., 5° to port. When launching from the axial deck and recovering on the angled deck, the wind should be adjusted to favor the recovery operation and be kept 10° to port.

With modern aircraft and the powerful catapults installed in our carriers today, relative wind is not so critical as before. If the catapult is sufficiently powerful for the aircraft under consideration, crosswind—or even downwind —launches may be made. It is the resulting *airspeed* of the aircraft at the end of the catapult that determines the safety of the getaway, and a satisfactory airspeed may be achieved with a sufficiently light aircraft even though no component of wind relative to the carrier was favorable during the catapulting. With modern equipment, if other operational requirements dictate, launching and recovery can be conducted safely with relative winds up to 20° to either side of the optimum direction.

From the above discussion it can be seen that the conning officer of the aircraft carrier must have an appreciation for the true wind, the ship's motion, and the vector combination which generates relative wind. A flight of aircraft returning to the ship low on fuel will require an expeditious turn into the wind by the carrier, so it is basic that the conning officer of the carrier know at all times the direction and velocity of the true wind. This will permit him to turn to a heading and set a speed which will combine to provide the correct direction and velocity of relative wind for the recovery operation.

By keeping cognizant of the present and forecast true wind velocity, the conning officer can estimate the boiler power he will require to obtain the desired wind over the deck. If a breeze of 15 to 20 knots is predicted, only moderate boiler power will be required, for a ship's speed of 15 knots can generate the 30 to 35 knots required for flight operations. In light airs or in a flat calm, full boiler power will be required since the ship must generate by her own speed nearly all, or all, of the required relative wind for her flight operations.

In modern naval ships, the power available depends not only upon the number of boilers in use, but also upon the temperature of the superheated steam. Furthermore, when a ship is using her superheaters, she cannot change her steaming condition very rapidly because of thermal expansion and contraction problems. Finally, speed ranges and limits vary with different combinations of boilers and superheat.

The conning officer of the carrier must plan ahead, basing his plans on the present and forecast wind velocities, the aircraft to be flown, and the speed-boiler combinations of the ships in company. He should assume the responsibility of advising the escort vessels of expected speed requirements, and do this sufficiently in advance to allow them time to make the necessary adjustments in an orderly and efficient manner. Especially should he remember that after the speed range for the operations has been selected, any change may require considerable time for the escort ships to adjust their own boiler arrangements.

Another matter of concern to the conning officer of the carrier is when, where, and how to turn into the wind for the air operations. Restrictions in sea room, or the desire to make good a general advance downwind, may require that the time in which the carrier is headed into the wind be held to the shortest duration possible. In that case the conning officer will wish to be sure that all is ready for the launch or recovery before he turns into the wind. Further, if high speed is required, he will wish to build up to high speed while still running downwind, thus conserving precious distance to windward. Some speed will be lost during the turn—as much as 5 to 7 knots at high speeds. Therefore, if the conning officer wishes to start recovery or launching immediately upon completing the turn, he must have a margin of speed above that required for flight operations when he begins his turn. In this way he will make allowance for the loss of speed in the turn, and, as he comes out of the turn, he will have adequate relative wind over the deck to begin air operations at once. The engine RPM can be reduced after the turn has been completed to hold the desired speed.

Carriers list outboard in a turn, because of their extensive above water structure. The degree of list will depend, of course, on the speed and radius of the turn. If the turn is made through the trough of the sea, a roll may be superimposed on top of the list. Aircraft unsecured or being moved about the deck when such a list occurs, may skid or roll out of control. Obviously the conning officer must be aware of this possibility, and must give adequate warning throughout the ship before executing a sharp turn.

Just as the mariner in a sailing ship abhors a lee shore, so does the carrier captain regard with distrust an obstruction to windward. If the obstruction is a shore line or shoal water, it may not allow sufficient room to windward to permit the planned launch or recovery. A fog patch to windward carries a double threat: it will advance *toward the ship* with the wind as the ship moves *toward it* against the wind. Whatever the restriction, the conning officer must measure the situation and insure that he has sufficient clearance to remain on the launching or recovery course for the required time.

Plane Crash

Air operations include the possibility of aircraft accidents for which the conning officer should have well-thought-out procedures. One of the most urgent situations is that in which a plane's engine fails on take-off and the plane lands in the water dead ahead. A careful study of the turning characteristics of the carrier will show that for a certain distance ahead (depending on the speed), putting the rudder over either way will tend to force the survivors into the side of the ship and possibly under the keel. When the ship responds to the rudder, her bow moves one way and her stern moves the other about her pivot point. It is the side force developed by the water against the inclined side of the ship that forces the ship around in her turn, and, for a certain distance, the ship proceeds forward in this inclined orientation before she leaves her initial path. In this process, tremendous currents are spilling under the keel, and these might draw the survivors under the ship. In a turn, the ship sweeps a broader path through the water than when on a steady course, because of the characteristic inclination of the ship's keel to her actual direction of motion. Thus, if we turn, we increase our chances of hitting the survivors because of our wider path, and we increase the possibility of injuring them, should we strike them, because of our direction of motion and the current spoken of above.

One would think that by putting the rudder over one way, and then, after a change in heading of a few degrees, reversing it, the ship could be displaced far enough to the side to clear the men in the water. This can indeed be done, depending upon the speed of the ship and the distance to the men in the water; however, a careful study of the specific maneuvering characteristics of the ship will show that a very *considerable* distance ahead is needed for this maneuver. The conning officer should remember that using the rudder will induce large currents under the stern, and its injudicious use could mean the death of the men in the water.

On the other hand, if the rudder is held amidships and if the aviators have cleared the plane and are floating in their life jackets, their chance of being struck directly by the stem is very small, and in any other position the bow wave will tend to push them aside. They will most probably be in good shape if they are not drawn into the screws. Our problem then is to stop the great indraft of water to the propellers. The conning officer should order STOP SHAFTS as soon as it becomes apparent that the men in water are going to pass close aboard. Even if the throttlemen are not able to completely stop the shafts in time, the indraft will cease as soon as the propellers stop driving.

When the survivors are actually alongside the ship and there is no doubt at all as to which side they will pass on, the rudder can be ordered over to move the stern *away* from the men in the water. But any confused or unreliable information should be a signal to the conning officer to keep his rudder amidships. Though there is some advantage to the men in the water if the stern is moved away from them, it will be very dangerous to them should a mistake be made and the stern be thrown *into* them.

If a plane is seen to go over the side anywhere else than at the bow, the situation is clear and the rudder may be put over immediately toward the side to which the plane was seen to go over.

A more difficult situation which occasionally arises is that in which an airplane goes over the side and remains caught in the bight of the arresting wire. When this happens, the steady pull on this wire causes it to be pulled out to its extreme length. This often means that the plane is already in the water, and if the arresting crew doesn't cut the wire immediately, the plane may be towed through the water backwards. The only indication of the situation visible from the bridge will usually be the two parts of the arresting wire leading over the side. Stopping all shafts and putting the rudder over a small amount toward the plane will help the situation. Backing the engines to kill headway is not acceptable, because the plane is usually in the vicinity of the screws, and the swirling turbulence caused by backing might augment an already bad situation. On the other hand, turning with a small rudder angle will tend to move the stern away from the plane and prevent damage from the ship's structure. A large rudder angle might cause the plane to tow too far out from the side for access in rescue operations from the ship.

When a plane goes into the water during a recovery or launching, the conning officer of the carrier must keep in mind the safety of the fliers in the other planes aloft. If the downed plane will pass clear of the ship, and if the ship has been handled in such a way as to minimize the hazards which she herself creates, then it is usually best to turn the rescue operations over to the rescue destroyers and complete the air operations. If planes, low on fuel, are not recovered promptly, they may be forced to ditch. The distraction of having a plane in the water must not lead the conning officer to forget the general situation.

Operating with a Task Force

A carrier is seldom at sea unless she is in company with other ships. With a task force, the conning officer will wish to know the general capabilities and characteristics of the other types in the formation. Fuel capacity, maximum speed for the boiler combination in use, time required to change this condition, etc., are all items of interest to the conning officer of the carrier. Though all ships are expected to use fleet standards for speed changes and turns, it behooves the conning officer to check the speed and turning characteristics of the other ships in the formation. The shift of the formation guide from a carrier to a cruiser might be the occasion for us to get off station during the next subsequent maneuver until we are familiar with that type of guide. Perhaps the cruiser loses less speed in a turn or regains her speed more promptly, and thus causes us to lose our position, even though all ships are using Fleet standards with the engines and rudder. We must learn and remember the peculiarities of each of the ships of our formation in order to be ready to conform to them should that ship be designated guide. To have a bit of difficulty keeping station on a new guide can be forgiven for a few maneuvers, but the conning officer who plods ahead blindly, dogmatic in the accuracy of his own ship's calibration, and so repeatedly arrives off station—well, such a shiphandler does anything but gain the admiration of the other shiphandlers of the force.

In war or in peace, a carrier will almost invariably be at sea with destroyers doing her screening and plane guarding. It is appropriate, then, that the conning officer of the carrier be thoroughly acquainted with all destroyer types. Characteristically, destroyers need fuel, and there will be frequent fuelings from the carrier. During combat operations it is customary to keep destroyers fueled to above 65 per cent capacity as long as the operational demands permit. It is necessary that these ships have ample fuel for the high speed steaming that air action requires. To accomplish this, the carriers are kept rigged for fueling destroyers at all times, and the destroyers are called alongside with little warning as soon as a lull develops. The alert carrier conning officer will insure that his crew, as well as his rigging, is ready on a moment's notice for this vital service to the destroyer.

Courtesy among seamen requires, also, that the assigned destroyers be queried about other logistics requirements; many things which are plentiful on the carrier might be badly needed on the destroyer. Passengers, light freight, and mail must also be passed under most circumstances. The "high line" is a busy rig when a destroyer is alongside.

If a destroyer is alongside for other purposes than fueling, it is advisable to take her at one of the after transfer stations. When alongside at these stations, only the bow of the destroyer overlaps the carrier, and her stern is free to swing without danger of fouling the carrier's side. Transfer stations on each side of the fantail afford an area for working the lines and landing passengers and freight, and the underside of the flight deck provides an elevated point for attaching the rig.

Because of the working area and relative size of her crew, it is best to use the carrier's rig when using the high line. When a transfer is ordered, the destroyer will appreciate a prompt message designating the transfer point and stating that the carrier's gear will be used. This will obviate the requirement for the destroyer to rig her own gear on her wet forecastle as she makes her approach.

With a destroyer alongside for fuel, or at the quarter for personnel, mail,

**Figure 90. USS MARS (AFS-1) and USS WALKE (DD-723)
prepare to fuel from USS SACRAMENTO (AOE-1).**

or stores, the conning officer's job is simple, since the carrier has only to steer a very steady course at a steady speed. He should be careful, however, about his own ship's actual course and speed. He must quickly detect and remedy any casualty. The engine-rooms and steering station aft should be kept informed as the destroyer makes her approach, rides alongside, and finally clears. The personnel in these stations must be aware that special vigilance is in order. The conning officer should also keep an eye on the destroyer so that he can take assisting action should a casualty occur aboard her.

If a course or speed change is ordered with a destroyer alongside, it can be made safely if made slowly, with complete information going to the destroyer at all times. It is usually best to make the change in moderate increments instead of one steady change. The carrier should make the course change with a small rudder angle, notifying the destroyer continuously of the carrier's heading to the half degree. The carrier should steady up for a couple of minutes about every 30° in order to allow the destroyer to settle down. Speed changes can be made in a single increment if desired, however, because the carrier accelerates or decelerates so slowly that the destroyer has little trouble keeping pace with the change. Further, the destroyer can surge farther off station fore and aft than she can to the side, and there is little danger of a collision inherent in a speed change when alongside.

When a carrier goes alongside an oiler or a storeship at sea, we have some of our most interesting shiphandling opportunities (See Figure 90). Our

Figure 91. Deck layout of USS FORRESTAL (CVA-59).

carrier may go alongside as many as four other ships during a day of replenishment because of the requirement to take aboard aviation fuel and ammunition in addition to the usual ship requirements. She is usually placed to port of the supply vessel in consideration of her offset conning station. The techniques of bringing a carrier alongside are the same as for the other large warships described in Chapter XII, so they will not be explored here; but it is worthwhile to note that carriers can be handled alongside as effectively as any of the other fleet types.

Pinwheel

In a discussion of the handling characteristics of aircraft carriers, there is one last shiphandling maneuver which should be covered that is unique in this type. This is given the operational title "Pinwheel," and is the employment of the power of the carrier's aircraft in maneuvering the ship.

In Pinwheel, four groups of aircraft are ranged along the edges of the flight deck with their tails pointing outboard. The aircraft are securely lashed down so that their engines can develop high thrust without moving the planes across the deck. Each group is at the extreme end of the deck on its side of the ship, and the groups are numbered from one through four for the forward starboard, forward port, after starboard, and after port groups respectively. Each group is controlled by hand signals from a controller, who stands directly in front of the group and receives his orders from the bridge by telephone.

To move the ship to starboard, groups two and four are ordered to apply power. To move the ship to port, groups one and three are ordered to apply power. To twist to the right, Groups two and three are ordered to "rev up"; to the left, groups one and four. The power obtained from the aircraft depends on the number and type of planes used in the groups, but the power available is considerable. This operation gives the aircraft carrier an agility not possessed by any other type. It is as though she had four tugs available at all times!

Obviously, with something as useful as this there must be some disadvantages. These lie in the fact that applying high power at low airspeed is not good for the aircraft engines. They heat up. However, if the engine temperatures are watched and the power is governed to prevent overheating, it is an acceptable employment for the aircraft.

CHAPTER XIV

SUBMARINES

OF ALL OF THE VARIOUS TYPES of vessels plying the oceans of the world, the **Submarine** is one of the most unusual. She is propelled by propellers, uses a rudder, and is manned by seamen, but beyond that she differs in almost every respect from conventional ships. The handling of a submarine is so different from that of a normal ship that naval officers are sent to an extensive course at the Submarine School in New London before they are assigned to submarines for duty. To qualify for submarines, and especially to qualify for command of a submarine, an officer must serve for an extended period in these "boats" and meet rigid requirements. Mistakes in handling the submarine can spell the death of all hands, so in the submarine service the greatest emphasis is placed on good shiphandling.

The submarine lives in a three-dimensional world instead of the two-dimensional world of the surface craft. To enable the submarine to operate under the surface, many modifications must be made to conventional ship design. The hull must be completely closed and strengthened to withstand the pressures of the depths. Additional control surfaces must be added, and most of the normal superstructure must be eliminated to allow efficient operation submerged. Normal steam power plants are unacceptable for underwater work, and only power plants which do not require a supply of fresh air are acceptable for running completely submerged. Making a ship habitable, operable, and efficient with these restrictions obviously requires the most radical departure from normal ship design.

Though the design limitations required just to allow the submarine to operate under the surface are severe enough, modern submarines must be designed to do much more. As the submarine art progresses, with the anti-submarine art in hot pursuit, submarines must be designed for deeper submergence, higher speeds, greater maneuverability, and increased offensive capacity. Each improvement carries with it certain limitations, and these limitations add an increased burden on the shoulders of the shiphandler.

All new construction submarines will be nuclear powered and their special handling characteristics will have to be determined later. The mainstay of the submarine force, however, is still the GUPPY-type, so this chapter will be devoted mainly to discussing the handling characteristics of these more numerous boats.

Construction Characteristics of the Submarine

As indicated in Figure 92, the GUPPY submarine is a slim, cigar-shaped ship with a minimum of superstructure. The heart of the ship is contained in a long cylindrical pressure hull which is somewhat smaller than the external shell and extends nearly to the ends of the ship. Within the pressure hull are all of the propelling machinery, control equipment, and living accommodations of the ship. On top of the pressure hull is a cylindrical tank known as the conning tower in which certain control equipment is housed. On the later classes of submarines, i.e., Fast Attack, Nuclear and Guided Missile boats, this conning tower has been replaced by a small vertical trunk to provide access from the pressure hull to the bridge. Surrounding the pressure hull are the majority of the fuel and ballast tanks, and extending from the pressure hull are the propeller shafts, control surfaces, periscopes, snorkel, torpedo tubes, etc. The whole is blended together into the streamlined form indicated in the figure by a free-flooding fairing. The result is a long, slim hull surmounted by the streamlined "sail" which provides fairing around the submarine's upper works. An exception to this long, slim hull is the ALBACORE hull, to be discussed later, which is designed for higher submerged speed.

As a result of the streamlining required to give the modern submarine the desired underwater capability, most of the normal deck and navigating equipment has disappeared. As a matter of fact, the deck remaining on the modern submarine is hardly worthy of the name and the bridge has been reduced to something slightly larger than the cockpit of an airplane. The lifelines, deck cleats, capstans, etc., are either portable and unrigged at sea, or they can be recessed in place when not in use. Deck guns are a thing of the past, and propeller guards have been eliminated.

Characteristics Which Affect Handling

The principles of handling a submarine on the surface are generally the same as for the surface ship, but the submarine has many distinctive features that affect her handling. The first item that will impress the conning officer is the tiny bridge and the limited equipment thereon. There is space on the bridge for only a few men. Normally, the Officer of the Deck is accompanied on the bridge at sea by only two lookouts; the quartermaster stands his watch in the conning tower (control room on boats not having a conning tower), and the helmsman is also located below. The bridge, particularly if on the top of the sail as in the latest types, provides excellent all-around visibility, including the advantage of permitting the conning officer to view the whole length of the ship from bow to stern. When handling alongside this

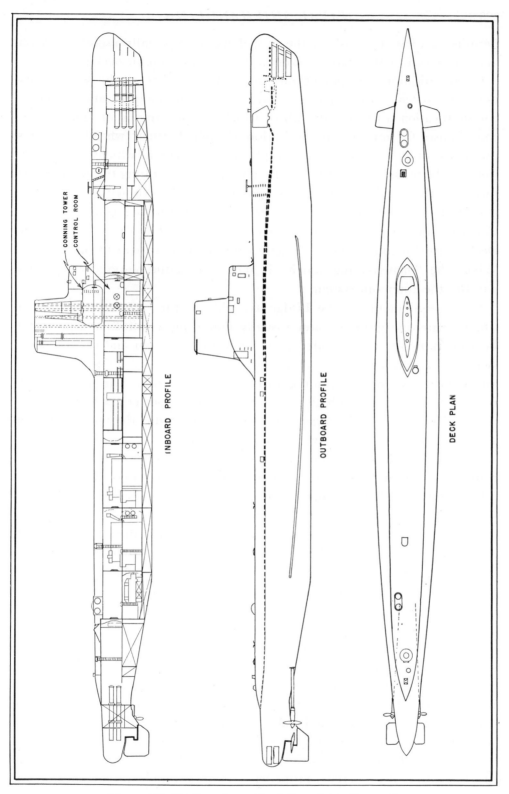

CONNING TOWER

CONTROL ROOM

INBOARD PROFILE

OUTBOARD PROFILE

DECK PLAN

Figure 92. Outboard profile, inboard profile, and
plan view of a "Guppy" submarine.

permits viewing the wash of the propellers, an especially useful check on motor orders since there are no motor order indicators on the bridge.

Communication equipment on the bridge consists of the general announcing system transmitter, a sound-powered phone outlet, and the intercommunication unit or units, all of which are pressure-proof. The "intercom" is used for normal communications to the helmsman (who also operates the motor order annunciators), except on those boats in which communication can be maintained directly through the upper conning tower hatch. By means of the intercom, bridge can communicate directly with the quartermaster, radar, maneuvering room (where the motors are controlled), the Captain, torpedo rooms and the control room. Thus the Officer of the Deck is able to communicate directly with every compartment on the ship. When the "maneuvering watch" is stationed, sound-powered telephones parallel the Intercom system.

Other equipment on the bridge available to the conning officer are a single centerline gyro repeater (usually mounting a binocular-type target bearing transmitter), a rudder angle indicator, collision and diving alarm switches, and the whistle operating lever or lanyard. The whistle is air operated and mounted in the lower forward part of the sail. Its efficiency is doubtful, especially in high winds, due to its low power and highly directional character, so it is always good practice to mount the portable signal searchlight and have it ready for use in emergency.

Due to the lack of space on the bridge, the Navigator usually works in the conning tower and uses the periscope for visual bearings. The conning officer must therefore be sure he has his conning chart (see page 138) and pay particular attention to "navigating by eye."

A feature of concern to the submarine shiphandler is the vulnerability of his stern. The ship's propellers and stern diving planes extend well out from the sides of the ship and there are no propeller guards! The stern torpedo tube shutters are also easily damaged and must be kept from contacting solid objects.

The bow planes and the bow torpedo tube shutters make the bow also somewhat vulnerable. Generally speaking, however, the bow itself is the strongest section of the ship, and in case of collision the bow should always be presented to absorb the impact and to reduce the danger of rupturing the pressure hull. The value of this was strikingly demonstrated in the bow-on collision of GROWLER and a Japanese gunboat during World War II, and when ARGONAUT collided with HONOLULU shortly after the war.

The diesel-electric drive of the conventional submarines provides smooth, precise control of the screws. Propeller response is rapid, and the same motor power is available astern as ahead. Due to the loss of efficiency of the screws when backing, however, the resultant power astern is slightly less than when using the same motor power ahead. From ahead at standard speed (about 14 knots) the GUPPY submarine can be stopped by BACK EMERGENCY in approximately two ship lengths. The boat can be maneuvered easily on the battery also (provided the state of charge is sufficient), and maneuvering on the battery permits quiet smokeless operation while going alongside or clearing a pier. The quietness of battery propulsion is also advantageous when creeping through a dense fog where listening for the whistles of other vessels, or the sounds from bell and whistle buoys, Klaxons, and foghorns is so important.

Though submarines normally maneuver alongside with only one 1,600 horsepower diesel generator per shaft and thus have only 3,200 horsepower available, this is not a handicap because in emergency, propulsion can be shifted to the battery in a moment, thus making maximum power available. For this reason some boats make it a standard procedure to answer BACK EMERGENCY on the battery, but this leads to trouble if during a landing using the diesel-generators, BACK FULL is followed by BACK EMERGENCY because precious backing power and time is lost in shifting from the diesel generators to the battery.

Among her favorable characteristics the submarine has a small turning diameter and her low superstructure makes her less sensitive to the wind than most ships.

Though she answers her rudder well when moving ahead, her propellers are less effective than normal for twisting the ship. This is due not only to the fact that the propellers are relatively close together, but also because the propeller shafts diverge from the centerline of the ship by about 2°. The actual thrust lines of the propellers extended forward thus cross the centerline very nearly at the pivot point of the ship and result in little actual twisting moment although the screws themselves are twelve feet apart. In addition the circulating current effect is reduced because there is extensive underwater structure forward as well as astern of the screws. Submarines habitually use, therefore, a twisting combination of BACK FULL and AHEAD STANDARD under similar conditions where a destroyer might use the TWO-THIRDS twisting combination.

The single, "balanced" type rudder is mounted about 10 feet aft of the propellers. It thus receives the full discharge current when the propellers are going ahead, but it feels little screw current when the propellers are backing. Maximum rudder is 35° and full rudder is normally 30°. Standard rudder is a term not used in submarines. At low speeds full rudder is normally

required to change the heading at an appreciable rate. Since rudder effectiveness is reduced when the screws are stopped, when making a landing, ahead
power is kept on as long as possible in order to increase maneuverability.

While the limited superstructure of the submarine reduces the conning
officer's concern for the wind, it at the same time raises a more serious problem. The silhouette of a submarine is misleading to other ships, and it is
difficult to tell her course and speed by visual observation. She is so low in
the water that she is difficult to see at even moderate ranges. At night her
side lights are low, she has only a masthead light and no accompanying
range light, and her stern light is very close to the water, often being
obscured by waves. A submarine is also a small radar target, and this combined with her visible characteristics frequently results in her being identified as a fishing vessel or other small ship. Hence she is expected to be shorter
and to have much greater maneuverability than is actually the case. The
ramming and sinking of s-51 by CITY OF ROME in 1925 resulted primarily
from failure of the latter to identify s-51 as a submarine on the surface at
night.

A last general feature of handling the submarine is the ever-present concern for safety. Collision spells mortal danger if the pressure hull is ruptured.
Although technically the submarine can survive with any two compartments
flooded (except the end ones), the reserve buoyancy required to replace the
buoyancy lost in the flooded compartments normally cannot be gained in
time to prevent the boat from sinking. More often than not in a collision,
not only is positive buoyancy lost from the flooding of compartments, but it is
also lost through the rupture of ballast tanks. Because of this danger from
collision submarine crews are thoroughly trained in collision procedures, and
submarine officers are trained to take early avoiding action and to liberally
interpret the General Prudential Rule to prevent collision situations from
developing. In this regard the cardinal rules are: (1) take action early;
(2) change course early and make the change great enough to be readily apparent to the other vessels; and(3) use the signal searchlight freely to insure
mutual identification.

One final feature that is a limitation at sea in company with other ships is
the lack of CIC facilities. Designed primarily for "lone wolf" operations,
there is no need nor space for a CIC comparable to that of a surface ship.
The conning officer on the bridge must depend entirely upon his JOOD (if
there is one available), quartermaster and radar operator to work out track-
ing and maneuvering board problems. Any radio traffic must be sent by
Intercom to the radio room to be handled by the radioman. The submarine
is therefore not equipped for operations in formation with other ships on a

continuing basis. For this reason, when submarines accompany a surface ship formation they should be given maximum freedom of action. They should habitually be given orders to operate clear of the force when they are not involved in a particular exercise.

Lines and Deck Equipment

Though her deck space is at a minimum, a submarine must be equipped to meet all of the mooring requirements of other ship types. Through impressive ingenuity she has ben equipped with all of the necessary equipment, yet at no sacrifice to her underwater performance. The bull-nose, capstan heads, cleats, lifelines, etc., are all either removable or retractable. She is smooth and trim when rigged for operations at sea, yet completely equipped when coming alongside the pier or nest.

There is a capstan forward and aft, the latter being electrically powered, single speed, and the former hydraulically powered at variable speed. They can be used to good advantage to bring the ship bodily in when desired.

Four 5-inch manila mooring lines are normally used to secure to the pier or nest, but 3-inch Nyon lines have become popular because they are easier to handle and to stow. Submarine cleats were designed for 5-inch lines so the smaller Nylon lines cannot be held under strain as easily as the manila, but with due care they can be used just as effectively and because of their long life are less expensive in the long run.

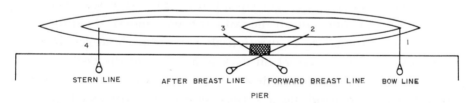

Figure 93. Mooring lines of a submarine.

Lines are normally rigged as shown in Figure 93. When alongside a pier, due to the necessity of adjusting short breast lines for the rise and fall of the tide, it is normal practice to rig the bow line to tend forward and the stern line to tend aft, which produces the result of breast lines but requires a minimum of adjustment. Because of the tendency of a submarine to pivot on her belly point, it is necessary that the bow and stern lines be set to restrain this pivoting.

The submarine's ground tackle consists only of a single, 2,200 pound, standard stockless anchor and either 105 or 180 fathoms of ¾-inch chain.

The only unusual feature of the anchor gear is the special set of jaws provided at the exit of the chain pipe to act as the chain compressor when securing the chain, there being no space or provision for normal chain stoppers to be used. An indicator is provided on deck to show the amount of chain out. In using the anchor it is difficult to see the chain clearly because of the location of the hawse pipe, and care must be exercised to prevent straining the chain.

In preparing the anchor for letting go, it should be walked out slightly to insure that it will drop when the brake is released. This precaution is necessary due to the recessed housing of the anchor which permits it to be housed flush with the ship's side. Once prepared for letting go, the anchor projects from the side so that it must be housed prior to going alongside if it is on the engaged side.

Towing, Fueling, Alongside Operations

Though submarines can be towed, they are poor ships for the towing vessel role since there is little deck space aft for the rigging of the towing gear and the stern planes and propellers are especially susceptible to fouling. Though not equipped with a towing hawser a submarine can disconnect her anchor chain and rouse it out on deck for the purpose. This is not an easy task and should be avoided when possible, especially in any kind of sea; just receiving a towing hawser or wire rope aboard a submarine from another towing vessel can be difficult enough.

Most submarines are no longer equipped for fueling at sea since the special fueling-at-sea connection in the sail has been removed. Fueling at sea to the normal in-port fueling connection aft is possible, however, in weather that permits putting personnel on deck to accomplish the task.

Handling a submarine alongside another ship at sea for transfer or fueling is no different than handling a surface ship of her size. Such operations should be conducted at low speed, however, to avoid waves breaking over the deck while personnel are exposed. Transfer at sea can be conducted when it is too rough to put men on the main deck by handling the lines from the bridge, but this method is not as easy nor as efficient as having personnel on the main deck to handle the lines.

Getting Underway

Because of the absence of projections from the hull, it is often quite satisfactory to back straight out when clearing the side of a pier or a large ship, but it is better to move the stern out by snubbing the bow in with number two line. This is particularly important when clearing from alongside other submarines. A good check can be made of the current, if there is any, when the bow is heaved in by observing how easily the stern is moved out. If it appears that the current would set the stern back to its original position once number one line is taken in, allowance should be made for this contingency by twisting the stern well out with the propellors.

Except in unusual cases (which should be planned beforehand with the Engineering Officer) the first bell astern should always be ONE-THIRD. If by error it were answered by ahead instead of astern, the low power would permit the error to be corrected easily. As a further safeguard, number two line should not be taken in until the boat starts astern. By retaining this line until the last minute, an error can be easily checked, and if there is no error no difficulty will be experienced in taking in the line as the boat moves astern, since this line tends aft. On the other hand, the use of, ALL BACK TWO-THIRDS (or FULL) as the first bell might cause considerable damage if it were erroneously answered in the ahead direction. This could be even more serious if the sequence of getting underway orders were: "TAKE IN ALL LINES, ALL BACK TWO-THIRDS, SOUND ONE LONG BLAST." There would be no lines to check the boat and the long blast would interfere with any corrective orders. The best procedure therefore is to give ALL BACK ONE-THIRD, and, when it is seen that screws are backing, order "Take in number two." ALL BACK TWO-THIRDS, should be given only after it is seen that all lines are clear, and the one long blast can be sounded as the boat actually gathers sternway. This latter is important when there are several boats at nearby piers, because in this case an approaching vessel can actually see *which* boat is getting underway. Since an air whistle does not emit a plume of steam, it is especially difficult for an approaching vessel to identify which boat has given the signal unless the boat is also moving.

Twisting

As previously mentioned, the submarine does not twist as effectively as a surface ship. For this reason the good rudder response of the ship should be used and slight headway should be maintained for twisting whenever possible. In any event, if the twist is to the right, right rudder should be used because it contributes the major part of the twisting force as it receives the thrust of the ahead screw. Likewise, if the twist is to the left, left rudder must be employed to twist effectively. This is true *even* if the vessel has sternway, *provided* sufficient power is used on the ahead screw, i.e., more than one-third. Thus, when backing out from a slip, should we be using left rudder to swing the stern to port and desire to continue the twist and swing the bow to the right after clearing, rather than ordering, PORT AHEAD ONE-THIRD, while clearing the pier, we should wait until it is safe to order, PORT

AHEAD STANDARD, which will rapidly kill our sternway and provide a powerful screw current for the rudder. When doing this, the conning officer should observe the propellor wash carefully and shift his rudder to RIGHT FULL as soon as he sees his ahead screw "bite in." The backing screw shoud not be increased to FULL until it is positively determined that the ahead screw is, in fact, going ahead. We should emphasize the value of habitually checking the screw wash after each order. Just as in using the rudder angle indicator, the habit of checking the actual response to an order will allow errors to be caught before they have produced serious consequences.

Twisting can be done easily, even by the novice, if a few simple rules are followed. First, get the rudder shifted to Full in the direction toward which the turn is desired once the ahead screw has started ahead; second, work the backing screw up to the maximum power suitable for the conditions, i.e. full when in the stream with plenty of sea room, and two-thirds when handling alongside or under close conditions; third, with the rudder fixed and the backing screw set, adjust the power on the ahead screw as necessary to control the ship's headway or sternway.

Going Alongside

When going alongside a nest or pier, it is normal to approach with a relatively large angle, 15° to 20°. In such an approach the bow can be placed alongside at the desired position and the stern worked in with the screws and the after capstan. In landing at a pier, the use of a spring line (number two) to check the headway and the bow line to hold the bow in will permit the ship to be brought bodily alongside. Springing should be avoided when going alongside a nest, since such action will disturb the whole nest.

The primary rule in going alongside is to keep the stern away from trouble and always clear for backing. This is not a difficult requirement, but it should be foremost in the mind of the shiphandler when planning the maneuver. It should also be remembered that in reference to turns, it is difficult to speed up or tighten a turn, but easy to slow it down. Thus, plenty of rudder should be used initially, and once the ship begins to swing, the amount may be reduced to adjust the turn as desired. Another important point to remember is to maintain a screw current past the rudder as long as possible to maintain better control.

In coming alongside the proper use of the lines makes for smart ship handling. They should not be put over too early and then walked up the length of the pier unless conditions require it. With the landing under reasonable control, complications are avoided by delaying putting the lines over until they can be sent directly to their proper cleats. Make sure the bow line is always in position to prevent the boat from pivoting and endangering the screws.

Handling a Nest of Submarines

Submarines alongside a tender are often moored in nests of as many as eight or nine boats. The entire nest must be maneuvered if the inboard boat has to get underway, as so often is the case. The availability of a tug makes the problem simple, but the operation can also be handled by the boats in the nest alone. First, all boats in the nest should be moored securely with little or no slack in their lines so relative movement between adjacent boats will be minimized. Second, the boats should be moored as parallel to each other as possible so that the sterns do not fan out. If these two conditions are met, the problem of maneuvering the nest as a whole is greatly simplified.

As in handling other nests of ships, the screws of the outboard and inboard boats are used. The propulsion should come from the diesel generators rather than the batteries to allow more precise control of the screws and the use of very low RPM. As soon as the boat getting underway has cleared, lines should be passed, and the movement of the detached part of the nest started in toward the tender. This can be accomplished by use of the inboard boat's capstans and using the propellers of the outboard and inboard boats as necessary. The conning officer of the inboard boat should be in charge, and he can adjust his own power while ordering constant power from the outboard boat. Considerable power can be used provided it is built up slowly. This maneuver should not be attempted without previous planning, and it is good practice to have another officer on the inboard boat ready to handle the lines so that the conning officer can devote his entire attention to maneuvering the nest as a whole.

Operating at Sea

When the protection of the harbor is left behind, the difference between the submarine and the surface ship becomes more apparent. Because of her very limited freeboard and rounded superstructure, the seas sweep completely over the deck of the submarine in weather that other ships would consider rather calm. There is little protection and few handholds on the deck of the submarine, and except in very calm seas, no one is normally allowed on the maindeck when at sea. Submarines are now equipped with a safety track extending from bow to stern on the main deck to which sliding safety lines can be attached when it is necessary to have men on deck during emergencies.

There is no flare to the bow of a GUPPY submarine, so there is no extra lift of the bow or deflection of the water as a wave strikes the bow. The nose of the boat tends to bury itself into oncoming seas, and she is swept from stem to stern by even small waves. In heavy weather the waves sweep completely over the bridge, and upon occasion the boat will be nearly submerged. Because of the constant threat of being swept out of the cockpit and over the side, all personnel on the bridge are provided with safety belts. Under such conditions the boat should *snorkel on the surface* with the bridge hatch shut to prevent entry of water into the boat.

In addition to its tendency to plow under the seas, the submarine is also inclined to roll heavily. The narrow, rounded hull of the submarine augments this tendency, even though the center of gravity of the boat is relatively low. This tendency is even more pronounced in the fatter ALBACORE type boat.

The most modern boats have the bridge on the top of the sail, affording much more protection from the seas for the bridge personnel. Due to heavy rolling, however, safety belts are still required in rough weather to prevent losing personnel over the side.

Submarines with the bridge on the lower level must always be alert to the dangers of a "pooping sea." The pooping sea normally occurs when the boat is underway in a moderate to heavy quartering or following sea. A wave coming from astern will completely submerge the deck aft and slowly pass over the bridge and forward deck, flooding water into the boat through the main induction valve and the bridge hatch if they are open. If there is any possibility of such a "pooping" sea, the boat should be sealed except for the snorkel, and the bridge watch secured with safety belts. Boats not equipped with a snorkel can shut the main induction and take the air supply through the upper hatch but even then a man should be standing by the hatch to shut it when required. Alternatively the bridge hatch may be kept shut and the OOD can order over the Intercom that the main induction be shut when necessary.

The Principles of Submerging

The greatest differences between the submarine and surface ships come into focus when we examine the problems of submerged operations. The design peculiarities which have been so troublesome for surface operation now demonstrate their worth. The principles and techniques of submerging and operating under the surface are quite foreign to the surface sailor, so we had better look into the basic principles and systems involved.

A submarine is submerged by flooding the ballast tanks with sea water until the reserve buoyancy is eliminated and the boat sinks beneath the surface. Once submerged, the weight of water contained within the submarine's tanks is adjusted until the weight of the submarine and all it contains is equal to the weight of the water displaced. In accordance with the principle of Archimedes, this would result in a balance of forces, and neutral buoyancy would have been attained.

Though in perfect neutral buoyancy, however, the distribution of weight versus buoyancy might be such that the boat would tend to rest with the bow or stern up. In order to avoid such a contingency the boat is equipped with trim tanks in the bow and stern. By adjusting the amount of water in the trim tanks, the boat can be balanced with a neutral pitching moment in addition to its neutral buoyancy.

We must become accustomed to the idea that once the boat is submerged and near neutral buoyancy, she may twist, turn, or drift up or down; and except for a small "squeezing" effect due to elimination of air bubbles and actual compression of the hull, the buoyant force does not change as the submarine changes depth. There is no certain depth to which the boat will sink for a given buoyancy condition. If the boat has negative buoyancy, she will sink until she strikes the bottom or until the buoyancy condition is changed. Conversely, if the boat has positive buoyancy and is not restrained, she will rise until a part of her structure emerges and changes the buoyancy condition.

These "ballast tanks" that we use to control the buoyancy and balance of the submarine are very interesting. They must be controlled accurately and rapidly if we are to depend upon them for diving control. For this purpose the submarine is equipped with an elaborate compressed air system and a versatile pumping system. Tanks which are to be emptied quickly are opened at the bottom to the sea, and compressed air is introduced at the top of the tank. The high pressure air quickly forces the water out of the tank. To fill such a tank quickly, vents at the top of the tank are opened, allowing the air to escape, and the water floods in to replace the air. If we are dealing with a closed tank that cannot be opened to the sea, we can empty it by blowing or pumping, and can flood it as desired through control valves.

The main ballast tanks provide the primary buoyancy control for the boat. They are used to dive and to surface the submarine, and are of such capacity that, when flooded, the reserve buoyancy of the boat is eliminated and the boat is nearly in the neutral buoyancy condition. These tanks have flood holes opening to the sea at the bottom and are equipped with vents at their tops. Thus they can be quickly "blown" or "vented" when surfacing or diving. These tanks are external to the pressure hull of the boat and, because they are free flooding, need not be built to withstand sea pressure

Though the flooding of the main ballast tanks will place the boat in near neutral buoyancy under "average" conditions, the actual conditions almost always differ from the average. Differences in displacement because of variations in fuel, stores, torpedoes, personnel, etc., or a difference in the density of the sea water, can alter the amount of ballast required to arrive at neutral buoyancy. The main ballast tanks, being free flooding and unable to withstand pressure differences, must be kept *completely full* of either water or air. If they were only partially full of water, with an entrapped volume of air above the water, the buoyancy of the boat would be changed as the depth changed. If the boat went deeper, the air would be compressed by the increased pressure, and then more water would enter the tanks. Thus the boat would lose buoyancy as she descended—an unstable situation. Because of this, we cannot compensate for differences from the average by *partial* venting or blowing of the main ballast tanks except as a momentary correction, only.

The adjustment to achieve perfect neutral buoyancy as well as to eliminate any residual pitch moment is made with the auxiliary ballast system. This system includes both the auxiliary ballast tanks near the center of gravity of the ship, and the forward and after trim tanks. The whole constitutes a closed pressure-proof system into which water can be introduced and distributed to adjust the "trim" of the boat. Incidentally, the term "trim," when applied to a submarine, includes both over-all buoyancy and fore-and-aft trim.

The Diving Officer (the conning officer in the vertical plane) must continually make adjustments to maintain the trim of the boat. If several men walked to one end of the boat when submerged, or sea water is admitted to or discharged from the sanitary tanks, the Diving Officer must compensate for the change. Corrections in trim are made by adding or discharging water from the auxiliary ballast system or by pumping the water already in the system from one tank to another. Even when the boat is on the surface, the Diving Officer makes trim adjustments. By noting all changes in weight and moment caused by consumption of fuel, discharging of water, flooding of tanks, etc., he periodically calculates the effect on his submerged trim and makes compensating adjustments in the auxiliary ballast system.

In addition to the tanks mentioned above, there are four other buoyancy control tanks to consider. These are the negative tank, the safety tank, the bow buoyancy tank, and the fuel ballast tanks.

Though flooding the main ballast tanks will eliminate the reserve buoyancy of the boat and cause it to sink beneath the surface of the water, there is no remaining force to carry the boat deeper since she is then in the neutral buoyancy condition. To overcome this and to allow faster dives, a negative tank is provided. When diving, this tank is flooded to give the boat a margin of negative buoyancy. When the desired depth is reached, this tank is blown and sealed by closing its flood valve, and the boat is returned to the neutral buoyancy condition. The negative tank is a pressure tank, and is located slightly forward of the submarine's center of gravity.

The safety tank is a pressure-proof tank which is normally kept full when submerged. The capacity of this tank is such that if the conning tower is flooded for any reason, the buoyancy gained by blowing this tank will just compensate for the loss. Flooding of the conning tower through error or through damage is a real possibility, and then the submarine would have to blow the main ballast tanks and surface in order to keep from sinking. This might not be acceptable in combat, so the safety tank provides a means of compensating for the lost buoyancy up to the extent even of loss of the entire conning tower. This tank has proved to be such a useful asset that later submarines, not having conning towers, are still provided with a safety tank.

The safety tank is also frequently used for surfacing when it is desired to conserve high-pressure air. In this case the safety tank is blown to bring the boat up to the surface, and then the water is eliminated from the main ballast tanks by means of the low presssure (LP) blow system. This system utilizes a large blower to create the relatively low air pressure necessary to force the sea water from the tanks when the boat is on the surface. If no high pressure air is available, the boat can also be surfaced by "planing" up to the surface and running the LP blower until sufficient water is blown from the main ballast tanks to give positive buoyancy.

Tht bow buoyancy tank is formed by the bow superstructure, and is similar in purpose and operation to one of the main ballast tanks. It is normally operated with the main ballast tanks, but it can be blown separately when desired. This tank is used when it is desired to get an *up* angle quickly, such as when surfacing or checking an unwanted *down* angle.

The fuel system of the submarine is also of interest. The fuel tanks are external to the pressure hull and are not pressure proof. As fuel is used from these tanks, water is introduced in equal quantity to compensate for the lost weight. This compensation is not exact because of the difference in density between water and diesel oil, but it is close enough to reduce to a second-order effect the loss in displacement. Since the fuel tanks are always full of either fuel and/or water, they can be relatively thin walled.

The fuel ballast tanks are a set of fuel tanks which are fitted with flood valves, vents, and air systems similar to the main ballast tanks. When the fuel from these tanks has been consumed—or in case of emergency—the flood valves can be opened and the tanks operated in conjunction with the main ballast tanks. This gives the boat increased reserve buoyancy when on the surface, with corresponding higher freeboard, and does not disturb the submerged trim.

With all of the "blowing" and the "venting" mentioned above, we must certainly be provided with an adequate air system. A fleet submarine is normally equipped with two large air compressors and a high-capacity system of air banks. These banks must provide the air for torpedo ejection and engine starting in addition to the requirements for buoyancy control. Obviously, once we are submerged, air consumed from the air banks cannot be replaced except by drawing air from the interior of the boat, and this is an insignificant source. Consequently, in controlling the boat, the Diving Officer of the submarine must be constantly alert to the consumption of air. It is a matter of grave concern to the Commanding Officer that the boat have sufficient reserve air in the air banks to meet emergencies.

Though we have only discussed the buoyancy tanks of the submarine and have not covered the entire list of tools available to the Diving Officer, we should examine the control procedure known as "hovering." By adroit use of the auxiliary ballast system the submarine can be maintained at a given depth and on an even keel by the use of this system alone at zero speed. This requires constant adjustment of the water in the auxiliary ballast tanks and the trim tanks. It is fairly difficult to control the depth of the submarine in this manner, but it is possible and is very useful when conserving battery power or when it is desired to eliminate the noise of the propellers.

Plane Control

A quicker and more effective way of controlling the depth and angle of the submarine when the boat is submerged *with way on* is by use of the depth control planes. These, the bow and stern planes, are horizontal hydrofoils located at the ends of the ship. By varying their inclination with respect to the water flowing by, forces can be applied to the ship in the amount and direction desired. The bow planes are well forward, and are mounted high on the hull so that they are clear of the water when the boat is on the surface. The stern planes are just aft of the propellers, and are in line with them in order to obtain the full force of the screw current.

Two sets of planes are provided, because it is necessary to control both ends of the boat. This would be similar in a surface ship to having both a bow and a stern rudder for maintaining the ship's head, so one might ask why wouldn't one set of planes do for a submarine, since one rudder suffices for a surface ship? If only one set of planes were provided, couldn't they be used to adjust the heading of the hull in depth, and let the shape of the hull itself provide the stability to maintain the direction of motion?

The answer of course, is *yes* but though one set of planes is adequate for a submarine at high speeds, two were installed for better control at low speeds. The unbalanced force on the hull can be large, and a relatively high speed is required to allow control from one end only. Even if reasonable control could be achieved at low speed, depth and angle could not be controlled independently. This would be most unsatisfactory when operating at periscope depth. Consequently, two sets of hydraulically controlled surfaces are provided, with the control wheels in the control room.

We should realize that a submarine normally operates in a layer of water only a ship length and a half deep. If, to draw a parallel, a destroyer did all of its cruising in a channel only 600 feet wide, she would probably be equipped with more than just controls at one end; she would probably have to be equipped with bow rudders also.

The submarine's instruments available for depth control are the depth gauge, which registers depth of the keel below the surface, in feet; and the inclinometer, which registers the "angle" for the boat from the horizontal, in degrees. Since operation of either set of planes affects both of these quantities, depth control could become a complex operation if there were no system for separating the control functions.

The bow planes are closer to the center of gravity of the boat than are the stern planes, because they are set back from the bow about 45 feet, and the center of gravity of the boat is forward of the midpoint of the hull profile. Consequently, though the bow planes produce a proportional amount of lift for a given inclination, they produce less angle moment on the boat because of the shorter lever arm. In addition, the change in angle resulting from bow plane action is such as to augment the action of the planes; that is, rise bow plane procedures *up* angle. For these reasons the bow planes are admirably suited for controlling depth, but poorly suited for controlling angle.

On the other hand the stern planes are nearly at the after extremity of the boat. They therefore produce a maximum angle moment on the boat for a given lift, because of the long lever arm from the center of gravity of the boat; but a plane inclination which moves the stern toward the surface results in *down* angle.

The accepted solution to this problem is to assign the bow planesman the task of *depth control,* and the stern planesman the ask of *angle control,* and thus have each planesman watch primarily *just one* instrument. By labelling the plane inclinations RISE and DIVE, we can have an unambiguous situation where RISE BOW PLANE causes the boat to rise in depth, and RISE STERN PLANE causes the boat to assume an *up* angle which will tend to cause the boat to rise (RISE STERN PLANE actually applies the force *downwards* on the stern in the process). DIVE plane angles, conversely, cause the boat to dive in depth and to assume a *down* angle.

Because of the above convention of labelling the control directions of the planes, it is necessary to interchange the functions of the bow and stern planesmen when the boat is backed down when submerged. Though the control directions for the stern planesman remain correct—that is, RISE STERN PLANES produces *up* angle and causes the boat to tend to rise— RISE BOW PLANE would cause the boat to *descend* in depth unless the angle reaction overcame the diving force. Since RISE BOW PLANE would produce *up* angle when going astern, the problem is solved by having the stern planesman control the *depth* and the bow planesman control the *angle* when going astern.

To summarize, then, the submarine is submerged by flooding the main ballast tanks. She is carried downward by the weight of the water in the negative tank, which is blown out upon reaching the desired depth. Trim is adjusted by adjustments in the auxiliary ballast system, and, throughout her underwater excursion, depth and angle control is affected by the use of the bow and stern planes. When it is desired to surface, *up* angle is induced by blowing the bow buoyancy tanks, and the boat is surfaced by blowing the main ballast tanks.

Stability of the Submarine

When a ship is on the surface of the water—and this includes the submarine —the *center of gravity* (CG) of the ship is usually above the *center of buoyancy* (CB). The center of buoyancy is that point within the ship where the total buoyant force can be considered to act on the ship. Since we will be concerned in this discussion only with the transverse effects, we can consider the relative locations of the center of buoyancy and the center of gravity to be at a mean cross-section of the ship, as indicated in Figure 94. The center of buoyancy can be considered to be at the midpoint of the submerged portion of the hull; that is, the center of the cross-sectional area below the waterline. If the center of buoyancy were *fixed* at a point below the center of gravity, and the ship were inclined from the vertical, she would roll right over. How can a ship remain upright then, if the center of gravity is above the center of buoyancy?

Because of the shape of the hull, the center of buoyancy *moves* as the ship

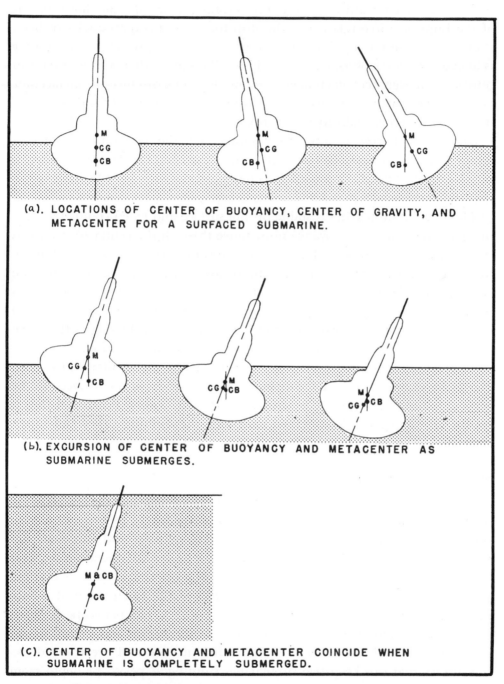

(a). LOCATIONS OF CENTER OF BUOYANCY, CENTER OF GRAVITY, AND METACENTER FOR A SURFACED SUBMARINE.

(b). EXCURSION OF CENTER OF BUOYANCY AND METACENTER AS SUBMARINE SUBMERGES.

(c). CENTER OF BUOYANCY AND METACENTER COINCIDE WHEN SUBMARINE IS COMPLETELY SUBMERGED.

Figure 94. Various aspects of the stability of a submarine.

rolls, as indicated in the figure. The midpoint of the submerged cross-section shifts to the side toward which the ship is rolling. If we plot the line of action of the buoyant force relative to the ship for each of several angles of heel, they will intersect at a point known as the *metacenter* (M). If the metacenter is above the center of gravity, the ship will be stable; that is, it will tend to return to an even keel when heeled to one side. The distance the metacenter is above the center of gravity is called the *metacentric height* and is a measure of the degree of stability of the ship.

Once a submarine is completely submerged, the midpoint of the submerged area no longer changes with roll, so the center of buoyancy is fixed, relative to the hull. Consequently, to be stable, the boat must be designed so that the center of gravity is *below* this *submerged* center of buoyancy.

Though the submarine is stable on the surface and when completely submerged, the center of buoyancy must move through the center of gravity as the boat dives or surfaces. This might give cause for concern about the stability of the boat, since we would seem to have no righting arm when the two centers coincide. Let's remember, though, that the center of buoyancy moves with heel unless the boat is completely submerged. The metacenter and center of buoyancy coincide at complete submergence. As long as the metacenter is *above* the center of gravity, we are in a stable condition.

The hull of a submarine is designed so that the metacenter will remain above the center of gravity throughout the transfer from the surfaced to the submerged condition, so she is actually stable at all times. Because of this, it is safe to run partially submerged with only the conning tower and superstructure above the surface.

Handling at Sea

At sea the submarine is handled on the surface much like the surface ship. The one great exception is that submarines are rarely in formation with other ships. However, submarines do operate in pairs and threes in formation when conducting coordinated attacks. This type of operation requires a precise sense of station keeping and a lively appreciation of relative motion, for there is no radar or visual information available when the boat is submerged. When at periscope depth during an attack, the periscope is raised only for a few moments at a time for attack observation and cannot be exposed long enough for other uses. Sonar information and prearranged tactics are all that can keep two submarines running at periscope depth from colliding while maneuvering in close company. When all else fails, the two boats can seek different depths, but this blinds the periscope of one or both of them, depending upon the depths so taken.

Diving and surfacing a submarine is normally carried out by the OOD and the section on watch. The evolution is kept as simple, as safe, and as rapid as possible, for the submarine's primary weapon, surprise, is dependent upon efficient diving and depth control. Submarines are always "rigged for dive" while cruising on the surface at sea. They are maintained continuously trimmed and properly compensated for diving on an instant's notice. The OOD always must keep the number of men on the bridge to a minimum, and can allow no loose gear topside which might foul the conning tower hatch. The first precautions when diving are to insure that all hands are below, that the main induction valve is closed, and that the conning tower hatch is shut. Since the average diving time of a submarine is about 45 seconds, this means rapid action.

When diving, the rudder is normally put amidships and careful attention must be paid to depth and angle control. More improperly executed dives result from improper use of the stern planes than from any other single cause. Loss of control on diving is generally due to excessive *down* angle on the boat. Dives are normally made at a down angle of from 7° to 10°, and angles over 15° are of little assistance in executing a rapid dive, because the stern remains on the surface for a longer time than when diving at a shallower angle. If the boat gets out of control and begins to assume an excessive down angle, in addition to shifting the planes to RISE, one or more of the following measures may be used to check the descent:

1. STOP or BACK the screws. This causes the stern to squat, tends to check the descent, and allows more time to correct the angle.

2. Use FULL RUDDER. This causes the stern to squat and kills way through the water.

3. BLOW BOW BUOYANCY TANK. This gives an upward force on the bow.

4. BLOW FORWARD GROUP OF MAIN BALLAST TANKS. This gives an upward force on the bow. (Note: Blowing all main ballast tanks aggravates the situation, because most of the air goes to the after tanks, which are higher in this case. This forces the stern up and increases the angle.)

A submarine will dive more readily when heading away from or across the seas than when heading into them. Depth control at periscope depth in a heavy sea is more difficult when heading into or away from the seas than when running in the trough. Though there is no increase in the buoyant force as a wave temporarily covers the submarine to a greater dept, there is a slight upward surge of the water as the wave passes over. This is troublesome to the Diving Officer and can cause the boat to broach. To counter this effect in a rough sea, it is normal to trim the boat "heavy" over-all so that she can be made to descend more quickly if she starts to "broach." or rises so rapidly after submergence that she breaks the surface and exposes herself. To prevent broaching, it is often advisable to increase speed to get better plane control; the larger "feather" when the periscope is raised is not so conspicuous when the surface is covered with waves.

In addition to normal use of the planes and ballast system for depth control and "hovering," as mentioned above, a submarine can, under certain conditions, be maintained at a constant depth by "balancing." To balance, the Diving Officer must find a layer of increasing density in the sea water and then carefully place and adjust the boat so that she will rest in this layer. These density layers are caused by changes in the temperature or salinity of the water at different depths. One might think that such changes would be insignificant, but this is not so. As the water temperature decreases, a normal fleet submarine, when submerged, experiences an increase in buoyant force of 850 lbs. per degree F. at a water temperature of 68° F. Furthermore, the salt content of sea water is normally about 35 parts in 1,000 by weight; but if this salt content is increased by only 1 part in 1,000, the submarine will experience an increase in buoyant force of about 3,500 pounds. Thus a temperature gradient or a layer of water of different salinity provides adequate means for balancing. Once the submarine is adjusted in the layer, she can remain motionless and silent, conserving the energy of her precious battery.

When diving the submarine, the Diving Officer retains speed control until he has levelled off and obtained the correct trim at the ordered depth. At other times the conning officer controls the submarine's speed, but he must be alert to assist the Diving Officer when depth control becomes difficult. The conning officer (normally the OOD) conns in the horizontal plane, and the Diving Officer conns in the vertical plane. The Diving Officer takes his orders for depth from the conning officer.

When running at high speeds submerged, the bow planes are not needed for depth control. It is normal to set them on zero degrees inclination or to rig them in. Though plane control must be more precise at high speed (the boat could broach or descend to a dangerous depth in a very short time), adequate control can be achieved with the stern planes alone.

An unusual effect with a GUPPY submarine at high speed submerged is that she heels *inboard* in a turn, instead of outboard as a surface ship does. This action is caused by the hydrofoil effect of the "sail." If we recall that a ship turns because the rudder forces the stern to the side and causes the whole hull to be inclined to the flow of water, we will remember that it is the side force of the water on the hull which forces the ship around in its turn. Since the "sail" is inclined to the water flow along with the hull, there is a strong side force developed on it also. Since the "sail" is *above* the hull of the boat, this side force creates an unbalanced rolling moment and causes the characteristic inboard heel during a turn.

The *snorkel* is a device for allowing use of the diesel engines while running at shallow submergence. It consists of an air intake tube which extends *above* the surface of the water, and an exhaust tube which extends *nearly* to the surface. Thus the engines can be supplied with fresh air and the exhaust expelled at low pressure, even though nothing but the tip of the intake pipe extends above the surface of the water. This intake pipe is equipped with a quick-closing valve which automatically closes whenever water enters the intake and opens when the intake head is once again above the surface. This allows use of the snorkel even though the intake is occasionally submerged due to wave action or errors in depth control.

It is most important, if the submarine is to escape detection, that the snorkel extend only the *minimum* distance necessary above the surface of the water. With skillful handling, the snorkel can be used with only a few inches exposed. This obviously calls for delicate depth control. A submarine may cruise on the snorkel for an indefinite period, so the shiphandler must provide the most expert depth control, day in and day out.

When running at periscope depth, or when snorkelling, care must be taken to prevent too large a "feather" when exposing either the periscope or the snorkel. The speed must be watched carefully when taking a "look," because the submarine decelerates slowly and it takes a long time to reach the very low speed that is acceptable for periscope observation. The smoother the surface, the smaller the allowable feather. In a flat calm, a periscope can be spotted at long range if it is making even a moderate feather.

When submerged, changes in power or the use of large rudder angles has a direct effect on depth control. If the engines are stopped or reversed, even though the boat is perfectly trimmed, there is a marked tendency for the stern to squat. If a large rudder angle is applied, the boat, in addition to turning, responds as though the stern planes had also been depressed. Because of this, the Diving Officer must be especially alert when power changes or course changes are ordered.

The reason for this unusual behavior is obscure and is buried in complex hydrodynamic phenomena. Some submarines have a greater tendency to respond to power changes and rudder angle than others. The reaction to power changes is due in part to the impingement of the helical propeller discharge currents on the stern planes, and the reaction to rudder angle is connected with the disturbance of the flow over the after part of the hull caused by the bridge fairwater. It is sufficient from the point of view of the ship-handler to understand that speed and rudder control have an effect on depth control.

Surfacing can also be most safely and expeditiously accomplished with the boat headed parallel to the trough. In this case, the lift of the sea acts all along the length of the boat as a wave passes and does not upset the trim as the boat is emerging. Surfacing into heavy seas is an uncomfortable evolution at best, occasionally involving submerging the bridge personnel and taking water down the conning tower hatch. Surfacing with the seas astern is not recommended, because a wave can crash down on the boat just as she breaks the surface, and this can completely upset the trim. Though surfacing in the trough may involve considerable rolling, it is the most acceptable solution. In any case, surfacing in heavy seas requires a fine sense of timing, careful control of speed and rudder, and a lively appreciation of the tremendous force of the sea.

The Single Screw Fast Attack Type

Submarines which are descendants of the experimental ALBACORE are entering the fleet and with them they bring special problems. As can be seen from Figure 95, ALBACORE has a short fat hull and only a single screw. Built to operate at high speeds submerged in the fast attack role, the surface han-

Figure 95. USS ALBACORE (AGSS-569), an experiment that has shown the way to the designers of future subs.

dling characteristics of ALBACORE leave much to be desired. Since her single propeller is mounted on the extremity of her stern cone and the conventional single screw hull form is not present, she cannot even be depended upon to "back to port" like a normal single screw ship.

It is in backing on the surface that ALBACORE shows her most difficult characteristics. The blimp-like hull form is designed for high submerged speeds ahead, and when moving astern this form has the tendency to sheer to one side or the other. When a sheer has started there is little that can be done to stop it. Once inclined to the flow of the water when moving astern, the hull is unresponsive to the feeble force of the rudders. Consequently controlled backing is out of the question.

Because of the difficulty of handling such a submarine on the surface, it is the normal practice to have tug assistance when handling alongside, and the conning officer should attempt a landing without assistance only under ideal conditions. Once such a boat is clear to maneuver ahead, however, she is capable of being handled as effectively as any other submarine.

The Nuclear Submarine

Except for their increased size and the absence of fuel ballast tanks, the general handling characteristics of the twin screw nuclear powered submarine is quite similar to the GUPPY. With her steam propulsion plant and greater displacement she will accelerate more rapidly but decelerate more slowly than the conventionally powered boat. Her greater draft causes her to twist more slowly in shallow water, and when backing she exhibits the tendency to sheer erratically seemingly unaffected by the direction of the

Figure 96. USS SKIPJACK (SSN-585)—streamlined hull plus nuclear power.

wind or the use of the rudder. However, the twin screw nuclear boats can be considered quite similar to their conventional sisters.

It is at sea where the unusual character of the nuclear boat comes into focus. As these boats are developed toward their role of the "true submersible," their surface handling characteristics become less and less important. Even their diving characteristics lose importance because there need be only one dive and one surfacing per exercise or war patrol. Deck seamanship evolutions at sea are of interest only as emergency rather than normal procedures. Fueling and replenishment at sea, man overboard, and even cruising on the surface are becoming less and less normal operations at sea in the nuclear submarine.

Submerged in her element the nuclear submarine is completely at home. She handles beautifully underwater and can operate at high speed and at great depth with excellent stability and control. Her controls have been combined into a control console at which a single "pilot" can control the boat in the same manner that a pilot flies an airplane.

Man Overboard

The methods used in submarines for picking up a man overboard are also similar to those used in surface ships, but here again there are disadvantages. The danger of placing a rescue party on the main deck, the fact that there are no boats available to assist, and the limited lookout and searchlight facilities available, all limit the submarine. One advantage which the submarine enjoys over the surface ship lies in its bow planes, which, when rigged out, provide a fine working platform a few feet above the surface for the rescue of personnel; another advantage is the short distance the rescued personnel have to be hoisted in order to get them on deck.

Submariners are alive to the dangers of "man overboard"—particularly the threat of being left topside when the submarine dives. The OOD, the lookouts, and the quartermaster must be adept at scrambling below through the conning tower hatch when the diving alarm sounds.

Bottoming

When under attack, or during ASW or salvage exercises, submarines are occasionally required to rest on the bottom. "Bottoming" must be done carefully to prevent damage to the boat, and it requires close coordination between the conning officer and the Diving Officer. A recommended procedure is to "plane" downward towards the bottom at slow speed, with little angle on the boat and with the fathometer continuously in use. A STOP TRIM should be attained before descending to the vicinity of the bottom. When about 50 feet from the bottom, the screws should be stopped and the boat trimmed slightly "heavy" over-all to allow her to sink slowly. The bow should be trimmed slightly down to prevent damage to the screws, rudder, or stern planes. When the bow has touched bottom, additional auxiliary ballast water should be taken into the tanks until the ship has settled firmly on the bottom. If there are bottom currents, the boat may bump along the bottom and change heading unless a sufficient measure of negative buoyancy is obtained with the auxiliary ballast system and the negative tank. We must remember not to move the rudder or turn over the screws while on the bottom.

Breaking clear of the bottom should be accomplished by retrimming the boat for neutral bouyancy and blowing the after group of main ballast tanks slightly (in order to free the stern first), and then venting these tanks as the boat begins to rise. The safety tank should then be blown to insure positive buoyancy while clearing the bottom. When about 50 feet clear of the bottom, the safety tank can be vented and the screws and rudder can be operated. If the angle is satisfactory, way can then be gotten on the boat and she can resume her normal underwater operations.

Occasionally it is desired to bottom at a specific location which permits the approach to be made on the surface. In this case a stationary dive can be made. Before diving, the anchor is dropped, and the boat is dived *using buoyancy control only*. The anchor insures that the boat will not drift from the spot while submerged, and it can be picked up again after surfacing.

Launching and Recovering Boats

Submarines, though not equipped with regular ship's boats, are usually equipped with rubber boats for emergency work and for special duties such as reconnaissance. The launching and recovering of these boats is quite interesting, since the submarine is not equipped with davits or other normal deck gear. One method of launching these boats is to slide them down the sides of the submarine and load them over cargo nets hung over the ship's side. Another method is to run with the main deck nearly awash and load the boats from the main deck. A last and most novel method is to load them on deck and then submerge out from under them.

When recovering the boats, the reverse of any of the above three methods can be used. In the third method—surfacing under the rubber boat—care must be taken to come up directly under the boat, or else it might be capsized. This method requires careful depth control at low speed.

At times, because of the proximity of the enemy, it is not feasible for the submarine to surface in order to retrieve the boats. In such cases the periscope can be used to tow the boats farther to sea, where a normal recovery can be made.

Though the actual handling of the submarine is not a part of the normal shiphandler's experience at sea, it is very interesting to examine the characteristics of this unusual type. The problems of the surface ship are multiplied many fold in the submarine. Shiphandling in two planes is a constant occupation when the boat is submerged.

This short chapter is not intended to acquaint the reader with the entire field of handling the submarine. It is not expected that the novice submariner could be prepared for his duties in so brief a span. The major purpose of this chapter is to acquaint the average mariner with the submarine as a type, to explain how it works, and to discuss its operations from a shiphandler's point of view.

CHAPTER XV

LARGE AMPHIBIOUS AND SERVICE SHIPS

Two MAJOR PARTS of the Fleet during and since World War II have been the mobile attack and support forces—the Amphibious and Service Forces. Both Forces operate with the Fleet, and both are required as an integral part of modern naval warfare. They are combatant forces in every sense of the word, though their missions are primarily those of amphibious attack and logistic support as opposed to the well-known mission of the striking forces. Though the roles and missions of the types being discussed in this chapter vary materially, and though their operations and tactics are dissimilar, they are grouped together because of their similarity from the shiphandling viewpoint.

The ships with which we will be dealing and which we will be mentally handling in this chapter all have one thing in common: relatively low power and low speed as compared to the cruiser, carrier, or destroyer. For example, our typical amphibious type (AGC, APA, or AKA) or service type (AD, AE, AF, AH, AK, AP, and AV) develops some 6,000 to 12,000 horsepower in turning up a maximum speed of about 17 knots. Though there are some ex-merchant ships in service of considerably greater tonnage and horsepower, their handling characteristics are similar and they will not be considered separately here. Our typical Fleet oiler (AO) develops some 13,000 horsepower at maximum speed 18 knots, and our SAN MARCOS-class Landing Ship Dock (LSD) develops some 7,000 horsepower at maximum speed 15 knots. We can see this differs greatly from our cruisers' 120,000 horsepower at a maximum speed of 34 knots, as indicated in Chapter XII.

All of these ships are distinctly different from the carrier, cruiser, and destroyer in that they all may vary considerably in tonnage and draft, and this materially effects their handling. For example, a typical amphibious transport may draw 22 feet when combat loaded en route to the beachhead. but may depart drawing a mean of only 15 feet, with her propeller barely underwater. Or, again, she might draw 28 feet when commercially loaded for her follow-up run to the combat area. The skipper or watch officer of an oiler likewise has to conn his ship under conditions of loading which vary the draft of this ship from that of a battleship (35 feet) when full of fuel, to that of a destroyer (18 feet) when in ballast.

Stemming in part from this greatly varying draft is another important difference from our cruiser or destroyer: the much larger sail area and the much smaller keel area resulting from light loading. These characteristics, combined with the greater top hamper in booms, boats, and bulwarks, make these ships quite susceptible to the wind. Though less powerful and less flexible than some types in the Fleet, these ships must take their place with even the most versatile ships afloat. They operate in the same restricted harbors under the same conditions of wind and tide as their fleeter sisters. This adds interest to the already challenging task of the conning officer of such a ship.

In some respects the low speed and lower power are an asset in handling ships of the amphibious and service type, since the lower power prompts greater care in executing any maneuver and the low speed patently allows greater time to perform the maneuver. Additionally, the single-screw, low-powered propulsion of most of these ships necessitates a nicety of control and command not required in handling our responsive twin-screw destroyer. Expressed another way, the conning officer of a heavy laden single-screw AKA or AE must employ many fundamentals of shiphandling which are seldom called into use by the destroyer conning officer. A destroyer has the ability to circumvent or prevent many situations through her large reserve of power and rapid response to controls, but the conning officer of a transport has to meet each situation head-on. The fundamentals of shiphandling are brought into play more completely with a single-screw, low-powered ship than with any other type.

THE SINGLE-SCREW SHIP

There are so many different types among the ships which make up the amphibious and service forces that space will not allow a complete exploration of each of them. However, since a majority of the ships in these forces are single-screw ships of approximately the same tonnage and horsepower, we can cover the basic shiphandling characteristics of most of them by discussing a typical ship. Let's commission a typical composite ship, uss AMPSER (Amphibious and Service), and examine her characteristics and behavior.

uss AMPSER (similar to the ships of Figures 97, 98, and 99), is a single-screw, low-powered large-ruddered, Maritime Commission design-World War II conversion, of high freeboard, of large sail area, and with a relatively thin skin. Her dimensions and characteristics are:

Length	489 feet
Beam	70 feet
Draft	
Full load	28 feet
Light	15 feet

Figure 97. Model of Attack Cargo Ship (AKA).

Displacement
Full load	13,000 tons
Light	7,500 tons
Total Shaft Horsepower	8,500
Maximum Speed	17 knots
Crew	35 Officers
	350 Enlisted

Though AMPSER can turn up 17 knots with her 8,500 horsepower, she backs sluggishly—and at times unpredictably as to direction. Under normal cruising conditions and at speeds over 12 knots she handles as nicely and precisely as a destroyer or carrier in routine maneuvers. "Close in" evolutions take a bit of "knowing"—knowledge which is readily attained by taking AMPSER on a short, independent cruise for calibration at the very first opportunity.

Before starting out on this important cruise it would also be propitious to review Chapter II and that portion of Appendix I dealing with single-screw effects. Figure 6 is particularly revealing and pertinent to the knowing required for close in handling. This review will remind us among other things, that AMPSER has a righthand screw which gives her a slight tendency to turn to port when going ahead, and a marked tendency to back to port until considerable sternway is picked up. Both these "normal" tendencies can of course be materially modified or even reversed either by the effect of wind or current. With these general characteristics and traits of AMPSER in mind let's begin handling AMPSER by getting under way. In describing the distinctive and unusual characteristics effecting getting AMPSER under way, with her

Figure 98. Amphibious assault calls for excellent seamanship at all levels. Here is shown the **LCVP Pre-Assault Pattern** of **USS ROCKBRIDGE** (APA-228).

single screw, under way, we will cover it in two situations: first, getting under way from anchorage; and secondly, getting under way from a pier.

Getting Under Way from an Anchorage

Because of AMPSER's rather limited maneuverability at low speed and relatively slow acceleration, it is particularly desirable to get more than 5 knots way on as soon as possible. For this reason it is frequently desirable to "cast" (twist about the anchor) to the direction desired for clearing the anchorage prior to getting under way, and then, immediately on getting under way, to build up speed which will permit more ready handling (a speed of at least 10 knots).

Although AMPSER has rather limited maneuverability, as compared to a multiple-screw warship or the twin-screw service type (Figure 99), she can be

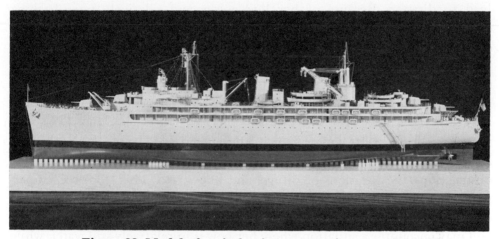

Figure 99. Model of typical twin-screw service type (AS).

turned smartly and handled nicely, under light wind conditions, by judicious use of her large rudder, coupled with her relatively slow acceleration rate. For example, a rapid change of course can be effected while at slow speed or even without steerageway by "kicking" the engine ahead (applying a short burst of ahead power) while holding full rudder in the direction of the desired course change. This kick, consisting of ringing up TWO-THIRDS or even STANDARD SPEED for a short interval, will produce a maximum turning effect for a short time but will not be of sufficient duration for the ship to gain much headway. If we wish to swing to the right (stern moving to port) we can kick the engines astern and the stern will move smartly to port. Unfortunately we cannot move the stern to starboard by kicking the engine astern, but, except for this, we can swing AMPSER nicely by using short bursts of power.

When clearing a crowded anchorage for a scheduled sortie, it is particularly desirable to cast AMPSER to the desired course prior to getting under way, so she can build up speed and join the formation smartly when her time of departure arrives. Once cast to the desired course, her heading can be maintained until the appointed sortie time by use of the above described kicks while at short stay. Once on her course and up to speed, AMPSER will handle equally as well as the more powerful twin-screw ships of the Force.

Getting Under Way from a Pier

Because of her characteristics, AMPSER requires a little more preparation for getting under way than most other naval types. It is essential that her loading and cargo stowage be carefully checked prior to getting under way. Abnormal draft or trim can materially complicate shiphandling, and shifting cargo may lead to disaster. Because of her low power and relatively poor backing characteristics, it is advisable to call for tug assistance under all but ideal conditions—particularly until AMPSER's characteristics are thoroughly learned by personal experience. The use of pilots and tugs will be discussed in Chapter XVIII; however, since there will certainly be times when tug assistance will not be available, let's consider handling our ship without the luxury of tugs.

Before taking in the gangway, it is advisable to walk to the end of the pier and study the situation—noting the general construction of the pier, any obstructions, the locations of pilings and buoys, etc. This "look-see" is particularly advisable when clearing from between two solid piers (as opposed to open or pile-supported piers), since AMPSER will be clearing relatively slowly and may encounter a situation where her bow is in relatively still water, while her stern is being acted on by the current in the channel. This situation can produce both a rapid drift and a radical turning moment which must be countered until the ship is clear of the piers. In the absence of tugs, our ship's boats will prove particularly useful in countering this effect.

In conning AMPSER from a pier, it is almost mandatory to take a station on the open bridge above the pilot-house because of the restricted visibility from the covered bridge. If there is any appreciable wind or current, it may be desirable to use an anchor and the ship's boats as described later under the section "Poor Man's Tug Boat." Under any circumstances we must make sure there are plenty of well-tended fenders available.

The first consideration in maneuvering AMPSER from the pier should be to keep her stern well clear. This can usually be accomplished by holding number two line and kicking AHEAD TWO-THIRDS, with the rudder toward the dock. When the stern has moved out a sufficient distance we can

clear with BACK TWO-THIRDS and adjusting the rudder to keep
AMPSER backing fair with her stern well cleared. If moored port-side-to a long
pier, we may have to kick ahead briefly to counter AMPSER's natural tendency
to back to port (into the pier). Once sufficiently clear of the pier face, it is
desirable to use more engine power in order to clear the pier head as rapidly
as possible.

Handling at Sea

While AMPSER may have some limitations in "close-in" handling, there are
no material differences in her maneuverability from that of a cruiser or carrier at speeds above 12 knots. Under normal conditions of wind and sea, her
condition of loading has no noticeable effect on her maneuverability. She
can maintain station in formation with any Navy type within her speed
range, and can perform all the common maneuvers handily. AMPSER's pivot
point is about under her bridge structure, and coincidentally, a good rule
for column movements is to apply rudder when the rudder kick of the ship
ahead is just forward of the bridge structure.

Although other ships normally come along her side during replenishment
exercises, she is on occasion required to go alongside other ships for transfer
of cargo. Going alongside under way presents no particular problems, but it
is prudent to make a wide approach and to maintain a distance of at least
100 feet from the other ship. An average value for surge when going along
side is about 50 yards per knot, but this will vary with loading.

For man overboard, because of AMPSER's limited backing power it is
usually preferable to put AMPSER in a 360° turn to return to the man rather
than to attempt to back and lower boats. In case the location of the man is not
known, the Williamson turn (See Chapter X) should be used.

In connection with the backing characteristics of AMPSER, though we know
that she will back to port, one might wonder what would happen should we
back the engines while moving ahead. It has been determined experimentally that backing while moving ahead is like applying FULL RIGHT
RUDDER (stern moves smartly to port). Thus if we back in an emergency
while going ahead, we must expect the ship to veer to starboard, and, as
heading is lost, even the use of FULL LEFT RUDDER will not prevent her
veering to starboard.

Though AMPSER maneuvers handily at sea, we must not overlook the heavy-
weather problems caused by her combat cargo and complex rigging. At the
first sign of heavy weather, all hands must be called to double-check the
stowage, lower and secure the cargo booms, and check the gripes on the boats.
There is so much topside gear that can break loose, and there are so many

things below decks that can be damaged by heavy rolling. It is significant to note that AMPSER's merchant sisters normally rig for heavy weather *prior to sailing* on any voyage.

Anchoring

Coming to anchor in a designated berth requires careful attention to piloting with any ship, but AMPSER requires extra care. She is sensitive to the wind and to the current, and she is restricted as to power and maneuverability at the low speeds required in the approach. If possible, the approach should be made from such a direction that the effect of the wind and the current is minimized, and this requires making the final approach directly into the wind. This is most desirable, but unfortunately the limitations of the harbor and the presence of other ships often make this impossible.

In the cases where it is not feasible to approach directly into the wind, the tendency to be set downwind should be countered by *large* course corrections *early* in the approach. It is much better to overcorrect than to undercorrect, because the drift effect increases as the ship slows. The penalty of "too little and too late" is to have the bow pass to leeward of the "Let go" point, and either have to anchor incorrectly and then correct later, or make another time-consuming pass at the anchorage. It is much more pleasant to arrive slightly to the windward of the center of the berth and make the necessary correction by simply waiting a few moments before letting go. (The wind will carry the ship down into the center of the berth after she has stopped.)

For making a normal straight approach to an anchorage, the following procedure has been found useful (but each ship should be calibrated individually at its normal loads):

Distance to Go	*Action*
1,000 yards	Be making 5 knots
750 yards	STOP
Zero yards	LET GO and BACK FULL

This will cause the anchor to be dropped while making slight headway, which is quite acceptable in this type, and the chain can be laid out and the anchor "dug in" as desired by continued backing.

Once riding to the anchor, we will find that AMPSER yaws considerably in the wind. It may be necessary to drop a second anchor underfoot to reduce the yaw; also, turning the screw over slowly ahead will ease the strain on the chain and moderate the yawing.

AMPSER's boats will also be found to affect her yawing. With several large landing craft riding to the booms, she will yaw more severely than with her sides clear. The boats do not ride well as she moves to a strong breeze, either. Though the landing craft are quite seaworthy by themselves, they ship water and veer into the side of the ship as the ship yaws. If the breeze is troublesome, it may be advisable to secure the boats to a long sea painter astern of the ship rather than to keep them at the booms; or, even better, to get them out of danger by hoisting them aboard or by sending them into a protected cove.

Going Alongside a Pier

Though it is usually prudent to have tug assistance when handling a large single-screw ship alongside a pier, we should be ready to take AMPSER alongside a pier without assistance. Before attempting such an evolution, however, we should review her handling characteristics at low speeds and as she is being brought to a stop. We must remember that although she handles reasonably well in either direction with the screw going ahead, she *always* backs to port. If we back the screw while going ahead, she will veer to the right, no matter what we do with her rudder. We must *allow* for at least a small turn to the right as she is brought to a halt, but it is nearly *impossible to produce* a turn to the left during the last moments before she stops.

If we remember that it is convenient to approach a pier at a small inclination (perhaps 10°) and then swing parallel to the face of the pier as we arrive at our berth, we will see that it is much easier to bring AMPSER alongside port-side-to than starboard-side-to the pier. Port-side-to, the stern will swing in alongside the pier nicely as the ship comes to rest; and if she is too far out, the stern can be worked in nicely with a couple of alternate kicks ahead and astern. Starboard-side-to, on the other hand, our inclination is *increased* as we back the engines to bring the ship to rest. Once stopped, if the stern is too far out, we can't work it in by alternate kicks as when port-side-to, because each time we back the engine, the stern moves to port. To work the stern in when alongside starboard-side-to, we usually have to run number two line to the pier and work against it with the engines ahead and with the rudder LEFT FULL. It takes us back to the days when we were handling motor launches and found it much easier to make the starboard accommodation ladders than the port ones.

The Poor Man's Tugboat

In handling our large low-powered, single-screw ship, we find her at her worst in the confines of the harbor where precise handling at minimum speed is required. In the well-developed ports of the world such a ship is met at the harbor entrance by a pilot and the necessary tugs to place her in her berth. The ship's engines, if used at all, are merely secondary in importance, and the big ship is babied into her berth as though she were completely helpless by herself.

Though tugs and pilots are comforting when available, there are many times, even in ports like Norfolk or San Diego, when neither is available, and the ship must either move unassisted or delay until such services become available. In the less-developed ports of the world, such niceties are just not available and the ship must move alone. What can we do to achieve this precise control that is just not provided in the design of our ship?

If we analyze our problem, we will discover a solution which has long been known to the Merchant Mariners. Our trouble lies in the susceptibility of our ship to the wind and current and in our inability to turn her without at the same time gaining speed ahead or astern. We cannot *twist* our ship in place. Our rudder is effective enough to give a large force at the stern if the engines are turning over rapidly enough, but this also produces headway. Going astern, we must be moving through the water with considerable speed before our rudder effectiveness is sufficient to control the direction of motion. How can we hold our ship against the wind or current? How can we eliminate the undesired headway coupled with turning?

The anchor, of course, is the solution. This "poor man's tugboat" gives us the means of restraining our ship while working the engines and rudder. This allows us to move with excellent control, even in very tight situations. It gives us a flexibility otherwise unavailable except through the use of tugs.

If we drop an anchor under our forefoot and work against it, it will restrain our forward motion but will have no effect on the sidewise swinging of the stern. We can therefore work our engines ahead at relatively high power and obtain good rudder forces from the resulting screw current without any forward movement. We can twist to the right or left and turn completely around the anchor if we desire. The anchor under our forefoot gives us the ability to twist in place without any forward motion.

When we have twisted to the desired heading and wish to move ahead, we can apply more power and drag the anchor. The anchor is normally held at a short scope of chain so that it will not dig in and will begin to drag when the screw is turning over for a moderate speed. The amount of fore-and-aft restraint provided will depend on the scope of chain in use and the character of the bottom, so we can adjust the scope of chain to provide the desired restraint. In a typical situation, in 7 fathoms of water, with a mud bottom, and with 20 fathoms of chain at the hawse, AMPSER would make about 2 knots over the ground when turning her screw for 8 knots ahead. Under these conditions she would be under excellent control—turning quickly to the desired heading in response to her rudder, and stopping nearly instantaneously when the power is reduced.

When working against the anchor, the ship will handle differently than when steaming unrestrained. The turning and fore-and-aft movements are made nearly independent, and, depending upon the scope of chain in use, the pivot point will shift. If the anchor is snubbed at short stay, the pivot point will move forward to the bow. If a long scope of chain is used, a strong side force will be produced by the chain (as indicated in Figure 100) when

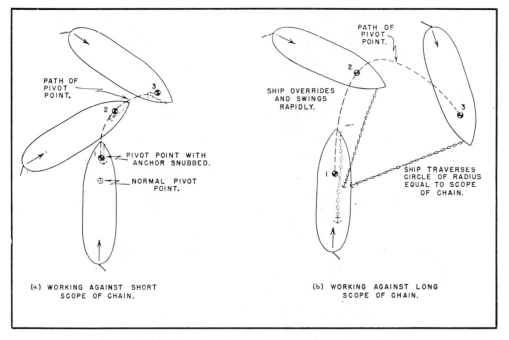

Figure 100. Turning by working against an anchor.

the ship "over-rides" the chain, and the ship will swing rapidly in an unaccustomed manner. It is worth while to experiment with a ship to determine the motion to be expected at different scopes of chain.

In addition to providing greater flexibility of control, the use of an anchor will hold the ship against a troublesome beam wind or current. When making a landing at a pier with the wind blowing onto the face of the pier, it is useful, even when being assisted by tugs, to drop an anchor to restrain the bow as it moves in against the pier. Though using the windward anchor is normal to insure a clear lead, when the situation is tight, it is often advisable to use the leeward or pier-side anchor and let the chain ride under the keel.

This will allow the bow to be snubbed up by the anchor in a much shorter distance than is required when using the windward anchor. When alongside, as mentioned previously, the chain can be slacked to the bottom, and it will prove useful later when clearing.

Another type of "poor man's tugboat" available to the conning officer of AMPSER is the landing craft (See Figure 101). Powered for storming through the surf with a heavy combat cargo, these boats are very effective aides in moving about the harbor. Several of these boats can handle AMPSER easily, and they can substitute for the harbor tug in the absence of the latter.

Because of their construction and bluff bows, these craft are well designed

Figure 101. Using ship's boats to "cast."

for pushing, and most ships equip one or two of their boats with large fenders on their bow ramps so they will not mar the side of the ship when so used. When used in conjunction with the ship's engines, the landing craft must be kept well clear of the propeller, but except for this, they can be placed anywhere along the side of the ship as desired. The boats, having no convenient tow point and handling poorly when towing to a cleat on the quarter, are not as well designed for pulling, therefore the conning officer should plan the employment of these boats so that they are pushing instead of pulling.

In order to employ the ship's landing craft effectively in moving the ship, it is mandatory that a reliable system of communications be set up between the conning officer and the coxswains of the boats. As will be outlined later in Chapter XVIII, it is usually best to rely on voice communications entirely and to make sure beforehand that the necessary telephone or loudspeaker system is set up and working. Though a system of hand and whistle signals can be set up, no code but the English language is needed if verbal commands are used exclusively.

Handling Boats Alongside

Though not exclusively a shiphandling problem, the conning officer of AMPSER must realize the part he can play in the employment of her "main battery"—that is, her boats. Hoisting and lowering these heavy landing craft is a herculean task which is made many times more difficult if the ship is rolling even slightly. Loading or unloading the boats alongside is greatly complicated by a running sea. The conning officer must be alert to improve the boathandling conditions by timely employment of the ship's engines and rudder.

If the ship is rolling at anchor to such an extent that it interferes with the boats, the roll can often be eliminated by twisting the ship (by working against the anchor) to another heading. If the boats alongside are having trouble with the waves, the situation can be eased by creating a lee by the same method. If the ship's roll is interfering with hooking on and hoisting, the situation can often be improved by weighing anchor and steaming slowly into the wind.

The conning officer should never sit idle while the boats are having a difficult time alongside. He should analyze his problem and take corrective action with the tools at his command. If his first attempt is not successful, he should try another solution; and he should keep working on the problem until he is sure that he has found the best solution possible under the circumstances.

Oilers

There are two terms in general use to designate ships built for the transportation of fuel cargoes; these terms are *tanker* and *oiler*. Tanker is the name for the general class of ships, and, specifically, for ships designed for transporting liquid fuels from port to port. Oiler is a naval term used to specify a ship designed and equipped to refuel naval ships at sea. Though tanker is widely used throughout the Fleet to indicate all ships of this type, oiler is more specific and will be used throughout this chapter. It is only the true oiler that is adequately equipped to meet the demands of fleet replenishment.

The older fleet oilers are basically a Navy conversion of a twin-screw merchant tanker of the Maritime Commission T-3 hull design with slight modifications.

Figure 102. Fleet Oiler, USS NEOSHO (AO-143).

The newer fleet replenishment oilers of the Neosho class (Figure 102) are very large ships with the following characteristics:

Length	655 feet
Beam	86 feet
Draft (Full Load)	35 feet (Same as FORRESTAL)
Displacement	
Full Load	38,750 tons
Light	13,521 tons
Shaft Horsepower	28,000
Maximum Speed (Full Load)	22 knots
Crew	13 Officers
	220 Enlished

The fleet oiler might be referred to a "seagoing service station" since its primary function is to provide fuel to the ships of the fleet while at sea. This fuel consists of "black oil," diesel oil, aviation gasoline, and jet fuels, and it is carried in the cargo tanks of the oiler and pumped to the receiving ship through the fuel transfer hoses. In addition to the bulk fuels, the oiler carries lubricating oils, bottled gasses, ammunition, stores, provisions, and other consumable supplies needed by the ships of the fleet; these latter are transferred to the receiving ship by "high line" while the ship is alongside fueling. As a matter of fact, it is because oilers have been modified to carry so many re-supply items that some have been redesignated as a special class known as "Replenishment Oilers."

In converting a ship designed as a commercial tanker for use as a Fleet Oiler, certain modifications must be made. Since she will be required to carry and handle several different kinds of fuels, the various fuel systems must be separated, and special pumping and protection equipment provided. In addition, guns, ammunition, radio, radar, and many other types of special Navy equipment must be installed. The weight added to the basic ship is appreciable, so the amount of cargo which can be carried must be reduced by an equal amount. This must be borne in mind when loading cargo, because, though there may be sufficient tank capacity available in the ship, her designed strength limit might be exceeded.

Effect of Load in an Oiler

The oiler, under any circumstances, is a heavy ship with limited power by Navy standards. With a full load she rides deep in the water and her inertia is tremendous. She is slow to accelerate, and once up to speed she wants to maintain her way. It takes a lot of backing to bring her to a halt. When empty, on the other hand, though she is more responsive to her engines, she is also very much more at the mercy of the winds.

The rudder of the oiler, though adequate for maintaining a steady course and for entering and leaving port, is relatively small and the ship has a large turning circle under all conditions. The effectiveness of the rudder, however, varies markedly with the degree of loading. Since the loading of the ship affects not only the total effective keel area but also the fore-and-aft distribution of the keel area, it produces both a change in rudder effectiveness and a shift of the pivot point. At full load the keel of the ship is nearly horizontal and the pivot point is in its normal location about 30 per cent of the ship's length abaft the stem. At light load, with the bow high, the center of the effective keel area moves aft, and the pivot point moves aft correspondingly. Generally speaking, at full load the ship is slow to respond to her rudder, while at light load she responds more quickly.

When her tanks are empty, the bow of an oiler may rise until the forefoot of the ship is actually at the surface of the water and the draft forward is *zero!* This means that the area of exposed hull and superstructure forward has been greatly increased while the counterbalancing keel area forward has been almost eliminated. To say that an oiler is sensitive to the wind when lightly loaded is a gross understatement; she is nearly at the mercy of the wind when empty.

Normally, when loaded and trimmed for an equal draft fore-and-aft, an oilers tend to head into the wind. As indicated in Figure 102 there is a pre-ponderance of superstructure aft, and the wind, acting on this, tends to carry the stern downwind more rapidly than the bow. At light loads, as indicated above, this situation might be completely reversed. There have been occa-sions where an oiler, forced to slow down when lightly loaded and with her bow high out of the water, has been swung completely around by the wind despite her engines and rudder.

Though greatly affected by the wind at light loads, we normally find the oiler at sea with a full cargo of oil, and in this condition she is one of the most stable of ships. The effect of the waves on a fully loaded oiler at sea is slight; in general she plows steadily through even heavy seas with little pitch and a slow, steady roll. Though her decks may be swept by combers in heavy weather, she can maintain her course very accurately, and she is ad-mirably suited for her role as reference ship in the evolution of refueling at sea.

Loading for Sea

Fleet oilers as a class are very seaworthy, provided they are properly loaded and ballasted. Since an oiler's hull is essentially a long series of tanks whose walls form the structure of the hull, the stresses on the hull will vary, de-pending upon which tanks are in use. A full tank adjacent to an empty tank will apply a shear stress to that section of the hull. Full tanks at the ends of the ship, with empty ones in the middle, will cause the ship to "hog"; full center tanks, with empty end tanks, will cause the ship to "sag."

To assist the shiphandler in insuring that no undue stresses are placed on his ship, a draft and stress computer, popularly called the "Ouija Board," has been provided for determining the load condition of the ship. Because of the tremendous cargo tonnages being handled, great care must be taken in the distribution of the cargo at all times. Essentially, the cargo should be distributed evenly throughout the length of the ship so that the ship rides with an even fore-and-aft trim. Should the cargo become depleted, sea water ballast should be taken on as necessary to insure the proper load distribution and stability. Under no circumstances should the ship be permitted to be-come so light forward that her bow comes clear of the water and can pound into the oncoming seas. The hull of a tanker is not as strong as the hull of a high-speed warship, and severe structural damage can result from pounding.

Problems of Deep Draft

When heavily loaded, the oiler draws more water than any other craft except the largest battleships and carriers. In the case of the oiler, with her limited horsepower and her great draft, the shallow water effect discussed in Chapter XII and the bank effect discussed in Chapter XI become major problems.

The keel of an oiler is often only a few feet from the bottom of the chan-nel as she moves about the harbor, and with her relatively small rudder, the shallow water effect makes her very sluggish. Large rudder angles must be used in shallow water, and the ship responds slowly. The conning officer must not expect to be able to turn in a short radius with the rudder alone when in a shallow harbor.

In a narrow channel with steep banks, the bank effect will be quite noticeable. The ship will tend to veer as she comes close to the edge of the channel or passes close to a shoal. The conning officer must anticipate this and must caution the helmsman to compensate promptly for the effect. A relatively large rudder angle may be required to overcome the tendency of the ship to veer when she is close to a bank.

Fueling Operations

It might be said with accuracy that the "main weapon" of the oiler is her fuel hose. It symbolizes her reason for being, and the operation of our modern fleet depends on the fuel that flows through the hoses of our fleet oilers. We then should examine carefully the handling of an oiler during the evolution of fueling at sea.

The task of the oiler's conning officer during fueling is to maintain a steady course and speed throughout the operation. This is not as simple as it sounds, because he must also keep station on the guide at the same time. He must adjust his position as necessary to maintain his station, but he must minimize all changes in course or speed. The conning officer of the oiler should maintain station with infrequent small alterations of course or speed rather than with the continual adjustment usual in normal station keeping. Each incremental change should be announced to the ships alongside so that they can compensate for the change as necessary.

The key to a safe and efficient fueling operation is excellent steering. The best helmsman in the ship should be used during fueling, and he should be backed up by a competent helmsman in the after steering station to take over in case of emergency. The stand-by helmsman in steering aft should keep abreast of all orders to the helm in order to be completely ready to take over in case of casualty.

If there is little wind or sea, replenishment may be accomplished on any course. However, if the wind and sea are appreciable, fueling is usually carried out on a course into the wind. Heading directly into the wind usually

allows the best course keeping, but, if the seas are rather large, severe pitch
ing may be experienced. A major disadvantage of heading into the wind
(the wind and waves are normally from the same direction at sea) is that the
decks of the fueling ships are frequently swept by seas endangering the line
handlers and the fueling rig. The wet decks and frequent interference by
the waves cause the operation to be slowed down seriously.

Downwind fueling is often preferable in rough weather because the ships
ride more easily and the decks are not swept by the onrushing seas. If a
course and speed can be selected which will minimize the yaw, downwind
fueling can be quite safe and comfortable. The fueling speed should be relatively high to insure good rudder control as the wave crests pass the stern.
The limiting factor in rough weather fueling of a task force is usually the
destroyer's ability to keep station close alongside the oiler. Though a destroyer may roll steadily on a downwind course, she can usually maintain
fueling station more easily than when beating into the seas. If there is any
doubt about the destroyer's ability to keep station alongside safely, a trial
run at double distance should be made to see how she rides. If all goes well
on the trial, she can move into normal distance and commence refueling.

Fueling operations should be conducted with the refueling ship between
80 and 180 feet from the oiler. Distances greater than 180 feet will part some
fuel rigs, and a ship riding closer than 80 feet will have an appreciable effect
on the steering of the oiler. The magnitude of the effect of a ship alongside
on the steering of the oiler will depend on the size of the other ship and its
distance from the oiler's side. Any ship in fueling station will affect the steering of the oiler, but with large ships the effect becomes severe. A large carrier
at normal fueling distance (120 feet) will require the oiler to use as much
as 15° rudder to compensate for her presence. As ships approach or leave
from alongside, the oiler's helmsman must alter his rudder angle accordingly,
and it is advisable to warn the helmsman when ships are approaching or de-
parting from alongside.

A large ship coming alongside will also affect the speed of the oiler; usually
the result is to decrease her speed, thus requiring her to increase her RPM
to keep on station. The reason for this effect on the oiler's speed is that the
wave systems created by the two ships interact. Depending on the relative
positions and sizes of the two ships, this interaction might tend to oppose
the motion of one ship while assisting the progress of the other. This will
result in real and apparent speed changes, and the conning officers of both
ships must be alert to correct for the effect. It is because of this interaction
that the conning officers of ships coming alongside seldom believe that the
oiler is actually making the speed that she should be making (they find they
must use a different shaft RPM than they expected to keep station alongside

for the formation fueling). It can be proved that the oiler is maintaining the proper speed because she is remaining on station with respect to the formation guide, so the difference must lie in the fact that the fueling ship requires a different RPM to maintain a given speed when steaming in the wave pattern of the oiler than she requires when steaming in open water well clear of other ships.*

An additional factor which may affect the speed of some oilers when operating at near maximum speed is the large amount of steam required to drive the cargo transfer pumps. This steam must be supplied from the main boilers and therefore during fueling operations is not available for driving the main engines. If we try to fuel at near the maximum speed of the oiler, we may experience fluctuations in her speed as the steam demand of the pumps and winches varies. For this reason it is best to fuel at a speed several knots slower than the maximum speed of the oiler.

Going Alongside Another Ship

Though the oiler is the reference ship during a normal fueling operation and though the other ship maintains station on her, an oiler is frequently required to go alongside another oiler at sea to transfer cargo ("consolidate cargoes"). The approach is similar to that described for other types, but the correct surge to use will vary with the loading of the oiler. A value of 70 yards per knot for surge has been found useful as an average value, but considerable variation will be found at different load conditions. When large quantities of fuel are being transferred, the change in draft and trim will affect the speed of the ship; but since these changes occur gradually, the conning officer can compensate for them by adjusting his RPM.

THE LANDING SHIP, DOCK

The Landing Ship, Dock (LSD) was developed during World War II to provide a ship suitable for launching heavily loaded landing craft in a seaway, and to provide a mobile landing craft repair base. Since that time this ship has proved to be such a useful addition to the fleet that a derivative version, the Landing Platform, Dock (LPD), has been developed with greater capacity, cargo flexibility, and helicopter facilities.

As indicated in Figure 103, the LSD is a unique type among the ships of the fleet. She is built around a dock or "well" in which she can carry her landing craft or amphibious tanks. Upon arrival at her destination, she can "ballast down" by flooding certain ballast tanks; then she can flood her well, open her tail gate, and let her cargo craft proceed out from the protection of

---

* For more information on the interaction of wave patterns, see Appendix II.

Figure 103. Landing Ship, Dock, USS SPIEGEL GROVE (LSD-32).

her hull under their own power. At anchor, with her well flooded, she is a floating small craft harbor. She can launch and retrieve large landing craft without the difficulties and hazards associated with the use of booms and davits.

The dimensions and characteristics of the LSD are as follows:

Length	510 feet
Beam	84 feet
Draft, normal full load	19 feet
Displacement	
Light	6,880 tons
Full load	12,150 tons
Total Shaft Horsepower	23,000
Maximum Speed (Full Load)	24 knots
Crew	16 Officers
	300 Enlisted
Dimensions of Well:	
Length	396 feet
Breadth	50 feet

Because of the presence of the large well in the center of the ship, her twin screws and rudders are mounted under the "wing walls" at the extreme edges of the ship. The rudders are relatively large and are mounted directly abaft the propellers. The combination of large twin rudders and the unusual distance between the screws gives this type exceptional turning characteristics.

The superstructure of the ship is concentrated forward, making the ship very sensitive to the wind. The wind will tend to blow the bow to leeward— so much so that she will often pivot rapidly when exposed to the wind with little way on. On the other hand, when steaming normally, the LSD tends to head up into the wind and turns downwind much less readily than upwind.

The concentrated superstructure forward also causes the ship to yaw badly at anchor. With high winds this becomes troublesome and may cause the anchor to drag. The use of an anchor underfoot is recommended under such conditions, and some shiphandlers have found it useful to turn the engines over slowly to ease the strain on the chain. The ship will ride much better at anchor if she is ballasted down, but the shiphandler must weigh this advantage against the possibility of having to get under way during a storm.

The hull shape of the LSD must be taken into account by the conning officer when handling his ship alongside a pier or another ship. The sides of the older LSDs are unusual in that they have an outward flare for the first few feet above the waterline, after which they rise vertically to the top of the wing walls. As the ship moves in against a pier, the structure of the pier will often bear against the flared portion, making it difficult to place fenders; so it is advisable to use camels or floats between the ship and a pier if they can be obtained. If there is any swell running, the height of the vertical sides of the ship will be of concern to the shiphandler. It takes a very small angle of heel to bring the deck edge of an LSD against the side of an adjacent ship even though their waterlines are separated by a sturdy fender.

Except for the characteristics mentioned above, the LSD handles similarly to other large twin-screw types of similar power and tonnage. Probably the only characteristic which is different is the vulnerability of her stern in a severe storm. Because of the stern gate and the danger of flooding the well during a storm, an LSD should head into the seas in heavy weather. If she were "pooped" by a large following wave, severe consequences might result. This is not a severe limitation, however, since she rides well head-on into the seas, but it is a characteristic which should be borne in mind when operating with this interesting type.

From Experience Comes Knowledge

This chapter was advisedly prefaced with the remark, "the ships . . . which we will be . . . mentally handling." While written rules may provide the mental preparation for handling these types, the real knowledge and full appreciation of their characteristics can only come through actual experience at sea. Since these ships are sisters to the vast majority of ships that ply the trade routes, we should study them closely to become more familiar with the ships we are most likely to encounter. Though less elaborately endowed than some other ships of the Navy, these ships are very capable at sea and in port, and they present the shiphandler with some of his most interesting problems.

CHAPTER XVI

LANDING SHIPS AND MINESWEEPERS

THE PROGRESS OF MODERN WARFARE has brought about a requirement that runs contrary to all that the mariner has learned and practiced. To gain flexibility in the movement of the masses of men and equipment it became necessary to develop the ability to land great quantities of cargo without the protection and facilities afforded by the normal port. Ships were to deliver their cargoes directly upon unprotected beaches. The mariner, who from the beginning of civilization has struggled to keep his craft clear of the treacherous shore, had to learn to run his ship aground deliberately. He had to learn the art of beaching his ship, of holding her firm while the cargo was handled, and of retracting her in the teeth of the pounding surf.

Boats have been landed through the surf since historic times, but such operations have always been accompanied by a distinct element of risk. Only the most skillful seamen were entrusted with the steering oar, and once the craft had touched the shore she was quickly withdrawn or dragged up on the beach beyond the reach of the surf. Double-ended boats were often provided for such operations to more easily cope with the waves from astern. The threat and danger of broaching (in a surface ship, falling off to a position broadside to the seas) was always present, and many a seaman was lost when boats capsized in the rolling surf.

If a conventional ship of any considerable size were to attempt to "beach" on an exposed shore, its first disadvantage would immediately become apparent: her forefoot would ground while the bow was still in water much too deep for cargo-handling. She would probably be hard aground while still beyond the breaker line, and she might as well still be at sea from the point of view of unloading her.

Next, even in cases where her bow was relatively close to the beach, unloading over the bow of a conventional ship would be about the most awkward way that could be devised. We *could* let her broach and try to unload while parallel to the beach, but we would find her sides no closer to the water's edge than was her bow, and after the waves had nudged her firmly aground, we would probably never be able to get her off. She would be hard aground from stem to stern, and any force we could exert with her own propellers would tend to move her along the beach, not away from the grip of the sand.

Even if we were satisfied with the position of the bow relative to the beach and had made suitable arrangements to discharge the cargo, it would still be difficult to hold the conventional ship perpendicular to the shoreline. She would tend to pivot on her pointed bow, since her propellers and rudder are not well suited for moving the stern in opposition to the waves. Furthermore, her screws are not protected from damage when she is aground. Lastly, we should have an anchor to seaward to keep from broaching—and few normal ships are equipped with stern anchors. Obviously, the conventional cargo ship is not suited to loading and discharging her cargo on an open, unprotected beach.

To meet the requirement of landing cargoes on unprotected beaches, a new type of ship had to be developed. World War II with its extensive amphibious campaigns saw the introduction of a new type of ship, the **Landing Ship.** These ships were developed to meet a number of different requirements, and several different sizes were built. All of them, however, had to meet the primary requirement of landing on an unprotected beach.

The LST

The largest and best known of the ships capable of direct discharge onto a beach is the Landing Ship, Tank, or LST. These ships are of about the same size and cargo capacity as an ocean going freighter; in fact two of the new LSTs can be considered equivalent to an APA and an AKA combined, from the point of view of troop and cargo capacity.

To allow the ship to ground securely on a sloping beach, the LST is designed with a flat bottom and a sloping keel. Fully loaded at sea she might draw 17 feet aft and 12 feet forward, but in "landing condition" (10% fuel and 500 tons of cargo) she draws only 4 feet forward and from 10 to 13 feet aft depending on the class. In all cases LSTs are designed to ground evenly on a beach with a slope of about 1 foot in every 50.

To facilitate unloading while lying bow to the beach, she is fitted with bow doors and a bow ramp. The bow doors swing open to the sides, allowing vehicles as wide as 15 feet to pass through. The bow ramp swings down from its protected position inside the doors and provides an inclined ramp over which vehicles can be driven from the ship to the beach. This ramp extends about twenty feet forward of the grounding point and thus allows discharge in even shallower water than indicated by the forward draft.

To hold her stern to seaward and keep her from broaching, the LST is equipped with a stern anchor and anchor winch. This winch is similar to the towing engine on a large tug, and allows a steady strain to be taken on the stern anchor wire.

Figure 104. USS GRAHAM COUNTY (LST-1176).

The propellers of the LST are well protected from damage while grounded by being set up clear of the base line and well inboard from the sides of the ship. Each propeller is protected by a skeg which extends forward from it and provides a sturdy "runner" beneath its blades. The twin rudders are mounted directly behind the screws, and thus achieve maximum effectiveness as a result of the propeller discharge.

A very interesting feature of the LST is the provision and use of her ballast tanks. She is equipped with an extensive ballast system which is very useful both during cruising and when beaching. The combined capacity of the "clean ballast" (water) tanks and the "dirty ballast" (fuel and/or water) tanks give the ship a ballasting capacity of nearly 4,000 tons.

In a normal beaching to discharge cargo, it is desirable to place the bow as close to the water's edge as possible. In preparation for beaching we discharge ballast forward and take on ballast aft to obtain the desired trim. Once the ship has grounded and has been driven as far up the beach slope as she will go by use of the ship's engines, it is desirable to take steps to insure that the ship will remain in place. Consequently, once the ship is aground, the ballast tanks are refilled to hold the ship on the beach more firmly. This also prevents the ship from working up the beach farther as the cargo is discharged and she becomes lighter. When ready to retract from the beach, the forward ballast is pumped out, lightening the bow and letting it come free from the sand more easily.

When beaching to load cargo, if we came in light, beached high up on the slope, and *then* loaded a heavy cargo, we would probably not be able to retract. For this reason, when beaching to load, we ballast the ship *down* for-ward before coming in. After the cargo has been loaded, we can pump out the ballast and thus compensate for any equal weight of new cargo taken on board.

At beaches where an extensive rise and fall of tide is experienced, our ship may be left high and dry at low tide. If it were not for fore-sighted designers, this could be uncomfortable, for one forgets how much a ship depends on the water in which she rides for various secondary services. Normally, for instance, a ship is continually taking in sea water for various purposes such as cooling machinery, supplying evaporators, supplying the fire main, provid-ing flushing water, etc. If special provisions were not made, the routine ship services such as electric power and fire protection would cease when the ship was left on the beach by a receding tide.

An LST solves this problem by utilizing the water in her "clean ballast" tanks to replace the water normally drawn from the sea. She can circulate her ballast water through her machinery as necessary, and can thus maintain her normal services regardless of the tide.

To summarize the dimensions and characteristics of the largest of the family of landing ships, the three classes of LSTs currently in service have the following characteristics:

	542 Class		*1156 Class*		*1171 Class*	
Length	328	feet	384	feet	442	feet
Beam	50	feet	55½	feet	62	feet
Full Load	4,080	tons	6,225	tons	8,650	tons
Draft forward	8	feet	10	feet	12	feet
Draft aft	14	feet	16	feet	17	feet
Landing Condition	2,400	tons	3,300	tons	4,600	tons
Draft forward	3.9	feet	3.8	feet	4	feet
Draft aft	9.8	feet	11.0	feet	13	feet
Total Shaft Horsepower	2,000		6,000		14,000	
Maximum Speed	11	knots	14	knots	18	knots
Crew: Officers	7		9		9	
Enlisted	110		150		160	
Troop Capacity	160		400		630	
Cargo (dry & liquid)	1,675	tons	2,300	tons	3,000	tons

Beaching

Beaching is an art which demands all the skill, judgment, and seamanship which the LST conning officer has to offer. Although his ship has been designed specifically for this job, the effects of the surf, wind, bottom character and "long-shore" current can be important in determining the success of the evolution. Poor judgment can turn a routine beaching operation into a salvage problem with disturbing rapidity.

The first requirement for successful beaching is that the ship be moving *directly perpendicular* to the waves as she grounds. This is normally perpendicular to the shoreline also, but, if there is a difference, make sure that the ship comes to rest with the breakers dead astern. The conning officer must weigh the direction of the prevailing wind, the character of the shoreline, and the direction and magnitude of the ground swell in estimating the final direction of motion of the breakers. If we end up with the surf on one quarter, we will have a continual fight to keep from broaching.

A next important step is to insure that the stern anchor is correctly placed and securely dug in. It takes careful calculation beforehand to estimate the point at which the ship will ground. If we place the stern anchor too far to seaward, we will lose the anchor and its wire. If we don't place the anchor far enough from the shore, and to windward of our beaching spot, it will be of little use in holding our stern into the oncoming surf.

If we know the gradient of the beach, we can quickly calculate the distance our forefoot will be from the beach when it first touches bottom. Assuming that our ship is trimmed in accordance with her design, if the beach gradient is steeper than 1 in 50, the first point which will ground will be the forefoot. We can measure the ship's draft forward just before making our approach, and by multiplying this draft by the beach gradient we can determine the distance from this point to the water's edge at the moment of grounding. For example, if the beach gradient is 1 in 40, and if we are drawing 6 feet forward, our *forefoot* will be 240 feet (6 × 40) from the water's edge at the moment of grounding. Should the beach gradient be less steep than 1 in 50, the *stern* will ground first, an undesirable condition resulting in our coming to a halt much farther from the water's edge than would have occurred had we trimmed down by the bow and thus raised the stern.

Having calculated the first point of grounding, we must now estimate how much farther up the beach we will move before the ship is brought to a stop. This will depend upon the speed of approach, the surf, the wind, and the manner in which the propellers and stern anchor are being used. For purposes of illustration, let's assume that the ship will slide forward until the point of grounding has been raised 1 foot. This means that we must allow for the ship sliding forward a number of feet equal to the numerical value of the denominator of the beach gradient. If the gradient is 1 in 50, we must allow for the ship to move forward 50 feet after touching bottom.

Our ship is equipped with 900 feet of wire on the stern anchor. If we come to rest on the beach riding to 600 feet of wire, we will have ample scope to the anchor and will have allowed ourselves a 300 foot margin for error. Consequently it is good practice to try to drop the stern anchor when the ship is 200 yards from her projected beached position. On a beach of 1 in 40 gradient, when we are drawing 6 feet forward we must drop the anchor when our forefoot is 800 feet (600 + 240 − 40) from the water's edge.

For a precise approach, "drop bearings" should be determined. These can be checked by seaman's eye if we know where the line of sight from the conning station to points on the surface of the water 600, 800, and 1,000 feet ahead of the bow intersect the ship's forward structure. As we approach our "drop bearing," the water's edge should come into line with these reference marks at the appropriate time.

When we beach, we wish to beach firmly in order to minimize the chance of broaching. We do not, however, wish to go aground so firmly that we cannot retract when we desire. Proper use of the stern anchor and ballast, however, will almost eliminate the likelihood of being unable to retract, so as we come in our thoughts should be concentrating on getting the ship firmly *on* the beach.

When an LST beaches on normal bottom, there is no sudden, jarring shock. It is more like a toboggan coming to the end of its run. The ship just stops. There is little chance of damage to the ship resulting from beaching at too high a speed if the beach is smooth and free from rocks, coral heads, and other obstacles.

To insure firm beaching and good control during the approach, it is advisable to approach at TWO THIRDS speed or even STANDARD speed. To reduce the stress at the bearing point, it is desirable to have at least 30 per cent of the area of the bottom aground, and this requires that the bow be forced well beyond its point of contact. (See Figure 105).

Even after the forward part of the ship is grounded, the ship can usually be kept at the desired inclination to the beach by use of the engines and rudders. With the screws driving ahead slowly, the rudders can be utilized to swing the stern from side to side as required. The conning officer can give the helmsman a course to steer, and the helmsman can steer in the normal manner. Should the helmsman be having trouble keeping the ship on the desired heading, more ahead power can be used and the effectiveness of the rudders will be increased.

If the ship has a tendency to broach, and, with a good strain on the properly placed stern anchor and liberal use of the engines and rudders, the stern still tends to move to one side, it is time to retract to avoid broaching.

The state of the tide and the range of succeeding tides should be carefully

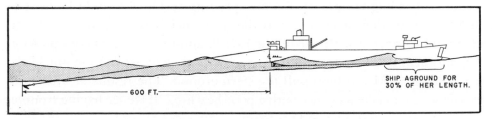

Figure 105. Sketch of LST correctly beached.

considered in beaching our LST. If we beach "light" at high tide and then load, we are inviting difficulty in retracting. To *beach* on an *ebb* tide and to *retract* on the next succeeding *flood* makes an ideal operation which insures the ship firmly holding her position during unloading and promises the best chance of a dry ramp during the intervening period. However, during an amphibious operation, the timing of scheduled events is such that we can seldom choose ideal situations. If we do beach on the ebb tide and remain beached for an appreciable period of time, we must be prepared to accept the fact that we may not be *able* to retract until the level of the water rises on the flood.

It should be apparent that the characteristics of the beach are of vital interest to the LST conning officer and also to the amphibious planner. All available information should be gathered during the planning period, for the remarkable flexibility of the LST can only be utilized if the beach characteristics are *known*. Once the operation has been started, the Underwater Demolition Teams (UDT) can provide a vital service to the LST. Their charts of the underwater obstacles, depth of water, surf and current conditions can make the difference between a successful beaching and utter chaos, for nothing is more useless than at LST solidly aground and unable to land her cargo. During assault landings, the information provided by the UDT may be all that is available at first, but as each LST makes her approach and beaches, the pool of information grows and should be passed on to ships that follow, for the LST officers themselves are the ones best qualified to advise their sister ships. For the normal non-combat beaching on an unfamiliar beach, reconnaissance by boat before beaching the ship should always be carried out.

The danger that the ship may broach is always at hand. Should she get out of control and be swept broadside to the surf, severe damage and even the loss of the ship could occur. The time to prevent broaching is just as the ship *begins* to move from her heading perpendicular to the waves, and not *after* she has already assumed a severe angle and is being swept nearer the beach by each succeeding wave. Vigorous action should be taken *as soon as* the change of heading is noticed. Engine speed up to FULL should be used to increase the rudder effectiveness. If the stern anchor is not properly placed, we should retrieve it with one of our LCVPs and place it in a better position to windward. If the surf conditions are not too severe, we can use our boats, or available LCMs, to help pull the stern around. The results of broaching are too severe to take a chance with a poor beaching. If we are having trouble, it is usually wise to retract and try again.

When beaching to land amphibian vehicles, the depth of water at the end of the ramp is not a problem, since the LVT and the DUKW type vehicles are quite at home in deep or shallow water, nor do we have any particular trouble with steep gradient beaches where the slope is about 1 foot in 40 or greater. When handling amphibians we normally do not use the stern anchor, since the evolution can be completed in a matter of a few minutes and there is little chance of broaching.

The Pontoon Causeway

Shallow gradient beaches with slopes of less than 1 in 50 present a difficult problem. On these beaches, we often find offshore sand bars and these may cause us to ground at the stern in 13 or 14 feet of water while still several hundred yards from the water's edge. On the other hand, if we ballast down forward to raise the stern to clear these obstacles, we may still come to a halt well short of fordable waters with 7 or 8 feet of water at the end of the bow ramp. Close-in sand bars often exist with deep water on the inshore side, and here again, we require some method of bridging the gap between our bow and dry land. The pontoon causeway has been developed to solve such problems.

A pontoon causeway is made up of specially designed sectional floats which are carried to the objective area on the sides of our LST. Floating piers extending several hundred feet from the beach can be constructed by assembling a number of causeway sections, and through the use of such a causeway an LST can be loaded with far more than the designer's 500-ton beaching load. Figure 106 shows an LST discharging the last of a *1,600-ton* vehicle load over such a causeway.

The problem of "marrying" the bow of the LST to the seaward end of the pontoon causeway is a delicate one requiring expert shiphandling and the very closest liaison between the bridge, where the conning officer is trying to make an eggshell landing on a mooring he can't see, and the bow where the First Lieutenant is coaching the ship in. An LCM to tend the causeway is most helpful in completing the marriage. The stern anchor is a *must* to assist the LST in maintaining her position married to the seaward end of such a semi-flexible floating pier, and the conning officer should insure that he has 600 feet of wire out and that the anchor is dropped up-wind or up-current from the causeway.

Retracting

When the time comes to retract from the beach, the normal procedure is to pump out the ballast forward, take a strain on the wire to the stern anchor, and back both engines. As the ship comes free, we must be careful not to overrun our stern wire or we may foul a screw. By keeping close contact with the crew handling the stern anchor, we can gauge our backward motion well enough to keep the wire out from under our stern. Constant information on the amount of wire still out and the direction toward which it tends must be sent to the conning officer as the ship moves away from the beach.

Though it is best to back directly out into deep water, as the ship comes free the wind and current may cause her bow to swing to one side. Normally we can let her swing and just use the engines to keep the stern wire taut and leading astern. If the beach is congested we may wish to drag a bow anchor underfoot to hold her more perpendicular to the beach until the stern anchor is aweigh.

The above procedure describes how the ship *should* come free, but unfortunately it is not always as easy as this. As the ship's weight is taken by the sand of the bottom, the thin film of water that separated the ship from the bottom is gradually squeezed out. The longer the ship stays in position, the more the water is squeezed and the more the ship's bottom comes into contact with the particles of sand. This increases the friction tremendously, and the force required to slide the ship toward deep water goes up with the friction.

To enable the ship to slide easily over the surface of the bottom, we must replace this lubricating film of water. This is not easily done, especially since the action of the waves may have built up shoulders along the edges of the bottom. The so-called "bottom suction" (the reaction to the ship rising and allowing the water to sweep in under her bottom) can be very great. To break this suction we must find some means of introducing water between the ship's bottom and the sand.

When the screws are backing, the discharge will tend to force water forward under the ship's bottom. See-sawing the stern with the engines and rudders will help break the suction. Further, the sidewise motion moves the stern out over areas from which the water film has not been squeezed. Also, as the stern moves to the side, any unevenness of the bottom will tend to open channels through which water can seep and restore the lubrication.

Turning the screws alternately ahead and astern at high power will at times help the situation. When turning ahead, they tend to draw out the sand from under the ship's stern; when going astern, they tend to move the ship astern and to force water under the ship. Using the ballast tanks in an effort to put a list on the ship may also help.

If continued work with the stern anchor, the engines, the rudders and the ballast system produces no result, patience, in the form of waiting for a higher tide, may be the best answer. If during the wait a low tide permits such action, fire hoses can be used to good effect to wash away the sand banked around the edges of the hull and to open channels under the bottom to break the bottom suction. Once the suction has been broken and the water film restored, the ship will come free with ease. One moment she seems cemented in place; the next, she is gliding effortlessly toward open water.

Handling Characteristics of the LST

The first characteristic that will strike an officer trained in other types is the location of the conning station on an LST. Her bridge is nearly at her stern. From his conning position, the conning officer can see four-fifths of his ship stretching out before him, instead of only the forecastle. He need not change his position to see all of his mooring lines. Far from being a disadvantage, this unusual conning location gives an excellent vantage point for observing the position of the ship relative to other objects. Conning "from the fantail" gives the LST skipper the same viewpoint for controlling his ship as that enjoyed by the coxswain of a motor launch; he can see the entire situation at a glance.

The bridge of the 1156 and 1171 classes of LST is similar to the bridge of a destroyer in both size and equipment; the older classes of LST are not nearly as well equipped. The 1156 class has, in addition, a main engine console on the bridge, from which the engines are controlled. This class, equipped with reversible pitch propellers, has most unusual shiphandling characteristics and the officer privileged to handle one has enjoyed a unique experience. The characteristics of ships with reversible pitch propellers will be discussed under Minesweepers.

The bridge is not the only thing that has moved aft: the pivot point has come after with it. Because of the very shallow draft forward, the deep draft aft, and the twin skegs, screws, and rudders at the extreme after end of the ship, the pivot point of an LST has moved aft almost as far as the bridge. An LST literally "spins on her heel."

Wind affects the LST to a marked degree. She has high freeboard fore and aft, and she draws relatively little water. With little power available to combat it, the ship is very susceptible to the wind. Because of her shallow draft forward, her bow is unusually prone to be carried downwind; so much so, that in all but the lightest airs an LST will invariably back into the wind regardless of her rudder.

Though not designed for high speeds, those equipped with diesel engines can almost instantly bring their full horsepower to bear either ahead or astern when maneuvering. The rudders, being directly in line with the propellers, are very effective when the engines are turning over Ahead, and though the propellers are tucked in under the sides, the lever arm between them is sufficient to insure some twisting moment when the screws are opposed.

Except when opposed by the wind, an LST turns in a remarkably small space. Because of her shallow draft forward and her flat bottom, she has much less effective keel area than other warships of comparable length. Once in her turn, however, she has a tendency to keep on swinging, especially when twisting in place. Once the angular momentum has been acquired, vigorous efforts must be employed to oppose it because keel area forward is not enough to quickly slow down the swing. When twisting to a heading, the engines must be placed in opposition to the swing well in advance of reaching the desired bearing, if the ship is to be stopped before swinging past the course.

The combination of relatively low power and excellent twisting characteristics is strikingly demonstrated when "backing and filling" to get out of a small turning basin. If, when the ship is moving slowly astern, both engines are ordered AHEAD at high power and the rudders put over FULL to one side, the LST, instead of gathering headway and commencing a normal turn, will seem to "squat" in place and spin rapidly in the direction dictated by the rudders. Though the side force produced by such a combination is ample to begin spinning the ship rapidly, the fore-and-aft component of propeller thrust is insufficient to kill the sternway and start the ship moving ahead within the same time interval.

We must remember that much of the side force available from the rudders is lost when the engines are backing. When the propellers are turning astern, the discharge current is not being directed on the rudders. They are subject only to the much less concentrated suction current. Consequently the ship, when backing, is much less sensitive to the rudders. To twist rapidly, the propellers must be turning ahead.

Handling Alongside

We should approach slowly when bringing our LST alongside. She is slow to respond to a backing bell, and if we are not careful we will overshoot. An

Figure 106. The Pontoon Causeway permits landing
heavier loads at shallower beaches.

easy approach, using the rudders and engines as necessary to maintain her
heading, is the best solution. Coming in wide and slow will avoid embarrassment.

The long, flat sides of the LST are an asset when handling alongside. Free
from projections, they provide an excellent bearing surface. The LST can
slide forward or aft alongside a pier, as necessary, with little chance of damage
to either the ship or the pier.

The wind is the greatest problem when handling the LST alongside. As
the ship slows, it becomes more and more difficult to hold her bow up into
the wind. The "poor man's tugboat," as described in Chapter XV, is most
helpful when we are faced with a cross wind in our approach to a pier. We
also have a stern anchor and powerful winches on the forecastle and the fantail, as well as our own LCVP "tugs." But perhaps our most unusual asset,
when required to back and fill awaiting a berth, is the beaching ability; we
need only to shove the bow gently onto a mud bank and stand-by until the
situation clears.

In going out, an LST can leave a berth alongside a pier even with a strong
wind setting her against the face of the pier if she is handled properly. By
opposing her engines and using FULL RUDDER, the stern of our ship can
be walked out from the pier even in the face of a 20-knot breeze. Her bluff

bow makes an excellent pivot, so her stern should be walked out from the pier until the ship is inclined as much as 45° to the pier face. Using FULL ASTERN, the ship should be backed smartly out of her berth and into the stream. If sea room permits, we should take advantage of her tendency to back into the wind instead of fighting it. These LSTs have a mind of their own when it comes to turning against the wind, particularly when they have little or no way on. It is often wiser to turn through the greater angle *with* the wind than to attempt a smaller turn *against* it! The angular momentum built up during the turn to leeward works to the advantage of the conning officer and helps achieve a heading into the wind that he might not have been able to make had he insisted on turning against the wind. This may not be a "pretty" maneuver, but when one sees an LST, in a heavy wind, squatting on her heel and turning through 270° or even 330°, one can be sure that there is an experienced LST shiphandler at the conn.

When anchoring, the LST enjoys a flexibility unknown to other more conventional types. She can use her bow anchor, her stern anchor, or both! It is often convenient to anchor with the stern anchor and ride with the bow to leeward; the bow doors can be opened, the ramp lowered, and the ship has a ready boat landing.

In addition to her duties as a primary carrier, an LST is frequently called upon to perform a task usually left to the smaller craft, that of unloading the transports. The transport usually rides at anchor and, if conditions dictate, drops a second anchor "under foot" to cut down the yaw. The LST approaches from astern, parallel and well out. She drops her off-side anchor about 125 yards off and slightly forward of the bow of the ship to be unloaded, then turns and maneuvers alongside the other ship, walking out her anchor chain as she approaches. Bow lines are passed and secured and the anchor is snubbed. The stern is twisted in until the two ships are parallel and about 10 feet apart; then the remaining mooring lines are passed and secured. While her bow is held firmly between her anchor chain and her forward mooring lines, her stern is held clear of the larger ship by opposed engines and *in* rudder. With this combination, the LST is moored securely alongside but held safely clear while the larger ship passes troops, vehicles and cargo. If we have calm waters, there is no need to use this "stand-off" mooring and the ship can be brought against the transport for a conventional alongside mooring. In rough weather, however, the use of an anchor by the LST is recommended to insure a safe separation between the rolling ships and it will be found the transfer can be made in weather too rough for smaller landing craft. In clearing after completion of the transfer, the anchor will be very useful in hauling the LST's bow clear of the transport.

At Sea

The LST has proved herself a seaworthy and sturdy ship. None were lost at sea as a result of weather during World War II, and they were at sea during the worst of it. Though seaworthy, the unusual hull structure gives the LST certain characteristics at sea not found in other types.

The sloping bottom and bluff bow of the LST cause her to slap and pound in a rough sea. The shallow draft at the bow allows the forefoot to come clear of the water even when pitching only moderately, and, once clear, the flat bottom produces a resounding slap as is comes down against the surface again.

When heading into the seas, a distinct pounding is felt when a wave crashes against the bluff bow. In a rough sea such a wave causes the ship to lose headway momentarily and to "shimmy" as though stunned. The hull structure of the LST, though strong enough to stand the stresses of beaching, is quite limber. One can actually observe the bending in the main deck as the force of the wave travels through the ship. If shimmying starts, we must do something to reduce it; continued flexure of the hull can cause failures.

To reduce the slapping and pounding, we can ballast down forward, change speed, or change course. Filling the forward ballast tanks will increase the draft forward and increase the moment-of-inertia opposing the tendency to pitch. Changing course or speed can change the frequency of the waves hitting the bow to one to which the ship responds less readily. Choosing a course upon which the ship rolls may ease the pounding because of the differing inclinations of the bow as the waves strike.

Except for her unusual motion in rough weather, the LST is quite conventional at sea. Her motion will change greatly as her displacement varies. She is a different ship at light displacement from what she is at full load. When "light," she bobs about like a cork. When heavily loaded, she is less responsive to the waves and tends to plow through them. To improve her sea-keeping qualities, it is usual to take on ballast when carrying no cargo.

Special Problems of the LST

The LST is often handled differently from other types because of her special features, and it is interesting to examine how she meets many of the ordinary problems which confront all ships. Her versatile bow access is a great asset in loading and unloading, but the shiphandler must be ready to depart from the conventional to position the ship so that this asset can be utilized.

Instead of the Mediterranean moor, the LST is frequently called upon to moor bow to the quay to allow loading through her bow doors. Since there is no necessity for the facilities of a pier for such an operation, LSTs are often handled at a sea wall or mole where they take up less berthing space and a larger number of them can be loading at the same time. When moored in this manner, the ship is secured so that the ramp can be lowered just to the edge of the mole. This allows vehicles to be driven in and out of the ship if desired in addition to the normal foot traffic.

When mooring bow to a sea wall, the ship makes her approach perpendicular to the sea wall and drops her stern anchor as far out from the face of the sea wall as practical. The bow doors may have to be opened before arriving at the mooring, because, if there is an obstruction at their height just in front of the bow, they cannot be swung open. This presents a problem, because, though the doors are quite sturdy in their closed position, should the ship ride against one of them in the open position, it might be sprung so that it could not be closed again. If available, a camel placed between the bow and the sea wall will usually provide enough clearance to allow opening the doors after mooring.

Doors open or closed, the approach should be made quite slowly, and it is advisable to use the ship's LCVPs as tugs to control the bow during the last stages of the approach. The wire to the stern anchor is eased gingerly as the bow nears the quay. Lines are sent over from each bow to the quay, and they are heaved in as the stern wire is eased out, until the ship is in position for using the bow ramp to the quay. In final position the ship is held in a taut moor between the bow lines and the stern anchor, with her bow just the right distance from the face of the quay so that the ramp will span the intervening space to the quay.

An LST is actually a large ship, but because she is designed for a specific task, she has many characteristics unusual in the normal ship. To handle her effectively, one must study her peculiarities and make use of her advantages while avoiding situations where her limitations will be restrictive. By employing her good characteristics and avoiding her bad ones, the shiphandler can meet almost any situation.

Smaller Landing Ships

In addition to the LST there is a complete family of smaller landing ships decreasing in size until we have the personnel landing boats that cannot be truly considered as ships. The general design and method of beaching are the same as detailed for the LST, but with each smaller class certain desirable equipment must be omitted. Each smaller type is simpler and carries less cargo, but can operate in shallower water than her larger sisters. Each one has an important role to play in an amphibious operation.

Of these smaller landing ships, the Landing Ship Medium (LSM) and the

Figure 107. Landing Craft, Utility (LCU) on the beach.

Landing Craft Infantry (LCI, LSIL, LSSL, and LSFF) are no longer in active service. The Landing Ship Medium Rocket (LSMR), built on the hull of an LSM, but designed for shore bombardment, is not a true landing ship in that she is not intended to beach, but since she operates with the other landing ships, she is usually classed with them. The LSMR is a small ship, being only 200 feet long with a beam of 30 feet and displacing 1,200 tons, but she packs a terrific wallop (equivalent in volume of fire to a division of destroyers) in her rocket batteries and 5-inch mount. However, she too is approaching obsolescence and will eventually be replaced by Inshore Fire Support Ships (IFS).

The Landing Craft Utility (LCU), formerly known as the LCT, is the smallest of the family of landing ships. Like the LST, she is very much a part of the modern Navy. These shallow-draft landing barges are slightly less than 120 feet long, have a beam of 30 feet, and a loaded maximum draft of less than 6 feet. They are normally carried in the well deck of the LSD, but, when empty, can be carried on the main deck of an LST. Loaded with three tanks and nested three to an LSD, these little ships carry an important load in an assault landing. After discharging her initial load, the LCU is used to shuttle the heavy equipment from the transports to the beach. Her large capacity compared to the smaller landing craft make her a most valuable ship in the ship-to-shore movement.

Because of her smaller size, the LCU has a problem when beaching usually not experienced with the larger landing ships. Frequently, her stern will be inside the breaker line and her tendency to broach will be increased. She is not equipped with a towing engine for her stern anchor, so the anchor winch will require careful attention and her conning officer will frequently have to use his engines to keep her perpendicular to the beach.

The landing boats such as the LCM (Landing Craft Medium) and the LCVP (Landing Craft, Vehicle and Personnel) are handled very much like the landing ships, but their high horsepower-per-ton ratio makes them much more nimble. As with all ships, once the basic principles are understood, these are found to apply to all situations, regardless of the size of the craft involved.

Minesweepers

As a result of the lessons learned during World War II and the Korean War, and to meet the threat of modern mines, new classes of Minesweepers have been developed and put into service. We have the Minesweeper, Ocean-going (MSO); the Minesweeper, Coastal (MSC); the Minesweeping Boat (MSB); and the Minesweeping Utility Boat (MSUB) in service today, with the MSO being the largest class of minesweeper in commission. To minimize their vulnerability to magnetic mines, all of these vessels have wooden hulls, special non-magnetic engines and auxiliaries, and non-ferrous hull fittings, and are built to additional rigid specifications which render them virtually non-magnetic. Since the MSO and MSC are fully commissioned vessels, and the MSB and MSUB are designed for operations within harbors, the following discussion will deal directly with only the first two classes, but the problems faced by all are similar. For comparison the general characteristics of the two largest classes of minesweepers are:

	MSO		*MSC*	
Length	173	feet	145	feet
Beam	35	feet	27	feet
Draft*	10¼	feet	8½	feet
Full Load Displacement	780	tons	384	tons
Total Shaft Horsepower	2,400		1,200	
Maximum Speed	15.5		14.7	
Crew: Officers	5		4	
Enlisted	67		35	

---

* Sonar extends below this draft.

The MSO

As shown in Figure 108, the MSO retains the high "Tuna Clipper" bow and low square counter of the old YMS, though she is considerably longer and broader than her predecessor. She is completely equipped to sweep all moored and influence mines except pressure mines, but she is fitted with a heavy duty towing winch aft for towing special equipment furnished from other sources when it is necessary to sweep pressure mines. Equipped with twin screws and twin rudders, the MSO handles beautifully. She is an ocean-going ship, and, were it not for a limitation in speed, she would be fully capable of operating with the fleet at sea.

Figure 108. USS ENHANCE (MSO-437), typical of the largest minesweepers in service today.

Variable Pitch Propellers

The MSO has four diesel engines which can be clutched singly or in pairs with suitable reduction gears to the corresponding propeller shafts. In principle, the engines turn at a pre-selected RPM and thus the propellers are turning at a constant speed. Ship speed (or power delivered by a propeller) is changed by changing the pitch of the propellers by means of a remote control hydraulic system. Propeller pitch can be varied from six feet (per revolution) ahead to five feet astern. The equivalent of STOP is achieved by setting the propellers at zero pitch. Pitch adjustments can be accomplished very quickly (12 seconds from six feet ahead to five feet astern), and thus changes in direction and level of power can be made much more quickly than with other propulsion systems.

Actually the situation is a bit more complicated than indicated in the preceding paragraph. Engine speed depends upon the manifold pressure and the output load, and the output load depends upon the propeller RPM and pitch. A change in pitch affects engine speed. As the output power varies, the manifold pressure must be adjusted to maintain the desired engine RPM. A rapid change in pitch can overload the engines, especially if only one engine per shaft is in use. Though there is a wide range of combinations of engine RPM and propeller pitch which will result in a desired ship speed, the propulsive efficiency is affected and, especially on long cruises, it is important to select the combination which results in the highest propulsive efficiency. As a general rule, *select the highest pitch setting and the lowest shaft RPM that will give the required speed but not exceed the recommended engine manifold pressure.*

Should the pitch control system become inoperative with a given pitch set on a propeller, the only way to stop the propulsion thrust of the propeller is to stop the engine. This can be done moderately quickly with the two inboard engines, but the two outboard engines, which are coupled to generators to provide power when making magnetic sweeps, are also fitted with very heavy flywheels to accommodate power surges and so take some time to stop. For this reason many skippers prefer to maneuver on only the two inboard engines when in a tight place. The available power is less, but they are better prepared to handle a pitch casualty.

Handling the MSO

The bridge of the MSO is located well forward and, because of its height and the shortness of the forecastle, the conning officer has the feeling of being immediately over the bow. From the bridge, the conning officer can easily observe the handling of the four mooring lines and the handling of the mine-sweeping gear on the fantail.

In addition to normal bridge equipment for a vessel of her size, we find controls and indicators for engine speed and propeller pitch. Normally throttle control is maintained in the engine room and propeller pitch is controlled from the bridge, but when sweeping mines, both throttle and pitch control are shifted to the bridge so all personnel below decks can be evacuated during a hazardous operation.

The variable pitch propellers call for a new propulsion control vocabulary. Instead of ordering, ALL ENGINES AHEAD ONE-THIRD, the MSO conning officer orders, ALL PITCH AHEAD ONE FOOT. Commands include the desired direction and the desired pitch in feet per revolution.

ZERO PITCH is ordered in the place of STOP, but this has effects different from that normally experienced with conventional drives. If the ship is moving through the water, even though pitch is set at zero, the propellers are turning and there will be an angle of attack between the propeller blades and the water as a result of rotation of the propeller and the ship's movement through the water. Consequently, zero pitch results in thrust to *oppose* the longitudinal movement through the water. Ordering ZERO PITCH therefore slows the ship much more rapidly than ordering STOP in a conventional ship, where the propellers would just "idle" with little resulting thrust.

Since the propellers rotate at a relatively high speed even when the ship is dead in the water, the adjustment for zero pitch (i.e. that pitch which will actually produce no thrust when the ship is dead in the water) is quite critical. Perfect adjustment is not normally achieved and MSOs have a tendency to "creep" with their propellers set at zero pitch. The conning officer should be familiar with the tendency of his particular ship.

The twin rudders are mounted directly astern of the propellers and normally afford excellent directional control, especially when ahead pitch is being used. When zero pitch (or a pitch appreciably lower than that for the speed being made through the water) is ordered, the effect of the rapidly rotating propellers is to blank off the normal flow past the rudders, so that rudder effectiveness is greatly reduced. When backing, speeds through the water greater than 8 knots must not be used because the rudders are not designed to stand the stress of backing at greater speeds.

With the variable pitch propeller system, full engine power can be employed ahead or astern, and the load on the engines can be changed rapidly. The conning officer must be aware of the pitch limitations for the engine combination and speed he is using and not overload the engines. For example, if we were proceeding through the water at 12 knots with pitch set at ahead five feet and using the corresponding engine speed, and we suddenly shifted the pitch to back five feet, we would increase the load on the engines several fold and would no doubt stall the engines. When operating near the allowable limits of a particular engine combination, the use of a large amount of rudder may add sufficient resistance to overload the engines. This does not imply that the propulsion system is unsatisfactory or difficult to use, it simply means that the conning officer must be familiar with the system and handle it within its limitations.

When going alongside to make a landing, it is better to approach slowly with a small amount of ahead pitch than to use the "stop-and-coast" method common in other types. The MSO has a moderately large sail area for her draft and is sensitive to the wind, and the improved rudder control gained by keeping ahead pitch on as long as practical is quite useful. During the last moments of the landing, an MSO can be stopped quite quickly using astern pitch.

When clearing a berth, opposed pitch will readily walk her stern away from the pier and, since her propellers do not project beyond her sides, clearing a berth by going out ahead is quite normal.

At sea, because of her size and lines, an MSO tends to ride up over the waves like a cork rather than to plow through them. She has no provision for ballasting and the lighter she gets, the more corky she becomes. The sea conditions have a great effect on her performance. When required to steam into the wind and seas, her fuel consumption per mile increases markedly. On long voyages, it is customary to carry a deck load of fuel in drums in addition to the load in her fuel tanks.

Minesweeping

A Minesweeper with her gear out is not the nimble craft we have been describing above. She cannot proceed at top speed because of the drag of her sweep, yet she cannot slow below a certain minimum speed because her sweep will sink to the bottom and be damaged or lost. Her small turning circle cannot be used with her sweep out, and with long multiple sweeps she must use tactical diameters as great as 2,000 yards.

Minesweeping is generally done at speeds of less than 10 knots and in waters of 30 fathoms or less. Frequently the sweeping area contains headlands, islands, reefs, navigation marks, etc., thus complicating the minesweeper's maneuvers and navigation, which must be precise with respect to the minefield. The conning officer must take these factors into consideration as well as watch his engine loading and keep his sweep properly streamed and off the bottom.

When making turns with gear streamed, it will be found that the tow will tend to oppose the effect of the rudder and that the amount of this opposition may vary during a turn because of the wind and sea conditions. Required to maneuver accurately, the conning officer must be alert to the effect of the sweep gear on the turning characteristics of his ship and compensate accordingly.

In addition to handling her sweep gear, a minesweeper is frequently called upon to lay and recover dan buoys or to act as a mine recovery ship. All of these operations require careful maneuvering and care in the use of propellers because all of the recovery equipment is located on the fantail.

The MSC

In operation the MSC (Figure 109) is very similar to the larger MSO with the exception that she has a normal diesel propulsion plant instead of variable pitch propellers. Through a remote control system her engines can also be controlled from the bridge and engine response is very rapid. She tends to maintain her way when her engines are stopped, and with conning offi-

Figure 109. USS WARBLER (MSC-206), coastal counterpart of the MSO.

cers accustomed to the braking effect of the MSO at Zero Pitch, there is a tendency to overshoot when making a landing.

An MSC is not designed for extensive open-ocean operation and severe weather should be avoided when possible. At sea in heavy weather, the MSC plunges and leaps in response to the waves. Proper securing for sea is *essential*. Because of her tendency to roll heavily in the trough, it is better to either steam slowly into the sea or to run with them. She will ride very comfortably in a following sea, but will yaw considerably and experience a certain loss of rudder control as the crests sweep past. She is short and light enough to ride up over the waves, so the danger of being pooped is not as great as with some other types.

If a really severe storm, such as a hurricane or typhoon, is approaching, an MSC should head for a protected anchorage. If available, a buoy is the safest mooring and she will ride well providing enough scope to the buoy is used to prevent the chain from being pulled taut with a jerk. Mooring to a pier in such a storm is not recommended unless it is certain that the wind will not be blowing the ship against the pier either before *or* after the passage of the "eye" of the storm. Should it be decided to remain alongside a pier during such a storm, the ship's anchor chain and heaviest cables should be used for mooring, but long leads should be used with these to insure that they are not brought up taut as the ship pitches and rolls, and also to provide for the rising storm tide. The MSC is equipped with two good anchors and it is much wiser to attempt to ride out the storm with a two-anchor Hammerlock moor (see Chapter VII) than to take a chance on being damaged against a pier.

CHAPTER XVII

ARCTIC SHIPHANDLING

BASICALLY, ARCTIC SHIPHANDLING (here meaning all shiphandling in the presence of ice, wherever it may be found) is no different from any other kind of shiphandling. Certain amplifications are necessary, however, to safeguard a ship from damage. Though maneuvers are performed at relatively slow speeds, situations change fast. Many things can and do happen during the course of a watch. All require an estimate of the situation and a course of action. But before we begin to deal with arctic shiphandling techniques, let us first take a look at the environment which makes all this necessary.

The two general kinds of ice which are of interest to the shiphandler are the iceberg and pack ice. One, because of its concentrated mass, should be avoided. The other usually can not be avoided by the ship because of its more common origin and far greater abundance. The ship must therefore negotiate it in order to reach her Arctic destination, selecting the weakest points and observing certain precautions to prevent damage to herself.

Practically everyone has read about icebergs, seen pictures of them, and knows that they are huge, fresh water ice masses which float in the ocean. But few people realize that to understand their origin completely they must go back to the Wisconsin Glacial Period—an epoch of low temperatures during which enormous ice sheets covered most of what are today the temperate zones. This so-called "ice age" had its apex about 100,000 years ago. So much water was scooped out of the sea and piled on shore in the form of ice that sea level the world over was lowered about 400 feet. Even today, if all the ice in the Arctic and Antarctic were suddenly to melt and run off, the water of the oceans would be raised about 130 feet.

Today most of the ice is heaped on the Antarctic continent and on Greenland. In those two regions ice still continues to perpetuate itself, though probably at a diminishing rate. Due to the plasticity of ice and the pull of gravity, the boundaries of the ice caps flow like great white rivers toward the sea. Sometimes, as in the Antarctic, the ice cap pushes itself for great distances out into the ocean. More frequently it sends tongues down valleys into the sea. Wave action and undercutting so weaken projecting sections that they break off from the parent and fall free. Currents then carry these broken-off ice masses, now known as icebergs, far out to sea until wave action and temperature changes eventually reduce them again to water.

Despite their dazzling beauty and excellent photographic possibilities, icebergs are not a mariner's delight. They are dangerous to an average ship and should be given a wide berth. As they are only slightly less dense than the surrounding water, the part that we see is only a fraction of the whole. Approximately nine-tenths of the berg lies under water. Dangerous underwater spurs or rams also frequently project from this mass. Bergs, too have been known to topple or to shift position as a result of change in their center of gravity.

Hence icebergs are best when viewed from a distance. Nevertheless their presence can on occasion be helpful. Because of the terrific amount of water they draw, for instance, they are apt to ground on any shoal spot. Therefore in an area where no hydrographic information is available, the bergs, if abundant, will mark the shoal spots, thus warning the navigator to steer well clear and avoid grounding himself. Another benefit hinges upon the destruction icebergs create. Because they travel at different rates than pack ice (due to being influenced more by sub-surface currents than by wind), and sometimes even in a different direction, they literally chew and tear sea ice to pieces, plowing through it as if it were mere cake frosting. The leads and polynas thus produced often come in handy for ships that must proceed through such areas.

To differentiate between the size of icebergs and their smaller derivatives, the following terms are customarily employed:

(a) *Berg*   (100 feet or more across)
(b) *Bergy Bit*   (20 feet to 100 feet across—cottage size)
(c) *Growler*   (6 feet to 20 feet across)
(d) *Brash*   (less than 6 feet across)

About 50,000 years ago sea ice covered the North Atlantic Ocean as far south as the latitude of Delaware. With the passing of the earth into an interglacial epoch, sea ice has retreated to the polar regions. There it circulates around the north and south geographic poles. In the Antarctic, the ice moves counterclockwise around the Antarctic continent, peeling off to the northward to join the circumpolar current. In the Arctic, on the other hand, the ice lies in the polar basin. There is but one principal avenue of escape—the East Greenland current. This is because Bering Straits are narrow and shallow; Robeson Channel, between Greenland and Ellesmere Island, is also very narrow. And the Gulf Stream holds the ice at bay between Spitzbergen and the coast of Norway.

In order that we may better understand the most important element that we will encounter with a ship in the Arctic (See Figure 110), let us review the

Figure 110. The channel left by an Icebreaker.

mechanics of sea ice formation and disintegration. Fresh water freezes at 32°F. This is not true of sea water because of its salt content. Thus sea water containing 35 parts salt to 1000 parts water does not begin to freeze until it has cooled to 28.6°F. Another deterrent to fast freezing is the effect of convection currents during the cooling process. These currents occur when the cold surface water sinks and is replaced by warmer sub-surface water, equilibrium being attained theoretically when all of the water has been cooled to the temperature at which it is densest. Actually, however, surface cooling usually progresses so fast as to mostly overbalance this exchange.

In the sea the first sign of freezing is marked by an oily appearance. The next step is the formation of slush having a thick, syrupy consistency. As freezing continues, the slush separates into pancake forms. Finally the pan-cakes adhere to each other and form a continuous sheet. (Surrounding brine is entrapped when the foregoing occurs, numerous salt crystals being inter-spersed in the resulting ice. As ice ages, it begins to lose this salt content, three- or four-year-old ice being quite potable when melted.)

Sea ice, after rapid initial growth (3 to 4 inches in the first 24 hours), con-tinues to develop until its insulating qualities offset the freezing of the water under it. Snow cover increases the insulating qualities. If unbroken through the second winter, then, sea ice may reach a thickness of 7 to 8 feet. In the Arctic Polar Basin three- or four-year-old ice may reach approximately 11 feet in thickness. However, most sea ice with which a ship will come into contact varies from 2 to 5 feet in thickness. "Rafting" (the piling up of blocks or floes forced over each other by pressure) accounts for the thickest concen-trations that will usually be encountered.

Essentially there are no physical differences between "fast" ice and "pack" ice, each being composed of sea water which has been frozen. Fast ice, as its name suggests, is attached to land. It forms in sheltered bays, gulfs, and fiords, and, except during the summer months, it remains stationary and does not break up. Pack ice, on the other hand, is sea ice frozen in the open sea. It is continually in motion as the result of wind, tide, and current. In its motion pack ice opens and closes. In winter, lanes of open water soon freeze over with young ice, but in summer, except in very high latitudes, they re-main open and allow opportunities for ship passage.

Disintegration occurs from melting and mechanical attrition—the sun, wave action, wind, and pressures all producing effects which cause the break-up and final disappearance of the ice. In the spring, as the sun appears above the horizon for increasing periods of time, the surface of the ice begins to thaw by direct solar radiation and by contact with warm air. In low humidity, most of the loss will pass into the atmosphere through evaporation, but if the relative humidity is higher, pools of water from the melted ice form on the surface. Such pools, being darker than ice, increase the heat absorbed. A further rise of temperature opens cracks which allow fresh water to run down to form a layer beneath the ice, an action that accelerates the rate of melting by reducing the heat normally lost to lower water layers. Warm currents may also contribute heat for melting. Wave action and wind help by providing a mechanical means of attrition which, once started, has progressively increasing effect. Thus, rubbing action between adjacent floes breaks off small blocks and brash, which enables the sea to come into contact with still greater areas of ice. Also internal pressures, such as those produced by entrapped air and salt deposits, may further speed the disintegration process. In the final stages, ice is reduced to small, water-carved remnants which tinkle like small bells when struck by the steel hull of a ship, and in the end only the appearance of a thin scum marks complete dissolution.

Terms which describe sea ice concentrations and size are as follows:

(a) Amount of Ice Covering Water
   Areas
   (1) *Open Water*   (less than 1/10 ice)
   (2) *Scattered Ice*   (1/10 to 5/10 ice)
   (3) *Broken Ice*   (5/10 to 8/10 ice)
   (4) *Close Ice*   (8/10 to 10/10 ice, with water)
   (5) *Consolidated Ice*   (10/10 ice, with no water)

(b) Size of Ice
   (1) *Brash*   (less than 6 feet across)
   (2) *Block*   (6 feet to 30 feet across)
   (3) *Small Floe*   (30 feet to 600 feet across)
   (4) *Medium Floe*   (600 feet to 3,000 feet across)
   (5) *Giant Floe*   (3,000 feet to 5 miles across)
   (6) *Field*   (5 miles and greater)

There are other important environmental elements which affect the ship in one way or other. A brief summary here may aid the shiphandler to know better some of his forthcoming duties while his ship is in the Arctic. Even though temperatures during some days of summer are mild so that personnel do not require additional clothing other than a standard foul weather jacket, more often greater warmth is needed. In the winter, when temperatures are considerably lower, the providing of sufficient protection from the weather for men stationed topside will ensure that they will perform at an accepted level of efficiency. The greatest factor in keeping warm is the wind. Actually a man can feel much colder at 20° *above* zero Fahrenheit with 25 knots wind, than at 20° *below* zero Fahrenheit with no wind—the reason being that wind removes body heat as soon as it is manufactured. This is called *wind chill* (See Figure 111). Low temperatures have their effect on materials, too, some of the resulting shipboard problems being: freezing of electrolyte in storage batteries; loss of lubricating qualities with normal oils and greases; freezing of water left in fire-main risers above main deck; coating of ship's rigging and decks with ice and snow. In each instance appropriate publications advise as to remedial or preventive action.

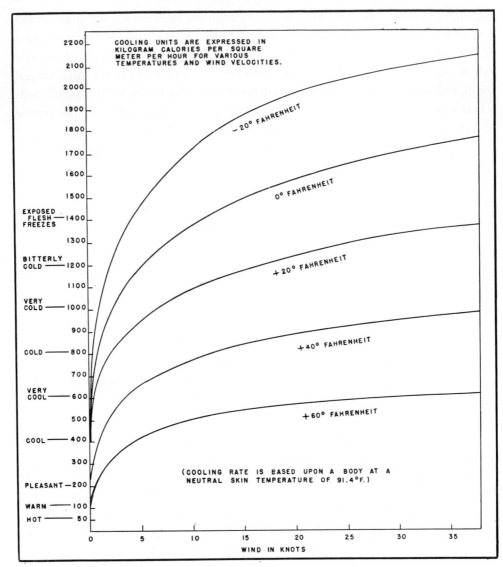

Figure 111. Wind chill on exposed personnel in a state of inactivity.

In the Arctic the ship's compasses will be affected by the weakening of directional and stabilizing forces. As a result, the magnetic compass (depending upon the proximity to the North Magnetic Pole, where the horizontal component of earth's lines of force is zero) becomes sluggish and unreliable. At the terrestrial poles, the conventional shipboard gyro-compass loses its effectiveness. Hence, beyond 70° North or South Latitude, a special correction table is necessary so that corrections can be applied to the latitude and speed adjustments on the gyro-compass.

Another disheartening feature of the Arctic, apart from ice and low temperatures, is its propensity for magnetic storms. The resulting conditions (radio blackouts) cause great difficulty in sending and receiving radio traffic, sometimes preventing it entirely. Radio Washington, however, broadcasts the schedule of such storms, so we will know when to expect them.

Ships in the Arctic

Let us take a look at the ships themselves (See Figure 112)—or, better yet, at the characteristics which have a direct bearing on operating capabilities in the Arctic. As a matter of fact, since almost all types of ships have at one time or another been in the Arctic, a list of the ships themselves would be very long indeed. What we are really interested in is what makes one ship a good operating ship in the Arctic and what makes another one a poor performer. We will therefore list those characteristics which affect Arctic operating ability, and will show in what way they affect it.

Length. In the ice fields, a long ship has difficulty in negotiating the sharp turns of the ice-free channels and in following the cleared channels made by

Figure 112. USS ARNEB (AKA-56) in ice off Cape Hallet.

an icebreaker. Since the hull of the normal long ship is thin and relatively unbraced amidships, it is not well designed to withstand the stresses of fending off the ice. When making a turn, a ship pivots about her Pivot Point, and her bow and stern are forced sideways into the ice alongside. A long ship swings her extremities farther to the side for a given turn, and can thus more readily be damaged from this cause.

Size. A large ship, with its greater mass, is usually more difficult to stop or to decelerate than a smaller ship. The sudden appearance of a floe ahead of such a ship may mean that damage would occur before she could slow down enough to take avoiding action.

Propellers. Protruding as they do outside the hull, propellers are very vulnerable to damage by the ice. Besides being poorly formed to resist damage from solid objects, the rotation of the propeller increases the force of any impact with the ice and insures the likelihood of damaging *all* of the blades when a piece of ice enters the propeller arc. The conventional propeller, constructed of bronze of relatively low tensile strength, can be deformed rather easily. Resulting dents and bends are quite troublesome because they cause an unbalance of the side forces (symptom—vibration) which can result in bearing failures and possible shaft misalignment. Cast steel propellers are much better for a ship operating in the Arctic because their stronger blades can better resist the effect of impact with the ice. Before installing them in a ship, however, it must be determined that a "safety link" still exists—that is, they should not be so strong that when a very heavy piece of ice strikes a blade, the propeller shaft itself will be twisted off or the reduction gears themselves damaged. A single-screw ship offers much more protection to her single propeller than a twin-screw ship does to hers, because of its centerline location behind and below the bulk of the ship.

Power. Generally, the greater the power, the more ability the ship possesses in maneuvering to avoid ice. Tug-type ships which develop maximum power at low speeds have the advantage, as speed in the ice must necessarily be low. The ability to effect quick power changes is also important. Bursts of power used in conjunction with the rudder greatly assisted in turning the ship.

Beam. A narrow ship offers less resistance to ice when moving directly Ahead or Astern than one of greater beam does, and such ships also are able to follow astern of wider ships with relative freedom from striking ice with the hull. A wide ship, on the other hand, gives more protection to her propellers by forcing the ice further to the side.

Hull Cross-section. The ideal Arctic ship has a hull of distinctive cross-section. The sides begin sloping inward immediately below the waterline and continue to the keel, giving the ship a nearly semi-circular underwater cross-section. This lends itself to great structural strength and prevents the ice from exerting its full pressure normal to the ship's side. If we remember that the greater bulk of the ice is below the surface of the water, we will see that under ice pack pressure such an underwater shape will cause the ship to be forced up and out of the ice like a pea being squeezed from its pod. When heavy ice bears against such a ship, the ship tends to ride up on the ice and its weight operates to break the ice and relieve the pressure. Nansen's FRAM, which successfully drifted across the Arctic Polar Basin, had the desired cross-sectional characteristic. Lieutenant DeLong's JEANNETTE, which was crushed in the ice off northern Siberia, did not.

Tumble-home. The form of the above-water hull structure and the rigging is important in a ship which is to operate in heavy ice. Projections from the ship's side could catch on the jutting pieces of the pack ice in a heavy ice field and either be damaged or retard the ship. For this reason, icebreakers and other Arctic ships are usually built with marked tumble-home to insure that all projections at the ship's rail and above are well within the extreme beam in the vicinity of the waterline.

Rudder. The more rugged and the more deeply mounted the rudder, the less chance it has of becoming damaged or deranged. Since it is mandatory that a ship in the ice be able to steer at very low speeds, the rudder(s) must be mounted directly behind the propeller(s) to insure that the full force of the screw current can be brought to bear for steering.

Draft. As stated before, the deeper the draft, the more protection afforded the propellers from floating ice. Shallow-draft ships, however, may at times have advantages over deep draft ships since they can cruise closer to the coastline, where the ice-free channels first appear.

Special Modifications. Ordinarily the first step in modifying a ship for ice operations in the Arctic is to strengthen that part of the ship which will bear the brunt of the ice. This is the bow. Strengthening can be accomplished by installing timbers or metal longitudinals to brace the stem; by adding additional stanchions; by adding extra frames; and by welding on additional side plating (this should extend at least four to five feet above and below the waterline and should extend aft to the turn of the bow). The second step is to provide stronger propellers, as mentioned above. They should be of cast steel, stainless steel, high tensile strength bronze, or of similar composition. The third step is to strengthen the entire length of the hull, mainly by adding frame members and welding steel plating externally along the waterline to augment that of the bow section. Further steps may consist of installing screens over sea chests, building shelters for lookouts and conning personnel, piping of steam topside to use when ridding the ship of ice accumulations, etc.

Icebreakers

At this point it is only natural to mention **Icebreakers,** for they embody all of the good characteristics previously mentioned. Let's take a look at the WIND-class icebreakers (Figure 113) which the Navy and the Coast Guard operate. They are 269 feet long, 63½ feet wide, and at full load they draw 29 feet. Propulsion is diesel-electric for economy and flexibility of operation. To withstand the tremendous stresses and impacts of breaking ice, these ice-breakers are equipped with 19-foot-diameter cast steel propellers, each weighing 22 tons. The propeller shafts themselves are 19 inches in diameter.

All icebreakers have a modified spoon bow with a sloping forefoot. When the ice is of sufficient strength and thickness to resist the forward horizontal crushing force of the ship, the inclined forefoot permits the ship to slide up on the edge of the ice a little way and thus exert a vertical force which tends to break off pieces from the edge of the ice. The stern is roughly similar to the bow to facilitate breaking ice astern.

A "quick roll" automatic feature is provided in these ships to heel the ship from side to side so as to free it from the grip of the ice. Using high speed pumps, sea water ballast is shifted from one set of heeling tanks to the other set on the opposite side of the ship to induce the necessary heel. The transfer of this water ballast can be made in about one minute. Occasionally the ice-breaker wedges into the ice and is unable to move ahead or astern. In this situation, heeling the ship breaks the hull loose from the grip of the snow and ice and permits the ship to back clear for another try. Admiral Peary, not provided with this luxury, had his crew rush from one side of ROOSEVELT to the other in order to break her out of the ice (a practice known as "sallying ship").

WIND-class icebreakers are equipped with a glass enclosed, electrically heated crow's-nest! It has a glare-proof glass roof and a comfortable chair for the single observer. In the ice, the conning officer often conns from this crow's-nest. Posted here, he can control the ship's course and speed by a rudder angle indicator to the bridge and an engine telegraph direct to the engines. He is also equipped with telephone communication with the bridge and the other control stations.

One feature which gives great speed and maneuvering flexibility to the icebreakers is the installation of engine *controllers* in three different locations on the bridge. These permit *direct* control of the propeller drive motors in

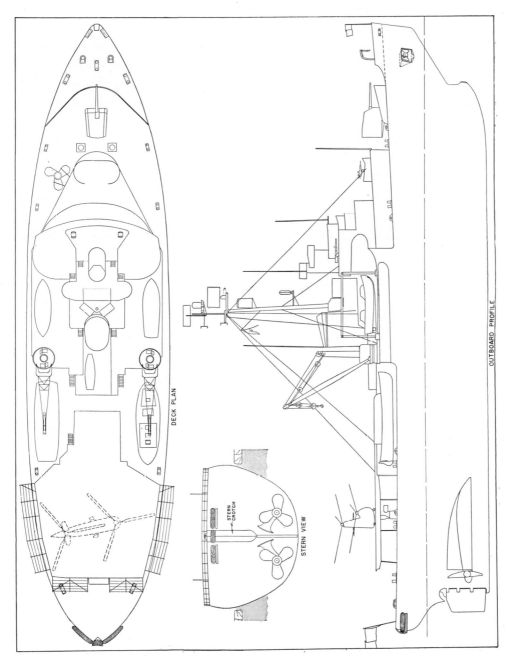

Figure 113. Plan, side, and end views of a WIND-class icebreaker. (Note: These ships were initially designed for a bow propeller which is not now installed.)

speed and direction. When not in the ice, the conning officer usually controls his engines with normal engine order telegraphs, but in the ice this direct control is very desirable.

Modern icebreakers are equipped with a small flight deck and two helicopters. For scouting ahead, finding open leads, and reporting on the conditions to be encountered, these aircraft are invaluable. They can see much farther ahead than is ever possible from the ship alone, and they can explore a full day's run in a fraction of the time it will take the ship to cover it. In heavy ice, the helicopter allows the icebreaker to find the best course and to take advantage of openings in the ice which would otherwise be undetected. With the help of the helicopter, the icebreaker need not dash blindly into promising leads, uncertain whether they will lead to open water or to a dead end.

How is icebreaking, or more properly "Ice Clearance," accomplished by the icebreaker?

It may be accomplished by one or all of the following:

(a) The weight of the ship, which exerts a downward bending moment on the edge of the ice, tending to break the ice off in chunks. This is made possible by the inclined forefoot of the bow below the waterline, and by the flare of the bow.

(b) The shock of ramming (See Figure 114), which tends to crack and split the ice.

(c) The shouldering or pushing action of the bow, which thrusts the small floes and debris to the side.

To break ice, the shiphandler applies the ship's power to the task through the medium of:

(a) Stern propellers.

(b) Bow propellers (if installed). Bow propellers set up a suction current forward of the ship, which suction draws the water out from under the ice ahead, causing it to sag and be more easily broken by the bow. The discharge current produced by such a propeller is also helpful in clearing the ice debris from the ship's sides as she makes her way through the ice. If desired, the bow propeller can be reversed while the ship is still being driven ahead. This throws water over the ice ahead, clearing it of snow and removing the cushioning effect from this source. A bow propeller is naturally very susceptible to damage because of being mounted at the end of the ship normally used for breaking the ice, and its use is usually restricted to fiords, inland waterways, and lakes, where the ice is level and homogeneous.

Figure 114. USS GLACIER (AGB-4) cutting through ice floe in Ross Sea.

(c) Rudder.

(d) Heeling system.

(e) Capstans.

If the ship's power is insufficient to clear the ice, resort to explosives may be called for. Often, however, the passive course of waiting for the forces of nature to do the job may be the best solution to the problem.

As the WIND-class icebreaker has three diesel generators supplying power to each of its two main drive motors, it is possible to have three different main propulsion combinations; namely, two-engine, four-engine, and six-engine combinations. The two-engine combination has the advantage of low fuel consumption, lessened possibility of damage when the propellers strike ice, and good opportunity for the ship's force to adjust and repair non-operating engines. The four- or six-engine combinations have the advantage of greater icebreaking ability, better maneuverability, and more rapid completion of the given mission. Usually the two-engine combination is employed in the open sea, and the four- and six-engine combinations when icebreaking or towing.

By shifting sea water ballast from the after to the forward trimming tanks, or vice versa, the icebreaker's trim can be changed. When the ship is down by the head, the added weight forward has the effect of increasing its ability to break hard ice. Such ice is broken by the ship's weight as the bow rides up on the ice, and the greater the weight, the greater the pressure on the ice. The disadvantages of being trimmed forward are that the ship does not answer her rudder as well, and the propellers and rudder are less well protected from the ice.

As mentioned before, pilot house engine control should always be employed when breaking ice. Being able to control the engines directly, the conning officer has the advantage of instant use of his engines. He can push the controllers ahead when he feels that the ship is slowing, or he can reverse engines for backing before the ship actually becomes deeply wedged into the ice. The engines can be quickly brought to bear when it is desirable to use them to assist the rudder in a turn.

How much ice can an icebreaker break? Icebreaker skippers are continually being asked this question. If they say three feet or twenty feet, either is correct, for icebreaking ability depends not so much on the thickness of the ice as upon other factors. A snow cover will cushion and dissipate the icebreaking effect. Solid or ten-tenths solid ice slows the icebreaker because it continually resists the ship's advance, besides allowing no opportunity for escape of ice displaced by the hull of the icebreaker herself. Ten-tenths slush can hold the ship back more than six-foot-thick ice of three-tenths concentration. If ice has water space into which it can be shoved, very thick ice can be broken. To elaborate further, young ice is more plastic than old ice. Antarctic ice is like a bed of feathers, compared to old Arctic ice. Even the temperature has its effect, the hardness of ice increasing with decreasing temperatures. At 32° F, ice has a hardness of 2 on Moh's scale; this increases to 4 at 50 degrees below zero, and 6 at about 80 below. The hardness of mild steel plate is about $5\frac{1}{2}$, and of glass about 6 on the same scale. To answer the question truthfully about how much ice an icebreaker can break, one should say, "It all depends." The answer must always be qualified.

The shortest distance between two points in the ice is seldom the most expedient for the icebreaker. The conning officer must often select leads and polynas which, although they do not lie along the desired base course, save time in the long run. If one has a choice between going through a gate or hopping a fence, he will naturally ascertain by which method he will conserve the most energy. The same is true when following leads. The choice between following a divergent lead or bulling through the ice by brute force often confronts the conning officer of an icebreaker (Figure 115).

Following leads at the expense of pushing through ice-bridges, however,

Figure 115. Where is the lead? (USS ARNEB moors to ice and waits.)

can be carried too far. Unless the conning officer watches his compass closely, he may find that his ship is describing a circle or working away from the intended destination. It is a good thumb rule not to follow leads which diverge more than forty-five degrees from the base course.

Air reconnaissance is our best means of determining which leads to follow. Long-range aircraft give the over-all ice picture as well as the conditions in certain selected areas. Helicopters give the close-up picture. We should not hesitate to use our helicopters. The pilots like to fly and to contribute to the success of the mission, and the aircraft serve no useful purpose sitting on deck.

When considerable brash is present, an icebreaker can clear her wake by "fishtailing." Slanting the screw currents at an angle to the channel tends to plaster the loose ice to the sides of the channel. Reversing the engines and "fishtailing" violently is also effective, but, when doing this, we must be careful that the ship never actually gains sternway. When the engines are backing, no screw currents are going astern to disturb the ice once it has been shoved aside. Fishtailing also widens the cleared path by levering the bow and stern against the ice. If a heavy concentration comes in astern between the icebreaker and a following ship when in soft ice, we can back down to disperse the concentration. Whenever paleocrystic (old) ice is present, how-ever, this is not a recommended practice as it may result in damaging the propellers.

When an icebreaker wedges herself in ice so securely that she cannot move by use of her engines alone, she must rely on heeling or automatic roll. As the ship begins to free herself as a result of the rolling motion, the engines should be backed FULL. As soon as momentum astern is gained, the engines are eased and the heeling discontinued. When about fifteen yards clear, the controllers are pushed ahead to Low Speed to clear out the ice debris in the ice "dock," or opening made by the icebreaker's battering. When the ice dock is once again clear, the breaker is in position and can make another ram.

Should the breaker become so fast in the ice that heeling and ice anchors cannot free her, explosives must be employed to relieve the pressure of the ice. This is usually accomplished by planting charges about thirty feet to leeward of the bow. The charges should parallel the keel from the bow back to about the bridge. Just before the blast is touched off, the engine controllers should be pushed FULL AHEAD. We must of course be sure that all per-sonnel are under cover and that the helicopters are away from the ship before touching off blasts.

Going North

To explore the shiphandling techniques of the Arctic in a manner easier to understand, suppose we steam a hypothetical ship northward from an eastern U.S. port and allow the problems to present themselves in logical order. As situations develop, we will pause to observe procedures which should be employed. We will assume that our ship has been adequately pre-pared for cold weather operations, and that all necessary planning has been accomplished. We are sailing in July.

During the first few days we set speed at fifteen knots and maintain a course that will provide a safe margin for clearance of land and shoal areas. As the sea remains calm, visibility good, and nothing out of the ordinary occurs, we decide to spend this period instructing officers and crew about what to expect on the coming cruise. Accordingly, we break out all manuals on cold weather operations, have top personnel with previous cold weather experi-ence conduct lectures, and show whatever appropriate Arctic films we have on board.

The *Ice Atlas,* a Hydrographic Office publication (H. O. 550), gives colored illustrations depicting general ice conditions over the entire Arctic for each month of the year. In it we will note that ice spreads over a considerable area, and that maximum coverage exists during February and March. Beginning in March this ice area commences shrinking, reaching a minimum during August and September. We observe that the maximum growth of sea ice lags in the coldest period of the Arctic year, and that the least ice occurs quite a bit after the sun has reached its zenith during the Arctic summer. This lag accounts for the fact that the most favorable period for ship operations in the North is between 1 August and 15 October.

Areas in which heavy glaciation occurs, and where strong currents are prevalent, have heavy concentrations of bergs, particularly in shoal areas. These berg concentrations may prevent certain operations in these regions from the middle of September through October. We should study the reports of previous expeditions and talk with experienced personnel who have operated ships in the areas into which we are going. There seems to be a general tendency to begin Arctic operations too early in the year, and to depart just when best operating conditions prevail. A shift to a later date, particularly during bad ice years, will pay off in reducing the possibility of ice damage to the ships.

No two years are ever exactly the same with regard to ice conditions in the Arctic. Seemingly, there exists no plausible explanation for an especially bad ice year. Sometimes the winter ice has been very light and a break-up has actually commenced ahead of schedule, so that everything points to a good ice year for the summer months. But something happens. Somewhere along the line, either lack of bad storms (which break up ice), undue amounts of cloud cover (which shields the warming effect of the sun), sudden and unexpected drops in temperature, small variations in current, or something else, apparently unrelated, causes the disintegration process to be slowed or even halted. Today, more and more is being learned about this. Arctic weather stations and special ice observers on long-range aircraft pool information so that forecasts can be made and transmitted to ships. In the past, ships took their chances in the Arctic; today they are much better prepared.

Meanwhile our ship is receiving daily ice broadcasts compiled by the Hydrographic Office. Ice charts are also being produced on our facsimile equipment. We should have one of the officers plot all this information on an acceptable overlay (with grease pencil) covering the applicable Arctic chart. We should instruct him to keep this presentation up to date, and to hold frequent conferences to point out ice trends to all conning personnel.

Ice Broadcasts usually include:

(a) The amount of sea ice, expressed in tenths, in relation to total sea area. Area limits are given by latitude and longitude coordinates.

(b) Size of sea ice.

(c) Presence of icebergs. The presence of bergs is usually reported by the words "many" or "few."

(d) Forecasts. These consist of statements concerning the trend of ice conditions in general and specific areas. (Whether leads will improve because of an impending period of clear weather or will close because of unfavorable winds is of definite value. Long-range forecasts assist ships in seizing favorable opportunities for Arctic operations when time is a factor to be considered.)

(e) Recommended routes for ship passage. Points along recommended routes are usually expressed by distances and bearings from navigational landmarks, distances and bearings from previously selected coordinates, or by latitude and longitude. Average direction and length also may be given. (Open water often exists adjacent to land because of early break-up of fast ice and the effect of off-shore winds. In other areas the direction and flow of comparatively warm water currents may cause early break-up.)

On the fourth day the ship enters into marginal or sub-arctic waters and the lookouts begin to report the presence of bergs. The outside air temperature falls to forty-two degrees Fahrenheit, and the water injection temperature goes down to thirty-five. Various articles of cold weather clothing make their appearance above decks. Appetites improve. Hot coffee and soup are most popular with all hands. Cameras are taken out of lockers. Everyone is anxiously looking ahead to what the Arctic has to offer. Then fog closes in so that we can barely make out the outlines of our jackstaff. We set special fog lookouts and reduce speed to five knots.

The stationing of lookouts during periods of low visibility is of the utmost importance when the ship is navigating in waters where icebergs are present. One lookout should be stationed in the bow, in a post sheltered from the wind. This lookout may provide us with our first warning of impending danger close ahead. Some ships make it a practice to station two bow lookouts, with instructions for one to watch ahead to starboard and the other ahead to port. Another lookout should be stationed in the crow's-nest in order to take advantage of layers in the fog or of a sudden clearing at mast height. Sometimes objects can be sighted from the crow's-nest when they are still obscured from sight at lower levels. Other lookouts, of course, are stationed on the wings of the bridge, as is normally done. All lookouts should be dressed warmly, should have ready communication with the bridge, should be instructed in detail about their duties and their importance, and should be relieved at intervals generally of no greater than thirty minutes duration

Icebergs produce "pips" on the radar scope the same as land masses do. We should make sure that the bridge scope is set on the proper scale and that the "gain" is properly adjusted. All bergs lying in the forward quadrant should continually be plotted both in CIC and on the bridge. A plot will prevent confusion when the ship is proceeding through an area of heavy berg concentration.

A watch should also be put on sonar, if a ship is so equipped. Have the operator search the sector from ahead to thirty degrees on either bow, reporting any contacts immediately. If an iceberg is within range, a good solid echo will result. Sometimes growlers which are too low in the water to show on the radar can only be detected by sonar.

The fog clears. We secure the special fog lookouts and change ship's speed back to fifteen knots. We make sure to give each iceberg a wide berth, approaching no closer than 500 yards. As we proceed north, we notice that the sun remains above the horizon more and more each day so that now there is only a short period of twilight at midnight! The Navigator relies more and more on crossing sun lines for his celestial fixes, and LORAN becomes more important. We see mirages frequently, and we begin to see the oddly distorted bergs that are common in the Arctic.

Finally our ship approaches the remnants of the pack ice. We see a seemingly impassable barrier of ice ahead. Speed is reduced and we proceed with caution. Closer, we begin to see the true picture. Instead of a solid mass of ice as first appeared, we now see that large areas of open water exist between the floes. This is the outer fringe of the pack—water-soaked floes in the last stage of disintegration. We estimate the ice concentration to be about two-tenths. Though a ship can operate unescorted in concentrations of three-tenths or less, we lie to in accordance with our previous instructions. This is where we rendezvous with the other ships and the icebreakers.

The Ice Convoy

On arrival of the other ships, we take our place in column in the "Ice Convoy" (See Figure 116) and begin Arctic shiphandling in earnest. Our job is to get our ship through to its destination in the far North without damage to the ship. The task, if correct shiphandling techniques are observed, will be interesting—and can be without mishap.

For the Ice Convoy, the column is the only practical formation. Icebreaker assistance is required to get a number of ships through an area containing three-tenths to nine-tenths coverage under summer conditions, and, naturally, the ships must follow in the path of the icebreaker if they are to benefit by the path she opens. Also, in a column each ship benefits by the action of the ships ahead in keeping the lead open.

When only one icebreaker is available, she should be placed ahead of the leading ship of the column (See Figure 117), but she should be free to range

Figure 116. USS EDISTO leads Coast Guard icebreaker NORTHWIND and British research ship RSS JOHN BISCOE through heavy Antarctic ice.

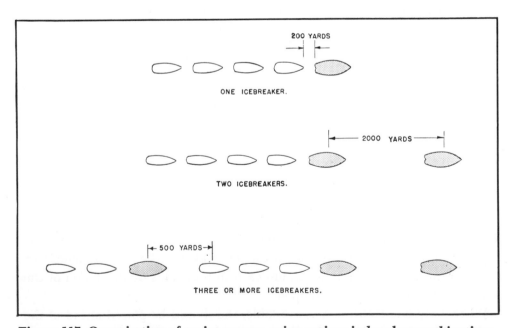

Figure 117. Organization of an ice convoy, using various icebreaker combinations.

ahead as necessary to break tough sections of ice. Frequently a particularly thick ice bridge will require extra work by the icebreaker in order to clear a channel through it. At times it will be necessary to stop the convoy and wait while the icebreaker makes repeated charges at any unusually tough section.

For these reasons, the first ship in the column astern of the icebreaker should be designated as formation guide. She should follow in the wake of the icebreaker, but should maintain as steady a speed as possible. The icebreaker will normally have little trouble staying ahead of the formation, but she should not range out too far ahead when in the ice. A station two to three hundred yards ahead of the leading ship is ideal when in heavy ice. This short distance is required, because the ice, once cleared by the icebreaker's hull, has a tendency to slide back into its original position because of the pressure being exerted upon it by other ice.

When two or more icebreakers are available for the convoy, one should be stationed two or three thousand yards ahead of the convoy to reconnoiter the pack. In this position she is free to search out promising leads and to make trial penetrations without retarding the main convoy. If other icebreakers are available, they should be interspersed at intervals in the convoy column to widen leads and keep them clear of ice. In such positions they will be readily available to help ships when they get stuck in the ice, thus avoiding the necessity of sending an icebreaker back from the head of the column.

The most powerful and rugged escorted ship should lead the column astern of the icebreaker. This is necessary because there are frequent bends in the channel left by the icebreaker as she seeks out the most favorable path. These changes in the ice channel must be widened and straightened after the passage of the icebreaker to allow the passage of longer and wider ships. The largest and most powerful ship is the one for this task, because if she can negotiate the channel, any of the other ships should be able to pass with no trouble. A weak ship in the lead position might hold up the entire convoy by getting stuck in a turn that a stronger ship could have passed through.

Because of her position in the column, the leading escorted ship is an excellent ship for the convoy commander. She is the convoy guide and the first escorted ship to encounter each new problem. With variable ice conditions, however, the convoy commander may find that a station aboard the leading icebreaker will give him better control of the situation.

The icebreaker naturally assumes course guide. Course signals are unnecessary and impractical because the course is the clearly marked channel left by the icebreaker. The leads between floes often vary from a few degrees to ninety degrees from the base course. Numerous changes of course, both voluntary and involuntary, will be made by the icebreaker in taking advantage of the weakest sections of the ice. The "shortest" distance between two points in the ice is seldom a straight line between them. Time can be gained by taking the *clearest* course, even though it does not lead directly toward our destination. The conning officer of the icebreaker should remember, however, that the other ships are "following the leader," and he should proceed as directly and with as few turns as the ice conditions allow.

After a day or two in the convoy, we begin to lose our initial fear of the ice. Although some of the other ships have lagged behind or strayed from the course, our ship has been on station all the time. We hear that one of the ships has suffered hull damage. Another has bent a screw. All of our old fears come rushing back.

We notice, however, that the ships that were damaged were the ones that have been the worst offenders in station keeping. They have often been out of column, and they have been slow in answering the signals. Maybe this damage can be avoided by alert smart shiphandling.

The damage reports emphasize that we have already begun to learn certain of the fundamentals in this ice business. Perhaps we can begin to enumerate the lessons we have learned.

We should never strike the ice *at high speed*. Hard shocks can rupture the hull plating and distort frames and strength members. We must never strike the ice with any part of the ship except the *stem;* it is the strongest part of the ship. Experience has shown that a speed of two or three knots in heavy ice and four or five knots in light ice are best. These speeds insure the maneuverability required for a safe passage, and spurts of higher engine speeds can be employed momentarily when greater rudder forces are required.

Our ability to push through a tough stretch of ice is dependent on our *momentum*. Our momentum is the product of our mass and our speed, so we must keep up our speed. When pushing through the ice debris left by the breaker, it may be necessary to use a good deal more power to maintain a given speed than is normal in open water. If we lose our headway in pushing through brash, we may soon find ourselves stuck and calling for an icebreaker.

All conning officers must be thoroughly instructed on *the danger of allowing chunks of ice to foul the propeller*. Special precautions should be taken to prevent the propellers and rudders from striking hard cakes of ice. It is useful to station men, equipped with police whistles, on the wings of the bridge to warn the conning officer when ice approaches the propellers. If the situation warrants, these men may be given permission to actually operate the engine telegraphs to stop the shafts. If, because of the construction of the ship, the water in the vicinity of the propellers is not visible from the bridge, men should be stationed aft to warn of this danger. This is a situation calling for STOP SHAFTS. Even with no power on the shaft, the rotational momentum of the propeller as she idles is enough to cause damage when a piece of ice enters the propeller arc. STOP SHAFT should be ordered promptly as soon as it is seen that ice is going towards the propeller.

Danger to the propellers and rudder also exists when the ice tends to squeeze under the ship due to the pressure of a dense pack. When the ice concentration is above nine-tenths, broken ice presses tightly against the sides of a ship. Often, as ice becomes pinched by the forward motion of the ship, chunks of ice upend and present their longest dimension downwards. Such chunks are very dangerous to the screws and rudders. The lateral motion of the stern as the ship pivots in a turn may also throw the ship hard against the ice.

Conning officers should make every effort to keep the ship *in the middle of the path* left by the ship ahead. Sometimes one may be forced to maneuver to avoid heavy ice which has come back into the channel, but the ship should be brought quickly back to the center as soon as the obstruction has been passed. Variations of course for any reason make it more difficult for the ship astern. It is the path traced by a ship's stern which determines the cleared channel, and course variations tend to increase in amplitude from the van to the rear of the column. Tail-end ships may find themselves unable to negotiate turns as a result of these increasing course deviations.

We should conn the ship from *the highest practical position*. The higher one gets, the better perspective one obtains of the ice ahead. From a high conning station one can estimate the action the ice will have on the ship, and can take preventive measures as necessary.

We must *keep closed up*. Ice has a tendency to close in astern of the ship ahead. The closer a ship follows, the better chance it has of finding a free channel. In close ice, a ship should never be more than 300 yards from the ship ahead.

Experienced shiphandlers only should conn. The ice is no place to learn the fundamentals of shiphandling. On most ships the Commanding Officer and the Executive Officer spell each other, so that either one or the other is on the bridge at all times.

Breaking Ships Out

On our imaginary trip all has gone well for perhaps two hours. The ship ahead finally is slow in making a turn to follow the channel cut by the icebreaker, and she "hangs up" on the ice. We see that she is in trouble, back our engines promptly, and notify the ships astern of our action. Fortunately we did not wait for the report from the ship in trouble, because her conning officer was so engrossed in trying to push through the ice that he forgot to notify the other ships that he was stuck. But we can't stop indefinitely in the ice without getting stuck ourselves, and soon the wind drifts us down against the ice to leeward and we too are caught in the grip of the ice. One by one the other ships report that they also are stuck and request icebreaker assistance.

Soon one of the icebreakers comes charging back, crashing through the pack as if it were nothing. We admire the purposeful way she goes about her job. One by one she breaks the ships out of the ice, and soon the whole convoy is moving once again.

To best perform the task of breaking out a convoy of ships, a brief estimate of the situation is necessary. As the object is to get all of the ships under way, in the shortest possible time—and to do so without damage—a review of the factors involved is in order.

A first consideration is the number of icebreakers we have at our disposal. If only one icebreaker is working the convoy, the job is more difficult because the breaker must end up in a position ahead of the lead ship in time to handle the next tough section of ice. In this case the icebreaker normally goes all the way to the stern of the column and then works forward, breaking out the ships in succession until finally the whole column is free and the icebreaker is again in her proper position ahead.

A ship can be freed from the ice by opening a channel close to her on her leeward side, and then providing means for her to get into this channel (See Figure 118). The wind will help carry the icebound ship into the cleared channel, since it is to leeward. A good system to use when breaking out a column of ships is as follows:

(a) Pass close to the lee side of the last ship in column on a converging course.

(b) Cut in as close as practical to her bow, and, when dead ahead, swing parallel.

(c) Have the stuck ship turn over her propeller for FULL SPEED AHEAD.

(d) There will be a last cake of ice between the icebreaker's stern and the stuck ship's bow. Back down and crack this piece.

(e) Kick ahead with plenty of power to get out of the way as the stuck ship begins to move.

(f) Proceed ahead to as near the stern of the next vessel ahead as practical, turn out to leeward, and repeat the process. Continue the process until all

**Figure 118. "Busting 'em loose" (NORTHWIND breaking
MT. OLYMPUS out of pack ice).**

ships are free and the icebreaker is once again in her place at the head of the
formation.

When more than one icebreaker is available, one can be left to her job of
breaking ice ahead of the column at reduced speed and the other can be
utilized for breaking out ships in succession from van to rear. As soon as ships
are broken out, they should quickly work up to speed to close up on the
icebreaker working ahead. This tends to keep the convoy moving and may
result in fewer ships becoming "restuck," especially if the convoy is a long
one. On completion of the breaking out operations, the icebreakers take their
former positions in the column. The series of maneuvers used when breaking
out a column from astern or from ahead is shown in the accompanying figure
(Figure 119).

Normally a ship can extricate herself if the ice accumulation ahead of her
bow is broken and cleared, but she may have difficulty returning to the convoy course if her stern is not free to move or if the wind is holding her hard
against the ice. In such circumstances it becomes necessary to clear the ice
away to leeward. This can be accomplished by the icebreaker coming up

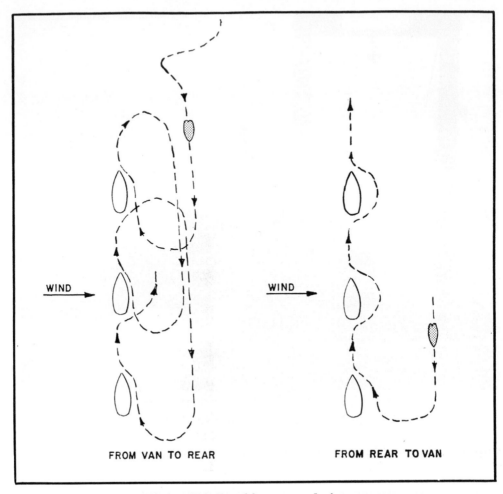

WIND

WIND

FROM VAN TO REAR

FROM REAR TO VAN

Figure 119. Breaking-out techniques.

astern and paralleling the ship on her leeward side. Enough clearance should be allowed to prevent the ship from drifting down on the icebreaker. If this fails because the wind is blowing too hard, the icebreaker can tow the ship to a more favorable location. Several tries may be necessary before the convoy is clear and moving again.

But to get back to our imaginary convoy, our ship is back in position and we begin to think about turning in for a well deserved nap, when suddenly the fog closes in and we can't even see the other ships. A signal is received to stop until the fog lifts. As no icebergs are closer than two miles, we take advantage of this lull, and turn in for the much needed nap. Once we vaguely hear the OOD report that two ships are readjusting positions, but nothing else disturbs us. This is a moment of rest, not the harrowing experience of fog in a busy seaway.

After several delightful hours the fog lifts, and the convoy gets underway once more. The sea ice conditions improve so that the convoy speed is boosted to five knots. We begin to notice the natural characteristics of the ice pack which can aid the ship. For instance, we realize that we can estimate the distance our ship has travelled through the ice by taking ranges and bearings on the icebergs in the pack. We learn to notice the distinct white and dark splotches in the overcast. These are made by ice reflection or "ice blink"; open water makes a dark or "water" sky. If we head toward the highest dark spot in the sky, we will end up in the closest area of open water. The radar also works well for detecting open leads; open water is indicated by the absence of pips on the scope.

About this time, perhaps, the leading icebreaker launches its two helicopters for ice reconnaissance. One aircraft proceeds out ahead about 30 miles to scout the general area to be encountered, while the other works at short range with the icebreaker to assist in locating favorable leads. By tuning in on the helicopter voice radio circuit, we can keep abreast of the information being passed to the mother breaker.

Now our ship is approaching the Arctic Circle and we prepare for the Crossing-the-Arctic-Circle ceremonies (similar to Crossing the Line except that Polaris Rex replaces Neptunus Rex, and the Court is composed of Arctic land and sea creatures). Bright sunlight around the clock which glints from the white ice and snow reminds us to have all personnel wear sunglasses topside. When one is "snowblind," his eyeballs feel on fire. All ships going to the Arctic should make sure that they have plenty of sunglasses for all hands.

Towing in the Ice

The ship with the damaged propeller finally reports that she has wiped a shaft bearing and must stop. The whole convoy is halted while one of our guardian icebreakers goes back to take her in tow.

Towing in the ice is a very important evolution. In addition to the necessity of towing when a convoy ship has sustained damage to her propulsion or steering equipment (a common enough occurrence), towing may be advantageous under other conditions. When transit through an ice area is urgent, or in an area where the ice is very thick or very dense, towing may be the best method of getting a single ship through. An icebreaker can break through a heavy pack with a relatively large ship in tow.

The towing problem with an icebreaker is complicated by the necessity of keeping the tow close to the breaker's stern. If this were not done, the ice passage might close before the tow got through. A WIND-class icebreaker is equipped with a towing engine and a strengthened "crotch" in her stern (against which the towed ship's bow can be placed). Towing can be accomplished by either of the two methods outlined below:

Crotch Method. By using the towing engine on the icebreaker, a ship with a relatively low bow can be brought up firmly against the icebreaker's stern so that her bow actually rests in the crotch. Puddings and other chafing gear should be used to reduce the effects of friction. In this method the towing wire is shackled to the towing bridle or to both anchor chains of the towed ship, and the towing engine is used to hold the towed ship firmly against the breaker's stern. Two large mooring lines can also be passed from the breaker's quarter-bitts to the towed ship's forecastle bitts to help keep the towed ship pointing fair. When using the crotch method, the towed ship's engines can be used if desired; but should the tow begin to "jackknife," the towed ship's engines should be immediately slowed until the situation is again under control. A fire hose must be kept handy at the crotch when the towed ship's engines are used, because the friction often causes fires in the chafing material.

Short Scope Method. A high-bowed ship does not lend itself to the crotch method, because the towing wire and other lines tend nearly vertically when her bow is in the breaker's crotch. In such a case the ship can be towed at short scope in the conventional method. It is best to use both anchor chains as a towing bridle in order to provide some weight to the short catenary. A scope of 50 to 100 yards can be maintained with use of the towing engine. With this method the towed ship's engines cannot be used steadily, because they would cause the towed ship to overrun the breaker. It is necessary to use the towed ship's rudder, however, to keep the towed ship in the icebreaker's path, and occasional kicks with the propeller may be necessary to obtain a sufficient twisting force. It may also occasionally be necessary to back the towed ship to keep from riding up on the icebreaker's stern, but usually the wash from the breaker's propeller is enough to hold the towed ship back.

In a convoy with only a single icebreaker, towing will have to be done by one of the convoy ships. While in the ice, all ships should be kept ready for towing and for being towed, for towing is frequently resorted to, and any time that can be saved means less chance of getting stuck.

With our broken-down companion safely in tow, the convoy once again proceeds. The leads are more open, no more ships get stuck, and our general progress is more rapid. At last we reach our destination. We enter the harbor, find our assigned berth, and commence off-loading our valuable cargo. In a few hours, however, we begin to become alarmed about the floes and growlers which are drifting down upon us.

Figure 120. Bergy Bits like this must be pushed or towed away from moored ships.

Currents in a harbor will often carry bergy bits and floebergs down upon an anchored ship, and there is real danger that they may foul the anchor chain or damage the ship. If we cannot move away from them, we must find a means to move them away from us. The ship's boats can be used for this task.

No matter how large a bergy bit may be, it can always be rotated by a good shove with a boat. If we keep such a body rotated so that it doesn't engage either our chain or our hull, the current will eventually carry it away. When using the ship's boats for this purpose, the boat coxswains should be instructed not to ram the ice at high speed. Contact should be made with bare headway and then the engine speed increased slowly. We must be very careful to keep the boat's propeller from being damaged by the ice.

Sometimes it is more convenient to move the ship than to move the berg. At times simple veering and heaving on the chain will avoid the ice, but at other times it will be necessary to employ the ship's engines and rudder to swing the ship clear. If persistently troubled with drifting ice, we should shift berth to a safer anchorage. A few hours' observation will disclose the flow patterns of the ice and indicate the spots that are untroubled by this menace.

In some regions of the Arctic in the winter—and in most locations in the

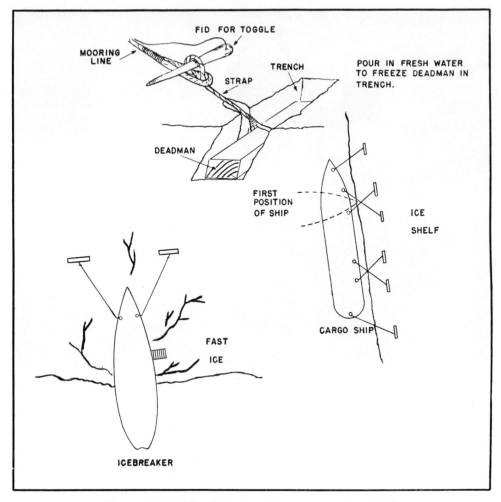

Figure 121. Using "deadmen" to moor to ice shelf.

Antarctic in the winter and summer—off-loading of ships must be accomplished over sea ice platforms. In the Bay of Whales in the Antarctic, ships moor directly against the edge of the bay ice just as they normally would along the side of a pier or sea wall. The mooring lines are secured to the ice with sea anchors or by using buried timber (deadmen) as indicated in the accompanying Figure 121. Deadmen are usually preferred, because the timbers can be left in the ice upon departure and need not be dug up again. A method occasionally employed by icebreakers when mooring to the edge of the ice shelf is to force the ship into the ice until she is jammed securely from the bow back to about amidships. Ice anchors can then be set to keep the ship from sliding back out of its dock. The figure indicates such a mooring.

In the Arctic patience many times pays off better than anything else. Generally it is one's nature to want to get things finished as soon as possible. Consequently we use power and strong arm methods, trying to force our way through ice when sometimes just the opposite is needed. The power of modern ships gives us the impression of great ability. Remember that the wind and current can move more ice in a few hours than the most powerful icebreaker can penetrate in several days. Ice leads tend to open during high tides and to close during low tides. Let nature work for us, not against us. We should study each situation thoroughly and then do it the easy way.

CHAPTER XVIII

PILOTS AND TUGS

HAVING MADE OUR LANDFALL and beaten our way to the harbor entrance, we pause momentarily just before we reach the dangers of the channel to pick up the pilot. The pilot boat swings smartly alongside in spite of the difficult chop. The very presence of this tiny vessel so far from the sheltered port bespeaks the competence of her masters. Catching the surge expertly, the pilot swings aboard by the jacob's ladder and soon is standing on the bridge. His hearty greeting to the Captain, his easy habit of command, and his weathered countenance mark him for what he is—a master mariner. "I'm ready to take her, Sir," he says, and we have the feeling that she should be in good hands.

Before we turn the ship over completely to this new master, however, we had better take a look at him and examine the extent of his competence. What is a pilot? Who qualified him? What can he do to assist us? These are good questions and require an answer.

Pilots

A **Pilot** is an expert on the waters for which he is qualified. He has made a study of the peculiarities of those waters and is required to have had extensive experience handling ships in them. He knows the vagaries of the currents, the latest shifting of the shoals, and the particular problems of each channel and each berth. His knowledge of local conditions extensively augments the information that is available from the charts and sailing instructions. He knows all of the harbor ranges, the landmarks, the habits of the local shipping. He can navigate in and out without a glance at the chart if need be, and he can steer a safe course through the harbor on the most meager visual information.

The licensing of pilots comes under the Coast Guard and is handled by the Marine Inspection Service. To obtain a pilot's license an applicant must give evidence of having served at sea for a minimum of three years in the deck department of a vessel and of having made a certain minimum number of round trips through the waters in question. In addition he must pass an examination on the following subjects, based on *Rules And Regulations For Licensing And Certificating Of Merchant Marine Personnel*, CG 191, June 15, 1953.

(a) *Pilot Rules* for the waters desired.

326

(b) Local knowledge of winds, weather, tides, currents, etc.

(c) Sketch a chart of the route and waters applied for showing courses, distances, shoals, aids to navigation, depths of water, and all other important features.

(d) Steering, handling, and maneuvering of steam and motor vessels.

(e) Such other written or oral examination as the Officer in Charge, Marine Inspection, may consider necessary to establish the applicant's proficiency.

As noted above, pilots are licensed for a specific locality and route. There is no universal license which is good for *all* waters. A new examination is required for a new route or an extension of an old one. Though a pilot may be licensed for several harbors, for instance, he must be examined for each of them.

In addition to the separate license as a pilot, a pilot's license may be granted as an endorsement to the license of a Master or Mate. This is a normal procedure, because to practice as a pilot it is usually necessary to have Master's papers. To obtain such an endorsement, however, an examination on the same subjects mentioned above must be passed.

Though the *legal* requirements for obtaining a pilot's license are quite rigid, in order to practice his profession (except in his own ship) a pilot must usually pass much more rigid requirements. In most U.S. ports the pilots used by naval vessels are either Civil Service Pilots or they belong to a Pilot's Association. In either case, a Master's license and extensive experience in handling large vessels under all conditions is required. For example, the following is an extract from the requirements for appointment as a Civil Service Pilot in the Twelfth Naval District for the waters of San Francisco Bay and tributaries:

Requirements

Note: It is useless to file application unless you meet the following requirements:

Experience. Applicants must have had at least three years of experience in piloting and moving vessels, in harbor and at berth or dock, which experience must have included handling of vessels of at least 10,000 gross tons and under each of the following conditions:

Entirely under their own power.

Partially under their own power, assisted by tugs.

Entirely with tugs.

Applicants must show in their applications the tonnage of vessels handled and the frequency with which vessels of 10,000 gross tons or more were maneuvered. They must have performed pilot duties at frequent intervals during the year prior to the announcement of this examination, which experience should preferably include acting as pilot for vessels entering or leaving dry docks.

License. Applicants must possess a current license as master of steam vessels of unlimited tonnage, and an unlimited license as first class pilot for vessels of unlimited tonnage, covering waters of navigation described above. These licenses must be submitted with application. . . .

Though the above discussion has been limited to U.S. ports coming under the control of the Coast Guard, similar regulations will be found in foreign ports. Handling ships in restricted waters and in the vicinity of wharves and moorings requires the nicest judgment, and the penalties for errors are costly. Throughout the world the title "Pilot" connotes the highest degree of skill, judgment, and knowledge.

Thus the pilot standing on our bridge is certainly an expert. He is an expert on the harbor in all of its details. He is an expert on handling ships in this harbor, and he has demonstrated his competence as a Master or he wouldn't have been standing there. Is he, however, an expert in handling *our* ship?

Though the pilot may have handled many ships of the same type as ours, he is not necessarily an expert in handling this particular ship. As described in the previous chapters, each ship must be studied and calibrated as an *individual* before she can be handled expertly. It takes time to learn her peculiarities and to become accustomed to her behavior. The best "expert" on a given ship should be her own Captain. He has lived with her and studied her habits, and he should know her as no one else could.

The question of responsibility arises as the pilot stands there. Though the harbor pilot is quite ready to "take full responsibility for the safety of the ship," this does not in any way decrease the responsibility of her Captain. Regardless of who has the conn or what assurances the pilot might have given, the basic responsibility for handling the ship never budges from the Captain's shoulders.

Thus the pilot should be looked upon as an exceptionally competent adviser and assistant especially hired for the occasion. He is very familiar with the harbor and the channel, and he can be depended upon as an experienced shiphandler of excellent judgment. He cannot, however, be depended upon to know *our* ship, and his presence on the bridge in no way alters the responsibility of the ship's Commanding Officer.

The Conn

Should we give the conn to the pilot? This must be weighed against the situation. Our decision should be that which will provide the greatest degree of safety and efficiency. When the pilot steps aboard our ship, he is being hired by the ship to assist in a given situation. Though he deserves and should be accorded the respect due a proven Captain, he should be used in the manner which can best benefit the ship.

If the situation is one where the intimate knowledge of the harbor is the key, then the *pilot* should be given the conn. If, on the other hand, the intimate knowledge of the ship and her handling characteristics is the key, the *Commanding Officer* should keep the conn. Unfortunately, this does not completely answer the question, because a full measure of familiarity with both the harbor and the ship is usually required.

A good system for handling the conn is to have the Commanding Officer give all orders to wheel and engines. In the case where he is maintaining the conn and using the pilot as an adviser, this would be the normal conning arrangement. In those cases where the pilot is given the conn, the pilot would give his commands through the Commanding Officer. In this system the Captain is always in direct control of the ship, and the pilot can be used as an adviser or as a director as the case may require. This arrangement blends the expert knowledge of the local conditions possessed by the pilot with the expert knowledge of the ship possessed by her skipper. The Captain automatically approves the recommendations of the pilot by the orders he issues. The question of responsibility is clearly solved, because in any case it is always the ship's Captain who issues the executive order.

Most Naval Shipyards and many canals have regulations which state that all ships must be moved "by a pilot" when within certain defined waters. This situation can be met by giving the pilot the conn in the manner described in the above paragraph. In such a situation, however, the Commanding Officer should follow the orders of the pilot unless he considers the safety of the ship to be in jeopardy. To take over from the pilot on a matter of taste would be a violation of the local regulation. However, no matter what the local regulations may be, the basic responsibility of the Commanding Officer is not altered.

Aside from the advantages mentioned above, having the Commanding Officer issue all executive orders is very useful for clarity and consistency of command. Engine orders used in the Merchant Marine such as AHEAD SLOW and HALF SPEED have either no naval counterpart or else carry a different meaning. AHEAD FULL means something different and produces drastically different results when ordered on the bridge of a destroyer than when ordered on the bridge of a Liberty ship. A pilot used to merchant ships is often caught unaware by the power and response of a warship. The ship's Captain can re-phrase and adjust the pilot's orders until the latter has gotten the feel of the ship.

Tugs

The companion of the pilot is the **Tug.** Without her we could not use the crowded wharves and intricate channels of our modern harbors. This workhorse of the harbor is short, squat, and of relatively deep draft (See Figure 122). She is powerful for her size, and she can deliver this power at low speeds through her large propeller. One of her most notable characteristics is her un-

Figure 122. Model of a large tug, showing typical structure.

usually large rudder. This enables her to deflect the discharge from her single screw to obtain adequate Side Forces even when dead in the water. She is built for the job of getting into and out of tight places and to apply her power to the task of moving ships in whatever locations they may be found.

The bow of a tug is covered by a large fender to allow her to work against the side of a ship without damage (See Figure 123). Her superstructure is set forward to allow her "towing point" to be well forward of her rudder and screw so that her stern can be swung easily even when towing astern. Her fantail is broad and long and her forecastle is short and stubby.

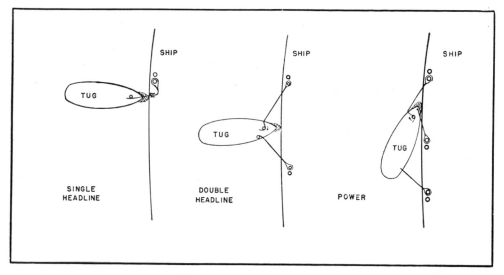

Figure 123. Tug tie-ups.

She usually has a powered capstan on her forecastle, and from stem to stern she is well equipped with bitts and chocks for handling lines.

A tug can either push or pull. In most harbors of the world, except those in the U. S., tugs habitually pull at the end of a hawser to assist a larger ship. Pulling avoids the ship-to-ship contact that requires large fenders and rubs off paint and fittings, and it insures that the full power of the tug is available in the direction of the hawser. Pulling has the disadvantage that it requires more space (because of the length of the hawser) and can't be used in closed berths where there is no open water from which to pull.

U. S. tugs are usually equipped with bow fenders which they place against the ship's side and secure themselves with one of the "tie-ups" described above. They are thus ready to push or pull (by backing down), and, by working engine and rudder in combination with their lines, can produce a force in almost any desired direction. They cannot, however, produce as strong and effective a pulling force as a tug pulling at the end of a hawser.

The simplest tug "tie-up" is the "single headline" or "backing line," shown in Figure 123. This is a single line led out through the tug's bullnose and secured to the ship. This tie-up is sufficient when the tug is going to push straight in or pull straight out; or when the tug is going to push steadily either forward or aft. If the tug must provide a force first toward the bow and then toward the stern of the ship, the "double headline" tie-up should be used. For general purpose use, especially when moving a dead ship, the "power" tie-up of Figure 123 should be used. This is the most versatile tie-up and can be readily adjusted to suit the situation. It holds the tug securely in position and allows free use of the tug's engine and rudder without moving the tug relative to the ship. With the power tie-up, the direction of the applied force can be altered over a wide range by simply shifting the tug's rudder.

Usually, the tug's skipper can be depended upon to select the best tie-up, but the situation should be studied and the tug instructed how to tie up, if necessary.

Handling Tugs

A case where it is nearly always advisable to turn the conn over to the pilot is when the ship is being handled by tugs. In this case the maneuverability is provided by the tugs, and the ship's engines and rudder are of secondary importance. The pilot is familiar with the tugs; in fact, he is often the skipper of one of them. He is accustomed to controlling tugs, and he knows intimately the capacity of each individual tug and her crew. In this case the pilot is certainly the unquestioned expert on both the motive power and the environment, so he is quite clearly the one best equipped to do the conning.

When handling a ship with tugs, a pilot prefers to station himself at the best vantage point on the ship for seeing both the ship and the tugs. This usually means that he is on the flying bridge, air defense station, or other location removed from the bridge. We must make certain that we have an effective means for putting his orders to the ship into action and of reporting back the action taken. The Captain will usually wish to be with the pilot and will be relaying the pilot's orders, so it is desirable to station an officer on the wing of the bridge with the specific duty of transmitting the orders from the Captain to the pilot house and reporting back to the Captain the action taken.

A pilot high in the superstructure of a large ship on a windy day cannot rely on his voice alone to transmit his orders to the tugs, so a system of hand and whistle signals has been devised to allow the pilot to control his tugs without the need for special communication equipment. Figure 124 shows the system of hand and whistle signals which has been approved for use in the United States Navy. Since the Captain of a ship often finds himself with tugs to help him but no pilot to control them, it is well worth his while to learn this system.

When we are called upon to handle our ship with non-Navy tugs in the absence of a pilot, we may prefer to rely on verbal orders. The general announcing system, the electric megaphone, or sound-powered telephones can

TUG BOAT SIGNALS

HAND WHISTLE (Police Type)

FROM STOP TO HALF SPEED AHEAD	1 BLAST
FROM HALF SPEED AHEAD TO STOP	1 BLAST
FROM HALF SPEED AHEAD TO FULL SPEED AHEAD	4 SHORT BLASTS
FROM FULL SPEED AHEAD TO HALF SPEED AHEAD	1 BLAST
FROM STOP TO HALF SPEED ASTERN	2 BLASTS
FROM HALF SPEED ASTERN TO FULL SPEED ASTERN	4 SHORT BLASTS
FROM HALF OR FULL SPEED ASTERN TO STOP	1 BLAST
CAST OFF, STAND CLEAR	1 PROLONGED 2 SHORT

NOTES:

1. A blast is 2 to 3 seconds duration.
   A prolonged blast is 4 to 5 seconds duration.
   A short blast is about one second duration.
2. In using whistle signals to direct more than one tug, care must be exercised to ensure that the signal is directed to and received by the desired tug. Whistles of a different distinct tone have been used successfully to handle more than one tug.
3. These signals may be transmitted to the tug by flashing light. However, flashing light signals should be restricted to use only when hand whistle or hand signals cannot be used.
4. Normally these whistle signals will be augmented by the hand signals given below.

HAND SIGNALS

HALF SPEED AHEAD OR ASTERN— Arm pointed in direction desired

FULL SPEED (Either)— Fist describing arc (as in "bouncing" an engine telegraph)

DEAD SLOW (Either)— Undulating movement of open hand (palm down)

STOP (Either)— Open palm held aloft facing tug

TUG TO USE RIGHT RUDDER— Hand describing circle as if turning wheel to right (clockwise) facing in the same direction as tug

TUG TO USE LEFT RUDDER— Hand describing circle as. if turning wheel to left (counterclockwise) facing in same direction as tug

TUG TO RUDDER AMIDSHIP— Arm at side of body with hand extended, swung back and forth

CAST OFF, STAND CLEAR— Closed fist with thumb extended, swung up and down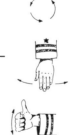

NOTE: Tug shall acknowledge all of the above signals with one short toot (one second or less) from its whistle, with the exception of the backing signal which shall be acknowledged with two short toots and the cast-off signal which shall be acknowledged by one prolonged and two short toots.

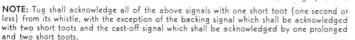

Figure 124. Tug Boat Signals.

be used effectively in this case. We should select the system best suited to our ship and make sure that it is rigged and working. When giving orders to tugs by this system, we should preface each order by the tug's name or number. The tug can acknowledge the order with her whistle using the following system, which is nearly universal among tugs:

Tug's Signal	*Meaning*
One Toot	Acknowledge all orders and instructions except backing orders.
Two Toots	Acknowledge an order to BACK.

Handling a Destroyer with Tugs

Let's begin our exploration of the use of tugs by considering handling a destroyer with her own engines and a single tug. As we diminish speed in the harbor we commence to lose control of our bow. Even when dead in the water, we can exert whatever side force we may need at the stern by proper use of our engines and rudders, but we have no means of controlling the bow. Obviously, we should place our tug forward to control the bow as we slow down.

Normally we take the tug alongside the forecastle in the location shown in Figure 125. She should use the double headline tie-up to allow her to help slow the ship down if necessary, yet be ready to swing her stern out to the side and provide an athwartships push. As we come abreast the berth, we have the tug swing perpendicular to us as indicated in the figure, and she controls the bow as we move the ship broadside into her berth. The fore-and-aft posi-

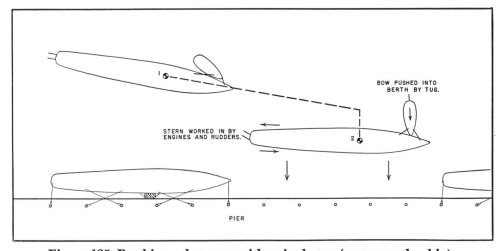

Figure 125. Berthing a destroyer with a single tug (power on the ship).

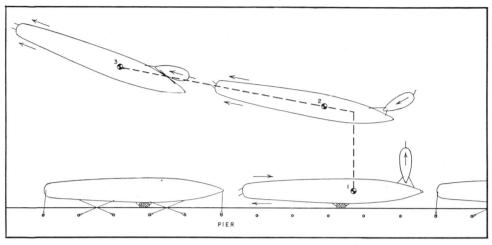

Figure 126. Unberthing a destroyer with a single tug (power on the ship).

tion of the ship and the athwartship position of the stern is controlled by the ship's engines and rudders. The tug should be used to maintain the ship parallel to the pier as she is "walked" in with her engines and lines.

When clearing a berth, we take the tug alongside the forecastle and with her stern out in the stream. As we twist our stern out from the dock with our engines, the tug pulls our bow out and keeps it away from the pier. When clear of the berth, we usually back out into the more open harbor, and the tug swings in alongside as shown in Figure 126. As she trails us out into safer water, she can be used as a "rudder" operating on the bow. As soon as the ship is clear of the congestion and heading for the channel, the tug can be cast off. Though she helps us for only a brief period, she permits us to utilize berths that would be beyond our reach without her.

With the ship's engines and rudders available for handling the stern and with a tug for handling the bow, a destroyer can be handled nicely at close quarters in all but the most extreme wind or current conditions. However, if the ship's power is not available for handling the stern, it is usually desirable to have a second tug. A destroyer can be handled without power by a single tug, but since the tug can work on only one end of the ship at a time, this is not very satisfactory if the wind is troublesome. A single tug can be considered to afford slightly more versatility than the ship's own engines, but not nearly so much power.

Two tugs afford complete flexibility of control. By placing one at each end of the ship, we can use them in combination to produce any translation or rotation desired. It is normally desirable to have them use the double head-line tie-up in order to be ready for any maneuver. Figure 127 illustrates a number of the combinations which will be found useful. The top right-hand example of the figure shows a special use of the power tie-up for moving a ship broadside when there is not sufficient room to place a tug perpendicular to the ship's side. In this combination, the two tugs are both turning their engines AHEAD with FULL outboard rudder. The fore-and-aft components cancel, but the athwartship components operate to move the ship broadsides. By various combinations of engine and rudder order on the tugs, the ship can be rotated and translated as desired without shifting the tug's position with respect to the ship

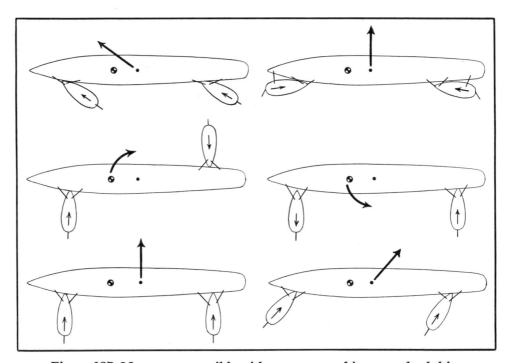

Figure 127. Movements possible with two tugs working on a dead ship.

Handling Large Ships with Tugs

Two tugs, if properly placed and handled, can be used to maneuver a ship in any manner desired, but with large ships the power available from two tugs is often not enough to overcome the inertia and the forces of the wind and current. With such ships it is customary to use more tugs in order to insure sufficient power.

The principles of handling a large ship with tugs are, of course, the same as for handling a small one. Speeds are so low when tugs are being used that the ship must usually be considered dead in the water. Her bow is at the

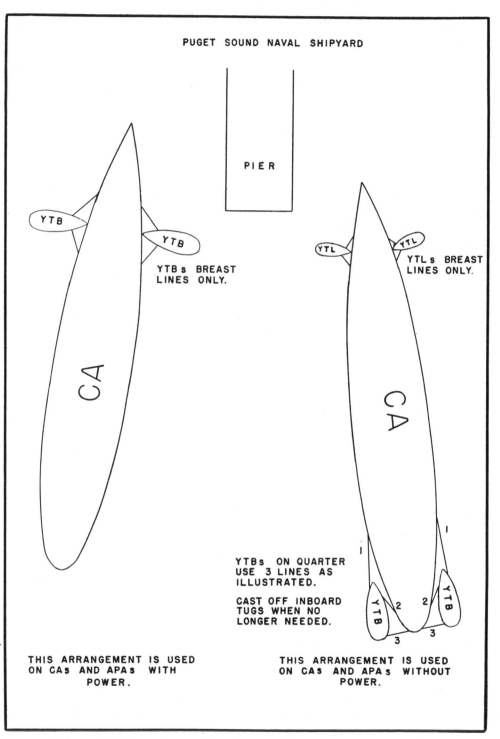

Figure 128. Tug arrangements for handling a cruiser or an APA.

mercy of the wind, so our first precaution is to provide tug assistance forward. With large ships, tugs are usually placed in pairs, so our first two tugs should be spotted one on each bow.

If the ship is being handled dead (no engines or rudder), we must have tugs aft as well as forward. It is common practice to place one on each quarter (using the power tie-up) to replace the engines. By using the engines and rudders of these two tugs just as we would the engines and rudders of the ship, we overcome the lack of the ship's power.

During a move, the tugs are placed and shifted as the requirements of the moment demand. If a ship is being placed alongside a pier starboard-side-to, obviously the tugs on the starboard side must be cleared before the ship is alongside. This might call for quick action on the part of the tugs. If a ship must be taken from her berth, turned around in the channel, and snaked into another berth, any single tug might have to shift her position several times. With each new position and task, a new tie-up might be called for. The tug masters must be on their toes and alert for each new role.

When planning a complex move with a large ship, the pilot usually has a conference with his tug masters before the move is started. Each phase of the move is examined and the part that each tug must play is explained. If each tug master understands his job, an intricate move can be executed with very few commands.

Though the tugs are frequently required to shift position during the moving of a large ship, it is worthwhile to have a standard arrangement for handling each type of ship. By studying a particular type ship and considering the tugs that might be made available for moving such a ship, a general purpose arrangement can be worked out which will meet most situations, and all other situations can be accommodated by modifying the standard arrangement.

Figure 128 shows the standard arrangement currently in use at Puget Sound Naval Shipyard for moving heavy cruisers and transports. The reader will note the tugs on the bow for all cases, and the use of the power tie-up for the tugs on the stern. A YTB is a large yard tug, and a YTL is a small yard tug.

Figure 129 is the standard arrangement at the same yard for a battleship. Essentially it is the same except for the addition of another pair of YTBs to help handle the bow of this heavier type.

Figure 130 is the arrangement for a large carrier. It is the same as for a battleship except for the special arrangement aft. Because of the overhang characteristic of the stern of a carrier, it is difficult to place tugs alongside the quarters. The illustrated arrangement overcomes this difficulty by placing

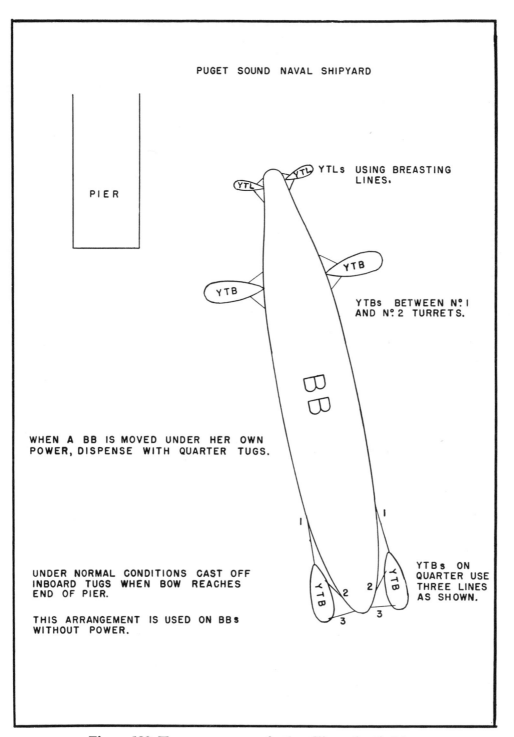

PUGET SOUND NAVAL SHIPYARD

PIER

YTLs USING BREASTING LINES.

YTBs BETWEEN N⁰ 1 AND N⁰ 2 TURRETS.

WHEN A BB IS MOVED UNDER HER OWN POWER, DISPENSE WITH QUARTER TUGS.

YTBs ON QUARTER USE THREE LINES AS SHOWN.

UNDER NORMAL CONDITIONS CAST OFF INBOARD TUGS WHEN BOW REACHES END OF PIER.

THIS ARRANGEMENT IS USED ON BBs WITHOUT POWER.

Figure 129. Tug arrangement for handling a battleship.

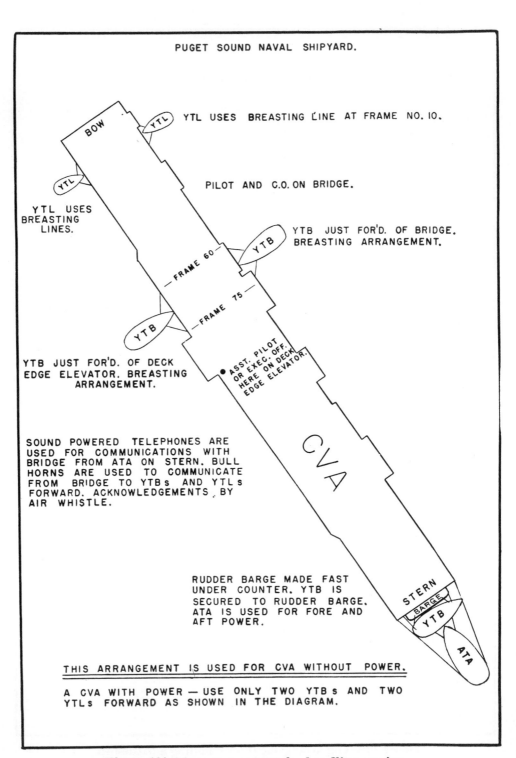

PUGET SOUND NAVAL SHIPYARD.

YTL USES BREASTING LINE AT FRAME NO. 10.

PILOT AND C.O. ON BRIDGE.

YTL USES BREASTING LINES.

YTB JUST FOR'D. OF BRIDGE. BREASTING ARRANGEMENT.

YTB JUST FOR'D. OF DECK EDGE ELEVATOR. BREASTING ARRANGEMENT.

ASST. PILOT OR EXEC. OFF. HERE ON DECK EDGE ELEVATOR.

SOUND POWERED TELEPHONES ARE USED FOR COMMUNICATIONS WITH BRIDGE FROM ATA ON STERN. BULL HORNS ARE USED TO COMMUNICATE FROM BRIDGE TO YTBs AND YTLs FORWARD. ACKNOWLEDGEMENTS BY AIR WHISTLE.

RUDDER BARGE MADE FAST UNDER COUNTER. YTB IS SECURED TO RUDDER BARGE. ATA IS USED FOR FORE AND AFT POWER.

THIS ARRANGEMENT IS USED FOR CVA WITHOUT POWER.

A CVA WITH POWER — USE ONLY TWO YTBs AND TWO YTLs FORWARD AS SHOWN IN THE DIAGRAM.

Figure 130. Tug arrangement for handling carrier.

one tug athwartships across the stern and the other working fore and aft against her side. An ATA is a large seagoing tug, and in this case the single ATA provides all of the fore-and-aft power when the forward tugs are in the breasting position.

In addition to assisting large ships in and out of their berths, tugs can be very useful when negotiating narrow, tortuous channels. If a large ship must make very sharp turns, a tug ahead with a towline to the bullnose can do much to make the job easy. By pulling the bow around in the turn, the normal turning radius of the ship can be considerably reduced. A second tug aft with a line from her bow to the ship's stern chock can augment the action of the tug ahead. Tugs can be used in this manner at speeds of over five knots, and this is especially useful in following a narrow channel with a swift current. The ship's engines provide the main driving power and the tugs add additional force to spin the ship in a tight turn.

General

The main reason for the existence of both pilots and tugs is to assist ships in restricted waters. They are provided for the safety and convenience of the ships using the waterway, and it is a foolish shiphandler who does not utilize their services when they could assist him. There is no honor or prestige attached to steaming about a harbor without a pilot, and there is no disgrace in flying HOTEL at the yard. Though a shiphandler should learn a harbor after having entered and departed a few times, he should devote adequate time to studying the chart and discussing the area with a qualified pilot to insure that he has adequate knowledge. The only *valid* reason for not having a pilot on board is that the skipper is so familiar with the harbor that he is absolutely certain he can proceed along his route with safety.

If there is any doubt as to one's ability to maneuver the ship into her berth with safety and efficiency, tug assistance should be requested. The tugs are provided to assist larger ships as needed, and they serve no useful purpose lying alongside a wharf. If tug assistance would materially expedite an evolution or simplify a difficult situation, it should be requested.

As in all other phases of shiphandling, the "smart" shiphandler is the one who uses all of the tools at his disposal. "Smartness" connotes intelligence, and is measured by the safety and efficiency with which the ship is handled.

CHAPTER XIX

SHIPHANDLING TIPS

ALTHOUGH we have explored shiphandling throughout the entire field of normal operations, our work would not be complete if we neglected to mention the little scraps of information and advice which make up the "folklore" of shiphandling. Most of these items would be supported by logic if they were traced to their source, but some of them clearly fall into the category of personal taste. They are the little rules that are picked up as one's experience broadens at sea, and they are the things that prevent one from repeating mistakes. They might be called the "Safety Precautions" of shiphandling.

In listing these shiphandling tips, no attempt has been made to record them in their order of importance, nor has any attempt been made to arrange them in groups. They are listed piecemeal for what they are worth.

KEEP YOUR STERN AWAY FROM DANGER. If your propellers and rudders become damaged, you are crippled. If your stern is free to maneuver, you can work your ship out of trouble.

DON'T TAKE A CHANCE. If you recognize it as a chance, it is probably too risky.

WHEN ORDERING RUDDER, LOOK IN THE DIRECTION YOU INTEND TO TURN. This is as good at sea as ashore.

CHECK TO MAKE SURE THAT THE RUDDER MOVED IN THE DIRECTION YOU ORDERED. Watch the helmsman move the wheel if you can see it. Check the Rudder Position Indicator to see what the rudder actually did. Check the compass for direction and rate of turn.

WHEN ORDERING RUDDER, TELL THE HELMSMAN YOUR INTENDED FINAL COURSE. You may be distracted during the turn, and the ship will continue to swing.

WHEN SWINGING TO A NEW COURSE, BRING THE RUDDER AMIDSHIPS A NUMBER OF DEGREES BEFORE REACHING THE NEW COURSE EQUAL TO ONE HALF THE RUDDER ANGLE BEING USED. When using 30° rudder, order the rudder amidships when you have 15° to go. This works remarkably well for coming smartly to a new course.

BEWARE OF A SHIP LYING TO. She is often moving imperceptibly.

DON'T TRUST YOUR SENSE OF DISTANCE IN A FLAT CALM. This sense is bad under any conditions, but it is at its worst across a glassy sea.

DON'T ATTEMPT PRECISE MANEUVERS WHEN GOING ASTERN. Ships handle awkwardly when going astern, and occasionally veer erratically.

GIVE BUOYS A WIDE BERTH. You can't see the cable to the buoy anchor from the surface. Many a screw has been damaged on a buoy which had been "cleared."

IF YOU ARE CONFUSED, CONSIDER THAT THE OTHER SHIPS IN THE FORMATION ARE, TOO. When the situation seems confused, a normal maneuver by another ship may catch you by surprise.

WHEN UNCERTAIN WHAT TO DO, COME TO FORMATION COURSE AND SPEED. This will give time to clarify the situation.

DURING A COMPLEX FORMATION MANEUVER, REMEMBER THE DIRECTION TOWARDS OPEN WATER. This is the avenue to safety; you may need it.

WHEN COLLISION IS IMMINENT AND A SAFE COURSE OF ACTION IS NOT APPARENT, BACK EMERGENCY AND TURN TOWARD THE DANGER. The backing will delay the collision and reduce the impact. The turn toward the danger will reduce the target presented, and we can withstand the impact better forward. A head-on collision crumples the bow; but we can be cut in two when hit from the beam.

NEVER TRUST A COMPASS OR A CHART. Keep checking the ship's heading by landmarks and auxiliary compass. A compass doesn't announce its departure when it goes out. And all charts have minor inaccuracies; some have major ones.

IF BLOWN AGAINST A SHIP OR DOCK WHEN GOING ALONGSIDE, STAY THERE UNTIL COMPLETE PREPARATIONS HAVE BEEN MADE TO GET CLEAR. We are normally quite safe resting there, but we can do major damage trying to pull clear without assistance.

NEVER TRUST A MOORING; CHECK IT. Anchor chains part, mooring shackles break, buoys break adrift, even bollards pull out of docks. Check the ship's position regularly.

IN LOW VISIBILITY, KEEP THE RADAR TUNED FOR SHORT RANGE. The power setting and tuning of the main control console should be selected for best coverage of the band 0—5,000 yards. Though we can expand the presentation by changing the scale setting on the remote scope on the bridge, we can't get optimum results unless the main console is properly adjusted. Remember, it is the contact at short range that presents the danger!

WHEN SOUNDING FOG SIGNALS, SHORTEN THE INTERVAL ONCE EVERY FEW MINUTES. We may be synchronized with another ship and not hear her signal because of our own.

SOUND THE DANGER SIGNAL EARLY. This is legal, and it declares that you do not understand the other ship's intentions. It will prompt her to commit herself and thus clarify the situation.

A SHIP ON A STEADY BEARING IS ON A COLLISION COURSE. Take precise bearings on approaching ships, and check the trend.

TAKE AVOIDING ACTION EARLY. Signal your intention early by taking a positive action that is clearly visible from the other ship.

AVOID PASSING STARBOARD-TO-STARBOARD CLOSE ABOARD. The other ship may evaluate the situation as being nearly head-on and cause a collision situation by altering her course for a Port-to-Port passing. It is safer to alter course to Starboard at an early stage and pass Port-to-Port.

JOIN OTHER SHIPS BY COMING UP FROM ASTERN. Relative speeds will be less and the whole maneuver will be more comfortable for yourself and your formation mates.

THE FASTER THE SHIP IS MOVING THROUGH THE WATER, THE BETTER CONTROL YOU WILL HAVE. The rudder force and the hull stability depend on speed. Wind and current are little felt by a ship moving at a good speed.

WHEN ADJUSTING POSITION ALONGSIDE WITH THE LINES OVER, DON'T WAIT FOR THE SHIP TO BEGIN MOVING BEFORE STOPPING THE ENGINES. The time lags are too long for this.

CHAPTER XX

RULES OF THE ROAD

SINCE THOUSANDS of vessels meet along the busy trade routes and in the teeming harbors of the world each day, the safety of such encounters cannot be left to chance. Ships are designed economically and are no more rugged than necessary to withstand the stress of the elements; the hull of a ship is proportionally no tougher than the shell of an egg. Ships are not built to stand up to the shock of a collision and the history of marine accidents is full of examples of seemingly minor collisions which resulted in the sinking of one or both of the vessels involved.

Individual judgment, even among experienced mariners, cannot be depended upon to provide for the safe passage of ships. The possibility always exists that just when one master decides on a certain turn to avoid another ship, the skipper of the second, sizing up the situation differently, might order a turn which exactly cancelled the precautionary maneuver of the first, and a collision would result. Personal judgment is too variable to be relied upon exclusively to prevent collisions.

The safe passage of ships can be assured, on the other hand, by the use of a universal system of rules which will insure that all ships maneuver predictably and consistently so that each mariner can know what he can expect of others and what is required of him. To provide such a universal system, the modern Rules of the Road were adopted by Great Britain and France jointly in 1863. The United States adopted these same rules the following year, and by 1885 most of the other major maritime powers had accepted them. These rules were revised in 1889 and again in 1948, and they stand today as the cornerstone to safety at sea. The International Rules of the Road are the effective law on all the high seas and in most of the coastal waters and harbors of the world—they are the governing law for more than 90 per cent of the navigable water of the world.

Though agreement has thus been found for the free ocean areas of the world, the rivers, inlets, bays, etc., that lie within the national jurisdiction of the various maritime countries present another problem. Geographic conditions, the nature of the water traffic, local customs, etc. tend to encourage the establishment of local rules, and in the inland waters of a country there is little compulsion to follow the provisions of the International Rules of the Road. The special rules which govern navigation in the Inland Waters of the United States are probably the most elaborate and complex in the world.

For the navigation of the Inland Waters of the United States, Congress has established the Inland Rules of the Road. In the same act that established these rules, Congress directed the Commandant of the Coast Guard to "establish such other rules . . . not inconsistent with the provisions of this act . . . as he may from time to time deem necessary for safety." Accordingly the Commandant of the Coast Guard has published the Pilot Rules for Inland Waters, which for the mariner have the same authority as the Inland Rules. The Inland Rules of the Road are couched in broad terms and generally give the regulations applicable to the normal vessels which frequent inland waters. The Pilot Rules re-state most of the Inland Rules, sometimes elaborating for greater clarity, and they also cover a great variety of special vessels and operations not provided for by the Inland Rules. Unfortunately, though there is no conflict between them, neither set of rules can stand alone and the overlap is extensive. In general, if one takes the Pilot Rules for Inland Waters and adds from the Inland Rules, Section II, on Lights, and Article 26 and Articles 29 through 32, on Right of Way of Sailing and Fishing Vessels, and on Good Seamanship, Suspension of Lights on Naval and Coast Guard Vessels, Distress Signals, and Orders to Helmsmen, he will have assembled the entire body of regulation that governs navigation in the Inland Waters of the United States. For brevity we shall refer to the combined regulations simply as the "Inland Rules."

In addition to the three sets of rules discussed above for navigating the high seas and the coastal waters of the United States, there are the following rules for particular inland water systems:

1. Great Lakes Rules
2. Pilot Rules for the Great Lakes
3. Western Rivers Rules (for Mississippi and tributaries)
4. Pilot Rules for Western Rivers
5. Corps of Engineers, Department of the Army, Rules and Regulations for the Great Lakes and Western Rivers
6. Panama Canal Rules

These rules are similar to the Inland Rules in scope but provide for the special conditions encountered in their respective areas. Since the normal naval vessel will traverse these waters only infrequently and will ordinarily employ a local pilot who will be thoroughly conversant with the special local rules, these special sets of rules are considered beyond the scope of this discussion.

There is one other special set of rules, the Motorboat Act of 25 April 1940, which is of interest to the average ship's officer because it regulates the operation of the ship's boats when in Inland Waters. Pertinent excerpts from this act are included in Appendix III.

As the reader will certainly have concluded by now, the United States mariner today is confronted with an imposing body of law. If he examines the literature of marine law, he will discover that it is not the apparently simple wording of the law, but the interpretation by the courts of the intent of the law, which in the final analysis defines the rule of navigation. A knowledge of the court decisions on the various controversial points of the rules is valuable to the shiphandler, and those readers interested in pursuing this aspect of the rules are referred to more complete texts on the subject, such as Farwell's *Rules of the Nautical Road.* (U. S. Naval Institute, 1964.) It is not, however, the intent of this treatment to explore the intricacies of Admiralty Law. The purpose of this chapter is to give the student shiphandler a working knowledge of the law of the nautical way.

On the roadways of our country, the average driver has proved to be safe and competent. He can abide by the law as he maneuvers in the confusing traffic of our metropolitan centers, yet he would probably be incapable of quoting a single traffic law *from memory,* and it would never occur to him to look up a court interpretation to establish the meaning of the law. It is the same for the law at sea. The ability to "parrot" the words of the various rules of the road is of no value if the mariner does not understand the principles of the law. The competent shiphandler must be able to tap his knowledge for the correct maneuver in the moment of emergency; he must have a feeling for the underlying reasoning behind the law. Accordingly, we shall apply ourselves to searching out the fundamental principles upon which the laws are based, instead of trying to commit the entire body of law to memory.

The Organization of the Rules

If we examine the International Rules of the Road, we will find that they are divided into the following major parts:

Part A. Preliminary and Definitions.

Part B. Lights and Shapes (this section contains a subsection entitled Sound Signals for Fog, and so forth).

Part C. Sound Signals and Conduct in Restricted Visibility.

Part D. Steering and Sailing Rules.

Part E. Sound Signals for Vessels in Sight of One Another.

Part F. Miscellaneous.

Annex to the Rules.

Of these sections the heart of the rules for the shiphandler is contained in Part D, Steering and Sailing Rules. The mariner must be sufficiently conversant with Part A to understand the meaning of the terms used, and he must have knowledge of the light and shape systems used at sea, etc., but he must above all understand the system of maneuver laid down by the Steering and Sailing Rules and be ready to put it into operation immediately. In a moment of emergency, the shiphandler's skill in applying the Steering and Sailing Rules (and the signal system used with them) may determine the safety of his ship. Because of the importance of the Steering and Sailing Rules, the discussion in this chapter will be led as directly as possible to them.

For each of the International Rules there is generally an equivalent rule effective for Inland Waters. Therefore it is customary to place the two sets of rules side by side and to study them simultaneously noting the similarities and differences in each particular rule. We will usually follow this system in the following discussion placing the International Rule to the left and matching it with the corresponding Article from the Inland Rules or the numbered section from the Pilot Rules for Inland Waters.

Our examination of the Rules in this chapter will be limited to those which affect a normal ship sailing the high seas or the coastal waters of the United States. We will examine the requirements for the vessels that she will frequently encounter in such waters, but we will not go into the details of highly specialized vessels infrequently seen. The complete texts of the three major bodies of effective rules, plus the Motorboat Act, are contained in Appendix III, and the details for any special vessel can be found there. It is suggested that after the reader has been exposed to the basic system of the Rules of the Road by the discussion in this chapter, that he turn to Appendix III and read the texts of all of the rules which affect the mariner who sails the seas adjacent to the United States. All qualified conning officers should be acquainted with the content of all sections of the rules and know where to look for infrequently encountered identification marks and special requirements. For ready reference when a strange craft is sighted, a complete collection of the effective rules, such as Appendix III, should be kept on the bridge.

GENERAL

Preliminary Definitions

Since there are distinct differences between the International and the Inland Rules, the first requirement is to define the line of demarcation between the waters governed by the two bodies of rules. As a first step in this determination the rules state:

International	*Inland*
RULE 1. (a) These rules shall be followed by all vessels and seaplanes upon the high seas and in all waters connected therewith	SEC. 80.01. **General Instructions.** The regulations in this part apply to vessels navigating the harbors, rivers, and inland wa-

navigable by seagoing vessels, except as provided in Rule 30. . . .

RULE 30. Nothing in these Rules shall interfere with the operation of a special rule duly made by local authority relative to the navigation of any harbor, river, lake or inland water, including a reserved seaplane area.

ters of the United States, except the Great Lakes and their connecting and tributary waters as far east as Montreal, the Red River of the North, the Mississippi River and its tributaries above Huey P. Long Bridge, and that part of the Atchafalaya above its junction with the Plaquemine-Morgan City alternate waterway.

These rules state the areas of application for the two bodies of rules, but they do not define the line of separation.

It is essential, of course, that the conning officer know precisely which body of rules is in effect in a given location, so the dividing line between Inland and International Waters must be readily apparent. The coastline and headlands of the United States, on the other hand, are so diverse in character that no simple rule of thumb is practical for all sections of the coast. For this reason the dividing line has been established on an individual basis for all of the sections of the coastline of the United States and is incorporated as a part of the rules. An example of the dividing line is shown in Appendix III, which shows how the line runs along the northeast coast of the United States. The reader will note that at times the line runs along the coastline itself and at other times it runs between salient navigational marks many miles at sea. The mariner should dispel any thought that there is a correlation between the division of International and Inland Waters and the Three-Mile Limit.

Next among the Preliminary Definitions we have the following:

International

RULE 1. (b) The Rules concerning lights shall be complied with in all weathers from sunset to sunrise, and during such times no other lights shall be exhibited, except such lights as cannot be mistaken for the prescribed lights or impair their visibility or distinctive character, or interfere with the keeping of a proper lookout. The lights prescribed by these Rules may also be exhibited from sunrise to sunset in restricted visibility and in all other circumstances when it is deemed necessary.

(c) In the following Rules, except where the context otherwise requires:

(i) the word "vessel" includes every description of water craft, other than a seaplane on the water, used or capable of being used as a means of transportation on water;

(ii) the word "seaplane" includes a flying boat and any other aircraft designed to maneuver on the water;

Inland

ART. 1. The rules concerning lights shall be complied with in all weathers from sunset to sunrise, and during such time no other lights which may be mistaken for the prescribed lights shall be exhibited.

(No Equivalent)

(No Equivalent, The Inland Rules do not deal separately with seaplanes.)

(iii) the term "power-driven vessel" means any vessel propelled by machinery;

(iv) every power-driven vessel which is under sail and not under power is to be considered a sailing vessel, and every vessel under power, whether under sail or not, is to be considered a power-driven vessel;

(v) a vessel or seaplane on the water is "under way" when she is not at anchor, or made fast to the shore, or aground;

(vi) the term "height above the hull" means height above the uppermost continuous deck;

(vii) the length and breadth of a vessel shall be deemed to be the length and breadth appearing in her certificate of registry;

(viii) the length and span of a seaplane shall be its maximum length and span as shown in its certificate of airworthiness, or as determined by measurement in the absence of such certificate;

(ix) vessels shall be deemed to be in sight of one another only when one can be observed visually from the other.

(x) the word "visible," when applied to lights, means visible on a dark night with a clear atmosphere;

(xi) the term "short blast" means a blast of about one second's duration;

(xii) the term "prolonged blast" means a blast of from four to six seconds' duration;

(xiii) the word "whistle" means any appliance capable of producing the prescribed short and prolonged blasts.

(xiv) the term "engaged in fishing" means fishing with nets, lines or trawls, but does not include fishing with trailing lines.

Preliminary Definitions

The words "steam vessel" shall include any vessel propelled by machinery.

. . . every steam vessel which is under sail and not under steam is to be considered a sailing vessel, and every vessel under steam, whether under sail or not, is to be considered a steam vessel.

A vessel is "under way," within the meaning of these rules, when she is not at anchor, or made fast to the shore, or aground.

(No Equivalent.)

ART. 11. . . . The length of a vessel shall be deemed to be the length appearing in her certificate of registry.

(No Equivalent.)

(No Equivalent.)

Part II

The word "visible" in these rules, when applied to lights, shall mean visible on a dark night with a clear atmosphere.

SEC. 80.03. **Signals.** The whistle signals provided in the rules in this part shall be sounded on an efficient whistle or siren sounded by steam or by some substitute for steam.

A short blast of the whistle shall mean a blast of about one second's duration.

A prolonged blast of the whistle shall mean a blast of from 4 to 6 seconds' duration.

(No Equivalent.)

Though these definitions are generally quite simple and clear, the following three relatively important changes were introduced in the 1960 revision of the International Rules:

1. By adding the last sentence to Rule 1. (b), it is made clear that there is no prohibition against showing the prescribed lights during daytime. (Merchant ships frequently leave their running lights burning at all times

when at sea—it eliminates the possibility of failing to turn them on when visibility decreases.)

2. The new rule (ix) makes it clear that the rules for maneuvering (Rules 17 to 24) and signalling (Rule 28) for vessels "in sight" of one another apply only when each vessel can be visually observed by the other; thus these rules do not apply when a vessel holds another by radar only.

3. Vessels which are simply trolling are excluded from the provisions for craft "engaged in fishing."

Governing Rules

Underlying the rules for the various rights and privileges of vessels on the nautical roads of the world we find the general principle that the more maneuverable vessel shall keep clear of the less maneuverable. This is specified not only between types of vessels but also among vessels of the same type under different conditions. Following this principle, a steam vessel must keep clear of a sailing vessel, but a vessel maneuverable enough to be overtaking another vessel must keep clear of her, even though the overtaking vessel be a sailing ship and the overtaken one a steamer. There is, of course, no legal basis for the naval practice of the junior (normally smaller and more maneuverable ship) giving way to the senior, nor is there any implication that the "privileged" ship in any situation can neglect, by reason of her maneuverability, any of the requirements placed upon her. However, in establishing the rules for a given situation, in the cases where there was a clear choice, the originators of the rules seem to have chosen to require the more maneuverable vessel to keep clear.

As we grow more familiar with the rules, a second basic principle will become evident. The below stated Governing Rules specifically require a vessel to keep to the right side of the channel, but after we have examined the rules for Meeting and Crossing situations we will see that the following is basic:

LOOK RIGHT—TURN RIGHT—KEEP RIGHT

The rules will tell the mariner to look to the right, on his starboard bow, and to avoid all ships he sees there. If a turn is required in such avoiding, his turn should be to the right. Finally, if he is in a restricted channel, he should keep to the right side of the channel.

To specify the relative rights of various vessels and to describe the action required of a "privileged" or "burdened"* vessel, a series of rules which we

---

* The "privileged" vessel is the one priviliged (and also required) to hold her course and speed; the "burdened" vessel is burdened to keep clear and is required to change her course and speed to this end if necessary.

shall call the Governing Rules apply. These are:

Steam Vessel vs. Sailing Vessel

International

RULE 20. (a) When a power-driven vessel and a sailing vessel are proceeding in such directions as to involve risk of collision, except as provided in Rules 24 and 26, the power-driven vessel shall keep out of the way of the sailing vessel.

(b) This rule shall not give to a sailing vessel the right to hamper, in a narrow channel, the safe passage of a power-driven vessel which can navigate only inside such channel.

(c) A seaplane on the water shall, in general, keep well clear of all vessels and avoid impeding their navigation. In circumstances, however, where risk of collision exists, she shall comply with these Rules.

Inland

ART. 20. When a steam vessel and a sailing vessel are proceeding in such directions as to involve risk of collision, the steam vessel shall keep out of the way of the sailing vessel.

Duty of the Privileged Vessel

International

RULE 21. Where by any of these Rules one of two vessels is to keep out of the way, the other shall keep her course and speed. When, from any cause, the latter vessel finds herself so close that collision cannot be avoided by the action of the giving-away vessel alone, she also shall take such action as will best aid to avert collision. (See Rules 27 and 29.)

Inland

ART. 21. Where, by any of these rules, one of the two vessels is to keep out of the way, the other shall keep her course and speed. (See articles 27 and 29.)

Crossing Ahead Prohibited

International

RULE 22. Every vessel which is directed by these Rules to keep out of the way of another vessel shall, so far as possible, take positive early action to comply with this obligation, and shall, if the circumstances of the case admit, avoid crossing ahead of the other.

Inland

ART. 22. Every vessel which is directed by these rules to keep out of the way of another vessel shall, if the circumstances of the case admit, avoid crossing ahead of the other.

Duty of Burdened Vessel, If Power-Driven

International

RULE 23. Every power-driven vessel which is directed by these Rules to keep out of the way of another vessel shall, on approaching her, if necessary, slacken her speed or stop or reverse.

Inland

ART. 23. Every steam vessel which is directed by these Rules to keep out of the way of another vessel shall, on approaching her, if necessary, slacken her speed, or stop, or reverse.

Overtaking Vessel Always Burdened

International

RULE 24. (a) Notwithstanding anything

Inland

ART. 24. Notwithstanding anything con-

contained in these Rules, every vessel overtaking any other shall keep out of the way of the overtaken vessel.

tained in these rules every vessel, overtaking any other, shall keep out of the way of the overtaken vessel. . . .

Keep Right in Narrow Channels

International

RULE 25. (a) In a narrow channel every power-driven vessel when proceeding along the course of the channel shall, when it is safe and practicable, keep to that side of the fairway or mid-channel which lies on the starboard side of such vessel.

Inland

ART. 25. In narrow channels every steam vessel shall, when it is safe and practicable, keep to that side of the fairway or mid-channel which lies on the starboard side of such vessel.

Keep Clear of Fishing Vessels

International

RULE 26. All vessels not engaged in fishing except vessels to which the provisions of Rule 4 apply, shall, when under way, keep out of the way of any vessels fishing with nets or lines or trawls. This Rule shall not give to any vessel engaged in fishing the right of obstructing a fairway used by vessels other than fishing vessels.

Inland

ART. 26. Sailing vessels under way shall keep out of the way of sailing vessels or boats fishing with nets, lines, or trawls. This rule shall not give to any vessel the right of obstructing a fairway used by vessels other than fishing vessels or boats.

Note the difference. Under International Rules, *all* maneuverable non-fishing vessels are directed to keep clear of *all* vessels fishing. In Inland Waters, *only* sailing vessels are directed to keep clear of *sailing vessels* or *boats* that are fishing.

General Prudential Rule

International

RULE 27. In obeying and construing these Rules due regard shall be had to all dangers of navigation and collision, and to any special circumstance, including the limitations of the craft involved, which may render a departure from the above Rules necessary in order to avoid immediate danger.

Inland

ART. 27. In obeying and construing these rules due regard shall be had to all dangers of navigation and collision, and to any special circumstances which may render a departure from the above rules necessary in order to avoid immediate danger.

Neglect Not Tolerated

International

RULE 29. Nothing in these Rules shall exonerate any vessel, or the owner, master or crew thereof, from the consequences of any neglect to carry lights or signals, or of any neglect to keep a proper lookout, or of the neglect of any precaution which may be required by the ordinary practice of seamen, or by the special circumstances of the case.

Inland

ART. 29. Nothing in these rules shall exonerate any vessel, or the owner or master or crew thereof, from the consequences of any neglect to carry lights or signals, or of any neglect to keep a proper lookout, or of the neglect of any precaution which may be required by the ordinary practice of seamen, or by the special circumstances of the case.

As can be seen from the above, the Governing Rules are very similar for International and Inland Waters. International Rules prohibit a sailing vessel from "hampering" a power-driven vessel in a narrow channel, make provision for Seaplanes on the water, give somewhat more flexibility to the "privileged" vessel in the limit to which she must "Keep her course and speed," and give a good deal broader privilege to fishing vessels. In general, however, there are no major differences.

The significance of Rules 27 and 29 should be particularly noted. The General Prudential Rule points out that blind adherence to the letter of the rule is *not* the objective. Rule 27 cautions the mariner to note *all* dangers and special circumstances and to be ready to *depart* from the Rules should that be required to avoid immediate danger. This rule requires the mariner to keep the "whole picture" of the situation and be ready to apply prudent judgment as required.

Rule 29, the "rule of good seamanship," is even more specific in its requirements. In addition to cautioning the mariner against any neglect to "carry lights or signals, or of any neglect to keep a proper look-out," it specifically warns him of the consequences of the "neglect of any precaution which may be required by the ordinary practice of seamen, or by the special circumstances of the case." The rules require that all vessels sailing the seas be operated with care and prudence. Rule 29 specifically points out that, regardless of other factors or fault, a vessel shall not be exonerated in the case of collision or other damage if there is evidence of neglect or lack of ordinary precaution which contributed to the accident.

STEERING AND SAILING RULES

Preliminary

International	*Inland*
1. In obeying and construing these Rules, any action taken should be positive, in ample time, and with due regard to the observance of good seamanship.	*(No Equivalent.)*
2. Risk of collision can, when circumstances permit, be ascertained by carefully watching the compass bearing of an approaching vessel. If the bearing does not appreciably change, such risk should be deemed to exist.	Risk of collision can, when circumstances permit, be ascertained by carefully watching the compass bearing of an approaching vessel. If the bearing does not appreciably change, such risk should be deemed to exist.
3. Mariners should bear in mind that seaplanes in the act of landing or taking off, or operating under adverse weather conditions, may be unable to change their intended action at the last moment.	*(No Equivalent.)*
4. Rules 17 to 24 apply only to vessels in sight of one another.	*(No Equivalent.)*

The first preliminary section of the Steering and Sailing Rules for International Waters contains one of the most important principles of safe navigation, *the requirement to take positive action and in ample time*. The prudent mariner takes whatever action the situation requires of him at the

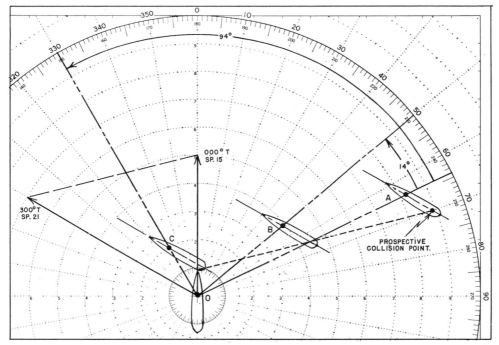

Figure 131. Collision *can* occur with True Bearing Changing. This figure shows last 800 yards of relative plot of collision situation. Own ship "O" taking bearings from C/L pelorus on Masthead light of approaching ship. Between positions A and B bearing changed 14°. Between A and C it changed 94°, but collision occurred anyhow! Own ship on course 000°T speed 15 knots, approaching ship on 300°T at 21 knots. Both ships of cruiser dimensions.

earliest practical moment, and his action is not only sufficient to meet the needs of the case, but also sufficient *so that the conning officer of the other ship will perceive that adequate action has been taken.* If in avoiding another ship a course change is called for, we should change course 20° or more so that it is clearly evident that we have changed course. If the situation calls for an appreciable reduction of speed, we should back our engines and give the appropriate whistle signal so that the other ship will know what we are doing. Though the rules for Inland Waters do not specify such action, this section should be considered universally good advice and applied in Inland as well as International Waters.

The second preliminary section concerns Risk of Collision provisions and is identical for both International and Inland Waters. If the bearing of an approaching vessel does not change, we are on a "collision course" with it. Watching the true bearing of other ships in the vicinity is the normal means used to detect a potentially dangerous situation. If the bearing is steady, action must be taken.

The converse of this rule, however, is not always true. At short ranges the bearing of another vessel may be changing and risk of collision can still exist. Figure 131 illustrates just such a situation. Here, though the true bearing was changing "appreciably," a collision would have occurred. Obviously the amount of bearing change required to insure safety is a function of range and the dimensions of the two vessels in question. Bearings are taken from point to point (from the starboard wing pelorus on our ship to the masthead light of the other ship, for example). Though change in point-to-point bearings insures that those two points will not collide, such change does not absolutely insure that other points on the two vessels will not collide.

Figure 132 shows the relative plot of the approach of a vessel which will clear us by 1,000 yards. The dimensions of vessels found at sea today are such

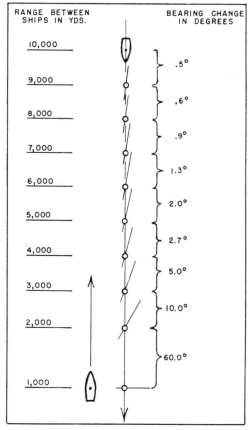

Figure 132. Bearing Change for each 1,000 yards decrease in range. Ships on reciprocal courses, and will pass 1,000 yards abeam. Same rate of bearing change per 1,000 yards of closing range holds good for ships approaching from any direction on such a course and speed that a 1,000-yard Closest Point of Approach (CPA) will result.

that if a point on one passes 1,000 yards from any point on the other at its closest point of approach, a collision cannot occur. A 1,000-yard separation at the moment of passing in the open sea might thus be considered as an acceptable minimum and Figure 132 lists the bearing change for each successive thousand yards decrease of range required to insure the 1,000-yard minimum separation upon passing. It will be noted between 10,000 and 9,000 yards only ½° of bearing change is required to insure the 1,000-yard passing separation, but between 6,000 and 5,000 yards this has grown to 2°, and between 4,000 and 3,000 yards the change must be 5° to insure this separation.

The third preliminary section to the International Steering and Sailing Rules deals with seaplanes, and we note again that the rules for Inland Waters are silent on the subject. The problem of seaplanes boils down to this: if a seaplane is on the water, it is supposed to keep well clear of all vessels (Rule 20 [b]); if, however, it fails to keep clear and finds itself in a situation where risk of collision exists, it is required to comply with the rules as a power-driven vessel (Rule 20 [b]); *but,* by this third preliminary rule, mariners are warned that seaplanes cannot always be depended upon to do that which is required of them. It should be noted that no part of the rules gives any special *right* to Seaplanes on the water.

Seaplanes in U. S. Territorial waters are governed by the Air Traffic Rules (which substantially conform to the Inland Rules applicable to vessels), but the Inland Rules themselves make no mention of Seaplanes on the water. A seaplane on the surface should be expected to maneuver approximately as would another power driven vessel, but the case is clearly one of Special Circumstance and the mariner should maneuver with due caution. The good *advice* given in preliminary section 3 of the International Steering and Sailing Rules should be considered to be just as valid in Inland waters as it is in International Waters.

Preliminary Section 4 to the International Steering and Sailing Rules emphasises that Rules 17 through 24, the basic system for maneuver when vessels encounter one another of the high seas, apply only to vessels in sight of one another—not to vessels obscured from one another by fog or precipitation, *even though they may be aware of each other's presence and movement by radar or other means.* As will be seen from a study of these rules, each vessel has an important part to play in the passage and, since it cannot be assumed that another vessel has an effective radar or other sensing device, one should not depend upon another vessel being aware of one's presence until one actually sights the other vessel. Advice on maneuvering when only radar information is available is the subject of the new Annex to the Rules, "Recommendations of the Use of Radar Information as an Aid to Avoiding Collisions at Sea."

Vessels Meeting

International

RULE 18 (a) When two power-driven vessels are meeting end on, or nearly end on, so as to involve risk of collision, each shall alter her course to starboard, so that each may pass on the port side of the other. This Rule only applies to cases where vessels are meeting end on, or nearly end on, in such a manner as to involve risk of collision, and does not apply to two vessels which must, if both keep on their respective courses, pass clear of each other. The only cases to which it does apply are when each of two vessels is end on, or nearly end on, to the other; in other words, to cases in which, by day, each vessel sees the masts of the other in a line, or nearly in a line, with her own; and by night, to cases in which each vessel is in such a position as to see both the sidelights of the other. It does not apply, by day, to cases in which a vessel sees another ahead crossing her own course; or, by night, to cases where the red light of one vessel is opposed to the red light of the other or where the green light of one vessel is opposed to the green light of the other or where a red light without a green light or a green light without a red light is seen ahead, or where both green and red lights are seen anywhere but ahead.

Inland

ART. 18. RULE I. When steam vessels are approaching each other head and head, that is, end on, or nearly so, it shall be the duty of each to pass on the port side of the other; and either vessel shall give, as a signal of her intention, one short and distinct blast of her whistle, which the other vessel shall answer promptly by a similar blast of her whistle, and thereupon such vessels shall pass on the port side of each other. But if the courses of such vessels are so far on the starboard of each other as not to be considered as meeting head and head, either vessel shall immediately give two short and distinct blasts of her whistle, which the other vessel shall answer promptly by two similar blasts of her whistle, and they shall pass on the starboard side of each other.

The foregoing only applies to cases where vessels are meeting end on, or nearly end on, in such a manner as to involve risk of collision; in other words, to cases in which, by day, each vessel sees the masts of the other in a line, or nearly in a line, with her own, and by night to cases in which each vessel is in such a position as to see both the sidelights of the other.

It does not apply by day to cases in which a vessel sees another ahead crossing her own course, or by night to cases where the red light of one vessel is opposed to the red light of the other, or where the green light of one vessel is opposed to the green light of the other, or where a red light without a green light or a green light without a red light, is seen ahead, or where both green and red lights are seen anywhere but ahead.

RULE III. If, when steam vessels are approaching each other, either vessel fails to understand the course or intention of the other, from any cause, the vessel so in doubt shall immediately signify the same by giving several short and rapid blasts, not less than four, of the steam whistle.

At first glance it appears that, except for signals, the two systems of rules require approximately the same action for two vessels meeting on nearly reciprocal courses. It is true that the basic idea that the two vessels shall normally maneuver so as to pass port-to-port is expressed in both systems, but there are important differences between the two.

In International Waters, the Rules state clearly and unequivocably that in the case of power-driven vessels meeting end on or nearly end on, so as to involve risk of collision, they shall *each* alter course to starboard so as to pass port-to-port. There is no choice at all. If the meeting is end on so as to involve risk of collision, *both* vessels are *required* to act. Whistle signals should be sounded as the changes of course are made, but there is no requirement that prior sound signals be exchanged.

In Inland Waters, on the other hand, three permissible methods of passing are prescribed; i.e. port-to-port passing with mutual change of course, port-to-port passing without change of course, and starboard-to-starboard passing. In each case, before the passing is attempted, an agreement as to the method of passing must have been reached by an exchange of identical whistle signals. Should the two vessels fail to agree, the vessel not understanding (or not agreeing with) the intention of the other is required to sound the Danger Signal.

The rules for International Waters are positive and clear and are excellent for use in the open sea where there is normally adequate sea room. The one weak point is the case where vessels are meeting on courses which would pass slightly to the starboard of each other. In this case if one vessel considers the situation to be a head-and-head meeting while the other considers it to be a clear starboard-to-starboard passing, requiring no action, a dangerous situation can result. Normally in such cases, as soon as one vessel considers the meeting to be head-and-head, she changes her course significantly to the right and blows one blast on her whistle. This ordinarily precipitates action on the part of the other vessel and a normal port-to-port passage results.

The Inland Rules, with their greater flexibility in the method of passing and the requirement for an agreement between the vessels before the passing is attempted, is more suitable for narrow channels where ships are often required to pass with only a few yards clearance and there may not be sufficient sea room to arrange a port-to-port passing.

Vessels Crossing

International	*Inland*
Rule 19. When two power-driven vessels are crossing, so as to involve risk of collision, the vessel which has the other on her own starboard side shall keep out of the way of the other.	Art. 19. When two steam vessels are crossing, so as to involve risk of collision, the vessel which has the other on her own starboard side shall keep out of the way of the other.

RULE 28. (b) Whenever a power-driven vessel which, under these Rules, is to keep her course and speed, is in sight of another vessel and is in doubt whether sufficient action is being taken by the other vessel to avert collision, she may indicate such doubt by giving at least five short and rapid blasts on the whistle. The giving of such a signal shall not relieve a vessel of her obligations under Rules 27 and 29 or any other Rule, or of her duty to indicate any action taken under these Rules by giving the appropriate sound signals laid down in this Rule.

SEC. 80.7. **Vessels approaching each other at right angles or obliquely.** When two steam vessels are approaching each other at right angles or obliquely so as to involve risk of collision, other than when one steam vessel is overtaking another, the steam vessel which has the other on her own port side shall hold her course and speed, and the steam vessel which has the other on her own starboard side shall keep out of the way of the other by directing her course to starboard so as to cross the stern of the other steam vessel, or, if necessary to do so, slacken her speed or stop or reverse.

If from any cause the conditions covered by this situation are such as to prevent immediate compliance with each other's signals, the misunderstanding or objection shall be at once made apparent by blowing the danger signal, and both steam vessels shall be stopped and backed if necessary, until signals for passing with safety are made and understood.

The rules for the crossing situation are very similar under the two bodies of rules except for the differences in whistle signals. In International Waters it should be remembered that only the vessel with the right of way may blow the Danger Signal, whereas in Inland Waters either vessel may use this signal in case of misunderstanding or disagreement.

Vessels Overtaking

International

RULE 24. (a) Notwithstanding anything contained in these Rules, every vessel overtaking any other shall keep out of the way of the overtaken vessel.

(b) Every vessel coming up with another vessel from any direction more than 22½ degrees (2 points) abaft her beam, i.e. in such a position, with reference to the vessel which she is overtaking, that at night she would be unable to see either of that vessel's sidelights, shall be deemed to be an overtaking vessel; and no subsequent alteration of the bearing between the two vessels shall make the overtaking vessel a crossing vessel within the meaning of these Rules, or relieve her of the duty of keeping clear of the overtaken vessel until she is finally past and clear.

(c) If the overtaking vessel cannot determine with certainty whether she is forward of or abaft this direction from the other

Inland

ART. 24. Notwithstanding anything contained in these rules every vessel, overtaking any other, shall keep out of the way of the overtaken vessel.

Every vessel coming up with another vessel from any direction more than two points abaft her beam, that is, in such a position, with reference to the vessel which she is overtaking that at night she would be unable to see either of that vessel's side lights, shall be deemed to be an overtaking vessel; and no subsequent alteration of the bearing between the two vessels shall make the overtaking vessel a crossing vessel within the meaning of these rules, or relieve her of the duty of keeping clear of the overtaken vessel until she is finally past and clear.

As by day the overtaking vessel cannot always know with certainty whether she is forward of or abaft this direction from the vessel, she shall assume that she is an overtaking vessel and keep out of the way.

other vessels she should, if in doubt, assume that she is an overtaking vessel and keep out of the way.

ART. 18. RULE VIII. When steam vessels are running in the same direction, and the vessel which is astern shall desire to pass on the right or starboard hand of the vessel ahead, she shall give one short blast of the steam whistle, as a signal of such desire, and if the vessel ahead answers with one blast, she shall direct her course to starboard; or if she shall desire to pass on the left or port side of the vessel ahead, she shall give two short blasts of the steam whistle as a signal of such desire, and if the vessel ahead answers with two blasts, shall direct her course to port; or if the vessel ahead does not think it safe for the vessel astern to attempt to pass at that point, she shall immediately signify the same by giving several short and rapid blasts of the steam whistle, not less than four, and under no circumstances shall the vessel astern attempt to pass the vessel ahead until such time as they have reached a point where it can be safely done, when said vessel ahead shall signify her willingness by blowing the proper signals. The vessel ahead shall in no case attempt to cross the bow or crowd upon the course of the passing vessel.

Both sets of rules are definite on the principle that an overtaking vessel, regardless of her type, must keep clear of the vessel being overtaken. They define an overtaking vessel as one that approaches another from a direction "more than $22\frac{1}{2}°$ abaft her beam" and state that no subsequent change of bearing shall change the situation so as to relieve the overtaking vessel of her duty to stay clear. They further state that if a vessel is in doubt as to whether she is approaching from more than $22\frac{1}{2}°$ abaft the beam, she should assume that she is an overtaking vessel and act accordingly.

As in all situations of vessels approaching one another, the system of sound signals is different between the two bodies of rules, but in the overtaking case the exchange of signals in the Inland Rules changes significantly the relative legal positions of the two vessels. First, the overtaken vessel is required to sound the Danger Signal in case she thinks the passage unsafe, and should she fail to do this (or sound a signal of agreement) in the face of apparent danger, she could be held at fault. Second, having agreed to a given passing, the overtaken vessel is then bound not to "attempt to cross the bow or crowd upon the course of the passing vessel." Because of these added responsibilities the overtaken vessel should examine the situation very carefully before agreeing to a passing under difficult circumstances.

Vessels Meeting, Summary

Having considered the meeting of two vessels in each of the three cases specified by the rules, let's consider the general system of maneuver. While conning a ship at sea it is often difficult to classify a given situation and then remember the corresponding rule. It would be better if we could relate the situation to our point of observation as we stand on the bridge of our ship.

All of the rules regarding the avoidance of collision utilize the relative bearing of one ship from the other in determining the status of privilege and in prescribing the required maneuvers. This is logical because, if there is going to be a collision, it will, in principle, occur ahead on our projected course at the point where the projected course of the other ship crosses ours. The action required of us under the rules always depends on the position of the other ship with respect to our bow.

If, as in Figure 133, we lay out the governing sectors for the various meeting situations, we will see that the recognition of relative Right of Way is very simple. All rules require that we keep clear of ships on our starboard hand that are approaching so as to involve risk of collision, except for ships that are overtaking us. By definitions contained in the rules, therefore, we must keep clear of all ships approaching between the relative bearings, of dead ahead and two points abaft the starboard beam ($000°$-$112\frac{1}{2}°$ relative). Ships on our port side, on the other hand, are required to keep clear of us, with the exception of vessels that we are overtaking and sailing vessels. All ships approaching from more than two points abaft our beams (between $112\frac{1}{2}°$ and $247\frac{1}{2}°$ relative) are overtaking vessels and are required to keep clear of us. Dead ahead there is a sector of approach where either the head-and-head case or the overtaking case can apply. In Figure 133, the sector from which an approaching ship has the right of way is shown in white, the sectors of shared responsibility are shown in light grey, and the sector from which an approaching ship must keep clear of us is shown in dark grey. The diagram tells the conning officer to look on his starboard bow and avoid all ships approaching from that sector, to look on his port bow for a vessel he is overtaking or a sailing vessel, that vessels dead ahead are a special case, and that vessels approaching from all other directions are required to keep clear of him. This of course does not imply any relaxation of the universal requirement to maintain an adequate lookout in all sectors.

Section 80.13 (c) of Pilot Rules for Inland Waters contains a series of diagrams which very simply illustrate the meeting situations and the actions required by the vessel involved in Inland Waters. These diagrams, in placard

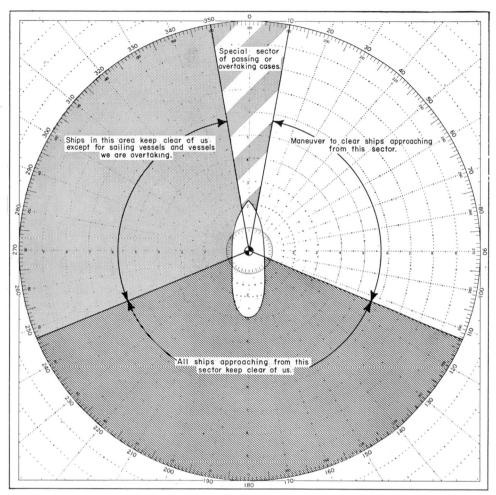

Figure 133. Sectors of relative Right of Way as related to own ship's bow.

form, are required to be posted in the pilothouse on all large steam vessels, and all steam vessels larger than motorboats are required to carry them in one form or another.

One of the most trying experiences of a mariner comes when his vessel is the "privileged" vessel and he is required to hold his course and speed on a collision course with a "burdened" vessel, which is giving no evidence of taking the necessary action to avoid the collision. Under either set of rules he may sound the Danger Signal, but an actual maneuver is required to avoid the danger. How long must be hold on?

Neither set of rules intends that the privileged vessel hold her course and speed right into the "jaws of collision." The International Rules specifically release the "privileged" vessel to maneuver when the collision cannot be avoided by the action of the "burdened" vessel alone, and good judgment applied under the General Prudential Rule in Inland Waters dictates a similar release. In practice, the prudent conning officer should conservatively estimate the maneuverability of the approaching ship, taking account of the weather conditions, her loading, and any other factor which might adversely affect her ability to turn or stop, and as soon as he has a reasonable doubt of the ability of the other vessel to take the required action, he should apply the General Prudential Rule and take vigorous avoiding action, making certain that he indicates his action by appropriate whistle signals.

SAILING VESSELS

International

RULE 17. (a) When two sailing vessels are approaching one another, so as to involve risk of collision, one of them shall keep out of the way of the other, as follows:—

(i) When each has the wind on a different side, the vessel which has the wind on the port side shall keep out of the way of the other.

(ii) When both have the wind on the same side, the vessel which is to windward shall keep out of the way of the vessel which is to leeward.

(b) For the purposes of this Rule the windward side shall be deemed to be the side opposite to that on which the mainsail is carried or, in the case of a square-rigged vessel, the side opposite to that on which the largest fore-and-aft sail is carried.

Inland

ART. 17. When two sailing vessels are approaching one another, so as to involve risk of collision, one of them shall keep out of the way of the other as follows, namely:

(a) A vessel which is running free shall keep out of the way of a vessel which is close-hauled.

(b) A vessel which is close-hauled on the port tack shall keep out of the way of a vessel which is close-hauled on the starboard tack.

(c) When both are running free, with the wind on different sides, the vessel which has the wind on the port side shall keep out of the way of the other.

(d) When both are running free, with the wind on the same side, the vessel which is to windward shall keep out of the way of the vessel which is to leeward.

(e) A vessel which has the wind aft shall keep out of the way of the other vessel.

To understand the logic behind the Inland Rules for the meeting of sailing vessels, we must remember that they were drawn up for square-rigged sailing ships, not the sleek fore-and-aft-rigged sailboats of today. A full-rigged ship sailed handsomely before the wind, but was much less maneuverable when working to windward. A square-rigger that could make good a course within six points of the wind was doing very well. Following the principle that the more maneuverable vessel must keep clear of the less maneuverable one, the order of privilege as specified by the rules, in descending order, is: vessel closehauled; vessel running free; vessel with the wind aft.

The new International Rule governing the encounter of sailing vessels, adopted in the 1960 change, is taken from the yachtman's racing rules and is simplicity itself. If the wind is on different sides, the vessel with the wind on the port side keeps clear: if the wind is from the same side, the vessel to windward keeps clear! This uncomplicated, practical system has been thoroughly tested in thousands of regattas and should be considered as a distinct improvement over the old system still in force under the Inland Rules.

The separation among the three major conditions of sailing under Inland Rules is not precisely defined. The courts have considered that a vessel which is sailing within two points of her highest heading is still "close-hauled" within the meaning of the rules, and they also have held that a vessel with the wind within 1½ to 2½ points of dead astern was sailing "with the wind

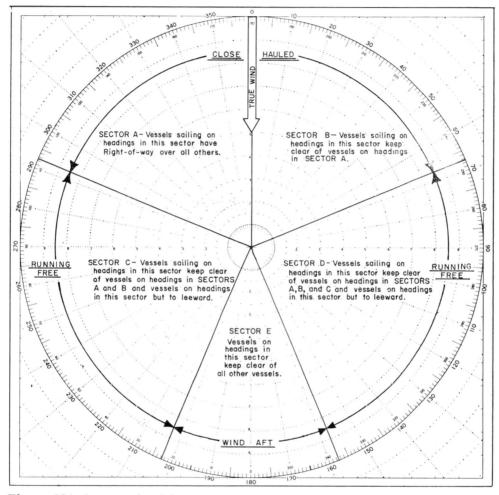

Figure 134. Sectors of privilege for Sailing Vessels in Inland Waters as related to direction from which True Wind is blowing.

aft."* Since modern sailing vessels are close-hauled when sailing about four points from the wind, we can, from a practical point of view separate the conditions of sailing into the sectors indicated in Figure 134 in relation to the direction of the true wind. A vessel with the true wind more than two points forward of her beam should be considered to be close-hauled; a vessel with

---

* *Knight's Modern Seamanship* (New York, N.Y.: Van Nostrand, 1958), 12th edition, page 385.

the true wind within two points of dead astern should be considered to be sailing with the wind aft; all others should be considered to be running free.

The meeting of two sailing vessels close-hauled on opposite tacks under Inland Rules follows the right hand principle governing the meeting of steam vessels, i.e. the one which has the other on her starboard bow shall keep clear. The same holds true when running free with the wind forward of the beam, but this does not hold true as the wind shifts aft. We must therefore commit to memory that, for sailing vessels running free with the wind on opposite sides, the vessel on the starboard tack has the right of way.

With two sailing vessels running free with the wind on the same side, it is logical that the one to windward should keep clear of the other. She is not only sailing with the wind farther aft, if the courses are converging, but she is also farther from a possible lee shore.

The Inland Rules are silent on the relative rights of two vessels close-hauled on the same tack or two vessels sailing before the wind. Should either be clearly an overtaking vessel, she would, of course, be required to keep clear under Rule 24. On the other hand, it is quite possible that two sailing vessels on nearly parallel courses sailing at approximately the same speed should converge when working to windward or running before the wind, and in the absence of specific provisions for such cases, we would have to rely on the General Prudential Rule to provide safety.

WHISTLE SIGNALS

International

RULE 28. (a) When vessels are in sight of one another, a power-driven vessel under way, in taking any course authorized or required by these Rules, shall indicate that course by the following signals on her whistle, namely:

One short blast to mean, "I am altering my course to starboard."

Two short blasts to mean, "I am altering my course to port."

Three short blasts to mean, "My engines are going astern."

International

RULE 28. (b) Whenever a power-driven vessel which, under these Rules, is to keep her course and speed, is in sight of another vessel and is in doubt whether sufficient action is being taken by the other vessel to avert collision, she may indicate such doubt by giving at least five short and rapid blasts on the whistle. The giving of such a signal shall not relieve a vessel of her obli-

Inland

SEC. 80.03. **Signals.** One short blast of the whistle signifies intention to direct course to own starboard, except when two steam vessels are approaching each other at right angles or obliquely, when it signifies intention of steam vessel which is to starboard of the other to hold course and speed.

Two short blasts of the whistle signify intention to direct course to own port.

Three short blasts of the whistle shall mean "My engines are going at full speed astern."

Inland

ART. 18. RULE III. If, when steam vessels are approaching each other, either vessel fails to understand the course or intention of the other, from any cause, the vessel so in doubt shall immediately signify the same by giving several short and rapid blasts, not less than four, of the steam whistle.

(See also Sec. 80.1, Pilot Rules, Appendix

gations under Rules 27 and 29 or any other Rule, or of her duty to indicate any action taken under these Rules by giving the appropriate sound signals laid down in this Rule.

(c) Any whistle signal mentioned in this Rule may be further indicated by a visual signal consisting of a white light visible all round the horizon at a distance of at least 5 miles, and so devised that it will operate simultaneously and in conjunction with the whistle sounding mechanism and remain lighted and visible during the same period as the whistle signal.

(d) Nothing in these Rules shall interfere with the operation of any special rules made by the Government of any nation with respect to the use of additional whistle signals between ships of war or vessels sailing under convoy.

A, designating this as the danger signal).

SEC. 80.2. **Cross signals.** Steam vessels are forbidden to use what has become technically known among pilots as "cross signals," that is, answering one whistle with two, and two whistles with one. (Former Pilot Rule II.)

SEC. 80.3. **Vessels passing each other.** The signals for passing, by the blowing of the whistle, shall be given and answered by pilots, in compliance with the rules in this part, not only when meeting "head and head," or nearly so, but at all times when the steam vessels are in sight of each other, when passing or meeting at a distance within half a mile of each other, and whether passing to the starboard or port.

The whistle signals provided in the rules in this part for steam vessels meeting, passing, or overtaking are never to be used except when steam vessels are in sight of each other and the course and position of each can be determined in the daytime by a sight of the vessel itself, or by night by seeing its signal lights. In fog, mist, falling snow, or heavy rainstorms, when vessels cannot so see each other, fog signals only must be given.

NEARING A BEND

RULE 25. (b) Whenever a power-driven vessel is nearing a bend in a channel where a power-driven vessel approaching from the other direction cannot be seen, such vessel, when she shall have arrived within one-half mile of the bend, shall give a signal by one prolonged blast of her whistle, which signal shall be answered by a similar blast given by any approaching power-driven vessel that may be within hearing around the bend. Regardless of whether an approaching vessel on the farther side of the bend is heard, such bend shall be rounded with alertness and caution.

NEARING A BEND, ETC.

ART. 18. RULE V. Whenever a steam vessel is nearing a short bend or curve in the channel, where, from the height of the banks or other cause, a steam vessel approaching from the opposite direction cannot be seen for a distance of half a mile, such steam vessel, when she shall have arrived within half a mile of such curve or bend, shall give a signal by one long blast of the steam whistle, which signal shall be answered by a similar blast given by any approaching steam vessel that may be within hearing. Should such signal be so answered by a steam vessel upon the farther side of such bend, then the usual signals for meeting and passing shall immediately be given and answered; but, if the first alarm signal of such vessel be not answered, she is to consider the channel clear and govern herself accordingly.

When steam vessels are moved from their docks or berths, and other boats are liable to pass from any direction toward them, they shall give the same signal as in the case of vessels meeting at a bend, but immediately after clearing the berths so as to be fully in sight they shall be governed by the steering and sailing rules.

Every vessel sailing the high seas or inland waterways is required to have an efficient sound-making device to be used to signal other vessels of her presence, her actions, or her intentions. Such sound-making device may be a steam whistle, a siren, an air "foghorn," or an electric horn depending on the class and type of vessel, and the word "whistle" as used in the rules is meant to indicate any such device. A power-driven vessel larger than a motor-boat is required to have both an efficient whistle, sounded by steam or a substitute for steam, *and* an efficient foghorn to be sounded by mechanical means. There are systems of signalling with the whistle in both clear and foggy weather, but we will discuss the former here, leaving the latter to the section on Rules in Fog and Reduced Visibility.

Before getting involved in the details of the whistle signals, however, we should make sure that we appreciate the limitations of these signals. The very definition of an efficient whistle is not adequately set forth in the rules. How far and under what conditions must such a signal be heard? What is the allowable frequency range of its tone? Must a small coaster have a whistle equal to that required of a transatlantic liner?

Actually, due to the effect of the wind and ambient ship noise, the exchange of whistle signals is often haphazard, and one learns to depend on the sighting of the plume of white steam emerging from an approaching steamer's whistle rather than upon hearing the sound and it is for this reason that the new white synchronized light described in International Rule 28 (c) has been adopted. However, the reader should not get the impression that whistle signals are useless or superfluous. The use of whistle signals by ships operating in the vicinity of one another is one of the most important means of preventing collisions.

International and Inland Whistle Signals Compared

The difference between the International and Inland Rules is nowhere so marked as in the use of whistle signals. Under International Rules the one and two blast signals are required whenever ships are in sight of each other to indicate all course changes actually being made, whereas the Inland Rules prescribe the use of these whistle signals only in certain meeting situations to propose actions or to signify agreement.

In International Waters, when in sight of another vessel, a single blast is given each time a power-driven vessel changes her course to the right, and two short blasts are given each time she changes her course to the left. (These signals are prescribed no matter how slight the change of course may be.) Should she back her engines for any reason she so indicates by three short blasts, and should it be required to call the attention of a burdened vessel to the fact that the conning officer of the privileged vessel is not satisfied with the adequacy of the burdened vessel's action, the five blast signal is available. It should be emphasized that in International Waters the Steering and Sailing Rules are considered completely adequate to control the maneuvers of vessels encountering each other, and the signals are used only to indicate the action actually being taken.

A completely different philosophy is used in Inland Waters. Here ships in sight of one another may change course in silence and utilize the whistle only to make agreements about passing, to call attention to danger or doubt, or to signify backing. It is only when vessels are passing, crossing, or overtaking *so as to involve risk of collision* that whistle signals for course changes are prescribed at all. The Pilot Rules elaborate upon the point and state that whistle signals must be exchanged "when passing or meeting within half a mile of each other" (this is close for large ships), but this is quite different from the International requirement for whistle signals when ships are "within sight of one another."

The Pilot Rules, in Sec. 80.03 on Signals, state:

One short blast of the whistle signifies intention to direct course to own starboard, except when two steam vessels are approaching each other at right angles or obliquely, when it signifies intention of steam vessel which is to starboard of the other to hold course and speed.

Two short blasts of the whistle signify intention to direct course to own port.

These statements are misleading because in practice the majority of the times that a vessel sounds either one or two blasts following Inland Rules she does not change her course at all and does not intend to. Most head-and-head meetings and most overtaking maneuvers are executed with no appreciable course change, yet a complete exchange of whistle signals is required.

It is much better to keep the following definitions in mind:

One Blast—"I propose (or agree to) a passing which will leave the other vessel to my port."

Two Blasts—"I propose (or agree to) a passing which will leave the other vessel to my starboard."

These definitions are applicable to all situations, whether involving the head-on case, the crossing case, or the overtaking case.

In Inland Waters, it is illegal that the passing should be undertaken before a satisfactory exchange of signals is completed; and should the proposing ship not receive a response of agreement from the other vessel, she is bound by the rules to sound the Danger Signal and stop or reverse her engines as the case might require, and maneuver with caution until the mode of passing is agreed upon by an exchange of identical signals (General Prudential Rule for all situations, Sec. 80.7 for crossing situation). The only acceptable response to a one or two blast signal is an identical signal.

Once an exchange of identical signals is made, thus establishing the mode of passing, the vessels then maneuver in accordance with the requirements of the Steering Rules, i.e. the privileged vessel must hold her course and speed and the burdened vessel must maneuver if necessary to keep clear. In the head-on case, as clearly stated in the rules, neither vessel is privileged and both must maneuver if necessary to effect a safe passage.

The most serious flaw in the Inland system of passing signals becomes apparent in a busy harbor where there are many ships maneuvering in close proximity. A whistle is non-directional, and with more than two ships in one area, it is difficult to determine which ship has sounded a particular signal, and it is often impossible to determine to which ship it was intended.

Though the one and two blast signals in Inland Waters are used only when vessels are passing and are in close proximity, the three blast signal, indicating that one's engines are going astern, is identical with the same signal under International Rules and is used whenever vessels are *in sight of one another*. Though the language actually used in the rule states that the three blast signal shall indicate that "my engines are going at *full speed* astern," the court interpretations have made it clear that this signal shall be used when the engines are going astern regardless of their speed.

One whistle signal in Inland Rules which is clearly more useful than its International counterpart is the Danger Signal of four or more blasts. This signifies danger or doubt and clearly states that the vessel which sounds it is concerned about the situation. It is an invaluable means of alerting the conning officers of other vessels to a potentially dangerous situation, and there is never any doubt as to its meaning. Contrary to the International Danger Signal, which can be used only by a privileged vessel, the Inland Danger Signal can be used by any vessel when in danger or in doubt. The conning officer should feel free to use this signal without hesitation.

Though both sets of rules prescribe a long blast (10 seconds for Inland Waters, five seconds for International Waters), for use by a power-driven vessel as she approaches a blind bend in the channel, there is a distinct difference in philosophy between the rules. Under International Rules, whether an answering signal is heard or not, the bend shall be rounded with "alertness and caution." Under Inland Rules, on the other hand, if an answering signal is not heard, the vessel is to "consider the channel clear and govern herself accordingly." This Inland Rule seems fraught with danger, and the wise mariner should round any blind bend with "alertness and caution" at the very least.

The Inland Rules allow the use of the 10-second blast when getting underway from a dock or berth, and this is a very useful signal to warn the shipping in the vicinity that our vessel, previously moored, is now underway and entering the harbor traffic.

Half-Mile Rule

Since Inland Rules so clearly require that the exchange of signals be completed *before* the passing is attempted, the question naturally arises as to the minimum separation between the vessels allowable before such agreement is reached. The Pilot Rules state that signals must be exchanged "when passing or meeting within half a mile of each other," but the rules for passing are prescribed for cases which "involve risk of collision," and certainly the passing of two fishing vessels on parallel courses a quarter of a mile apart would not ordinarily be considered to involve risk of collision. Obviously the statement in Sec. 80.3 of the Pilot Rules concerning the "half mile" is not clear and appears not to apply to the closest point of approach between two passing vessels, but rather to their separation as they mutually approach a point of possible collision.

Obviously when two vessels are approaching so that their passing will involve the danger of collision, it is to their mutual benefit to arrive at an agreement as to the mode of passing at the earliest moment possible. Thus the prudent mariner in Inland Waters initiates his passing signal at the earliest moment that he believes the other ship will be able to hear it and recognize that it is intended for her. If his first attempt fails to produce a response, he tries again in a few moments. In any case he does not approach closer than one-half mile before having obtained an exchange of identical signals. The "Half-Mile Rule" should thus be considered to define the point at which one must blow the Danger Signal, back his engines, and maneuver with caution if agreement on the manner of passing has not been reached.

Signals When Moving Astern

Inland and International Rules are silent on the passing signals to be used by a ship moving astern. Frequently when moving about a confined harbor it is most practical to proceed astern and one would prefer to have appropriate signals available for use when encountering other vessels. It is common practice for mariners to use passing signals appropriate for the direction of motion; i.e., consider the stern as the bow when moving astern and sound passing signals accordingly. Closer examination of the problem, however, reveals that this practice is hazardous because of the uncertainty of achieving a mutual understanding.

In the first place, the Steering and Sailing Rules are intended to apply to vessels in sight of one another navigating on steady courses apparent to other vessels. A vessel proceeding astern is frequently *not* on a steady course, her speed through the water is often difficult to estimate, and at night the lights she shows astern are quite inadequate for indicating her heading. Further a vessel moving astern is not as maneuverable as when moving ahead (especially a single screw vessel) because of decreased rudder effectiveness and the effect of her hull form. Also, since the practice of exchanging signals in such a case is not supported by statutory law, it is quite possible that one of the two conning officers involved might not be aware of this "common practice" and a hazardous misunderstanding result. Accordingly, proceeding astern should be considered a Special Circumstance and the General Prudential Rule should govern the situation.

In view of the above, when a vessel backing or making sternway sights another vessel, she should immediately sound the Three Blast Backing Signal. If the other vessel is approaching, the backing vessel should maneuver with caution conforming to the principles of the Steering and Sailing Rules (with respect to method of passing) in accordance with her direction of motion, but she should not engage in an exchange of passing signals in Inland Waters nor sound the Course Change signals in International Waters because such whistle signals might be misunderstood. Maneuvering with caution, stopping, and early sounding of the Danger or Doubt Signals are the appropriate actions to be taken in such a situation.

RULES IN FOG OR REDUCED VISIBILITY

General

International	*Inland*
Preliminary	
1. The possession of information obtained from radar does not relieve any vessel of the obligation of conforming strictly with the Rules and, in particular, the obligations contained in Rules 15 and 16.	*(No Equivalent.)*
2. The Annex to the Rules contains recommendations intended to assist in the use of radar as an aid to avoiding collision in restricted visibility.	*(No Equivalent.)*
RULE 15. (a) A power-driven vessel of 40 feet or more in length shall be provided with an efficient whistle, sounded by steam or by some substitute for steam, so placed that the sound may not be intercepted by any obstruction, and with an efficient foghorn, to be sounded by mechanical means, and also with an efficient bell. A sailing vessel of 40 feet or more in length shall	ART. 15. All signals prescribed by this article for vessels under way shall be given:
	1. By "steam vessels" on the whistle or siren.
	2. By "sailing vessels" and "vessels towed" on the fog horn.
	The words "prolonged blast" used in this article shall mean a blast of from 4 to 6 seconds' duration.

be provided with a similar fog-horn and bell.

(b) All signals prescribed by this Rule for vessels under way shall be given:

(i) by power-driven vessels on the whistle;

(ii) by sailing vessels on the fog-horn;

(iii) by vessels towed on the whistle or fog-horn.

(c) In fog, mist, falling snow, heavy rainstorms, or any other condition similarly restricting visibility, whether by day or night, the signals prescribed in this Rule shall be used as follows:

A steam vessel shall be provided with an efficient whistle or siren, sounded by steam or by some substitute for steam, so placed that the sound may not be intercepted by any obstruction, and with an efficient fog-horn; also with an efficient bell. A sailing vessel of 20 tons gross tonnage or upward shall be provided with a similar fog horn and bell.

In fog, mist, falling snow, or heavy rain storms, whether by day or night, the signals described in this article shall be used as follows, namely:

Steam Vessel

RULE 15. (c) (i) A power-driven vessel making way through the water, shall sound at intervals of not more than 2 minutes a prolonged blast.

(ii) A power-driven vessel under way, but stopped and making no way through the water, shall sound at intervals of not more than 2 minutes two prolonged blasts, with an interval of about 1 second between them.

(a) A steam vessel under way shall sound, at intervals of not more than 1 minute, a prolonged blast.

Sailing Vessel

(iii) A sailing vessel under way shall sound, at intervals of not more than 1 minute, when on the starboard tack one blast, when on the port tack two blasts in succession, and when with the wind abaft the beam three blasts in succession.

(c) A sailing vessel under way shall sound, at intervals of not more than 1 minute, when on the starboard tack, one blast; when on the port tack, two blasts in succession, and when with the wind abaft the beam, three blasts in succession.

At Anchor

(iv) A vessel when at anchor shall at intervals of not more than 1 minute ring the bell rapidly for about 5 seconds. In vessels of more than 350 feet in length the bell shall be sounded in the forepart of the vessel, and in addition there shall be sounded in the after part of the vessel, at intervals of not more than 1 minute for about 5 seconds, a gong or other instrument, the tone and sounding of which cannot be confused with that of the bell. Every vessel at anchor may in addition, in accordance with Rule 12, sound three blasts in succession, namely, one short, one prolonged, and one short blast, to give warning of her position and of the possibility of collision to an approaching vessel.

(d) A vessel when at anchor shall, at intervals of not more than 1 minute, ring the bell rapidly for about 5 seconds.

Towing, Not Under Command, Etc.

(v) A vessel when towing, a vessel engaged in laying or in picking up a submarine cable or navigation mark, and a vessel under way which is unable to get out of the way of an approaching vessel through being not under command or unable to maneuver as required by these Rules shall, instead of the signals prescribed in subsections (i), (ii), and (iii) sound, at intervals of not more than 1 minute, three blasts in succession, namely, one prolonged blast followed by two short blasts.

(vi) A vessel towed, or, if more than one vessel is towed, only the last vessel of the tow, if manned, shall, at intervals of not more than 1 minute, sound four blasts in succession, namely, one prolonged blast followed by three short blasts. When practicable, this signal shall be made immediately after the signal made by the towing vessel.

(e) A steam vessel when towing, shall, instead of the signals prescribed in subdivision (a) of this article, at intervals of not more than 1 minute, sound three blasts in succession, namely, one prolonged blast followed by two short blasts. A vessel towed may give this signal and she shall not give any other.

Vessel Aground

(vii) A vessel aground shall give the bell signal and, if required, the gong signal, prescribed in sub-section (iv) and shall, in addition, give 3 separate and distinct strokes on the bell immediately before and after such rapid ringing of the bell.

(No Equivalent.)

Fishing Vessels

(viii) A vessel engaged in fishing when under way or at anchor shall at intervals of not more than 1 minute sound the signal prescribed in sub-section (v). A vessel when fishing with trolling lines and under way shall sound the signals prescribed in sub-sections (i), (ii) or (iii) as may be appropriate.

(No Equivalent.)

Miscellaneous

(ix) A vessel of less than 40 feet in length, a rowing boat, or a seaplane on the water, shall not be obliged to give the above-mentioned signals but if she does not, she shall make some other efficient sound signal at intervals of not more than 1 minute.

(f) All rafts or other water craft, not herein provided for, navigating by hand power, horsepower, or by the current of the river, shall sound a blast of the fog horn, or equivalent signal, at intervals of not more than 1 minute.

Speed in Fog or Reduced Visibility

RULE 16. (a) Every vessel, or seaplane when taxi-ing on the water, shall, in fog,

ART. 16. Every vessel shall, in a fog, mist, falling snow, or heavy rainstorms, go mist, falling snow, heavy rainstorms, or any other condition similarly restricting visibility go at a moderate speed, having careful regard to the existing circumstances and conditions.

(b) A power-driven vessel hearing, apparently forward of her beam, the fog signal of a vessel the position of which is not ascertained, shall, so far as the circumstances of the case admit, stop her engines, and then navigate with caution until danger of collision is over.

at a moderate speed, having careful regard to the existing circumstances and conditions.

A steam vessel hearing, apparently forward of her beam, the fog signal of a vessel the position of which is not ascertained shall, so far as the circumstances of the case admit, stop her engines, and then navigate with caution until danger of collision is over.

Pilot Vessel

(x) A power-driven pilot-vessel when engaged on pilotage duty may, in addition to the signals prescribed in subsections (i), (ii), and (iv), sound an identity signal consisting of 4 short blasts.

(No Equivalent.)

(c) A power-driven vessel which detects the presence of another vessel forward of her beam before hearing her fog signal or sighting her visually may take early and substantial action to avoid a close quarters situation but, if this cannot be avoided, she shall, so far as the circumstances of the case admit, stop her engines in proper time to avoid collision and then navigate with caution until danger of collision is over.

(No Equivalent.)

Effectiveness of Fog Signals

Fog, snow, mist, heavy rain, or other atmospheric condition which limits visibility interferes with many of the Rules of the Road, because they are based upon the fact that vessels are clearly in sight of one another. With the loss of visual contact there is no natural means for discovering other ships and perceiving their movements. To overcome the crippling effect of reduced visibility, both sets of rules prescribe sound signals which shall be used under such conditions. These signals, in general, are sounded on the ship's whistle or bell.

It was mentioned before that whistle signals are quite uncertain at sea because of the wind and ambient noise, and the reader might be wondering about the usefulness of this elaborate system of signalling. The fact is that fog signals are surprisingly effective. For normally fog occurs under conditions of flat calm, and ships proceeding in the fog do so very carefully and with an especially alert watch. The moment the wind picks up, the fog normally disperses. A raging blizzard or torrential thunderstorm is another thing—under such circumstances the low visibility signals are nearly useless. Under normal fog conditions, however, a ship's whistle can be heard for more than a mile, and a ship's bell or gong can be heard for several hundred yards.

Fog Signals—International Waters

When at sea under International Rules, a ship making way in the fog is required to sound one prolonged blast (a sounding of the whistle from four to six seconds), at intervals of not more than two minutes. Practically this means that the conning officer requires his Quartermaster or Messenger to sound a five-second blast on the whistle every two minutes by the clock, shortening the interval occasionally to insure his signal is not in synchronism with and blanking that of another vessel.

When at sea with engines stopped and not making way through the water, the rules require that two five-second blasts with a one-second interval between them be substituted for the single blast of the ship underway. This is quite a useful signal when "feeling" one's way past another vessel in a fog. Ships normally move slowly and carefully in a fog, but it is especially helpful to know that the other ship is actually not making headway and can be depended upon to remain dead in the water at least for the present.

At anchor in International Waters, a ship is required to ring her bell rapidly for about five seconds at intervals of not more than one minute. If the ship is more than 350 feet long—this includes destroyers and larger—she must ring a bell forward and a gong aft. Both the bell and the gong must be sounded for five seconds each minute and in such a way that they cannot be confused. It is normal practice for the gong to be rung for five seconds immediately after the end of the five-second ringing of the bell.

Because of the greater effectiveness of the whistle as compared to the bell, International Rules prescribe a whistle signal ROMEO ($\cdot - \cdot$), a one-second blast followed by a five-second blast followed by a one-second blast, to be used at the discretion of a ship at anchor to warn approaching vessels of her position. For this provision to be useful, the watch officer in addition to manning his surface search radar, must insure that he has steam to the whistle (a normally omitted provision in former days) and has someone posted on the bridge to operate the whistle lever.

In addition to the normal underway and at-anchor signals, International Rules prescribe a Not-Under-Command whistle signal of one five-second blast followed by two one-second blasts for a vessel underway but unable to maneuver because of the work in which she is engaged or because of a breakdown. This signal is especially intended for vessels towing, laying cables, tending buoys, or conducting underwater work, but the conning officer of a Navy ship should use this signal in exactly the same circumstances in which he would use his Breakdown Lights.

For a vessel being towed under International Rules, a signal of one five-second blast followed by three one-second blasts is prescribed. In a multiple tow, only the last vessel of the tow shall sound this signal. When practical, the towed vessel's signal shall follow immediately the signal of the vessel towing. It is most curious to note that this signal is required only if the tow is manned, and that there is no requirement for manning.

International Rules continue and specify special fog signals as follows:

Vessel Aground—Normal signals for a vessel at anchor except that immediately before and immediately after the normal signals she shall sound three separate and distinct strokes of the bell.

Fishing Vessels—Same as for Towing, Not Under Command, etc. the whistle signal DELTA (——— · ·).

Small Vessels—Any sound signal at intervals of not more than 1 minute.

Pilot Vessel—A power-driven Pilot Vessel, *in addition to the signals for a normal power-driven ship,* may sound an identity signal of 4 short blasts.

The elaborate system of sound signals, summarized in Figure 135, seems cumbersome until one realizes that he ordinarily will hear only the one and two blast signals of a vessel underway and the bell and gong of vessels at anchor. The other signals will be heard only infrequently and will be immediately distinguished as unusual. As soon as they are heard, the mariner is warned to proceed with extra caution, and a rapid reference to his bridge copy of the rules will clear up any doubt.

Fog Signals—Inland Waters

The system of fog signals prescribed by the Inland Rules is much simpler than that prescribed by the International Rules. The rules affecting steam vessels are only the following three:

Underway—A steam vessel underway shall sound a five-second blast at intervals of not more than *one minute.*

At Anchor or Moored—Rapid ringing of the bell for five seconds at intervals of not more than *one minute.*

Towing—A steam vessel towing shall sound, at intervals of not more than one minute, a five-second blast followed by two one-second blasts. A vessel being towed *may* sound this same signal and no other.

It is apparent that these rules are almost identical with the major provisions of the International Rules except that the interval for a vessel underway is reduced to one minute, there is no special signal for a vessel underway but with no way on, and there is no requirement for a gong on large ships.

Sailing Vessel in Fog or Reduced Visibility

Sailing vessels are treated identically under both sets of Rules, which provide:

"A sailing vessel under way shall sound, at intervals of not more than one minute, when on the starboard tack, one blast; when on the port tack, two blasts in succession; and when with the wind abaft the beam, three blasts in succession."

The blasts required of sailing vessels of longer than 40 feet (International) or greater than 20 tons, (Inland) shall be made on a fog horn (normally a mechanically operated air horn) and are of unspecified duration but are normally of about one second's duration. Smaller vessels may sound the signals with any efficient sound-making device.

At anchor, sailing vessels make exactly the same signals required for other vessels of equivalent size or tonnage.

Speed in Fog or Reduced Visibility

Both sets of rules are identical in meaning with respect to speed in fog. They require that under conditions of reduced visibility all vessels shall "go at a moderate speed, having careful regard to the existing circumstances and conditions." They also provide that a "vessel hearing, apparently forward of her beam, the fog signal of a vessel the position of which is not ascertained shall, so far as the circumstances of the case admit, stop her engines, and then navigate with caution until danger of collision is over."

The "moderate speed" required by this rule has been the subject of much discussion, and the most frequently found fault in cases involving collision in the fog has been that one or more of the vessels was proceeding at an immoderate speed. As a result of the numerous cases involving this point, a fairly clear definition of the permissible speed has evolved. On the basis that all ships in reduced visibility should be proceeding with equal prudence, a ship that can stop within one-half the distance at which another vessel can be sighted is certainly doing her part to be ready to prevent a collision. Consequently "moderate speed" in a fog or reduced visibility is normally considered to be a speed not more than that from which a vessel can stop in a distance equal to one-half the range of visibility. Since it is quite difficult to know with any accuracy the true limit of visibility at any moment only very low speeds would be found beyond reproach in case of an accident.

Radar in Fog or Reduced Visibility

Since most modern ships are equipped with efficient radars, the whole system for maneuvering in reduced visibility seems to be obsolete. According to the above discussion of "moderate speed," a vessel would have no choice but to lie-to or anchor in "pea-soup" fog when the forecastle cannot be seen from the bridge, yet we know that modern radar-equipped ships can continue their voyages and even enter and leave port safely under conditions of almost zero visibility. Are these ships flouting the law?

SIGNAL		INTERNATIONAL RULES	INLAND RULES
	Visibility	Interval	Interval
▪▪	Clear	CHANGING MY Course to MY RIGHT.	a. INTEND to leave other vessel to PORT, or b. AGREE to YOUR Signal.
 ▪ ▪	Clear	CHANGING MY Course to MY LEFT.	a. INTEND to leave other vessel to STBD. or b. AGREE to YOUR Signal.
 ▪ ▪ ▪	Clear	MY Engines are BACKING.	MY Engines are BACKING.
 ▪ ▪ ▪ ▪ etc.	Special	a. DOUBT (Privileged vessel, in sight only) b. Following normal Fog Signals, Pilot vessel.	DANGER or DOUBT, clear or Fog.
▬▬▬	Fog	Underway in Fog, way on. 2 min.	Underway in Fog. 1 min.
▬▬ ▬▬	Fog	Underway in Fog, but dead in water. 2 min.	NONE
▬▬▬▬▬ 5 sec. International 10 sec. Inland	Special	Approaching Blind Bend.	a. Approaching Blind Bend, or b. Getting Underway from Dock or Berth.
▬▬▬ ▪ ▪	Fog	a. Towing. b. Working Sub Cable or Nav. Mark. c. Broken down, unable to maneuver. d. Fishing Gear caught on bottom. 1 min.	a. Steam vessel TOWING. b. Any vessel being TOWED (Signal is optional and made on Foghorn only!) 1 min.

At top of table:

▪ Whistle, Siren, Foghorn.   ▭ Foghorn only   Bell   ⊙ Gong

Signal and Duration Indicated

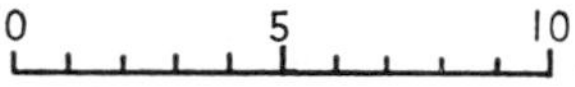

0   5   10 —Time Scale for Blasts in Seconds.

Figure 135. Meanings of Sound Signals.

▬▬▬▬ ■ ■ ■ Fog	Vessel being TOWED (Whistle or Foghorn)	NONE
🔔 5 Sec. Rapid Fog	ANCHORED (under 350') 1 min.	ANCHORED 1 min.
🔔 5 Sec. Rapid ◉ 5 Sec. Rapid Fog	ANCHORED (over 350') 1 min.	NONE
■ ▬▬▬▬ ■ Fog	ANCHORED, optional Danger Warning Signal. As required.	NONE
🔔 3 Stks 🔔 5 Sec. Rapid ◉ 5 Sec. Rapid 🔔 3 Stks Fog	AGROUND 1 min.	NONE
▭ Fog	SAILING, STBD TACK. 1 min.	SAILING, STBD TACK. 1 min.
▭ ▭ Fog	SAILING, PORT TACK. 1 min.	SAILING, PORT TACK. 1 min.
▭ ▭ ▭ Fog	SAILING, WIND AFT. 1 min.	SAILING, WIND AFT. 1 min.
ANY SOUND SIGNAL	SMALL VESSEL 1 min.	RAFT or UNPOWERED VESSEL. 1 min.

Notes: "Fog" means Fog or Reduced Visibility; "Clear" means vessels are in sight of one another.

Radar is an aid to the conning officer which complements his eyes and ears. If the conning officer is certain that the radar is showing him *all* of the other vessels in his vicinity and by adequate plotting he is being kept informed of their movement, he is justified, from the practical if not the legal point of view, in proceeding at the same speed that he would use if there were no fog. He must take into account the fact that the other vessels he might encounter cannot be depended upon to have efficient radars and they might not be aware of his presence and movement. He therefore must *not* expect other vessels to maneuver correctly even though he has the right of way. However, with *certainty* about the adequacy of his radar and his plotting, it is still in the realm of good judgment to proceed even at high speed in fog or reduced visibility.

On the other hand, should there be any doubt about the adequacy of the ship's radar to supply the necessary data which the fog is denying to the human eye, it is culpable irresponsibility to proceed at a greater speed than that from which the ship can stop in half the range of visibility. The dangerous factor in relying on the radar is that it is often difficult to make sure that the radar is actually showing all that is required. The conning officer must constantly check the performance of his radar and utilize land, other vessels, and even waves to make sure that his radar merits the confidence that he is placing in it.

If a collision were to occur while a ship was proceeding at a high speed and depending upon her radar, the ship would almost certainly be found at fault. The only possible defense in such a collision would be to prove that the speed of the vessel could not have contributed at all to causing the collision—a most unlikely event.

Thus the use of modern radar to allow a ship to continue her voyage at the desired speed is a matter of judgment which involves both the efficiency of the radar and the skill of the personnel using it. If, in balancing all of the factors involved, the conning officer decides to proceed, he must recognize that *he will find no comfort in the courts if a collision occurs.*

The 1960 revision of the International Rules recognizes the existence of radar as a modifying influence on the maneuvering of ships in restricted visibility, but they do not yet equate the capability of the electronic "eye" to that of the human eye. The Inland Rules do not yet take cognizance of radar.

Under International Rule 16(c) a vessel detecting another by radar (or other means), prior to sighting such vessel or hearing her fog signal, is specifically permitted to take "early and substantial" avoiding action, however, if a "close quarters situation" cannot be avoided, the normal stopping of engines and navigating with caution is prescribed. This specific permission, though important in itself, is accompanied by some very sound recommendations in the new Annex to the Rules:

International	*Inland*
ANNEX TO THE RULES	
Recommendations on the use of radar information as an aid to avoiding collisions at sea.	
(1) Assumptions made on scanty information may be dangerous and should be avoided.	*(No Equivalent.)*
(2) A vessel navigating with the aid of	*(No Equivalent.)*

radar in restricted visibility must, in compliance with Rule 16(a), go at a moderate speed. Information obtained from the use of radar is one of the circumstances to be taken into account when determining moderate speed. In this regard it must be recognized that small vessels, small icebergs and similar floating objects may not be detected by radar. Radar indications of one or more vessels in the vicinity may mean that "moderate speed" should be slower than a mariner without radar might consider moderate in the circumstances.

(3) When navigating in restricted visibility the radar range and bearing alone do not constitute ascertainment of the position of the other vessel under Rule 16(b) sufficiently to relieve a vessel of the duty to stop her engines and navigate with caution when a fog signal is heard forward of the beam.

(No Equivalent.)

(4) When action has been taken under Rule 16(c) to avoid a close quarters situation, it is essential to make sure that such action is having the desired effect. Alterations of course or speed or both are matters as to which the mariner must be guided by the circumstances of the case.

(No Equivalent.)

(5) Alteration of course alone may be the most effective action to avoid close quarters provided that:
　(a) There is sufficient sea room.
　(b) It is made in good time.
　(c) It is substantial. A succession of small alterations of course should be avoided.
　(d) It does not result in a close quarters situation with other vessels.

(No Equivalent.)

(6) The direction of an alteration of course is a matter in which the mariner must be guided by the circumstances of the case. An alteration to starboard, particularly when vessels are approaching apparently on opposite or nearly opposite courses, is generally preferable to an alteration to port.

(No Equivalent.)

(7) An alteration of speed, either alone or in conjunction with an alteration of course, should be substantial. A number of small alterations of speed should be avoided.

(No Equivalent.)

(8) If a close quarters situation is imminent, the most prudent action may be to take all way off the vessel.

(No Equivalent.)

Lookout in Fog or Reduced Visibility

The whole problem of maneuvering in a fog turns about the lack of visibility. The more one can see, the less he must depend upon the artificialities of the rules. The harder we try and the more skillful we are, the more likely we are to see what we are looking for, *and our eyes and ears are those of our lookouts.*

The rules deal with the problem of lookouts negatively by stating in Article 29 that "Nothing in these rules shall exonerate any vessel . . . from the consequences . . . of any neglect to keep a proper lookout. . . ." The conning officer must be positive that he is giving himself the best possible chance to see or hear an approaching vessel. He must post his lookouts to see and to hear—not just to comply with a law. The lookouts must be competent, must be adequately instructed, must be properly placed, and must be sufficiently numerous for the circumstances. *Officers and petty officers* should be used in difficult situations, and under any circumstances only *alert, intelligent* men should be entrusted with this important duty. Since fog is often in thin layers, visibility might change markedly at different heights, and it is frequently much better near the surface of the water than at bridge height. When entering or leaving port in thick fog in a modern destroyer, the author normally stationed an officer and two petty officers in the eyes of the ship, experienced seaman on each wing of the bridge, looking to the sides and astern, and a petty officer as far up the mast as was safe with the radars operating. These men know they were part of the team helping to conn the ship, and they frequently detected important elements well before they were perceived by the conning personnel.

LIGHTS AND SHAPES FOR NORMAL SEAGOING VESSELS

Under all the rules vessels are required to carry lights, not only to insure that they will be sighted during darkness, but also to give an approaching vessel an indication of the heading of the vessel. Vessels engaged in special operations restricting their maneuverability or according them certain rights are required to carry special lights so that approaching vessels can recognize them and maneuver accordingly. By day the rules prescribe that special shapes be shown to insure recognition of such vessels. Twelve of the thirty-one International Rules are devoted to the specification of the lights required by various vessels; an equal number of the Inland Articles are devoted to the same subject, and a much larger portion of the Pilot Rules for Inland Waters deal with the requirements for special lights and shapes. In total, the rules concerning lights and shapes form an impressive body of law.

Rather than commit such a mass of rules to memory, let us examine them and determine which parts must really be a part of the shiphandler's working knowledge as he stands on the bridge of his ship.

The shiphandler must be able to recognize the type of ship he is encountering, estimate with reasonable accuracy her course and special occupation, if any, and then maneuver appropriately, if required, during the passing. Dimensions and spacing of lights, required distances of visibility, exact arcs of visibility, etc. are of primary interest to the shipbuilder or periodically to the commanding officer. The conning officer can turn his lights on and check that they are operating, but in general he has no control over their characteristics. As for the lights of the other vessel, he has no control over them at all, and he would probably never recognize any minor deviation from the rules should there be such.

To suit the needs of the average conning officer of a major ship, the following discussion will examine the rules applying to a large sea-going vessel in both International and Inland Waters and then, by brief discussion and the use of figures, cover the special classes of vessels covered in the rules. Should the reader wish to examine the detailed wording of the rules applying to other than major sea-going vessels, he is referred to Appendix III, where the complete texts of the rules are given.

Running Lights

International	*Inland*

MASTHEAD AND RANGE LIGHTS

International	*Inland*
RULE 2. (a) A power-driven vessel when under way shall carry:	ART. 2. A steam vessel when under way shall carry—(a) On or in the front of the foremast, or if a vessel without a foremast, then in the fore part of the vessel, a bright white light so constructed as to show an unbroken light over an arc of the horizon of 20 points of the compass, so fixed as to throw the light 10 points on each side of the vessel, namely, from right ahead to 2 points abaft the beam on either side, and of such a character as to be visible at a distance of at least 5 miles.
(i) On or in front of the foremast, or if a vessel without a foremast then in the forepart of the vessel, a white light so constructed as to show an unbroken light over an arc of the horizon of 225 degrees (20 points of the compass) so fixed as to show the light 112½ degrees (10 points) on each side of the vessel, that is, from right ahead to 22½ degrees (2 points), abaft the beam on either side, and of such a character as to be visible at a distance of at least 5 miles.	
(ii) Either forward of or abaft the white light mentioned in sub-section (i) a second white light similar in construction and character to that light. Vessels of less than 150 feet in length, and vessels engaged in towing, shall not be required to carry this second white light but may do so.	(e) A seagoing steam vessel when under way may carry an additional white light similar in construction to the light mentioned in subdivision (a). These two lights shall be so placed in line with the keel that one shall be at least fifteen feet higher than the other, and in such a position with reference to each other that the lower light shall be forward of the upper one. The
(iii) These two white lights shall be so	

placed in a line with and over the keel that one shall be at least 15 feet higher than the other and in such a position that the forward light shall always be shown lower than the after one. The horizontal distance between the two white lights shall be at least three times the vertical distance. The lower of these two white lights or, if only one is carried, then that light, shall be placed at a height above the hull of not less than 20 feet, and, if the breadth of the vessel exceeds 20 feet, then at a height above the hull not less than such breadth, so however, that the light need not be placed at a greater height above the hull than 40 feet. In all circumstances the light or lights, as the case may be, shall be so placed as to be clear of and above all other lights and obstructing superstructures.

vertical distance between these lights shall be less than the horizontal distance.

(f) All steam vessels (except seagoing vessels and ferryboats, shall carry in addition to green and red lights required by article two (b), (c), and screens as required by article two (d), a central range of two white lights; the after light being carried at an elevation at least 15 feet above the light at the head of the vessel. The headlight shall be so constructed as to show an unbroken light through 20 points of the compass, namely, from right ahead to 2 points abaft the beam on either side of the vessel, and the after light so as to show all around the horizon.

SIDE LIGHTS

(iv) On the starboard side a green light so constructed as to show an unbroken light over an arc of the horizon of $112\frac{1}{2}$ degrees (10 points of the compass), so fixed as to show the light from right ahead to $22\frac{1}{2}$ degrees (2 points) abaft the beam on the starboard side, and of such a character as to be visible at a distance of at least 2 miles.

(v) On the port side a red light so constructed as to show an unbroken light over an arc of the horizon of $112\frac{1}{2}$ degrees (10 points of the compass), so fixed as to show the light from right ahead to $22\frac{1}{2}$ degrees (2 points) abaft the beam on the port side, and of such a character as to be visible at a distance of at least 2 miles.

(vi) The said green and red sidelights shall be fitted with inboard screens projecting at least 3 feet forward from the light, so as to prevent these lights from being seen across the bows.

(b) On the starboard side a green light so constructed as to show an unbroken light over an arc of the horizon of 10 points of the compass, so fixed as to throw the light from right ahead to 2 points abaft the beam on the starboard side, and of such a character as to be visible at a distance of at least 2 miles.

(c) On the port side a red light so constructed as to show an unbroken light over an arc of the horizon of 10 points of the compass, so fixed as to throw the light from right ahead to 2 points abaft the beam on the port side, and of such a character as to be visible at a distance of at least 2 miles.

(d) The said green and red side lights shall be fitted with inboard screens projecting at least 3 feet forward from the light, so as to prevent these lights from being seen across the bow.

STERN LIGHT

RULE 10. (a) Except where otherwise provided in these Rules, a vessel when under way shall carry at her stern a white light, so constructed that it shall show an unbroken light over an arc of the horizon of 135 degrees (12 points of the compass), so fixed as to show the light $67\frac{1}{2}$ degrees (6 points) from right aft on each side of the vessel, and of such a character as to be visible at a distance of at least 2 miles.

ART. 10. A vessel which is being overtaken by another, except a steam vessel with an after range light showing all around the horizon, shall show from her stern to such last-mentioned vessel a white light or a flare-up light.

The running lights are the lights that a vessel must show during the hours of darkness or reduced visibility when she is underway, i.e. not anchored or moored. They consist of a central range of two lights, of which the forward light is called the masthead light, and the after one, which is mounted distinctly higher, is called the range light; the red and green side lights; and in the case of a sea-going vessel, the stern light. The running lights are required to be turned on at sunset when underway and they must be kept on until sunrise.

It will be noted that in Inland Waters, a non-sea-going vessel may show an all-around range light in lieu of the combination of the 20-point range and 12-point stern light, but in any of the allowed arrangements, a white light will be visible from any point of the compass, at least upon the approach of another vessel.

Anchor Lights

International

RULE 11. (a). A vessel under 150 feet in length, when at anchor, shall carry in the forepart of the vessel, where it can best be seen, a white light visible all round the horizon at a distance of at least 2 miles. Such a vessel may also carry a second white light in the position described in section (b) of this Rule but shall not be required to do so. The second white light, if carried, shall be visible at a distance of at least 2 miles and so placed as to be as far as possible visible all round the horizon.

(b) A vessel of 150 feet or more in length, when at anchor, shall carry near the stem of the vessel, at a height of not less than 20 feet above the hull, one such light, and at or near the stern of the vessel and at such a height that it shall not be less than 15 feet lower than the forward light, another such light. Both these lights shall be visible at a distance of at least 3 miles, and so placed as to be as far as possible visible all round the horizon.

Inland

ART. 11. A vessel under 150 feet in length when at anchor shall carry forward, where it can best be seen, but at a height not exceeding 20 feet above the hull, a white light in a lantern, so constructed as to show a clear, uniform, and unbroken light visible all around the horizon at a distance of at least 1 mile:

Provided, That the Secretary of the Army may, after investigation, by rule, regulation, or order, designate such areas as he may deem proper as "special anchorage areas"; such special anchorage areas may from time to time be changed, or abolished, if after investigation the Secretary of the Army shall deem such change or abolition in the interest of navigation:

Provided further, That vessels not more than 65 feet in length when at anchor in any such special anchorage area shall not be required to carry or exhibit the white light required by this article.

A vessel of 150 feet or upward in length when at anchor, shall carry in the forward part of the vessel, at a height of not less than 20 and not exceeding 40 feet above the hull, one such light, and at or near the stern of the vessel, and at such a height that it shall be not less than 15 feet lower than the forward light, another such light.

All major ships are required to show two all-around anchor lights when at anchor, one near the stem of the ship and one "at or near" the stern, the forward one being at least 15 feet higher than the after one under all rules. Small vessels, those under 150 feet in length, are required to show only one anchor light, mounted forward where it can best be seen, and vessels under 65 feet in length, when anchored in specially designated anchorage areas in Inland Waters, are not *required* to show any light at all.

Anchor Ball

International	*Inland*
RULE 11. (c). Between sunrise and sunset every vessel when at anchor shall carry in the forepart of the vessel, where it can best be seen, one black ball not less than 2 feet in diameter.	SEC. 80.25. Vessels of more than 65 feet in length when moored or anchored in a fairway or channel shall display between sunrise and sunset on the forward part of the vessel where it can best be seen from other vessels one black ball not less than 2 feet in diameter.

The anchor ball is an unusually useful signal. As one enters a harbor filled with shipping it is often impossible to distinguish between the vessels which are actually at anchor and those which are lying-to. Many a hair-raising moment has been caused by cutting across the bow of a ship assumed to be anchored when in fact she was just starting ahead. It is often not possible to see the anchor chain of a vessel at anchor, so the anchor ball is depended upon in cases where the chain cannot be seen.

In Inland Waters, the anchor ball is specified not only for a vessel at anchor but also for a vessel moored to a pier or aground. International Rules do not require the signal when moored and specify *three* black balls in a vertical line for the vessel aground.

Breakdown Lights

International	*Inland*
RULE 4. (a). A vessel which is not under command shall carry, where they can best be seen, and, if a power-driven vessel, in lieu of the lights required by Rule 2 (a) (i) and (ii), two red lights in a vertical line one over the other not less than 6 feet apart, and of such a character as to be visible all round the horizon at a distance of at least 2 miles. By day, she shall carry in a vertical line one over the other not less than 6 feet apart, where they can best be seen, two black balls or shapes each not less than 2 feet in diameter.	*(No Such Provision.)*

In case of steering failure, machinery breakdown, or other casualty which interferes with the normal maneuverability of the ship, the International

Rules prescribe the Not-Under-Command Signal, more descriptively known as the "breakdown lights." In case of material casualty which interferes with the maneuverability of the ship, the conning officer in International Waters, should immediately turn off his masthead and range lights, and turn on his breakdown lights, two all-around, red lights in a vertical line. While the vessel has way on, the side lights must also be shown. If a casualty occurs in daylight, the equivalent signal is the display of two black shapes in a vertical line, usually two anchor balls.

Lights for Sailing Vessels

International

RULE 5. (a). A sailing vessel under way and any vessel or seaplane being towed shall carry the same lights as are prescribed by Rule 2 for a power-driven vessel or a seaplane under way, respectively, with the exception of the white lights specified therein, which they shall never carry. They shall also carry stern lights as specified in Rule 10, provided that vessels towed, except the last vessel of a tow, may carry, in lieu of such stern light, a small white light as specified in Rule 3 (b).

(b) In addition to the lights prescribed in section (a), a sailing vessel may carry on the top of the foremast two lights in a vertical line one over the other, sufficiently separated so as to be clearly distinguished. The upper light shall be red and the lower light shall be green. Both lights shall be constructed and fixed as prescribed in Rule 2(a) (i) and shall be visible at a distance of at least 2 miles.

Inland

ART. 5. A sailing vessel under way and any vessel being towed, except barges, canal boats, scows, and other vessels of nondescript type, when in tow of steam vessels, shall carry the same lights as are prescribed by Article 2 for a steam vessel under way, with the exception of the white lights mentioned, therein, which they shall never carry.

(No Equivalent.)

Sailing vessels are required to carry side lights and a stern light but, in International Waters, may additionally carry a red light over a green light at the masthead. They are specifically forbidden to carry the central range of white lights.

Vessels being towed carry the same lights as a sailing vessel, except in Inland Waters where there are special Pilot Rules covering the lights which shall be carried by barges, canal boats, scows, and other vessels of nondescript type.

Naval Lights

International

RULE 13. (a). Nothing in these Rules shall interfere with the operation of any special rules made by the Government of any nation with respect to additional station and signal lights for ships of war, for

Inland

ART. 13. Nothing in these rules shall interfere with the operation of any special rules made by the Government of any nation with respect to additional station and signal lights for two or more ships of

vessels sailing under convoy, or for seaplanes on the water; or with the exhibition
of recognition signals adopted by shipowners, which have been authorised by
their respective Governments and duly registered and published.

war or for vessels sailing under convoy, or
with the exhibition of recognition signals
adopted by shipowners, which have been
authorised by their respective Governments, and duly registered and published.

This rule authorizes the use of special lights required by naval authorities
such as red truck lights for warning aircraft when anchored or moored, the
use of speed lights when in the vicinity of other naval vessels, the use of
yardarm blinker lights, etc. Without such a rule, many lights used by the
Navy could be interpreted as clear violations of the law of the sea. This rule
does *not* authorize "Darkened Ship," and while a warship is steaming darkened she must maneuver to avoid an approaching vessel.

LIGHTS AND SHAPES FOR SPECIAL CLASSES OF VESSELS

Though most vessels are easily identified by sight during the daytime, there
are many times when it is impossible to tell by casual observation what operations a particular vessel might be conducting. The rules recognize that certain vessels are unable to maneuver freely because of the work in which they
are engaged and cannot be expected to met the requirements of a normal
vessel. In some cases the rules require all other vessels to keep clear of such
vessels, but in most cases the rules only state that such vessels be considered
as vessels "Not Under Command." To enable the mariner to recognize such
vessels, the rules prescribe special lights at night and special signals for daytime. These rules are very complex and are quite different in the various
waters. In general the inability of a vessel to maneuver is indicatd at night
by displays containing red lights; the greater the number of red lights, the
greater the degree of non-maneuverability. To some extent this principle
extends to the day signals; in general, the greater the number of shapes in
the required display, the less the vessel is able to maneuver. A summary of
the various lights and shapes required under the rules is shown in Figure 136.

Restrictive Operations (International Waters)

In International Waters, a vessel engaged in operations which restrict her
ability to get out of the way of an approaching vessel (such as replenishment
at sea, launching or recovering aircraft, working a submarine cable, working a navigation marker, surveying, conducting diving operations, etc.) must
not show the masthead and range lights, but in their place must show three
all-around lights in a vertical line, the top and bottom ones being red and
the middle one white. By day the three lights are replaced by shapes of the
same colors as follows: top and bottom, globular and red; middle, diamond-
shaped and white. When such vessels are not making way through the water,

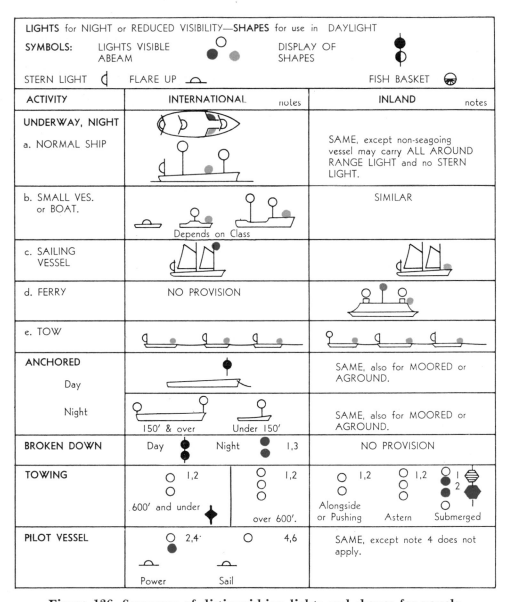

Figure 136. Summary of distinguishing lights and shapes for vessels.

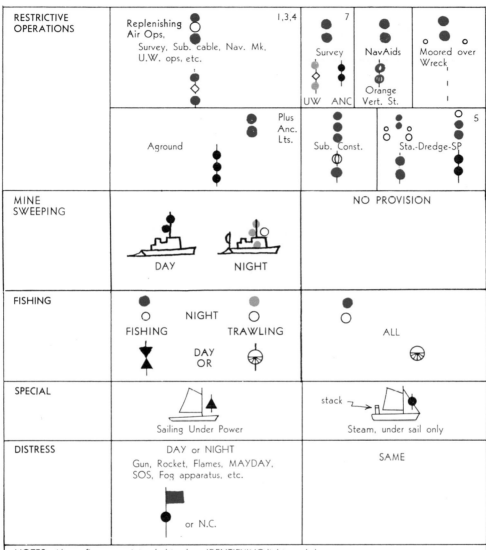

RESTRICTIVE OPERATIONS	Replenishing Air Ops, Survey, Sub. cable, Nav. Mk, U.W. ops, etc.	1,3,4	Survey	7	NavAids	Moored over Wreck
			UW	ANC	Orange Vert. St.	
	Aground	Plus Anc. Lts.	Sub. Const.		Sta.-Dredge-SP	5
MINE SWEEPING	DAY NIGHT		NO PROVISION			
FISHING	NIGHT FISHING TRAWLING DAY OR		ALL			
SPECIAL	Sailing Under Power		stack → Steam, under sail only			
DISTRESS	DAY or NIGHT Gun, Rocket, Flames, MAYDAY, SOS, Fog apparatus, etc. or N.C.		SAME			

NOTES: Above figures are intended to show IDENTIFYING lights and do
       not include minor variations and special cases.

1. Plus Stern Light when Underway (Special provisions for Tugs and Tows).
2. Plus Side Lights when Underway.
3. Plus Side Lights when Underway with Way On.
4. Plus Anchor Lights when at Anchor.
5. Plus Complex special provisions.
6. Also Show Side Lights on approach of another vessel.
7. Plus Flare Up Light as necessary.

they must not show side lights, nor stern lights, but when they are making way they shall show them. The showing of these lights and shapes is to be interpreted by other vessels as indicating that the vessel is "Not Under Command" and is unable to maneuver to get out of the way.

Restrictive Operations (Inland Waters)

Inland Rules are silent on the subject of vessels engaged in restrictive occupations, but the Pilot Rules for Inland Waters devote a large section to the subject. Though no attempt will be made to go into detail, in brief summary the requirements are:

Vessels Working on Wrecks—By night, two red lights in a vertical line plus bow and stern white lights on each outside vessel of a group. By day, two red hexagonal shapes in a vertical line.

Stationary Dredges—By night, two red lights in a vertical line and a white light at each corner of the dredge plus white lights at each outboard corner of scows or lighters moored alongside. By day, two red balls in a vertical line.

Self-Propelled Suction Dredges, when Dredging—By night, in addition to regular running lights, two red lights of the same arc as the masthead light and in a vertical line below the masthead light, and two red stern lights showing two points either side of dead astern. By day, two black balls in a vertical line.

Vessels Engaged in Underwater Operations—By night, three red lights in a vertical line. If there is a line of vessels or barges engaged in the operation, a horizontal line of amber lights, not more than 50 feet apart shall mark these vessels. By day, two balls in a vertical line, the upper with vertical black and white stripes, and the lower painted bright red.

Floating Pipelines—By night, a string of amber lights along the entire length of the pipeline, being spaced not more than 30 feet apart where such line crosses a navigational channel. No day marking.

Floating Plant Moorings (this applies to any of the above types of special vessels)—When any type of floating plant is using a combination of bow, breast, and stern anchors while working in a navigable channel, such anchors shall be marked by a barrel or buoy, and at night these buoys shall either be lighted by red lights, or they shall be illuminated by playing a spotlight on them on the approach of another vessel. This rule is not applicable in certain parts of New York Harbor.

Coast and Geodetic Survey Vessels Surveying—By night, underway, normal running lights. At anchor in a fairway, two red lights in a vertical line with a flare-up light ready for use. By day, underway, three shapes in a vertical line, top and bottom globular and green, middle one diamond and white. At anchor in a fairway, two black balls in a vertical line.

Coast Guard Vessels Servicing Navigation Aids—By night, two red lights in a vertical line. By day, two orange and white vertically striped balls in a vertical line.

Miscellaneous Vessels (Inland Waters Only)

Vessel Towing Submerged Objects—By night, in place of the regular towing lights, four lights in a vertical line, the top and bottom being white and the two middle ones red, all lights to be of the same character as the regular towing lights. By day, two hexagonal shapes in a vertical line, the upper with black and white horizontal stripes, and the lower painted bright red.

Double Ended Ferry Boats—Normal side lights for the direction of intended travel and a central range of two all around white lights placed at equal heights forward and aft. Officers in charge of Marine Inspection may designate a third light, white or colored, to be mounted amidships in line and above the two white lights.

Towing Lights

Though a tug and tow are easily recognized in broad daylight, at night it is not at all easy to distinguish a vessel towing another astern from two vessels following the same track, and a tug with tow alongside often has her identifying lights obscured by the vessel towed. For this reason a special system of identification lights has been provided for vessels involved in towing operations. Though the rules differ in detail between the International and Inland Rules, the systems are very similar.

In both sets of rules, a vessel towing another alongside, in addition to her side lights shall show an additional white light of the same characteristics and mounted above or below in a vertical line with the masthead light. All vessels towing astern in Inland Waters, and vessels towing a long tow astern in International Waters, shall show a third white light in the vertical line with the masthead light. The rules next become somewhat complicated by optional features which may or may not result in a central range of lights in addition to the vertical line of towing lights, and in the case of Inland Rules allows the option of forming the vertical display around and with the characteristics of the range light (an all-around light in Inland Rules), but the chance of confusion is slight. When we see either two or three white lights in a vertical line, we know we are encountering a tug and tow. By day in International Waters a vessel with a long tow shows a black diamond shape.

On the high seas, the vessel being towed shows her Side Lights and her Stern Light, and this is the same in Inland Rules except that the last vessel of a multiple tow shows two stern lights. Under Inland and Pilot Rules, however, the regulations become much more complicated in the cases of multiple tows of barges, lighters, and nondescript vessels. In these extensive rules, normally affecting only special harbors or inland rivers and canals seldom frequented by sea-going ships, various assortments of white and colored lights are used to identfy the various arrangements of barges. It is sufficient for the sea-going conning officer to know that these rules always result in ends of narrow tows and all corners of wide tows being clearly marked by a light.

The mark of a towing operation is two or three white lights in a vertical line. Once this sign is spotted, the mariner is warned, and he can proceed cautiously until he has identified the character and extent of the tow.

Vessel With Both Sail and Power

A vessel proceeding under the combination of sail and power in International Waters is considered under the rules as a power vessel in spite of her sails and must display forward, where it can best be seen, a single black conical shape, point upwards. In Inland Waters, the opposite case, that of a steam vessel (with her funnel up) proceeding under sail only, *may* indicate her condition by displaying her anchor ball forward.

Mine Sweeping

Vessels engaged in minesweeping operations at night are required, in International waters, to shown (in addition to masthead light, side lights and stern light) a green all-around light at the fore truck and a similar light or lights at the ends of the fore yard to the side or sides to which their sweep gear is streamed. Thus two or three green lights in the upperworks marks a minesweeper. By day such vessels are required to carry black balls in the same position as the green lights. When not making way through the water, such vessels show the green lights and the masthead light but extinguish the side lights and the stern light.

Seaplanes

In International Waters a seaplane on the water at night is required to carry a white light similar to a masthead light mounted forward on the centerline, a tail light showing aft, and red and green side lights mounted on the wing tips. In case of breakdown, a seaplane may show normal breakdown lights at night and, by day, she may show the breakdown signal of two black balls.

Inland Rules are silent on the subject of seaplanes, but mariners can assume that seaplanes encountered in Inland Waters will show at least side lights and an all-around white light.

Lights For Pilot Vessels

Pilot vessels, when waiting to provide pilots to vessels coming in from sea, lie-to or maneuver slowly in the vicinity of the designated rendezvous point, which is normally the last harbor channel marker to seaward. A harbor entrance is a busy place, and there may be so many vessels in the vicinity of the sea buoy picking up or dropping pilots that an incoming vessel has difficulty in spotting the pilot vessel among them. Further, since a pilot vessel must maneuver constantly as she goes from vessel to vessel, she does not hold her course and speed for any predictable length of time, and this would be very confusing for a vessel attempting to pass her in the normal way. For these reasons special lights and sound signals are designated for Pilot Vessels so they can easily be distinguished from other vessels entering or leaving the harbor.

A sailing Pilot Vessel—and a large number of pilot vessels in use today are sailing vessels—is required to show an all-around white light at the masthead and also to exhibit a flare-up light or flare-up lights at short intervals. She does not normally carry side lights, but on the approach of other vessels she is required to "flash" or show them at short intervals to indicate her heading.

Small Pilot Vessels, of a class which goes alongside another vessel to put a pilot aboard, may merely "show" the white masthead light instead of carrying it at the masthead, and may use a combination colored lantern in place of side lights when needed.

A power-driven Pilot Vessel, on the other hand, in addition to the white masthead light and the flare-up light prescribed for the sailing Pilot Vessels, is required to carry a red all-around light on the mast 8 feet below the white light, and also she must carry the normal side lights of a vessel underway.

In many cases Pilot Vessels can perform their duties at anchor, and while so doing, they continue to show the distinguishing lights for their class as indicated above, except that they must never exhibit side lights while at anchor. In Inland Waters, these are the only lights shown by a Pilot Vessel, but in International Waters, Pilot Vessels at anchor show normal anchor lights in addition to their special Pilot-Vessel Lights. This is the only significant difference between the two bodies of rules in this case.

In all waters, Pilot Vessels, not engaged in piloting duties, shall show the lights of a normal vessel of her size and type.

Fishing Vessels (International Waters)

Vessels fishing with nets or heavy rigs of one sort or another are often unable to maneuver freely because of the drag of the rig. In addition, many of these expensive rigs float close to the surface of the water, and a vessel cutting through them could cause considerable loss. Consequently the rule prescribes special lights and signals to enable the mariner to distinguish a vessel actually engaged in fishing.

First, a fishing vessel not engaged in fishing or a vessel engaged in trolling (towing simple fishing lines astern is not included in the special provisions for fishing vessels, and such vessels must show the normal lights for their class.

Vessels engaged in fishing, whether under way or at anchor, shall carry aloft in a vertical line an all-around red light over an all-around white light. Vessels engaged in trawling shall similarly carry a green light over a white light and may carry a masthead light, but lower and abaft these identifying lights. Whether fishing or trawling, fishing vessels must show side lights and stern lights when making way through the water but extinguish them when not making way through the water. Vessels fishing with outlying gear extending more than 500 feet horizontally into the seaway shall carry an additional white light in the direction of the gear. Thus, red-over-white or green-over-white marks the fisherman and if he shows an extra white light separated to the side, there is danger in that direction.

In addition to the lights specified above, any fishing boat is permitted to use a flare-up light to attract the attention of another vessel, and she is also permitted to use working lights.

By day, the sign of a fisherman is a black shape consisting of two cones one above the other with their points together; small fishing vessels may substitute a basket for this black shape. If the outlying gear of a fishing vessel extends more than 500 feet horizontally into the seaway, the vessel shall additionally show one black cone, point upwards, in the direction of the gear.

All vessels not engaged in fishing, except those to which Rule 4 (Not under command, replenishing, flight operations, minesweeping, etc.) applies, shall keep out of the way of vessels engaged in fishing. This Rule does not, however, give any vessel engaged in fishing the right to obstruct a fairway used by other than fishing vessels.

Fishing Vessels (Inland Waters)

In Inland Waters, *all* vessels when trawling, or fishing with any kind of nets or lines, must carry, where it can best be seen, a display of two all-around lights, the upper of which shall be red, and the lower (from 6 to 12 feet below and displaced not more than 10 feet horizontally from the upper) shall be white.

When not fishing, fishing vessels must carry the normal lights for a vessel of the same class, except that fishing vessels of less than 10 tons may, instead of carrying normal side lights, exhibit a suitably colored combination lantern to indicate her heading to an approaching vessel.

Small Vessels and Boats (International Waters)

Power-driven vessels of less than 65 feet in length may show the normal lights of a larger vessel, but if they do not, they are required at least to show a masthead light and side lights and stern lights. The side lights may be mounted separately or may be combined in a single lantern showing only the correct color in the prescribed arcs.

Sailing and rowing boats of less than 40 feet in length, if they do not carry the normal side lights of a sailing vessel, shall carry a combination lantern showing green in the starboard side light arc and red in the arc of the port side light. If it is not possible to fix this light, it shall be kept ready for immediate use and exhibited in ample time to warn an approaching vessel.

Small rowing-boats, whether under oars or sail, are required only to show a flashlight or hand lantern in time to warn approaching vessels of their presence.

Rule 6, which, now applies to vessels of any category, provides that in bad weather or for other good reason, when it is impossible to fix the side lights of a vessel, these lights shall be kept lighted and ready for use, and on the approach of another vessel they shall be exhibited on their respective sides in time to prevent collision.

Small vessels in International Waters are not required to have breakdown lights or shapes or the day signal for a vessel aground. They are, however, required to show a single anchor light at night and the anchor ball during the day.

Small Vessels and Boats (Inland Waters)

The Motorboat Act covers all vessels propelled by machinery not more than 65 feet in length, except tugboats and towboats propelled by steam. Under this Act, large motorboats, defined as being between 26 and 65 feet in length, are required to show a masthead light, and all-around range light, and separately mounted side lights. Small motorboats, up to 26 feet in length, show an all-around white range light aft, and a combination lantern forward, showing red and green in the appropriate arcs for the side lights.

When such boats are being propelled by sail alone, they shall not exhibit the white lights mentioned above, but shall carry only their side lights. When not showing their white lights, however, they shall have a flashlight or white lantern ready for use to warn approaching vessels of their presence. Article 7 of the Inland Rules requires that rowing boats have a similar white lantern ready for use in warning other vessels.

Vessels under 150 feet in length are required to show only a single all-around white light when at anchor, and vessels under 65 feet in length, when anchored in officially designated "Special Anchorage Areas" are not *required* to show any light at all.

In Inland Waters, vessels under 65 feet in length are excluded from the requirement to show an anchor ball during the day.

SIGNALS

Special Signals

International

RULE 12. Every vessel or seaplane on the water may, if necessary in order to attract attention, in addition to the lights which she is by these Rules required to carry, show a flare-up light or use a detonating or other efficient sound signal that cannot be mistaken for any signal authorized elsewhere under these Rules.

Inland

ART. 12. Every vessel may, if necessary, in order to attract attention, in addition to the lights which she is by these rules required to carry, show a flare-up light or use any detonating signal that cannot be mistaken for a distress signal.

The intent of this rule is clear: Every mariner is to consider himself at liberty to utilize for attracting attention any light or sound signal available to him that cannot be mistaken for one of the other signals under the rules. The problem often lies in finding an appropriate light or sound device for making such a signal.

On a warship, the ship's whistle (and siren, if so equipped) and the signal searchlights are normally the only means at hand for such signalling. A series of blasts on the whistle will usually attract attention, and even if such a series should be interpreted as the Danger Signal, this is often the interpretation desired. Flashing a signal searchlight at an approaching ship and then playing it on the object to which one desires to draw attention is also an effective signal. With a little opportunity for preparation, a Verys Pistol or a rifle can serve for use in attracting attention.

Distress Signals

International

RULE 31. (a) When a vessel or seaplane on the water is in distress and requires assistance from other vessels or from the shore, the following shall be the signals to be used or displayed by her, either together or separately, namely:

(i) A gun or other explosive signal fired at intervals of about a minute.

(ii) A continuous sounding with any fog-signal apparatus.

(iii) Rockets or shells, throwing red stars fired one at a time at short intervals.

(iv) A signal made by radiotelegraphy or by any other signalling method consisting of the group · · · – – – · · · in the Morse Code.

(v) A signal sent by radiotelephony consisting of the spoken word "Mayday."

(vi) The International Code Signal of distress indicated by NC.

(vii) A signal consisting of a square flag

Inland

ART. 31. When a vessel is in distress and requires assistance from other vessels or from the shore the following shall be the signal to be used or displayed by her, either together or separately, namely:

In the daytime—

A continuous sounding with any fog-signal apparatus, or firing a gun.

At night—

First. Flames on the vessel as from a burning tar barrel, oil barrel, and so forth.

Second. A continuous sounding with any fog-signal apparatus, or firing a gun.

having about or below it a ball or anything resembling a ball.

(viii) Flames on the vessel (as from a burning tar barrel, oil barrel, etc.).

(ix) A rocket parachute flare showing a red light.

(x) A smoke signal giving off a volume of orange-colored smoke.

(xi) Slowly and repeatedly raising and lowering arms outstretched to each side.

Note—Vessels in distress may use the radiotelegraph alarm signal or the radiotelephone alarm signal to secure attention to distress calls and messages. The radiotelegraph alarm signal, which is designed to actuate the radiotelegraph auto alarms of vessels so fitted, consists of a series of twelve dashes, sent in 1 minute, the duration of each dash being 4 seconds, and the duration of the interval between two consecutive dashes being 1 second. The radiotelephone alarm signal consists of 2 tones transmitted alternately over periods of from 30 seconds to 1 minute.

(b) The use of any of the foregoing signals, except for the purpose of indicating that a vessel or seaplane is in distress, and the use of any signals which may be confused with any of the above signals, is prohibited.

A vessel "in distress" is a vessel in severe danger and is requesting assistance in the most urgent manner. From the above list, it is seen that a great variety of spectacular sound and light signals are prescribed, and the entire International list should be considered effective in Inland Waters also. When a vessel is in such a precarious situation that she is signalling for help, it is no time to apply the fine distinctions between the bodies of rules.

CHAPTER XXI

MARINERS AT WORK

EXAMPLE 1

Problem

USS THOMAS J. GARY (DE 326) was moored stern to the quay at Admiralty Dock, Port Said, with a slightly modified Mediterranean Moor. Due to the proximity of other ships, the anchors had been dropped nearly dead ahead, well out in the Suez Canal. As the ship prepared to depart, a 15-knot wind sprang up, blowing GARY down on the other ships moored to the quay. A British submarine was next adjacent to leeward. The wind was too strong to allow the moor to be broken in the normal manner without the ship being set hard against the submarine lying only 5 yards to leeward. No tugs were available and departure could not be delayed until the wind subsided.

Solution (Figure 137)

GARY commenced heaving on her windward anchor as she eased her stern line. As soon as the stern began to come away from the quay, the engines were opposed; the starboard engine BACK TWO THIRDS and the port engine AHEAD ONE THIRD. This kept the stern upwind and maintained a steady strain on the chain while heaving short, thus keeping the bow away from the ships to leeward. As the stern line was eased, it was found that the stern actually walked to port (upwind). By the time the stern was abreast the conning tower of the submarine, 15 yards of clear water showed between the ships, and GARY was still working farther to windward. When the stern was abreast the sub's bow, the stern line was cast off, and the Starboard engine was slowed to BACK ONE THIRD. With this combination the anchor was readily heaved to short stay and held thus for a moment. The engines were stopped and the ship swung to the wind, with the stern clearing the submarine and the other ships quite readily. The first anchor was then picked up and the ship was allowed to ride back with the wind while the second anchor chain was shifted to the wildcat. The ship rode well clear of the other moored ships, the second anchor was weighed easily, and GARY proceeded on her way.

400

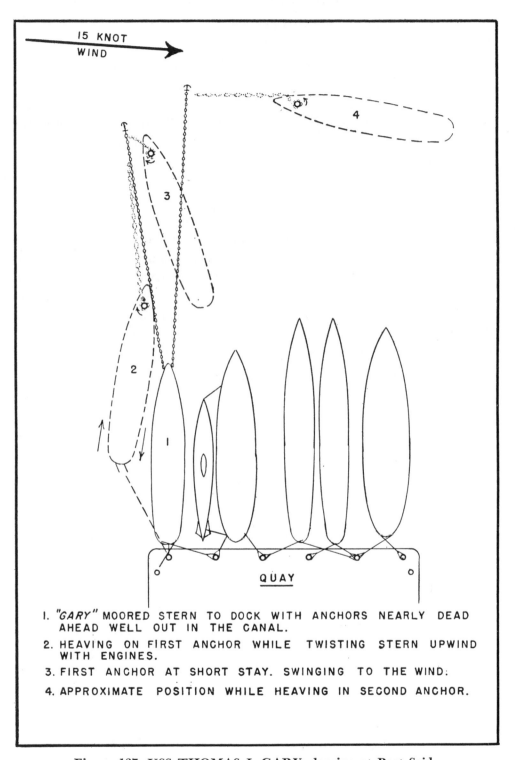

15 KNOT WIND

4

3

2

1

QUAY

1. *"GARY"* MOORED STERN TO DOCK WITH ANCHORS NEARLY DEAD AHEAD WELL OUT IN THE CANAL.

2. HEAVING ON FIRST ANCHOR WHILE TWISTING STERN UPWIND WITH ENGINES.

3. FIRST ANCHOR AT SHORT STAY. SWINGING TO THE WIND.

4. APPROXIMATE POSITION WHILE HEAVING IN SECOND ANCHOR.

Figure 137. USS THOMAS J. GARY clearing at Port Said.

EXAMPLE 2

Problem

USS THOMAS J. GARY (DE 326) and USS FINCH (DE 328) were assigned to a single buoy in Hong Kong harbor. Upon arriving at the assigned berth it was found that the berth was fouled by two wrecks and an improperly anchored Liberty ship, as indicated in the figure. Because of minesweeping operations going on at the time, berths were in short supply, and the American ships did not wish to complain to the British SOPA. How could they make a safe mooring in this berth?

Solution (Figure 138)

GARY snatched the buoy and kept it snubbed to the bow while FINCH came alongside bow to stern. As soon as FINCH had doubled up, GARY began veering chain and twisting her stern away from the closest wreck. She veered about 75 fathoms of chain, using more power on her backing engine than on her ahead engine in order to keep the chain taut. When sufficiently clear, FINCH dropped her anchor and the moor was equalized between the buoy and FINCH's anchor. This mooring proved snug and safe during several days of windy weather.

When the time came to break up this improvised moor, the above procedure was simply reversed. After weighing her anchor, FINCH cleared by going out ahead around GARY's stern.

EXAMPLE 3

Problem

USS COGSWELL (DD 651) was ordered to load ammunition at the Naval Ammunition Depot, Charleston, S.C., during daylight. The Ammunition Pier is located at a sharp bend in the Cooper River a few miles north of the Navy Yard, and the current conditions in the river are severe. At maximum ebb, the current runs at a full 5 knots, and at maximum flood it passes the Ammunition Pier at more than 2 knots. Because of other schedules the arrival had to be made at maximum flood, and the departure made while 3 knots of ebb tide was running. Tug and pilot assistance, normally provided, were not available.

Solution (Figure 139)

COGSWELL approached upriver, with the flood current of 2 knots as indicated in the figure. As her bow passed over a carefully pre-selected point

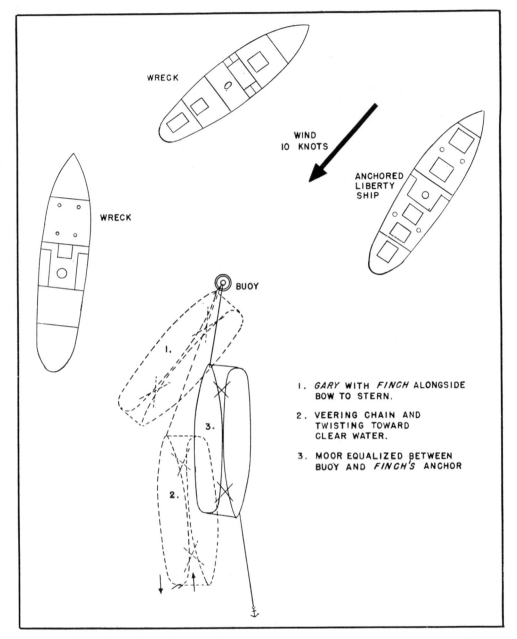

Figure 138. USS THOMAS J. GARY and USS FINCH mooring at Hong Kong.

120 yards (60 fathoms) abreast the pier, she dropped her Port anchor. She swung to her anchor nicely, and working against her anchor, made a smooth, controlled landing in spite of the current. As soon as her lines were doubled up, the anchor chain was slacked to the bottom to clear the channel.

On departure (the current now running at 3 knots downstream), the stern

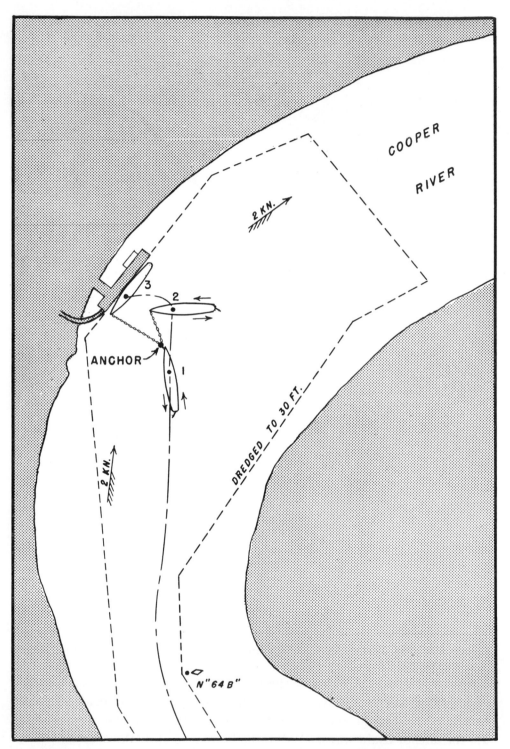

Figure 139. USS COGSWELL going alongside at NAD, Charleston.

was walked away from the pier with the engines while the bow was controlled between the chain and number two line to the pier. As the ship moved broadside into the channel, she was held parallel to the current and in the desired fore-and-aft position by using the engines. As the bow came over the anchor, number two line was cast off, and the ship was held in place with her engines alone while the anchor was weighed. Care had to be exercised during this part of the evolution to avoid any athwartships strain on the anchor chain which might twist the ship cross-current. Once the anchor was in sight, the ship could proceed down stream with ease from her position well out in the channel.

EXAMPLE 4

Problem

USS COGSWELL (DD 651) was moored outboard of USS EATON (DDE 510) at Railway Wharf, Kingston, Jamaica. Just before the ships were to depart, a 30-knot wind sprang up from the starboard quarter, forcing COGSWELL hard against EATON. No tugs were available to assist. How could COGSWELL clear without raking EATON?

Solution (Figure 140)

COGSWELL dipped her port anchor as a first precaution to eliminate any possible damage from this source. Next, she ran her "strong line" to the next pier to windward and heaved her bow about 10 feet upwind with her capstan. Casting off the after lines, her stern was walked upwind by opposing the engines at TWO THIRDS. The forward lines were used for control as the stern slowly worked to windward.

When the stern was sufficiently upwind, all lines to EATON were taken in and BACK FULL was ordered. Just as the ship began to move astern, the strong line to the windward pier was slacked and cast off (provision had been made to let the bitter end of this line run out in case the men on the pier were unable to cast it off). The ship backed clear beautifully, never closing EATON appreciably.

EXAMPLE 5

Problem

USS CORAL SEA (CVA 43) was moored starboard-side-to the stone breakwater at Mers-el-Kebir (the Naval Harbor), Oran, Algeria. At the time set to get underway, a 23-knot wind was blowing steadily against the port bow,

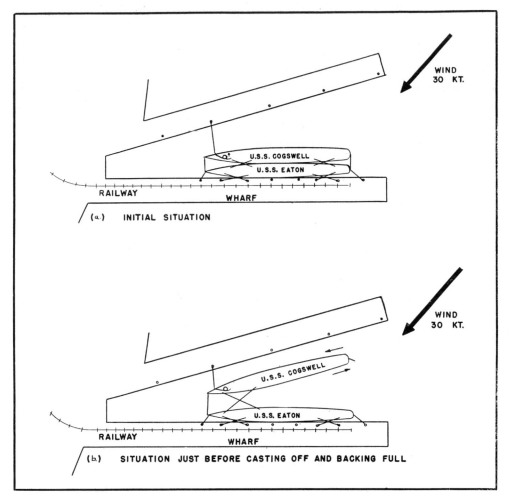

Figure 140. **COGSWELL** clearing **EATON** at Kingston, Jamaica.

setting the ship hard against the camels on the face of the breakwater. The harbor entrance was about 700 yards astern, as shown in the figure, but it was desired to turn the ship inside the harbor and proceed to sea going ahead rather than to back through the entrance. A sunken battleship 300 yards ahead prevented maneuvering in that area, so it was decided to turn the ship in the clear area abeam to port. Two French tugs and a pilot were provided, but when the pilot attempted to breast out the ship directly, using one tug on the bow and one on the stern, the pressure of the wind held the big ship solidly against the face of the breakwater. How could the ship get clear and turn?

Solution (Figure 141)

Both tugs were put on the bow. The stern was moved out by opposing

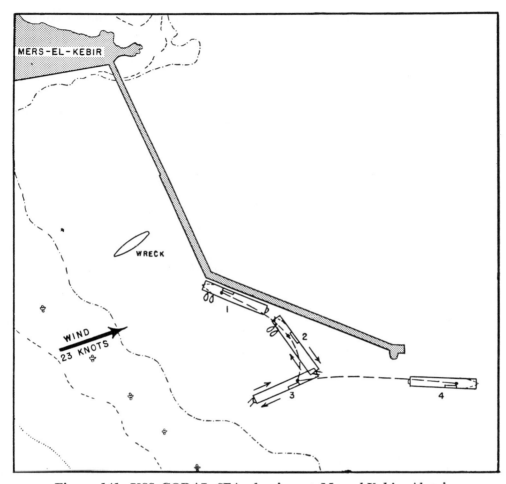

Figure 141. USS CORAL SEA clearing at Mers-el-Kebir, Algeria.

the ship's engines at ONE THIRD and pivoting the ship against the forward camel. When the ship reached an angle of about 10° with respect to
the breakwater, all engines were backed FULL with the rudders LEFT 30°,
and the tugs were directed to pull straight out at maximum power. The ship
came away from the breakwater nicely, with the stern moving rapidly into
the wind. The pull of the tugs, assisted by the wash of the backing screws
along the solid face of the breakwater, held the bow clear of the breakwater
as she backed into the wind. As soon as clearance forward permitted, the
port engines were worked ahead and the rudders shifted to RIGHT 30° to
increase the rate of turn, but care was taken to insure that the ship did not
move toward the breakwater.

When the ship had finally been worked perpendicular to the breakwater,
the tugs were cast off and the turn completed with the engines and rudders
alone. By using more ahead power than back power during the last part

of the turn, sufficient headway was achieved to insure good rudder control for passing through the harbor entrance.

EXAMPLE 6

Problem

USS PRINCETON (CVA 37) was moored port-side-to the pier at Alameda, California, heading out into the channel. At the time set for getting under way, a 10-knot wind was setting the ship against the pier, but the pilot, with two tugs at his disposal, thought he could handle the job.

Solution (Figure 142)

The pilot placed the tugs as indicated in the figure, and when the ship had been breasted only about a yard clear of the face of the pier, he ordered ALL AHEAD ONE THIRD. As the ship commenced to move forward, the tugs trailed aft and were unable to supply as great an athwartships force as previously because of their inclination. With the breasting force thus reduced, the wind carried the ship down against the pier and she scraped against the end of the pier for about one-third of her length. Fortunately, little damage was done.

Criticism

With tug power barely sufficient to move the ship away from the face of the pier, the pilot should have waited until he had a much greater margin between the ship and the pier, and then he should have moved the ship Ahead very slowly in order to avoid the loss of his breasting force as the tugs trailed aft. Additional tugs or the use of "Pinwheel" would have insured a safe operation.

EXAMPLE 7

Problem

USS CORAL SEA (at anchor, as shown in the figure, in the Bosphorus, Istanbul, Turkey), was the first heavy ship to get under way in the sortie of a visiting U.S. force. The current in the vicinity of the ship was running at about 5 knots, and 500 yards downstream lay three rows of merchant ships moored bow-and-stern to buoys. Inshore, towards Istanbul, three Turkish destroyers were at anchor, and upstream lay two heavy cruisers. The current was the strongest in the vicinity of the heavy ship berths, and, flowing south, it divided on a point of land about 1,500 yards from CORAL SEA, part flowing out into the Sea of Marmora, and part flowing into the Golden Horn. The current into the Golden Horn formed a counter-current along the Istanbul

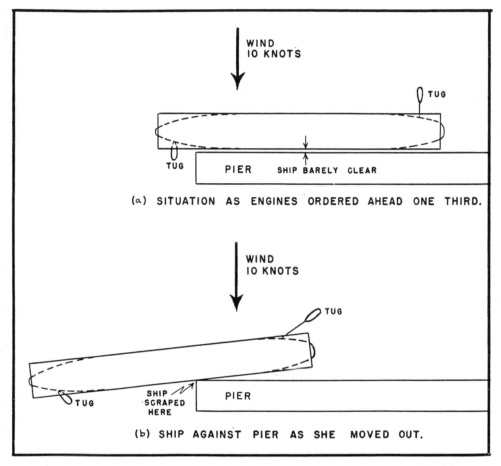

WIND
10 KNOTS

TUG

TUG   PIER   SHIP BARELY CLEAR

(a) SITUATION AS ENGINES ORDERED AHEAD ONE THIRD.

WIND
10 KNOTS

TUG

TUG   SHIP SCRAPED HERE   PIER

(b) SHIP AGAINST PIER AS SHE MOVED OUT.

Figure 142. USS PRINCETON clearing pier at Alameda, California.

shore, and the Turkish destroyers were riding with sterns upstream. The *Coast Pilot* stated that there were many old anchor chains on the bottom, so there was a real danger that the carrier's anchor might be fouled. How should she turn to head out to sea?

Solution (Figure 143)

Full boiler power was made available and pinwheel was set up with 8 planes at each of the four corners of the flight deck. A party of shipfitters with cutting torches and boatswain's chairs was standing by ready to go over the side to cut any cable which might have fouled the anchor. The ship steamed against the current as the chain was heaved in, and the bow was held over the anchor until it came into sight. Fortunately, the anchor was clear.

Once under way, the ship was moved ahead close to the cruiser next upstream and as far to the left towards the Turkish destroyers as comfort would

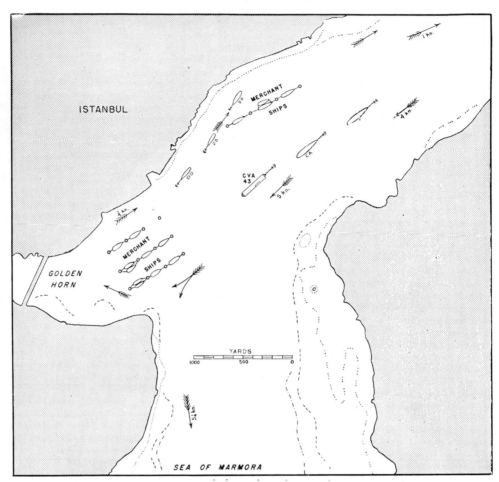

Figure 143. USS CORAL SEA twisting out of the Bosphorus.

permit. When ready to start the turn, the rudders were put HARD RIGHT, the engines were opposed at high power, and groups two and three of pinwheel were turned up to maximum safe power. During the turn, the cross-channel position was controlled by varying the power on the engines.

As the ship turned, she was carried downstream with the current, but she turned rapidly enough to complete her turn before being swept into the merchantmen. About 30° before reaching the heading desired for departure, all engines were ordered AHEAD STANDARD and all pinwheel groups were idled. This permitted the swing to be stopped with the rudders and headway to be built up quickly for standing out of the harbor.

Note

Had there been less congestion, a more rapid turn could have been made by getting the stern in the counter-current along the Istanbul shore while the bow was being carried downstream in the main current. At other times heavy ships have used this current difference to good advantage.

EXAMPLE 8

Problem

USS LST 859 was required to go inside the harbor at Canton Island to unload cargo alongside the pier. The entrance channel is about 150 feet wide, the turning basin is small, and beyond the turning basin are dangerous coral heads. A strong current flows through the channel at all times except at high water and low water slacks (which last only about twenty minutes), and it was undesirable to wait for slack water. The tide was flooding through the entrance and a wind of 15 knots was blowing from the East. How could the ship enter the harbor and go alongside the dock without being swept into the coral heads?

Solution (Figure 144)

The initial intention was simply to enter and go alongside port-side-to, without turning. Once in the channel, however, the current was found to be so strong that the ship was swept past the pier and into the center of the turning basin in spite of her engines. To keep from being swept into the coral heads, the anchor was dropped and the ship spun rapidly to her anchor. Once heading into the current, the anchor was heaved in, and a starboard-side-to landing made at the pier with no trouble. To hold the bow against the wind, the anchor was dragged at short stay during the last part of the approach.

EXAMPLE 9

Problem

In a small undeveloped port in Korea, LSTs bringing in supplies are confronted with a difficult shiphandling problem. The harbor is exposed to the prevailing wind and the ships must unload through their bow doors onto a sea wall which is nearly parallel to the wind. The busy little harbor is usually congested with numerous barges and small craft, and, in the winter, the wind may have a velocity as high as 25 knots. How can an LST be handled to moor crosswind under a typical situation as depicted in the figure?

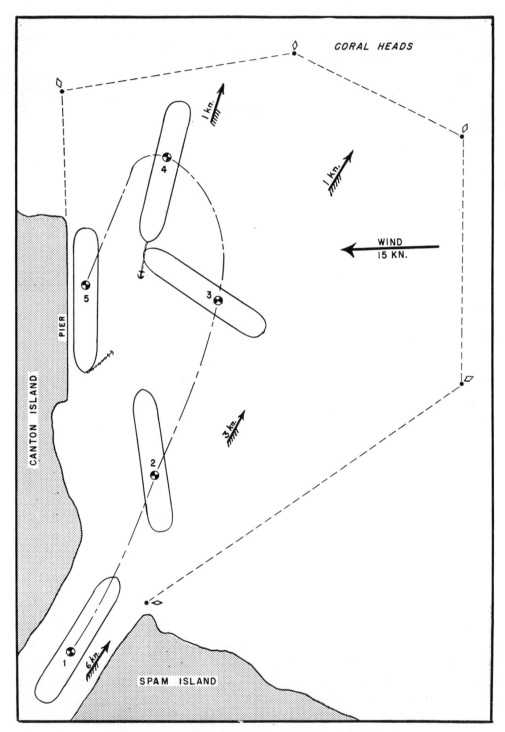

Figure 144. LST 859 recovers at Canton Island.

Solution (Figure 145)

As the LST approaches the harbor, both her LCVPs are lowered to act as tugs. The approach up the channel is made at 6 knots to insure good control, and, as the ship turns into the harbor, the stern anchor is dropped in mid-channel about 700 feet from the intended berth. As the ship moves into the restricted part of the harbor, the two LCVPs are placed on the port bow to push the bow to starboard. As the ship comes abreast the sea wall, she is inclined to the wind by a combination of the engines, rudders, and the boats working on the port bow. As soon as possible, the starboard bow line is passed to the sea wall, and the bow is worked gently in to the sea wall by the combination of the bow line and the boats. Once the bow has been secured, the ship can be brought perpendicular to the sea wall by adjusting the stern anchor cable.

In clearing, the reverse of the above procedure is used, with the addition of using the bow anchor to help hold the bow from being swept to leeward after the bow lines are cast off. If control is lost when getting clear, the wind will carry the bow down on the lee shore, so care must be taken to insure that every shiphandling aid is ready for use. When the stern anchor has been

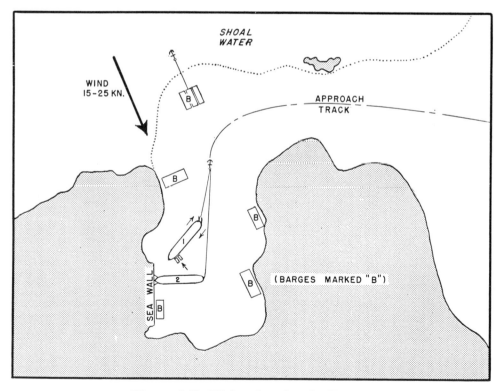

Figure 145. Tight situation in Korea.

picked up, the ship can back into the wind to the edge of the shoal water to insure sufficient room to square away on her departure course.

EXAMPLE 10

Problem

During World War II an LST was stuck on "Brown" beach, Nakagasuku Wan (later Buckner Bay), Okinawa, and could not retract. She was enveloped in a cloud of diesel smoke for a long time as she tried every trick in the book to get free. Several tugs had been used singly and in combination to try to get her off, but she wouldn't budge. How to get her off?

Solution (Figure 146)

After having taken careful soundings to insure there was sufficient water alongside the LST, two LSMs were backed in alongside, as indicated in the accompanying figure. The stern anchor wires of the LSMs were secured to the forward bitts on the LST, and the ships were securely married with

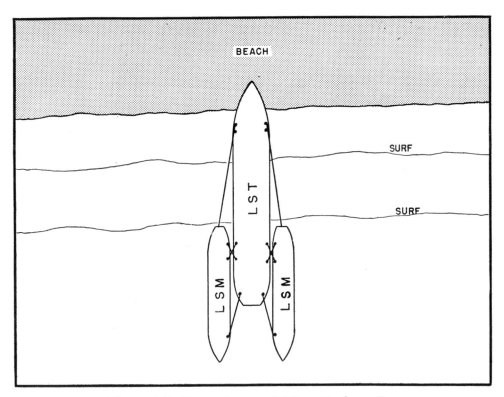

Figure 146. Retracting an LST at Buckner Bay.

mooring lines as indicated. The stern anchor of the LST had already been recovered.

When all was ready, the engines of all three ships were applied to the task of getting the LST free. By alternately reversing the LSMs, a strong twisting motion could be applied, and when all engines were working together, a very strong force was applied to pulling the LST off the beach. After a moderate amount of effort, the balky LST was pulled free.

EXAMPLE 11

Problem

USS CARPELLOTTI (APD 136) was frequently required to berth between two other APDs at the finger piers, Naval Amphibious Base, Little Creek, Virginia. The usual procedure for the three ships was for the first ship to go alongside the windward pier, the second ship to moor to the leeward pier, and the third ship, usually CARPELLOTTI, to slide in between the two and moor to the ship alongside the windward pier. The space remaining after the first two ships were alongside was only about a ship width and a half, and CARPELLOTTI often had to "thread the needle" with a strong crosswind. How could she make her berth without raking one or both of the other ships? Her crosswind angle, even for a fast approach, would be so large that she could not fit into the remaining space.

Solution (Figure 147)

Having passed the cable crossing and arrived at a position with her bow in line with the slot, the windward anchor was dropped and snubbed at short stay. The remainder of the approach was made working against this anchor at relatively high power and dragging the anchor as the ship moved into her berth. This moved the pivot point forward near the bow and allowed a controlled approach to be made into the tight berth. The restraint at the bow, coupled with the much higher side forces from the rudders and propellers allowable with this method, easily countered the side force from the wind, and the ship could move into her berth on a heading nearly parallel to that of the other two ships.

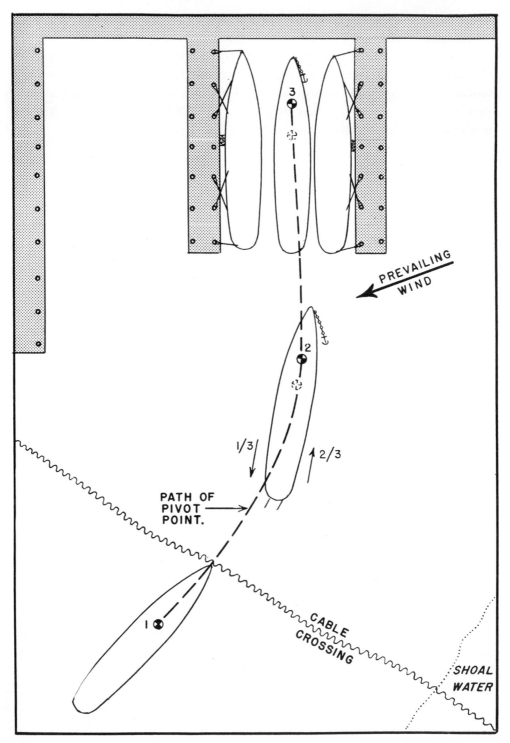

Figure 147. CARPELLOTTI makes a tight berth at Little Creek.

EXAMPLE 12

Problem

USS EDSALL (DE 129), alongside a pier at Miami, Florida, on a windy day had to get under way and proceed to sea through the main ship channel astern. A brisk breeze was blowing from astern, and the situation was complicated by a slight current from the Inland Waterway which cut across the small turning basin. The tendency of a destroyer escort to back into the wind, and the difficulty of twisting such a ship in the confines of the basin, had just been demonstrated by a sister ship. After much unsuccessful backing and filling, this ship had ended up against the end of one of the piers, still not turned around, and with a damaged side to show for her efforts.

Solution (Figure 148)

EDSALL backed into the wind until clear of the piers and then started a turn to her port—the direction the current tended to carry her stern. When she neared the opposite extremity of the basin, her engines were kicked AHEAD with the Rudders RIGHT FULL, and, as the ship commenced to move ahead, the starboard anchor was let go and snubbed underfoot. As soon as her stern was sufficiently across the wind, her engines were stopped, and the wind and the current carried the ship completely around until she was headed fair for the main ship channel. Once squared away, the anchor was weighed and the ship proceeded to sea.

EXAMPLE 13

Problem

A division of DDEs, returning from operations off the coast of Korea, upon arrival at Yokosuka was ordered alongside the destroyer tender. A strong wind was blowing and the tender lay with her stern so close to a point of land that there was scarcely a boat passage between her stern and the adjacent sea wall. The first ships had backed in alongside the tender, but the operation had been awkward, hazardous, and time consuming. How could USS TAYLOR (DDE 468), the last ship to go alongside, make her landing more efficiently and with less hazard?

Solution (Figure 149)

As the ship next ahead of her was backing in alongside, TAYLOR made a broad sweep and came up nearly abreast the nest, heading into the wind. As the other ship was getting her lines over, TAYLOR was inclined to the wind

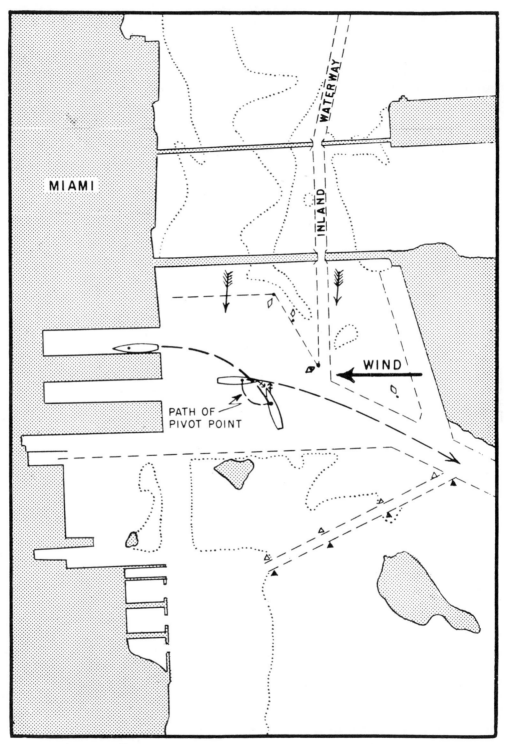

Figure 148. Working a DE out of harbor against wind and current.

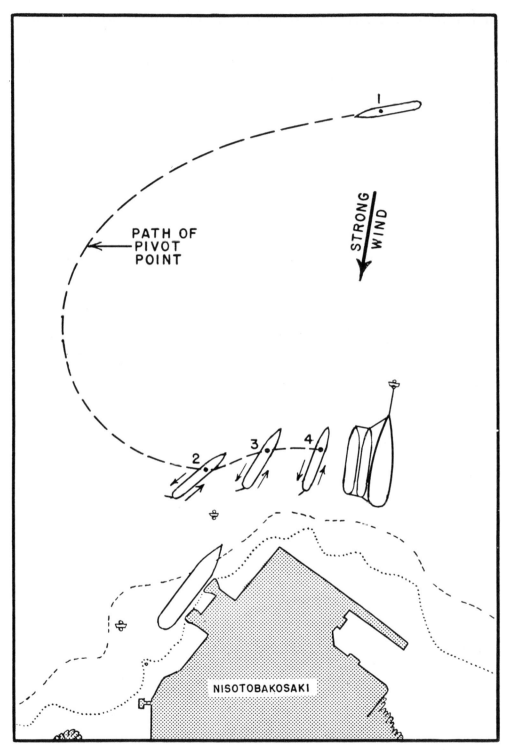

Figure 149. **TAYLOR** makes a difficult landing at Yokosuka.

and "controlled" in, half sailing and half twisting, as indicated in the figure. When the other ship was ready to receive her, she moved in alongside under complete control, never having been exposed to the awkwardness and hazard of a sternward approach.

EXAMPLE 14

Problem

The destroyer USS TAYLOR (DDE 468), was in a narrow slip congested with other craft, and had to be moved across the basin from the submarine base, Pearl Harbor, T.H., to the Naval Shipyard where she was to be squeezed through a narrow opening near the head of a slip and then worked broadside into a berth. There was not room at either slip for a tug to swing perpendicular to the ship and push against her side. The move called for moving broadside as well as fore-and-aft, and the margin allowable for error was only a few feet. How to handle a dead ship under such conditions?

Solution (Figure 150)

The pilot placed two tugs on the port side of the ship, one at the bow, the other at the stern, heading in opposite directions with their sterns towards the ends of the ship. The tugs secured firmly with the "power tie-up" parallel to the ship and snubbed in so nicely under the flare of the bow and against the quarter that the three ships were scarcely wider than the destroyer alone. With this arrangement the pilot could produce motion in any direction he desired without requiring either tug to shift its position.

With the rudder of the lead tug amidships, and steering with the trailing tug, the pilot snaked the ship out of its narrow berth, across the channel, and into the slip on the opposite side. She skinned through the restrictions without a hitch, but the most interesting part of the move occurred as the ship was brought opposite its new berth. The pilot ordered both tugs to drive ahead with their rudders full outboard, as seen from TAYLOR. The forward components of the tugs' propeller thrusts cancelled, but the sidewise component, controlled by the rudders, breasted the ship into her berth perfectly.

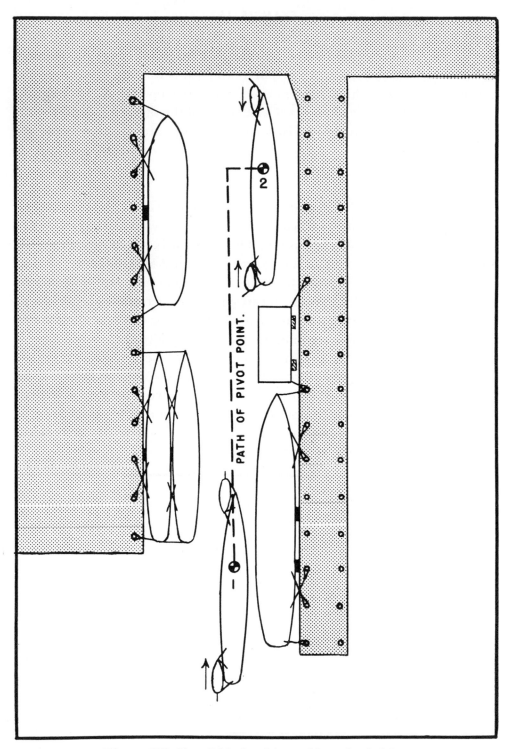

Figure 150. Broadside berthing with a dead ship.

EXAMPLE 15

Problem

The amphibious group had arrived in the transport area for the landing exercise and each ship was anchored in its assigned berth, but a 30 knot wind, gusting to 50 knots, threatened to upset the entire operation. Though the boats could manage the choppy sea when clear of the ships, it was nearly impossible to load them alongside. How could the ships provide a lee so the offloading could continue?

Solution (Figure 151)

USS SARASOTA (APA 204), riding to 60 fathoms of chain to the port anchor in the 8 fathoms of water, kicked AHEAD into the wind at ONE THIRD until the chain tended directly astern. Throwing the bow to port with FULL LEFT RUDDER, the engine was slowed to about 2 knots, and as the ship continued to work against the chain, the wind on the starboard bow carried the ship downwind. This movement carried the ship across the anchor chain, and a state of equilibrium was finally reached with the chain tending under the ship at Frame 30. The chain under the keel provided the equivalent of a fulcrum against which the ship could be levered with her engine and rudder. By this method the ship could be held steadily at a constant angle across the wind, with no yawing. This maneuver provided an excellent lee for loading the boats, and the ship's operations went off on schedule. It was interesting to note that as a result of eliminating the yawing, the anchor never budged, though several other ships were dragging alarmingly.

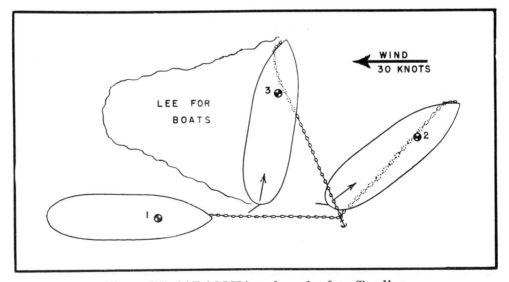

Figure 151. SARASOTA makes a lee for offloading.

EXAMPLE 16

Problem

Ships mooring to the piers at the Minecraft Base, Charleston, South Carolina, are required to moor bow downstream. On a full ebb tide the current sweeping down past the ends of these piers may be as fast as 6 knots, so a conventional landing, moving with the current, adds the ship's way to the velocity of the current and results in a dangerously fast landing.

At full ebb uss TOWHEE (AM 388) was standing up the Ashley River to moor to Pier B at the Minecraft Base. There was a breeze of 10 knots blowing from across the river. How to make this tough job easy?

Solution (Figure 152)

Selecting the last suitable turning basin before arriving at the Base, TOWHEE headed into the wind and made her turn in the mouth of Wappoo Creek. She then commenced backing upstream to her berth. When the ship had built up to about 6 knots sternway through the water (1 knot over the ground), she began moving upstream, and except for carrying a little rudder

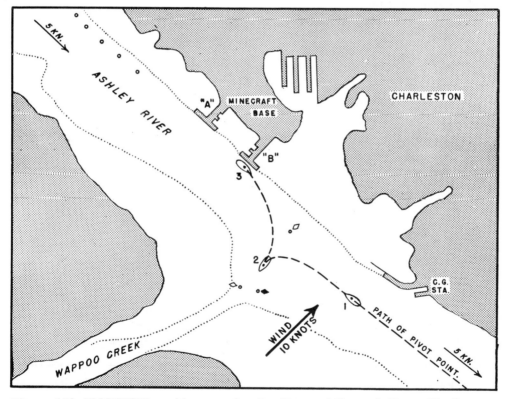

Figure 152. TOWHEE avoids a too fast landing at Minecraft Base, Charleston.

to compensate for the wind, she answered her helm satisfactorily. She was backed upstream to a point about 100 feet abreast her berth and held there with her engines while her lines were sent over. When all lines were set, she was worked in slowly toward the pier, and finally, when nearly against the pier, her engines were slowed and the strain was taken by the lines. This method of making the landing allowed a controlled evolution instead of a frantic "grab" at the pier as the current swept the ship downstream.

EXAMPLE 17

Problem

USS NEW KENT was often faced with the problem of making a landing un-assisted, with the wind blowing directly against the face of the pier. She had her landing craft available, but these would have to work on the windward side during the last stages of the landing and a more expeditious method was desired.

Solution (Figure 153)

When still well clear of the pier, the windward (off-pier) anchor was dropped and veered to about 30 fathoms. Working against this anchor at an engine speed of 8 knots, the ship made a wide approach, dragging her anchor, at about 1 or 2 knots to a point about 100 feet abreast her berth. At this point the engines were slowed to 4 knots, the dragging ceased, and the ship was held dead in the water, parallel to the pier, by working her engine and rudder against the taut chain. In slowing the engine speed from 8 to 4 knots,

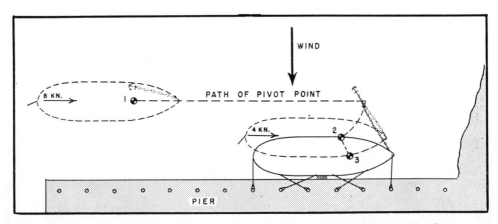

Figure 153. NEW KENT makes an unassisted landing with the wind blowing directly onto the pier.

the ship had "sagged" downwind until now she lay only about 30 feet from the face of the pier and slightly astern of her berth. From this position her lines could be run to the pier as desired. When all lines were in place, the ship was eased in against the face of the pier by veering the chain and adjusting the engine speed to achieve the desired fore-and-aft position. Once in her berth, her chain was slacked to the bottom, and she had a friend in mid-channel ready to help her when the time came to get under way again.

EXAMPLE 18

Problem

The new skipper was handling the ship for the first time, and he had been ashore for the past two years. USS CUSHING (DD 797) lay alongside a nest at Yokosuka, Japan, a fresh breeze was blowing from nearly astern, and she had to depart through the entrance to windward. She cleared the nest nicely, threaded her way between the tender and a line of station ships as she Backed into the wind, and reached a clear area to the northward where she could turn. The skipper put her stern to port, opposed the engines, and commenced to turn her into the wind. Twisting with the engines alone would not do the trick. She would come almost broadside to the wind, and then she would turn no further. The shoal water astern and the ships ahead limited her motion, and as she backed and filled with high engine power, the wind was carrying her relentlessly to leeward. Soon she was in a veritable cul-de-sac between the tender and a nest of minecraft. The sea wall was getting ominously close, and in spite of twisting at maximum power the ship was not going to make it. The new skipper was getting desperate.

Solution (Figure 154)

Sensing the mounting tension, the Commodore whispered "Don't forget your anchor." The starboard anchor rattled to the bottom, and the ship pivoted smartly into the wind, and in a few moments the ship was standing safely towards the entrance—a lesson in shiphandling permanently engraved in the new skipper's mind.

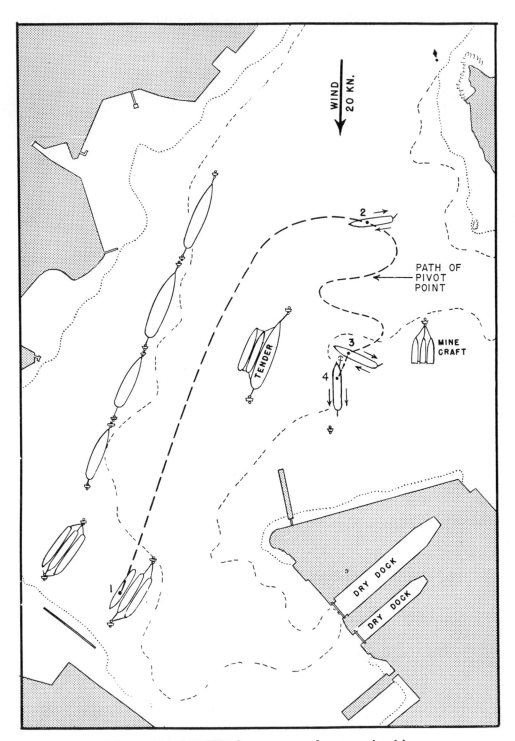

Figure 154. **CUSHING** uses an anchor to twist ship.

EXAMPLE 19

Problem

USS WISCONSIN (BB 64) was ordered to moor bow and stern to Buoys A and B in Berths 5 and 6 in the Hudson River, New York City. In this part of the river, that part of the channel deep enough for a battleship is only slightly wider than the WISCONSIN's length. It was desired to moor the ship heading downstream.

Solution (Figure 155)

A pilot and 8 tugs were on hand. The mooring was timed to coincide with the changing of the tide from ebb to flood, and as the ship arrived at Buoy A, heading upstream, there was still a slight downstream current running.

The tugs, working in pairs, held the big ship in position while a heavy wire was secured to Buoy A. When this was completed, the ebb had ceased, and the first part of the flood commenced to carry the ship upstream. The bow wire was slacked to allow the bow to move near the Jersey side while the ship was turned by the tugs. The wire to Buoy A provided a positive control on the cross-channel position of the ship (her draft was 36 feet, and the Naval Base had provided a special chart to show the exact location of the 36-foot depth contours).

Upon completion of the winding, with the ship now heading downstream, the tugs moved her stern near Buoy B, and four heavy wires were secured to this buoy. Finally, the bow was heaved close to Buoy A and the port anchor chain was secured to the buoy. The moor was made taut by heaving in on the chain, and the big ship lay safely in her berth, having used all of the tools available to the shiphandler.

EXAMPLE 20

Problem

USS R. E. KRAUS (EDD 849) was again assigned an end berth at one of the piers at Naval Base, Norfolk, Virginia. A full ebb tide combined with a south-westerly wind of 25 knots gave an off-pier wind and current. It was known from previous experience that though the bow could be brought in with the capstan, it would be impossible to twist the stern in with the engines and rudders alone. No tugs were available, and operational commitments required a landing without delay.

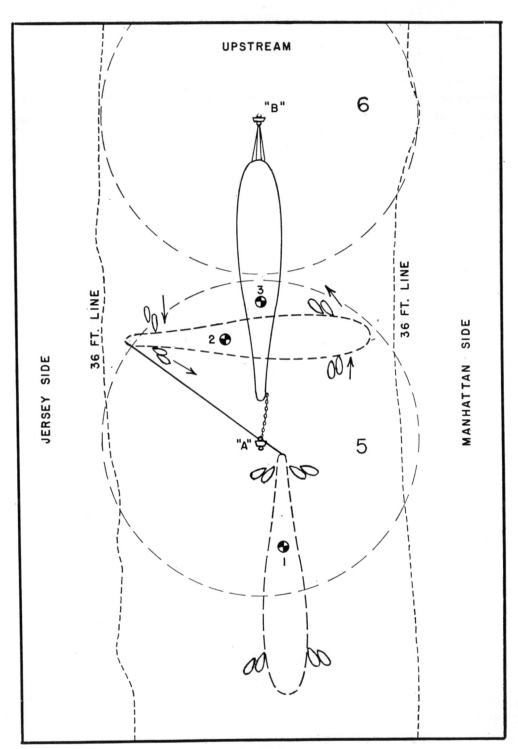

Figure 155. Mooring the WISCONSIN in a narrow channel.

Solution (Figure 156)

KRAUS had a trick up her sleeve. Long experience with this situation had caused the crew to carefully re-examine their resources. The strongest mooring line was made ready on the fantail, and Mount 53 was trained around into her Starboard stops.

A fast approach put her close alongside, and the lines were quickly passed to the pier. The bow was snubbed and under control in the usual way, but the stern began to move away from the pier in response to the wind and current in spite of the engines being opposed at TWO-THIRDS.

The stern was snubbed by holding all after lines as soon as they were secured on the pier and turns were taken with the extra mooring line about the moving part of the base of Mount 53. When ready to move the stern in, a strain was taken on the special mooring line aft by training Mount 53 slowly to the right in "local." The powerful train drive of the 5″/38 twin mount provided adequate force to move the stern in against the pier in spite of the wind and tide. The stresses of such use are small compared to the stresses of firing, and this unusual employment of a gun mount did not harm the mount in any way. Had the mount trained all the way into its port stops, the stern could have been held with the other lines while the mount trained back to starboard and a new purchase was taken on the line. The use of the gun mount provided a solution to a troublesome shiphandling problem.

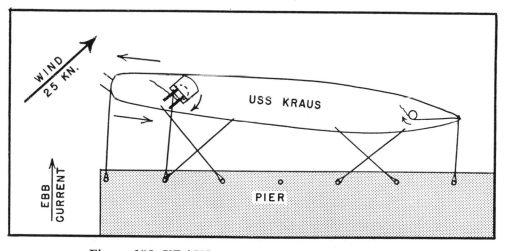

Figure 156. KRAUS uses a gun mount for a capstan.

EXAMPLE 21

Problem

A "Med Relief" was in progress, and most of the ships of the Sixth Fleet had crowded into the Harbor of Naples. YELLOWSTONE was already in port when the others arrived, and NEWPORT NEWS (NN), GOODRICH (G), LARSEN (L), and GRAND CANYON (GC), had Med-moored in the locations indicated in the figure. A 25-knot wind complicated the situation when the time came for YELLOWSTONE to get under way.

As YELLOWSTONE cast off her after lines and commenced heaving in on her anchors, Backing to hold her stern up against the wind, things began to happen. About the time her stern was even with the bows of the adjacent destroyers, their stern lines commenced to part from the combination of high wind, the strong screw currents from YELLOWSTONE, and the strain on GOOD-RICH's anchor chain (mentioned below). Soon both destroyers had broken free from the sea wall and were drifting across the harbor. As YELLOWSTONE heaved in her port anchor she found it fouled by *two* anchor chains (NEW-PORT NEWS' and GOODRICH's); when she tried her starboard, she found it had fouled GRAND CANYON's **chain.** Three chains fouled, two destroyers adrift— now what?

Solution (Figure 157)

Every man for himself! Luckily GOODRICH and LARSEN had steam up, and before they had drifted into NEWPORT NEWS or into the shoal water on the opposite side of the harbor, they were gotten under control with their own engines. Maneuvering nested together, they could exert a tremendous twisting moment as well as move fore-and-aft, and soon they had backed up to the sea wall and were securing again.

YELLOWSTONE held herself in position, Stern into the wind, and cleared her chains one at a time. This was accomplished by heaving the anchor clear of the water to work on it. By passing a wire under the bight of chain which had caught in the anchor's flukes and securing the wire back on deck, the offend-ing chain could be held suspended while the anchor was again lowered. When the anchor had been gotten past the chain by hoisting it a second time, the chain could be released by slipping the wire. Soon YELLOWSTONE was on her way clear of her entanglements, but all who had observed had learned a lesson about fouled anchors.

Comment

Had the anchors of all ships been clearly marked and had all concerned been alert to the danger, the anchors of all ships could have been placed in

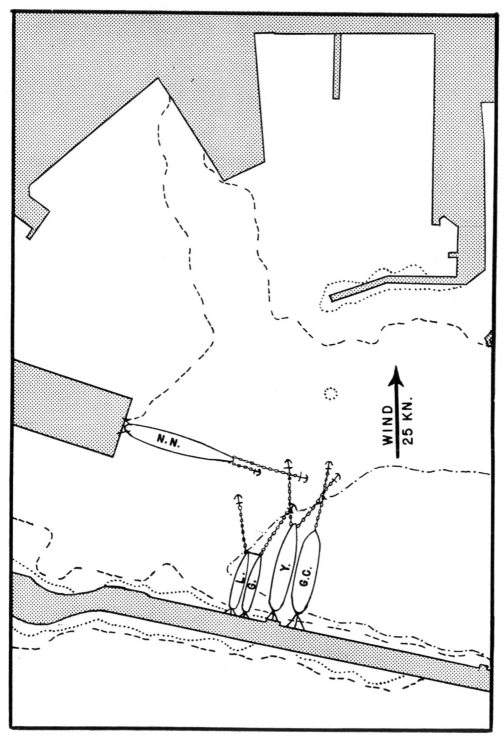

Figure 157. Crossed anchors mean a fouled-up getaway.

such a way that no anchors would have been fouled.

In cases where it is necessary to cross anchor chains, fouling is usually avoided if the last ship to arrive is the first to depart.

EXAMPLE 22

Problem

The night of 28 November 1943 had been a tough night for cruisers. It is now called the Battle of Tassafaronga, but most of that night it was a confusing nightmare. NORTHAMPTON had been sunk, PENSACOLA nearly cut in two by a torpedo, and MINNEAPOLIS and NEW ORLEANS had their bows blown off! The destroyers had been called back from the attack to stand by the stricken cruisers, and dawn found MAURY (DD 401) shepherding NEW ORLEANS (CA 32) into Tulagi harbor. As they approached the anchorage, it was suddenly realized that the anchors were in that part of the ship which had disappeared (she was sheared off between turrets one and two). How to secure the cruiser?

Solution (Figure 158)

NEW ORLEANS maneuvered to the spot where she wished to anchor, and stopped. MAURY came alongside, and as she secured to the larger ship, she dropped her inboard anchor. Both ships rode to MAURY's anchor.

When MAURY had veered to the desired scope of chain, a strong wire was run from the chain outside the hawsepipe to the foremost remaining set of bitts on NEW ORLEANS. The chain was secured with a detachable link just inboard of MAURY's stopper, so MAURY could quickly get free by breaking her chain and tripping her stopper. In this manner MAURY would be free to get under way in case of attack without leaving NEW ORLEANS adrift.

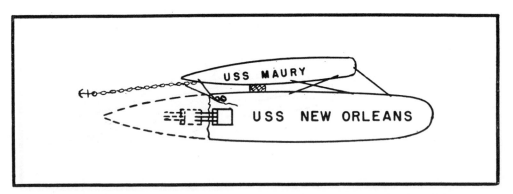

Figure 158. MAURY develops a jury anchor for an anchorless ship.

EXAMPLE 23

Problem

The five ships of TransDiv 128 (APDs) were assigned to berths at the finger piers at the submarine base, St. Thomas, Virgin Islands. A 20-knot breeze was blowing across the piers. TOLBERG (APD 103) was third in column and the only ship assigned to a berth on the leeward side of a pier. The two following ships could not berth until TOLBERG had cleared the area between the piers, and the crews of all ships were looking forward to a well earned liberty. How could TOLBERG expedite her landing and make way for the other ships?

Solution (Figure 159)

As she approached the finger piers, TOLBERG put all four of her LCVPs into the water and had them follow just off her port side. She made a fast approach and stopped with her bow close to the pier abreast her berth. As soon as the ship had come to rest, all four LCVP's were called in alongside and ordered to push on the port quarter. Heaving on number one with her capstan, twisting with her engines, and being pushed by the four powerful boats, the ship moved rapidly in against the pier and the lines were quickly secured. As soon as they could be spared, the boats were ordered to clear the side and the basin was ready for the next ships to enter.

EXAMPLE 24

Problem

USS BLACK (DD 666) was moored port-side-to O'HARE (DD 889) at Buoy 2, Hampton Roads. A fresh breeze was blowing from the north, but the strong ebb tidal current held the ships stern-into-the-wind. Under way time was 0800, and this could not be varied because BLACK was to take part in a scheduled sortie. Just before casting off, the wind overcame the weakening current (slack water was approaching) and the nest swung broadside to the wind and the remaining current. An LST, more sensitive to the wind than the current, had already swung to the wind and lay across BLACK's stern about 200 yards away. The time for departure was rapidly approaching. What to do?

Solution (Figure 160)

BLACK dipped her port anchor and all available fenders were made ready along the port side. The Chief Engineer was notified of the entended ma-

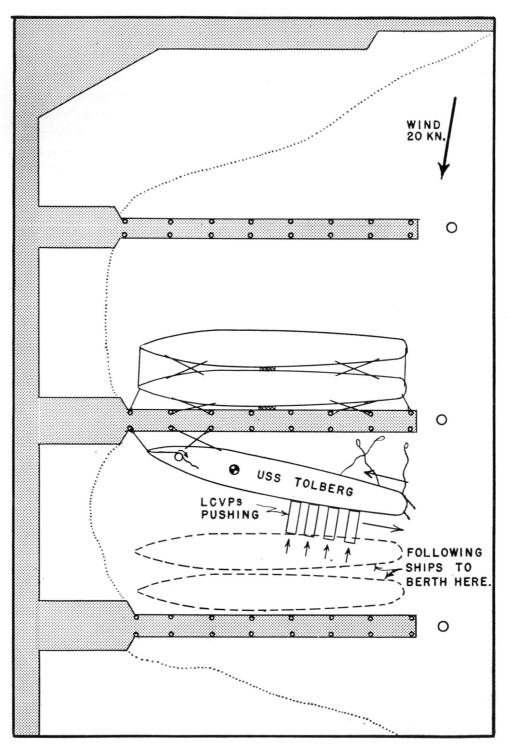

Figure 159. Quick mooring close quarters for an APD.

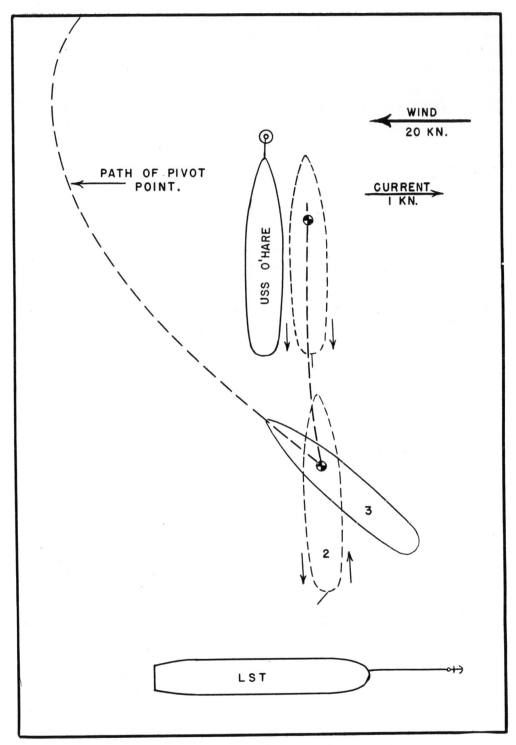

WIND
20 KN.

CURRENT
1 KN.

PATH OF PIVOT
POINT.

USS O'HARE

3

2

LST

Figure 160. Getting under way in variable wind and current.

neuver to insure that the throttlemen would be ready for it. All lines were cast off simultaneously and both engines were backed FULL. As soon as she had moved slightly astern, the rudder was ordered LEFT FULL to counter the tendency of the stern to go upwind and to keep the bow clear of O'HARE. As her bow came abreast of O'HARE's quarter, all engines were ordered AHEAD TWO-THIRDS and the ship was brought to a stop about 50 yards clear of O'HARE's stern. Once dead in the water, the engines were opposed, and the bow was twisted downwind easily. BLACK executed a broad sweep to leeward and stood out toward the channel on schedule.

EXAMPLE 25

Problem

USS STORMES (DD 780) had been damaged on Picket Station Fifteen at Okinawa. After waiting for a full two months, she was finally placed in a floating dry dock (an ARD) for emergency repairs to make her safe for the long trip home. In the interim, however, the summer of 1945 had worn on and it was now typhoon season. STORMES had been extensively damaged aft by the *Kamikaze,* and though the major structural members had been replaced, her hull plating had not been completely replaced. A typhoon was approaching, and Buckner Bay was in the center of its path. Sensing the imminent danger, the SOPA ordered the bay evacuated—that is, except for STORMES and her ARD. Deserted, she lay there alone as the velocity of the wind mounted. All hands donned lifejackets. The crew of the ARD seemed to be drifting aboard the destroyer; the crew of the destroyer seemed to be drifting over to the ARD. Anxiety seemed to say that the combination would certainly roll over in a typhoon—but the question was, would the destroyer fall out of the dock and sink, or would the dock founder and the destroyer float free?

Solution (Figure 161)

Anticipating severe rolling and heavy seas, a conference was held to decide upon measures to minimize the danger. It was decided that the real danger lay in the ship coming loose in the dock and rolling off the keel blocks. The spur shores were the key to the situation.

It was estimated that no amount of wedging could keep the ship from moving to some small extent with respect to the dock, and it was anticipated that should the destroyer roll away from one of the sides of the dock ever so

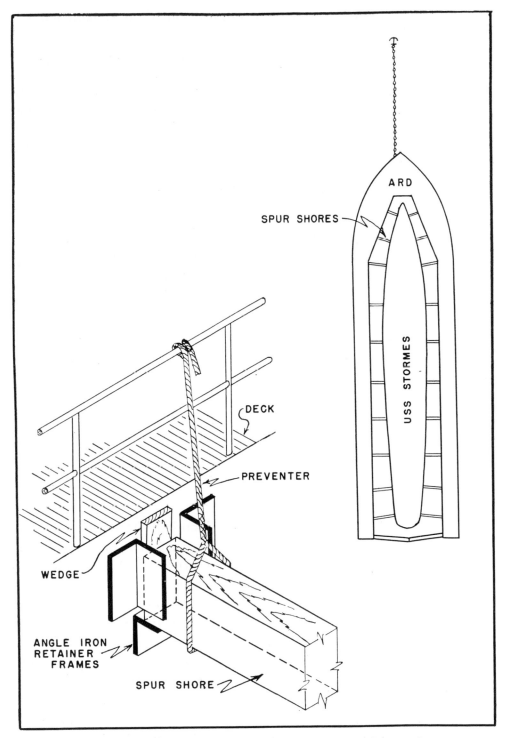

Figure 161. Securing a ship in a floating dock against typhoons.

little, the spur shore would thereby be released and fall to the bottom of the dock. If the spur shores began to go, the ship would most certainly slip off the blocks. The solution could not lie in tighter wedging alone.

After several suggestions were explored, it was decided to construct a small retainer frame around the ends of the shores. Thus, if the ship moved momentarily, the spur shore would be held in place and would not fall out from between the ship and the dock. The spur shores were backed up by "preventers" to hold the shore in place should the opening become larger than the retaining frame.

The storm came on, and though the center passed many miles away (over the center of the formation of ships which had evacuated Buckner Bay), the wind and waves were severe. The dock and ship rolled as much as 15° to a side, and half-inch gaps were observed between the ends of the spur shores and the side of the ship at the extremity of the roll. Each time a gap would appear, wedges would be driven between the end of the shore and the ship (or dock). By this means, all shores were held in place and kept bearing throughout the storm.

The ship didn't roll out of the dock, and the dock didn't founder. A severe situation had been alleviated, however, only by careful forethought and positive action.

EXAMPLE 26

Problem

The second Battle of Kula Gulf had gone poorly for GWIN (DD 433). She had been torpedoed aft, and she was awash for the after one-third of her length. MAURY (DD 401) and RALPH TALBOT (DD 390) had been ordered to stand by her, but as the morning wore on and the Japanese air attacks became more troublesome, it became apparent that they would never get her back to the now safe waters of Iron Bottom Bay (between Guadalcanal and Tulagi). After repeated attempts to tow her had been thwarted by the appearance of Jap planes, the Commodore finally decided to abandon her and ordered MAURY alongside to take off the salvage detail. (Most of the crew had been taken off earlier by RALPH TALBOT.)

Approaching a ship, the after third of which is submerged, presents its problems. If we get our screws over the submerged part of the ship, perhaps we too will become crippled and at the mercy of the dive bombers.

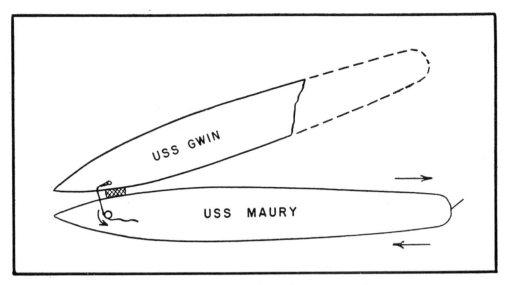

Figure 162. Rescue work under enemy threat.

Solution (Figure 162)

The Captain selected a spot on the GWIN's forecastle which was about the same height as MAURY's forecastle, and made a one-point one-line landing. Approaching smartly, he placed the flat of MAURY's forecastle against this point (abreast No. 1 gun), passed a single mooring line, and kept MAURY's stern away from GWIN's by gentle use of the engines.

After a few minutes alongside, all survivors had been transferred and GWIN's Captain had made his inspection to be sure that none had been forgotten. With all safely on board, MAURY backed clear. Twenty minutes later GWIN had been sent to the bottom by a torpedo from RALPH TALBOT and the two surviving ships were headed down the "Slot" at top speed. Coolheaded shiphandling had been essential in a "hot" situation.

EXAMPLE 27

Problem

In December, 1944, O'NIELL (DE-188) in Ulithi was ordered to the ammunition anchorage at the far end of the lagoon to load ammunition. The weather was marginal with 25 to 35 knots of wind and five to eight-foot swells. On approaching the AE, a converted Liberty Ship, the Commanding Officer of O'NEILL informed the Master of the AE that it would not be advisable to come alongside under existing weather conditions since damage to the DE's superstructure and gun sponsons was certain to occur.

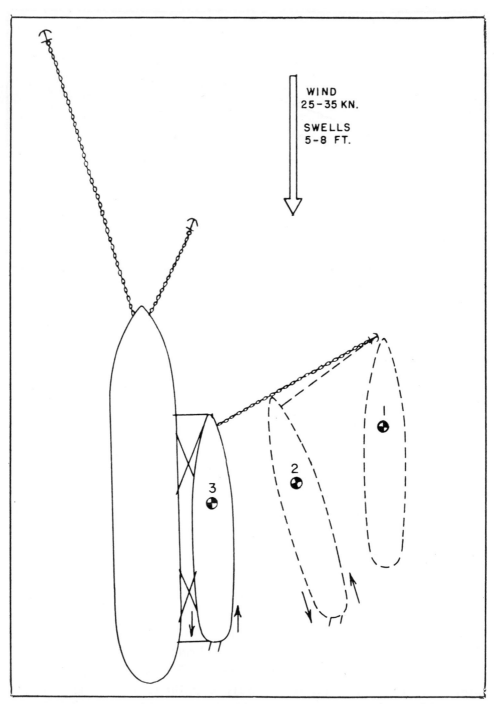

WIND
25–35 KN.

SWELLS
5–8 FT.

Figure 163. How to keep from rolling against the supply ship
when the weather is difficult.

Solution (Figure 163)

At the suggestion of the Master of the AE, O'NEILL proceeded to a point about 100 yards 60° on the starboard bow of the AE and dropped her *port* anchor. Then slowly paying out chain, she eased aft and worked in, using opposed engines and *in* rudder, until she was abreast the AE and mooring lines could be passed. With her bow controlled by the mooring lines and anchor chain, and her stern by the engines and rudder, O'NEILL was brought in parallel to the AE until about 6 feet of water separated the ships. Lines were secured and O'NEILL was held in her position by the combination of lines and chain and by maintaining low power ahead on the starboard engine, backing slowly on the port engine, and using left rudder.

Though the ships rolled heavily and O'NEILL pitched moderately, they never touched and the transfer was made safely and expeditiously.

EXAMPLE 28

Problem

STORMES (DD-780), in shakedown training at San Diego, was ordered to moor bow and stern to a pair of buoys near the Sonar School. The buoys were just off the mouth of a creek from which a strong current was flowing, and 20 knots of wind was blowing across the buoys to add to the difficulty. The bow was secured to the first buoy easily enough, but when the conning officer tried to work the stern up to the other buoy with the engines and rudder he didn't come close. After a half an hour of twisting and sweating, the conning officer gave up, declaring that it just couldn't be done.

Solution (Figure 164)

The skipper, who had a better comprehension of the forces acting on the ship, stepped in and pointed out that the chain to the first buoy was countering the twisting action of the engines. To eliminate this restraint on the vessel he veered chain and moved the ship forward, into the wind and current, until the chain led aft and the buoy was abreast the pivot point. Then twisting the ship with engines opposed with lots of power and full rudder, he turned the ship 180° until her stern was into the wind without putting any significant strain on the buoy. Once her stern was into the wind, he veered chain and "sailed" cross-wind, controlling the ship's orientation with engines and rudder, until the stern was in the vicinity of the other buoy. Once the stern was secured to the buoy, the engines were stopped and the ship brought into her proper position between the buoys by heaving in on the chain.

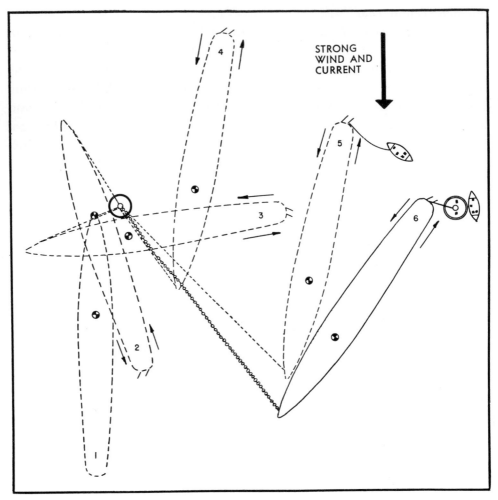

Figure 164. Snatching two buoys in a strong wind or current.

EXAMPLE 29

Problem

FORREST SHERMAN (DD-931) was ordered to Washington, D.C. for the Presidential Inauguration. She made her way up the frozen Potomac, often with only inches between her sonar dome and the bottom, and finally moored in the ice-clogged slip at the Municipal Pier. The visit was enjoyable, but when the time came to depart, a new problem arose. The channel was not considered wide enough for backing clear of the slip, and then turning and proceeding down the channel. Backing out all the way was unattractive because of the ice on the river and the great distance to the closest suitable turning basin. Though a tug was available, there was little room in the slip and the sheets of ice made maneuvering difficult.

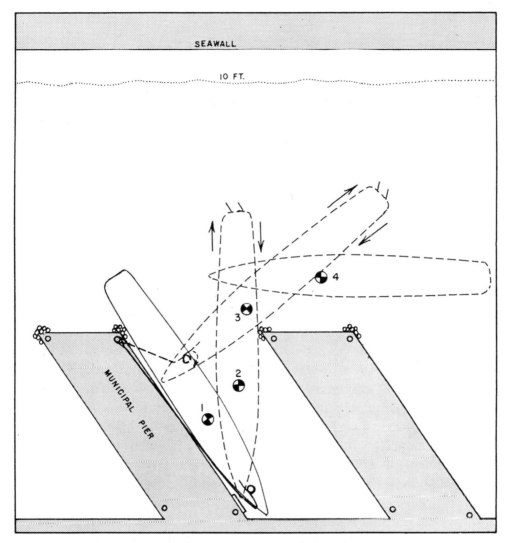

Figure 165. Using the slip as part of the "turning basin."

Solution (Figure 165)

A line was run from her bow to the channel end of the pier. The ship was then twisted, pivoting on a camel, until her stern had crossed the slip and her port side was close to the head of the adjacent pier. A strain was then taken on the line leading to the head of the Municipal Pier, and as the bow moved toward the channel, the stern was worked up channel with the engines keeping the port side close to the head of the other pier. As the ship came parallel to the channel, the bow line was cast off, the ship backed up channel slightly to clear the pier heads, and she finally proceeded down channel normally. The trick had been to use the slip as part of a turning basin and to find a means of moving the bow out to the end of the pier.

PROPELLER SIDE FORCES*

A. SIDE FORCE IN A SINGLE-SCREW SHIP

As A PROPELLER rotates to drive a ship through the water, in addition to producing *thrust* along the axis of the propeller shaft, it produces a *side force*
at the stern of the ship which is quite appreciable. This side force must
always be considered in the calculations of the shiphandler, and it often is
the determining factor in whether or not a particular maneuver can be
accomplished. It is of interest, then, to explore the origin of this unexpected
force.

An isolated propeller deeply submerged in a large body of water will experience no appreciable side force as it turns. All radial components of the
lift on the propeller blades will cancel, and the only force experienced will
be along the axis of the propeller. The case of a propeller being used in an
actual ship, however, is considerably different from this ideal case. The propeller is not deeply submerged, it is in the immediate vicinity of the ship's
underwater body, and it is surrounded by ship's structure such as the shafts,
struts, and rudders. The flow of water across the propeller disc is neither
parallel to the axis of the propeller nor uniform in intensity. In an actual
ship, side force is always experienced as the propeller turns.

As a vessel moves through the water, she tends to drag some of the water
along with her because of skin friction. If we measure the velocity of the
following wake at different distances out from the surface of the hull, we get
a picture similar to Figure 166. Close to the hull, the velocity of the water
relative to the ship is very small; that is, the water is being carried along with
the ship. At some distance out from the hull, the relative velocity approaches
the velocity of the ship. We can take some arbitrary point (such as where the
velocity of the following wake is 2 per cent of the ship's speed) as the limit of
the boundary layer and can thus examine the thickness of the frictional wake.
The frictional wake, starting from zero thickness at the bow, increases towards
the stern until it reaches a thickness of several feet in some cases. The net
effect is that an envelope of water immediately adjacent to the ship is given a
forward motion by the passage of the ship.

---

* This section is based on a paper prepared by the David Taylor Model Basin entitled,
"Propeller Action in a Single-Screw Ship."

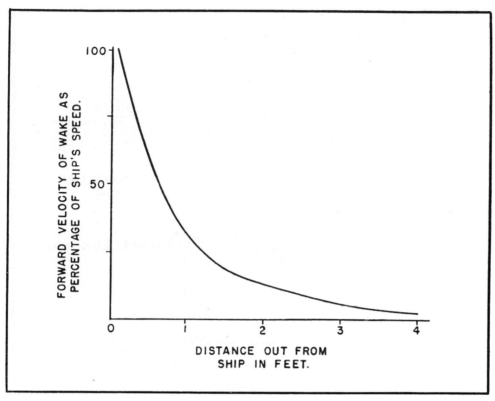

Figure 166. Thickness of Frictional Wake.

The propeller, being behind the ship, has to work in this wake. It is as though the propeller were advancing through the water at a lower speed than the ship. Thus if a ship moving at 15 knots had a following wake of 3 knots in the vicinity of the propeller, the propeller would be advancing at only 12 knots *relative* to the water.

Actually, due to the shape of the hull and appendages, the velocities in the wake may vary greatly from place to place. Behind blunt endings of the structure, the wake may be moving forward bodily with the ship. A variation in the wake pattern may cause unsymmetrical propeller forces.

The wake pattern has been measured on many models. A typical wake distribution for a single-screw merchant ship is shown in Figure 167. This indicates by contours the distribution of fore-and-aft velocity over the propeller disc. It will be seen that this fore-and-aft velocity relative to the propeller drops in places to 20 per cent of the ship's speed.

In addition to the fore-and-aft motion, the water also has an *upward* and *inward* motion in the vicinity of the propeller. As indicated in Figure 159, this motion is imparted to the water as it closes in behind the stern. This

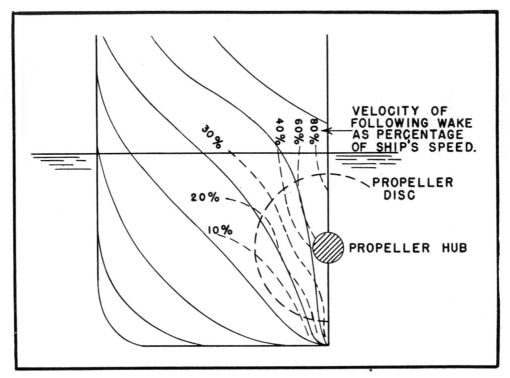

Figure 167. Wake behind a single-screw ship.

upward component of velocity of the wake also has an important effect on propeller behavior.

Having obtained a general picture of the wake pattern, we can now turn to the propeller. It is usual to simplify the study of propeller action by considering a typical section of the blade. Figure 169 indicates that the velocity of the blade section relative to the water is the resultant of two components:

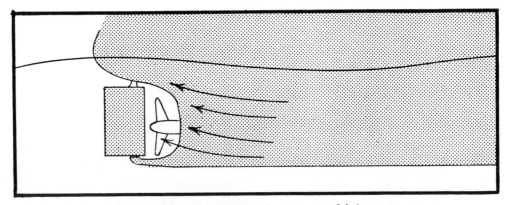

Figure 168. Movement of water at ship's stern.

1. A forward component, velocity V_A, equal to the ship's speed minus the wake velocity.

2. A tangential component due to the rotation of the propeller equal to $2\pi rN$ (r being the radius under consideration and N the RPM).

The velocity relative to the blade section, V_o, is found by combining the forward and rotational components as shown in the figure. The inclination of V_o to the face of the blade is the angle-of-attack (α). The effect of the current striking the blade at this angle is to develop lift and drag, and these forces can be readily resolved to give thrust, T, and torque, Q, as shown in the figure.

As a typical section rotates around the disc, it meets many different wake areas. The variation of V_A as the wake velocity varies will cause changes in α, T, and Q. Hence the propeller will not deliver a steady thrust nor absorb a uniform torque.

As a result of variations as it rotates, a propeller produces side forces in addition to thrust along the propeller shaft. The side forces produced by the propeller of a single-screw ship can be broken down into four parts as follows:

1. Following Wake Effect

In the vertical position behind the hull (blade A, Figure 170), the blade passes through a region of high following wake. This results in an increased

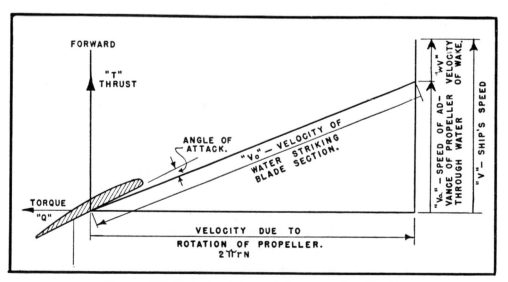

Figure 169. Velocity Diagram for propeller blade.

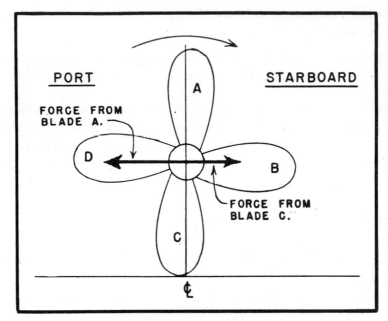

Figure 170. Side Force resulting from Following Wake on a single-screw ship.

angle of attack and greater thrust and torque when the blade is in this region. The reaction to this, with a right-hand screw, is a force tending to move the stern to port when going ahead. At the same time, a blade passing through the bottom part of the disc would experience an opposing reaction; but since the following wake in this lower region is much weaker and extends over a much smaller area, the action of the upper blade would predominate. *The following wake effect, then, is to produce a net force tending to move the stern to port and cause the ship to veer to the right.*

2. Inclination Effect

The axis of the propeller shaft is inclined to the axis of water flow past the propeller because of the inward and upward movement of the water under the stern. The inward movement is symmetrical on both sides of the stern and can be neglected, but the upward movement produces a marked effect. As a blade moves downward to its horizontal position (blade B, Figure 161), it meets water which is moving upward as well as aft. This is equivalent to increasing the relative velocity *and* the angle of attack at the same time, and thus an increase in thrust is experienced. On the opposite side, the port side for a righthand screw, a decrease in thrust is experienced. *The net effect of the reaction to the inclined flow, then, is a torque tending to twist the ship to the left.*

3. Helical Discharge Effect

The helical discharge from the propeller of a single-screw ship impinges directly on the rudder. That part of the discharge above the propeller hub creates a force on the rudder tending to move the stern to starboard, while the lower half creates a force tending to move the stern to port. Because of the increased blade angles of attack in the upper arc due to the following wake effect, the discharge current from the upper half of the arc is stronger. *The net effect of the helical discharge, then, is to tend to turn the ship to the left.* (This effect can be altered or increased by an unsymmetrical rudder, especially if the rudder does not extend across the entire disc.)

4. Shallow Submergence Effect

If a vessel is at light displacement, the propeller may break surface and cause a decrease in transverse force in the upper arc. When the ship has little way on, the propeller frequently draws air from the surface when appreciable power is applied, and experiments have shown that the effect is the same as if the blade broke the surface. In either case it is as though the blade were working in a less dense medium. *The shallow submergence effect, then, is to tend to move the stern to starboard and cause the ship to veer to the left.*

A single-screw ship, when going ahead, is therefore subject to several different actions—some opposing—and the actual behavior of a given ship will depend on the relative magnitude of the forces. One must experiment with a given ship to determine the magnitude and character of the side force that will be encountered. Experience shows, however, that most single-screw ships have a tendency to turn to the left when going ahead.

Getting Under Way

With the ship at rest and just starting to move, the stern usually moves to starboard. Since the forward motion of the hull is negligible, the wake is also negligible, and one must examine other conditions to find the source of the side force. Only the shallow submergence effect of those outlined above is independent of the wake.

If one observes the water in the vicinity of the propeller when the screw is started rapidly, he will notice a "churning" action as air is drawn down into the propeller disc even though the propeller is well below the surface. Experiments have shown that this air affects the upper half of the disc predominantly, and *the effect is a resultant force to move the stern to starboard.*

Backing

When turning the propeller astern with the ship dead in the water, the side force on the propeller arises from the same cause as when starting ahead, but the direction of the force is reversed. *From the propeller alone, then, the force on the stern is to port.*

When backing the propeller with the ship dead in the water or moving astern, the propeller is biting into undisturbed water, so the following wake effects that come into play when moving ahead are not present. The discharge of a backing propeller is directed against the stern of the ship, and the upper half of the spiral discharge tends to bank up against the starboard side of the counter while the lower half of the spiral hits the lower part of the skeg and spills under the keel. *The result is a force tending to move the stern to port.*

Since both effects tend to carry the stern to port, a *single-screw ship with a righthand screw has a strong tendency to back to port.*

Since the suction current is much less concentrated than the discharge current, it has little effect on the rudder of a single-screw ship when backing. Consequently, such a ship must rely nearly entirely on sternward velocity for rudder effectiveness. For this reason it is necessary for a single-screw ship to build up appreciable sternway before the tendency to back to port can be overcome by use of the rudder.

In summary then, in a normal single-screw ship, the side force acts in a direction as though the blades were bearing against the bottom, as described in Chapter II, and the direction of the side force depends only upon the direction of rotation of the propeller. When operating with little way on or Backing, this is clearly the case; but when proceeding ahead, the conflicting forces may reduce the side force markedly or even reverse it. There may be cases where a single-screw ship has a tendency to veer to the right when moving ahead.

B. SIDE FORCE WITH TWIN SCREWS

In the normal twin-screw installation, the propellers turn in opposite directions when driving ahead or astern, and the side forces then cancel. To increase the maneuverability of these ships, it has become the convention to allow the side force to augment the moment resulting from the shafts being offset from the centerline. Thus we find the propellers turning so that the blade tips are moving outboard during the upper half of their travel when driving ahead. This calls for a righthand screw on the starboard shaft and a lefthand screw on the port shaft.

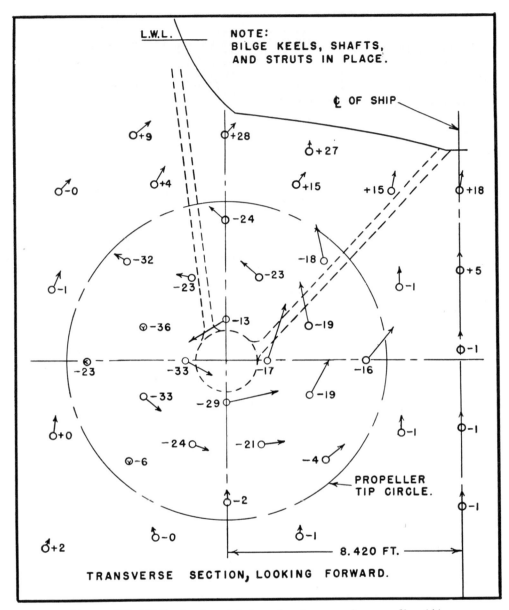

Figure 171. Wake in the vicinity of a destroyer's propeller (A).

To determine the magnitude of the side force to be expected in a twin-screw ship, we should consider the character of the flow in the vicinity of the propellers. Figure 171 shows the actual character of the wake in the vicinity of a propeller of a destroyer moving at high speed. The arrows indicate the transverse components of flow and clearly show the upward movement of the wake under the stern and the helical motion imparted to the discharge

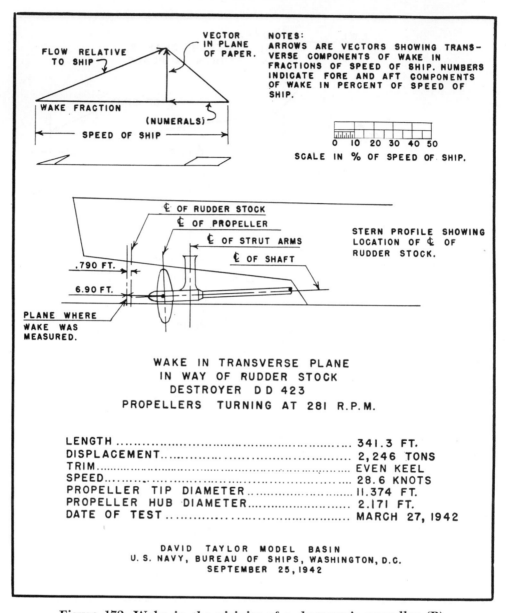

Figure 172. Wake in the vicinity of a destroyer's propeller (B).

stream by the propeller. The numbers indicate the velocity of the following wake as a percentage of the ship's speed—positive numbers indicating following wake, negative numbers indicating rearward motion with respect to still water.

Analyzing this wake pattern for the effects discussed above for the single-screw case, the following facts become apparent:

Following Wake Effect

The blade tips as they pass closest to the hull are working in a following wake of only 15 per cent of ship's speed, and throughout the majority of the propeller disc there is no appreciable following wake. Consequently, the following wake effect is considerably reduced with normal twin-screw design.

Inclination Effect

The inclination of the shaft axis to the direction of flow is just as marked with twin screws as with single. Not only is the upward motion of the wake still present, but, as shown in the side view of Figure 163, the inclination of the shaft is downward. Since the engine is inside the hull and hence the shaft must pass through the bottom to reach the propeller in any type of ship, the inclination effect is present in all types of ships.

Helical Discharge Effect

If the ship has a single rudder, it will probably not be within the region of helical discharge current, so this effect will be absent in such ships. In a twin-rudder ship, on the other hand, this effect is not only present but is greatly augmented by the shape of the rudder. Normal twin-rudder design for warships uses a spade rudder (narrower at the bottom than at the top, as seen from the side), and frequently the rudder extends only slightly below the axis of the propeller. Consequently such a rudder feels the upper half of the discharge current much more than the lower half, and the helical discharge effect is very large.

Shallow Submergence Effect

This effect is less common with twin-screw design, especially with warships, since it is most unusual that a propeller tip will break surface. The churning and air drawing is present, however, so this effect is still to be considered.

Since the only opposing effect—the following wake effect—has been diminished in twin-screw design, the side force on a righthand screw turning ahead is definitely to starboard, and the side force for a lefthand screw turning ahead is definitely to port. The directions of the forces are reversed, of course, when the direction of rotation is reversed.

With twin screws, then, the side forces are large and are uniformly in the direction indicated by the direction of rotation of the propeller. When moving steadily ahead, the force to starboard on a righthand screw is not appreciably diminished by a following wake effect, so we can expect strong side force to be present even though normally cancelled by the side force from the opposite screw. When the ship is dead in the water, the side forces experienced from the propellers alone are of the same magnitude as those encountered in a single-screw ship. When backing, the side forces from a twin-screw installation are usually somewhat smaller than with a conventional single-screw ship because the structure into which the helical discharge is directed is less extensive.

C. USE OF SIDE FORCE

In all types of conventional ships, a side force is experienced whenever the propellers are rotated. Though the magnitude of the force may vary with the type of ship, the direction is nearly always that indicated by the direction of rotation of the propellers (as though the blades were bearing against a more solid layer during the lower part of their travel). If the ship-handler has considered the origin of these forces, he will know what reaction to expect under any given set of conditions. For a certain ship, a little experimentation will indicate the magnitude and character of the side forces that can be expected, and the conning officer can turn these forces to good use in handling his ship.

RESISTANCE AND POWER*

IN HIS EXPERIENCE with ships, the mariner becomes curious about the power required to drive his ship through the water. On one hand it seems that relatively feeble power plants are sufficient to drive large ships at moderate speeds, yet on the other hand vast amounts of power are needed to drive even small ships at 30 knots or more. There seems to be a "wall" of resistance which suddenly appears as the ship approaches high speed.

A destroyer with 60,000 shaft horsepower can make only about 35 knots, yet a cruiser having six times the displacement of the destroyer can make the same speed with only twice the power. The battleship, the cruiser, and the destroyer have 3.7, 6.5, and 19 horsepower per ton, respectively, yet all have about the same maximum speed at sea. Though the greater horsepower per ton insures the ability to *accelerate* more rapidly at low speeds, it does not seem to provide a significantly higher maximum speed. The hulls of all fast warships are very similar in shape; is there a factor which depends simply on size? Why do we obtain better results with the larger ship?

We can begin our exploration of the power required to propel a ship by examining the resistance which the ship encounters as she moves through the water. One of the first things we must understand is that the resistance in question depends on motion. All fluid resistance results from motion and usually increases as a power of the velocity of motion. There is no static friction in the sea. If we apply a force, no matter how minute, on the ship, the ship will move and will continue to accelerate until a balancing resistance is created by the motion of the ship.

The resistance encountered by the ship also depends on the size and shape of the hull. In fluid resistance, it is the character of the immersed body which determines the magnitude of the retarding force. For this reason it is very advantageous that the underwater body have a smooth "streamlined" form.

Actually, as a perfectly streamlined body moves through the water, no power is required simply to displace the water to allow the ship to pass. In an ideal case, the pressures on the forward half of the body are exactly compensated by the pressures on the after half of the body, and there is no pressure difference to hold the ship back. We must look elsewhere than the

---

* This appendix is based on *Speed and Power of Ships* Book II —("Resistance") by Rear Admiral David W. Taylor, CC, USN (Ret.).

simple displacement of water to find the source of resistance which requires the expenditure of our ship's power. Many of the sources of resistance to the motion of our ship are not readily apparent.

The examination of the resistance encountered by a ship is complicated both by the complex form of the underwater body of the ship and the fluid nature of the medium in which it is travelling. Extensive experimental research over a number of years has established, however, that the resistance to motion encountered by a ship can be divided into the following categories: frictional resistance, wave resistance, eddy resistance, appendage resistance, and air resistance. These resistances are further modified by squat, the shallow water effect, and the effect of rough seas. In normal weather, the frictional resistance and the wave resistance are by far the predominant causes for the expenditure of power.

Frictional Resistance

As a ship moves through the water, the particles of water immediately against the skin of the ship move along with the ship, the particles next adjacent to these are dragged along to a certain extent by molecular friction, and the next layer of particles is dragged along to a lesser extent, etc. These particles form an envelope of water about the ship which is being more or less carried along with the ship. The thickness of the "boundary layer" which is being dragged forward by the movement of the ship varies from a few molecules in thickness at the bow to several feet near the stern. Energy must be expended to impart this motion to the boundary layer, and the resulting resistance has become known as the frictional resistance.

Extensive experiments, beginning with those of Mr. William Froude in England in 1874, have shown that the frictional resistance of a ship can be expressed by the formula:

$$R_f = fSV^n$$

where:

R_f = frictional resistance
f = coefficient of friction (dynamic)
S = total wetted surface of the ship
V = velocity of the ship through the water
n = index or power according to which water friction varies

Froude found that for rough surfaces, the index (n) was 2.00, but that for hard surfaces it might be as low as 1.83. After very elaborate experiments, supported by later investigations with only slight variation, Froude established in 1888 Froude's Frictional Constants which give the index (n) as 1.825 for all sizes of ships. Since later experimenters found the value to be slightly larger, it is customary to use the following formula for frictional resistance:

$$R_f = fSV^{1.83}$$

It is sufficient for the shiphandler, however, to remember that the frictional resistance is proportional to the total wetted surface and approximately to the *square* of the speed.

Wave Resistance

When a ship moves on the surface of the water, it creates waves. It is evident that these waves have energy (as one can observe when waves strike an obstruction), so the ship must have imparted this energy. The amount of energy being imparted to the waves by the ship could be determined if the energy of the waves could be measured. If we could evaluate the energy flowing away from the ship in the form of waves, we could evaluate the propulsive power expended in creating them.

The energy in a single wave has been found to be proportional to the breadth of the wave (its longest dimension) and the square of the height of the wave. The power (energy expended per unit of time) required to create a train of waves is equal to the energy per wave multiplied by the rate at which the waves are being created.

The principal waves which make up the wake of a ship are created at the bow and at the stern of the ship. It is as though two wave generators were travelling, one after the other, separated by one shiplength. These two wave systems interact with one another, and this interaction may increase or decrease the magnitude of the resulting waves.

As indicated in Figure 164, the waves created at the stern may tend to reinforce or cancel the waves created by the bow. If one of the crests of the bow wave system coincides with the first crest of the stern wave system, a reinforcement occurs, the resulting wake waves are higher, and the wave resistance (R_w) is increased. Should a crest of the bow wave system fall on the first trough of the stern wave system, a cancellation would occur, the resulting wake waves would be smaller, and R_w would decrease. The waves which are affected by this reinforcement and cancellation process are the transverse waves discussed in Chapter XI, the crests of which are perpendicular to the track of the ship and which travel initially at the speed of the ship.

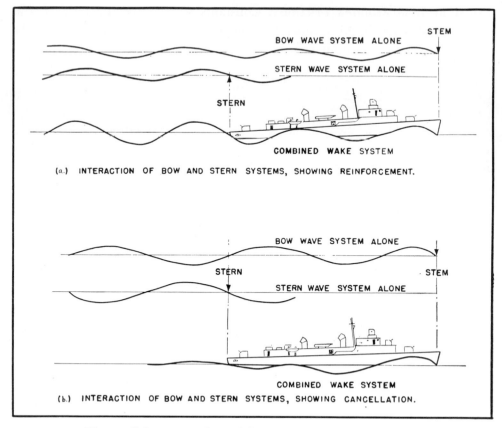

(a.) INTERACTION OF BOW AND STERN SYSTEMS, SHOWING REINFORCEMENT.

(b.) INTERACTION OF BOW AND STERN SYSTEMS, SHOWING CANCELLATION.

Figure 173. Interaction of bow and stern wave systems.

The formula for the length (distance between crests) of a wave at sea in deep water has been determined to be:

$$l = .557 \ V^2$$

where:

$l =$ length of the wave in feet

$V =$ velocity of the wave in knots.

Thus as the speed of the wave (which is equal to the speed of the ship for transverse wake waves) doubles, the length between crests will quadruple!

In observing the waves which make up the ship's wake, we will note that the bow system commences with a crest which is just abaft the ship's stem. The stern system commences, on the other hand, with a trough in the vicinity of the propellers followed by a crest a little abaft the stern. Considering the locations of the first crests, we can consider that the two initiating points are separated by approximately one shiplength (L). Whether we get a reinforcement or a cancellation from the interaction of the two systems will depend on the ratio of the length between crests (l) and the length of the ship (L), or l/L. If the length of the wake waves created at the bow is equal to the length of the ship, or is an even fraction of this length, we will experience a reinforcement and a consequent increase in resistance.

To compare the length of the wake waves to the length of the ship, we can state the ratio as:

$$\frac{l}{L} = \frac{.557 \ V^2}{L}$$

which varies as the ratio:

$$\frac{V^2}{L}$$

Because it is usually convenient to plot resistance against speed, the square root of this ratio:

$$\frac{V}{\sqrt{L}}$$

where:

$V = $ ship's speed in knots
$L = $ ship's length in feet

is used in considering wave resistance. This ratio $\frac{V}{\sqrt{L}}$, is known as the speed-length ratio and is very important in consideration of resistance and power in a ship.

Actually, the wave making length (distance between the first crest of the bow system and the first crest of the stern system) is not exactly equal to the length of the ship, so the regions of maximum R_w do not fall exactly where $\frac{V^2}{L}$ equals 1.0 or multiples thereof. The wave making length is usually slightly greater than the length of the ship (L) and will vary with the shape of the hull. However, the difference is not large and the speed-length ratio is a very useful key in studying the resistance encountered by a ship.

The amount of power consumed in creating waves is not easily expressed. If one were to attempt to find a simple formula in the form of $R_w = aV^n$, he would find that (n) varied from 1.5 to 11 for different parts of the speed range. Because of the reinforcements and cancellations mentioned above, any formula which expresses a smooth increase in resistance as speed increases is far from a correct representation of the situation.

By representing a ship by two disturbances, Professor T. H. Havelock of Armstrong College, Newcastle-on-Tyne, made an analysis which indicated that the wave resistance would be in the form indicated in Figure 165. The reader will note the distinct humps and hollows in the resistance curve which occur as the reinforcements and cancellations occur. The general decrease in resistance at very high speeds (speed-length ratio greater than 2), is experienced because, "when the travelling disturbance travels fast enough, the water does not have time to respond and is not disturbed as much as at lower speeds."[*] Actually, other experiments have shown that at very high speeds the ship rides up on its bow wave and a decrease in wave resistance is experienced.

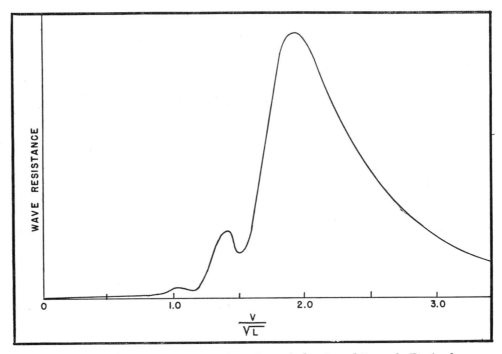

Figure 174. Wave Resistance as a function of the Speed-Length Ratio for two disturbances travelling through the water separated by one ship-length L. (Based on Figure 56 of "Speed and Power of Ships," by Rear Admiral David W. Taylor (CC), U.S.N. (Ret.).)

Eddy Resistance

As the water flows past the underwater body of the ship, if there are abrupt changes in the surface of the hull separation and turbulence may occur.

---

[*] *Speed and Power of Ships* by Rear Admiral David W. Taylor, CC, USN (Ret.), page 46.

When the flow of water breaks away from the skin of the ship, such as at the after edge of a square sternpost, an area of confused eddying results. This area is aft of the ship's structure and is characterized by a lower pressure than is found in the surrounding water; therefore, a drag force is exerted on the ship as a result of eddies. Though a well designed ship will have few such areas, the eddy resistance caused by blunt edges and projections must be considered.

Eddy resistance (into this category is lumped all resistance caused by separation and turbulence around hull endings and hull openings) varies as the frontal area of the surface causing the disturbance and the square of the velocity of the water flow. Thus, even small causes of eddying may become important at high speeds.

Appendage Resistance

The previous discussion has considered the simple hull of the ship without its appendages such as the propeller shafts, struts, rudders, bilge keels, etc. Each of these projections contribute to the resistance of the ship as it moves through the water, and, depending upon the nature and design of the appendage, any of the previous sources of resistance may apply.

In general, the underwater appendages of a well designed ship are deep below the surface of the water, so they contribute little to the wave making resistance of the ship. They are usually quite streamlined to minimize the eddy resistance, so our main source of resistance is the frictional resistance. Thus we can consider that the appendage resistance is generally proportional to the wetted surface of the appendages and the square of the velocity of flow past them.

Air Resistance and Wind Resistance

Determining the air or wind resistance of a ship with a complex superstructure is very difficult except by experiment. Though certain data are available on the resistance of flat plates at various inclinations, it would be nearly impossible to evaluate the effect of the multitude of interacting surfaces in the superstructure of even a small ship. Consequently there are no formulae which apply to this source of resistance.

Experiments on a number of ships show, however, that air resistance varies in the range of from $1\frac{1}{2}$ to 3 per cent of the total water resistance of the ship at maximum speed. This leads to the conclusion that the air resistance is only a minor factor as compared to the water resistance of a ship, and can be neglected in most considerations.

Though simple air resistance (the resistance to the ship's motion through still air) may be neglected, wind resistance cannot be overlooked. A ship steaming at 10 knots into a 20 knot wind (thus feeling a 30 knot relative wind) may be expending as much as 20 per cent of her power to overcome wind resistance. Another factor to be considered is that the maximum resistance to motion ahead may occur when the relative wind is on one bow instead of dead ahead. Thus the direction of the wind may have an effect in determining the resistance. A last factor in considering the wind is that a wind with a beam component usually necessitates the use of rudder to hold the ship on her course, and even a small rudder angle increases the drag of the ship appreciably.

Squat

As discussed in Chapter XI, as the ship increases speed she sinks bodily in the water, and then, at the critical speed (speed-length ratio about 1.2), the bow begins to rise and the stern begins to sink as the ship "squats." As the first crest of the bow wave system moves aft from the bow with increase of speed, the bow begins to be buoyed up by its own wave, and so the bow rises. If we remember the interaction of the bow and stern wave systems, we can see that the stern will sink into the hollow created as the first trough of the bow wave system coincides with and augments the stern system hollow near the screws. As the ship squats, her resistance increases abruptly.

Shallow Water Effect

As the ship enters shallow water, the character of the wave changes. A wave created at a given speed in shallow water has a longer wave length than a wave created at the same speed in deep water. Consequently, the reinforcements and severe squatting occur at lower speeds in shallow water than in deep water. Thus, in shallow water, the resistance of the ship rises more rapidly as the speed increases.

Because the severe reinforcements occur at a lower speed in shallow water, it is possible for certain very high speed ships to reach a higher maximum speed in shallow water than in deep water. This is possible because they are operating beyond the peak of the wave resistance curve (Figure 174), and as the whole curve shifts to the left as a result of the longer wave length in shallow water, the wave resistance at the speed they are steaming actually decreases!

Total Resistance

The combination of all of the above mentioned sources of resistance is shown in Figure 175. Though the particular curves shown do not illustrate

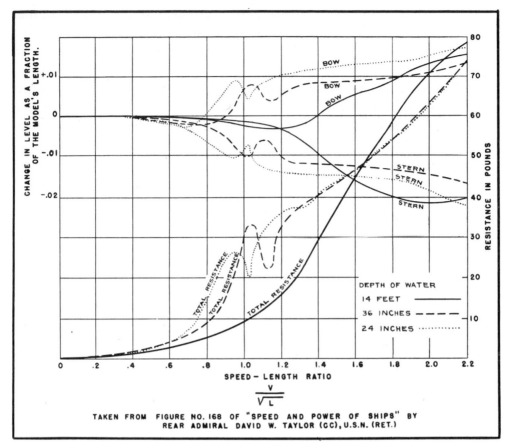

Figure 175. Resistance and changes in level of a 20-foot
model of a high-speed warship.

the hump and hollow character of wave resistance in deep water, this characteristic is quite marked in the shallow water curves. The general sinkage of
the ship at the lower speeds, and the squatting and abrupt increase in resistance as the speed is increased, can be clearly seen. The reader will note that if
a ship, scaled up from the model, had the power to overcome the equivalent
of 60 lbs. resistance for the model, she could make a higher speed (that is,
operate at a higher speed-length ratio) at this power in shallow water than
in deep water.

Rough Water Effects

In addition to the general sources of resistance which the ship encounters
in smooth water, there is additional resistance if the surface of the water is
not smooth. As the ship encounters seas from ahead, her trim is constantly
changing and she crashes into the approaching seas. As she rolls in response to

the waves, the shape of the submerged portion of her hull is constantly changing. These effects cause an increase in the resistance to her forward motion.

The pitching of the ship is the most severe deterrent to speed that is caused by rough water. It increases all the normal sources of resistance, and, additionally, may cause losses in propulsive efficiency as the screws race when they come near the surface.

Rolling, though causing increased resistance, is much less detrimental than one might think. It is difficult to determine experimentally the increase in resistance caused by pure rolling, but certain experiments indicate that inclinations up to 20° cause an increase in resistance of only a few per cent. Rough seas, however, do have a marked effect on the resistance of the ship and the power required to drive her.

Conclusion

It is seen, therefore, that the causes of the resistance encountered by a ship are very complex. Though the thumb rule long used by mariners that "the power required and the fuel consumed for a given speed go up as the cube of the speed" is applicable in certain speed ranges, the rule does not hold true for all ranges, especially when wave resistance becomes an important factor. The power required at any speed is equal to the total resistance multiplied by the speed (force × velocity = power), and for the "Cube Rule" to be correct, the resistance would have to vary as the square of the speed. We have seen that this is far from true for all cases.

The resistance of the ship is the sum of all of the factors mentioned above, and it is not susceptible to simple analysis. The shiphandler should be impressed, however, with the fact that the resistance encountered, the power required, and the fuel consumed increases drastically as the speed increases. When the speed is increased until squatting is encountered, the resistance increases even more rapidly, and the steaming efficiency of the ship is severely reduced.

The length of a ship is a very important factor in determining the resistance, and the speed-length ratio is an excellent index in considering the resistance. Two similar ships operating at the same speed-length ratio will require power in the ratio of the squares of their lengths. The higher the speed-length ratio, especially beyond critical speed ($\frac{V}{\sqrt{L}}$ greater than 1.2), the greater the proportion of total power which is expended uselessly in creating waves.

The wastage of power in creating surface waves leads one to the interesting realization that a streamlined submarine, cruising at a sufficient depth to be free from surface effects, can attain a higher speed for a given power than an equivalent ship on the surface at the same power. A deeply submerged submarine encounters resistance which is proportional to the square of her speed, but the surface ship encounters a much higher resistance for the same speed. It is because of this wastage of power in creating wake waves that inventors are constantly searching for ways of causing a ship to "plane" at high speeds and thus be able to escape this major source of drag on a conventional hull.

APPENDIX III

RULES OF THE ROAD

REGULATIONS[1]

TITLE 33-NAVIGATION AND NAVIGABLE WATERS

Chapter I—Coast Guard, Department of the Treasury

Subchapter D—Navigation Requirements for Certain Inland Waters

Part 82—Boundary Lines of Inland Waters

Sec.

---

[1] The regulations in this part are reprinted from the Code of Federal Regulations of the United States of America, as amended.

[2] The boundary lines of inland waters for the Gulf Coast of the United States were revised in December, 1953. For the original description of the revised lines, see the *Federal Register* of Tuesday, December 8, 1953. Subsequent changes in description have not affected the position of these lines.

82.230 Bahia de Jobos.

82.235 St. Thomas Harbor, St. Thomas.

82.240 Christiansted Harbor, Island of St. Croix, Virgin Islands.

82.245 Sonda de Vieques.

Alaska

82.275 Bays, sounds, straits, and inlets on the coast of southeastern Alaska between Cape Spencer Light Station and Sitklan Island.

AUTHORITY: §§ 82.1 to 82.275, inclusive, issued under Sec. 2, 28 Stat. 672, 33 U. S. C. 151.

General

SEC. 82.1 **General basis and purpose of boundary lines.** By virtue of the authority vested in the Commandant[3] of the Coast Guard under section 101 of Reorganization Plan No. 3 of 1946 (11 F. R. 7875), and section 2 of the act of February 19, 1895, as amended (28 Stat. 672, 33 U. S. C. 151), the regulations in this part are prescribed to establish the lines dividing the high seas from rivers, harbors, and inland waters in accordance with the intent of the statute and to obtain its correct and uniform administration. The waters inshore of the lines described in this part are "inland waters," and upon them the Inland Rules and pilot rules made in pursuance thereof apply. The waters outside of the lines described in this part are the high seas and upon them the International Rules apply. The regulations in this part do not apply to the Great Lakes or their connecting and tributary waters.

SEC. 82.2 **General rules for inland waters.** At all buoyed entrances from seaward to bays, sounds, rivers, or other estuaries for which specific lines are not described in this part, the waters inshore of a line approximately parallel with the general trend of the shore, drawn through the outermost buoy or other aid to navigation of any system of aids, are inland waters, and upon them the Inland Rules and pilot rules made in pursuance thereof apply, except that Pilot Rules for Western Rivers apply to the Red River of the North, the Mississippi River and its tributaries above Huey P. Long Bridge, and that part of the Atchafalaya River above its junction with the Plaquemine-Morgan City alternate waterway.

Atlantic Coast

SEC. 82.5 **All harbors on the coast of Maine, New Hampshire, and Massachusetts between West Quoddy Head, Maine, and Cape Ann Lighthouse, Mass.** A line drawn from Sail Rock Lighted Whistle Buoy 1 to the southeasternmost extremity of Long Point, Maine, to the southeasternmost extremity of Western Head; thence to the southeasternmost extremity of Old Man; thence to the southernmost extremity of Double Shot Islands; thence to Libby Islands Lighthouse; thence to Moose Peak Lighthouse; thence to the eastern extremity of Little Pond Head. A line drawn from the southern extremity of Pond Point, Great Wass Island, to the southernmost point of Crumple Island; thence to Petit Manan Lighthouse; thence to Mount Desert Lighthouse; thence to Matinicus Rock Lighthouse; thence to Monhegan Island Lighthouse; thence to Seguin Lighthouse; thence to Portland Lightship; thence to Boon Island Lighthouse; thence to Cape Ann Lighted Whistle Buoy 2.

SEC. 82.10 **Massachusetts Bay.** A line drawn from Cape Ann Lighted Whistle Buoy 2 to Boston Lightship; thence to Cape Cod Lighthouse.

SEC. 82.15 **Nantucket Sound, Vineyard Sound, Buzzard's Bay, Narragansett Bay, Block Island Sound, and easterly entrance to Long Island Sound.** A line

---

[3] By Reorganization Plan No. 26 of 1950, effective July 31, 1950 (15 F. R. 4935), the functions formerly vested in the Commandant, U. S. Coast Guard, were transferred to the Secretary of the Treasury with certain exceptions. The Secretary, however, by an order dated July 31, 1950 (15 F. R. 6521), delegated to the Commandant the functions formerly performed by him under Reorganization Plan No. 3 of 1946.

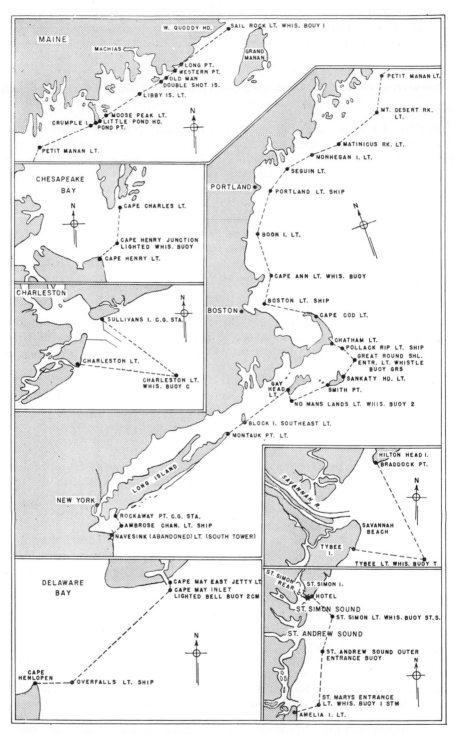

Boundary lines of Inland Waters, Atlantic Coast of the United States.

drawn from Catham Lighthouse to Pollock Rip Lightship; thence to Great Round Shoal Channel Entrance Lighted Whistle Buoy GRS; thence to Sankaty Head Lighthouse. A line drawn from the westernmost extremity of Smith Point, Nantucket Island, to No Mans Land Lighted Whistle Buoy 2; thence to Gay Head Lighthouse; thence to Block Island Southeast Lighthouse; thence to Montauk Point Lighthouse on the easterly end of Long Island, N. Y.

SEC. 82.20   **New York Harbor.** A line drawn from Rockaway Point Coast Guard Station to Ambrose Channel Lightship; thence to Navesink (abandoned) Lighthouse (south tower).

SEC. 82.25   **Delaware Bay and tributaries.** A line drawn from Cape May East Jetty Light to Cape May Inlet Lighted Bell Buoy 2CM; thence to Overfalls Lightship; thence to the northernmost extremity of Cape Henlopen.

SEC. 82.30   **Chesapeake Bay and tributaries.** A line drawn from Cape Henry Lighthouse to Cape Henry Junction Lighted Whistle Buoy; thence to Cape Charles Lighthouse.

SEC. 82.35   **Charleston Harbor.** A line drawn from Sullivans Island Coast Guard Station to Charleston Lighted Whistle Buoy 2C; thence to Charleston Lighthouse.

SEC. 82.40   **Savannah Harbor.** A line drawn from the southwesternmost extremity of Braddock Point to Tybee Lighted Whistle Buoy T; thence to the southernmost point of Savannah Beach, bearing approximately 278°.

SEC. 82.45   **St. Simon Sound, St. Andrew Sound, and Cumberland Sound.** Starting from the hotel located approximately ¾ mile, 63½° true, from St. Simon (rear) Lighthouse, a line drawn to St. Simon Lighted Whistle Buoy St. S; thence to St. Andrew Sound Outer Entrance Buoy; thence to St. Marys Entrance Lighted Whistle Buoy 1STM; thence to Amelia Island Lighthouse.

SEC. 82.50   **St. Johns River, Fla.** A line drawn from the east end of the north jetty to the east end of the south jetty.

SEC. 82.55   **Florida Reefs and Keys from Miami to Marquesas Keys.** A line drawn from the east end of the north jetty at the entrance to Miami, to Miami Lighted Whistle Buoy 2; thence to Fowey Rocks Lighthouse; thence to Pacific Reef Lighthouse; thence to Carysfort Reef Lighthouse; thence to Molasses Reef Lighthouse; thence to Alligator Reef Lighthouse; thence to Tennessee Reef Lighthouse; thence to Sombrero Key Lighthouse; thence to American Shoal Lighthouse; thence to Key West Entrance Lighted Whistle Buoy; thence to Sand Key Lighthouse; thence to Cosgrove Shoal Lighthouse; thence to westernmost extremity of Marquesas Keys.

Gulf Coast

SEC. 82.60   **Florida Keys from Marquesas to Cape Sable.** A line drawn from the northwesternmost extremity of Marquesas Keys to Northwest Channel Entrance Lighted Bell Buoy 1; thence to the southernmost extremity of East Cape, Cape Sable.

SEC. 82.65   **San Carlos Bay and tributaries.** A line drawn from the northwesternmost point of Estero Island to Caloosa Lighted Bell Buoy 2; thence to Sanibel Island Lighthouse.

SEC. 82.70   **Charlotte Harbor, Fla., and tributaries.** Eastward of Charlotte Harbor Entrance Lighted Bell Buoy off Boca Grande.

SEC. 82.80   **Tampa Bay and tributaries.** A line drawn from the southernmost extremity of Long Key, Fla., to Tampa Bay Lighted Whistle Buoy; thence to Southwest Channel Entrance Lighted Bell Buoy 1; thence to a spire on the northeast side of Anna Maria Key, bearing approximately 109°.

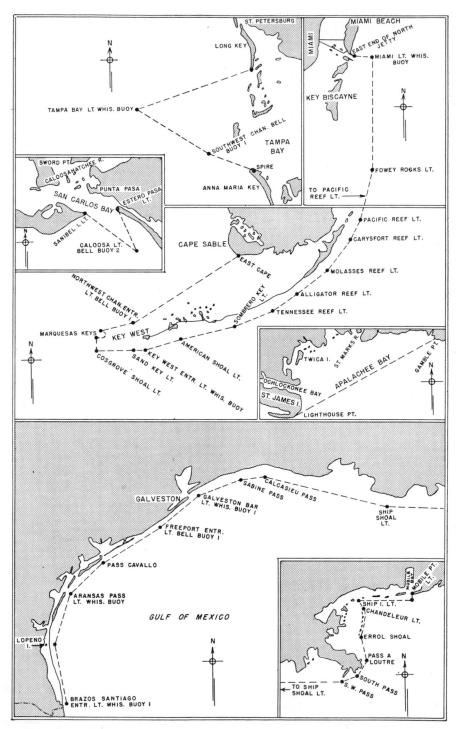

Boundary lines of Inland Waters, Gulf Coast of the United States.

Sec. **82.89   Apalachee Bay, Fla.** Those waters lying north of a line drawn from Lighthouse Point on St. James Island to Gamble Point on the east side of the entrance to the Aucilla River, Fla.

Sec. **82.95   Mobile Bay, Ala., to Mississippi Passes, La.** Starting from a point which is located 1 mile, 90° true, from Mobile Point Lighthouse, a line drawn to a point 5.5 miles, 202° true, from Mobile Point Lighthouse; thence to Ship Island Lighthouse; thence to Chandeleur Lighthouse; thence in a curved line following the general trend of the seaward, high-water shore lines of the Chandeleur Islands to the southwesternmost extremity of Errol Shoal (Lat. 29°-35.8′ N, Long. 89°-00.8′ W.); thence to a point 5.1 miles, 107° true, from Pass a Loutre Abandoned Lighthouse.

Sec. **82.100   Mississippi River.** The Pilot Rules for Western Rivers are to be followed in the Mississippi River and its tributaries above the Huey P. Long Bridge.

Sec. **82.103   Mississippi Passes, La., to Sabine Pass, Tex.** A line drawn from a point 5.1 miles, 107° true, from Pass a Loutre Abandoned Lighthouse to a point 1.7 miles, 113° true, from South Pass West Jetty Light; thence to a point 1.8 miles, 189° true, from South West Pass Entrance Light; thence to Ship Shoal Lighthouse; thence to a point 10.2 miles, 172° true, from Calcasieu Pass Entrance Range Front Light; thence to a point 2.5 miles, 163° true, from Sabine Pass East Jetty Light.

Sec. **82.106   Sabine Pass, Tex., to Galveston, Tex.** A line drawn from Sabine Pass Lighted Whistle Buoy 1 to Galveston Bar Lighted Whistle Buoy 1.

Sec. **82.111   Galveston, Tex., to Brazos River, Tex.** A line drawn from Galveston Bar Lighted Whistle Buoy 1 to Freeport Entrance Lighted Bell Buoy 1.

Sec. **82.116   Brazos River, Texas, to the Rio Grande, Tex.** A line drawn from Freeport Entrance Lighted Bell Buoy 1 to a point 4,350 yards, 118° true, from Matagorda Lighthouse; thence to Aranas Pass Lighted Whistle Buoy 1A; thence to a position 10½ miles, 90° true, from the north end of Lopeno Island (Lat. 27°-00.1′ N, Long. 97°-15.5′ W.); thence to Brazos Santiago Entrance Lighted Whistle Buoy 1.

Pacific Coast

Sec. **82.120   Juan de Fuca Strait, Wash., and Puget Sound.** A line drawn from the northernmost point of Angeles Point to Hein Bank Lighted Bell Buoy; thence to Line Kiln Light; thence to Kellett Bluff Light; thence to Turn Point Light on Stuart Island; thence to westernmost extremity of Skipjack Island; thence to Patos Island Light; thence to Point Roberts Light.

Sec. **82.125   Columbia River Entrance.** A line drawn from the west end of the north jetty (above water) to South Jetty Bell Buoy 2SJ.

Sec. **82.130   San Francisco Harbor.** A straight line from Point Bonita Lighthouse drawn through Mile Rocks Lighthouse to the shore.

Sec. **82.135   San Pedro Bay.** A line drawn from Los Angeles Harbor Lighthouse through the axis of the Middle Breakwater to the easternmost extremity of the Long Beach Breakwater; thence to Anaheim Bay East Jetty Light 4.

Sec. **82.140   San Diego Harbor.** A line drawn from the southerly tower of the Coronado Hotel to San Diego Channel Lighted Bell Buoy 5; thence to Point Loma Lighthouse.

Sec. **82.175   Mamala Bay.** A line drawn from Barbers Point Lighthouse to Diamond Head Lighthouse.

Sec. **82.200   Bahia de San Juan.** A line drawn from the northwesternmost extremity of Punta del Morro to Puerto San Juan Lighted Buoy 1; thence to Puerto

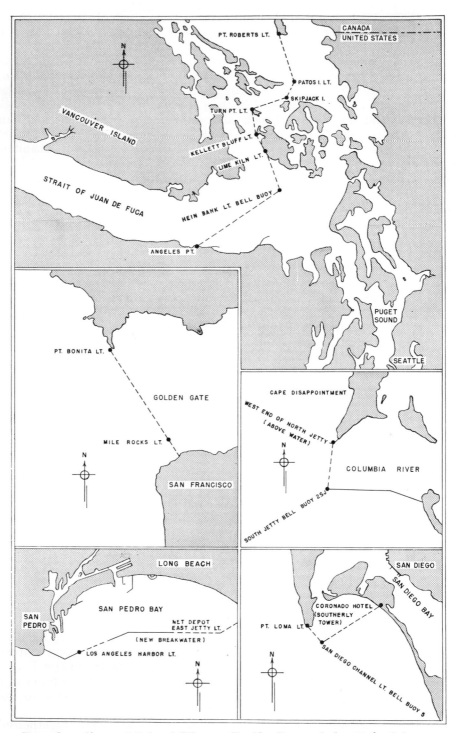

Boundary lines of Inland Waters, Pacific Coast of the United States.

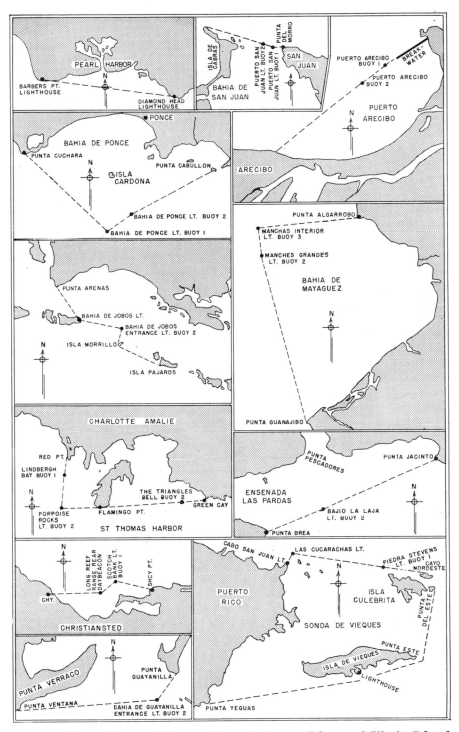

Boundary lines of Inland Waters, Hawaii, Puerto Rico, and Virgin Islands.

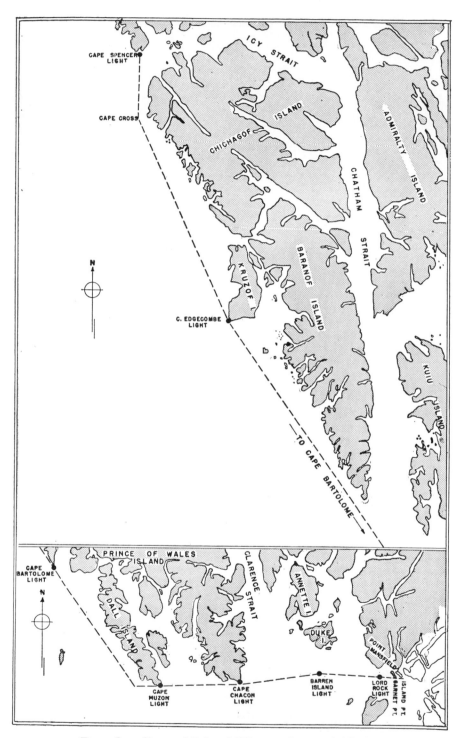

Boundary lines of Inland Waters, Coast of Alaska.

San Juan Lighted Buoy 2; thence to the northernmost extremity of Isla de Cabras.

SEC. 82.205   **Puerto Arecibo.** A line drawn from the westernmost extremity of the breakwater through Puerto Arecibo Buoy 1; thence through Puerto Arecibo Buoy 2; thence to shore in line with the Church tower in Arecibo.

SEC. 82.210   **Bahia de Mayaguez.** A line drawn from the southernmost extremity of Punta Algarrobo through Manchas Interior Lighted Buoy 3; thence to Manchas Grandes Lighted Buoy 2; thence to the northwesternmost extremity of Punta Guanajibo.

SEC. 82.215   **Bahia de Guanica.** A line drawn from the easternmost extremity of Punta Brea through Bajio La Laja Lighted Buoy 2; thence to the westernmost extremity of Punta Jacinto.

SEC. 82.220   **Bahia de Guayanilla.** A line drawn from the southernmost extremity of Punta Ventana through Bahia de Guayanilla entrance Lighted Buoy 2; thence to the southeasternmost extremity of Punta Guayanilla.

SEC. 82.225   **Bahia de Ponce.** A line drawn from the southeasternmost extremity of Punta Cuchara through Bahia de Ponce Lighted Buoy 1; thence to Bahia de Ponce Lighted Buoy 2; thence to the southwesternmost extremity of Punta Cabullon.

SEC. 82.230   **Bahia de Jobos.** A line drawn from Punta Arenas through Bahia de Jobos Light; thence to Bahia de Jobos entrance Lighted Buoy 2; thence to the southernmost extremity of Isla Morrillo; thence to the southernmost extremity of Isla Pajaros.

SEC. 82.235   **St. Thomas Harbor, St. Thomas.** A line drawn from the southernmost extremity of Red Point through Lindberg Bay Buoy 1; thence to Porpoise Rocks Lighted Buoy 2; thence to the southernmost extremity of Flamingo Point; thence to The Triangles Bell Buoy 2; thence to the Green Cay.

SEC. 82.240   **Christiansted Harbor, Island of St. Croix, Virgin Islands.** A line drawn from Shoy Point to Scotch Bank Lighted Buoy No. 1; thence to Long Reef Range Rear Daybeacon; thence to shore in range with stack at Little Princess northwestward of leper settlement.

SEC. 82.245   **Sonda de Vieques.** A line drawn from the easternmost extremity of Punta Yeguas, Puerto Rico, to a point 1 mile due south of the lighthouse at the entrance to Puerto Ferro; thence eastward in a straight line to a point 1 miles southeast of Punta Este Light, Vieques; thence in a straight line to the easternmost extremity of Punta del Este, Isla Culebrita. A line from the northernmost extremity of Cayo Nordeste to Piedra Stevens Lighted Buoy 1; thence to Las Cucarachas Light; thence to Cabo San Juan Light.

Alaska

SEC. 82.275   **Bays, sounds, straits and inlets on the coast of southeastern Alaska between Cape Spencer Light Station and Sitklan Island.** A line drawn from Cape Spencer Light Station due south to a point of intersection which is due west of the southernmost extremity of Cape Cross; thence to Cape Edgecumbe Lighthouse; thence through Cape Bartolome Lighthouse and extended to a point of intersection which is due west of Cape Muzon Lighthouse; thence due east to Cape Muzon Lighthouse; thence to a point which is one mile, 180° true from Cape Chacon Lighthouse; thence to Barren Island Lighthouse; thence to Lord Rock Lighthouse; thence to the southernmost extremity of Garnet Point, Kanagunut Island; thence to the southeasternmost extremity of Island Point, Sitklan Island. A line drawn from the northeasternmost extremity of Point Mansfield, Sitklan Island, 040° true, to where it intersects the mainland.

INTERNATIONAL RULES[1]

PART A. PRELIMINARY AND DEFINITIONS

Rule 1

(a) These Rules shall be followed by all vessels and seaplanes upon the high seas and in all waters connected therewith navigable by seagoing vessels, except as provided in Rule 30. Where, as a result of their special construction, it is not possible for seaplanes to comply fully with the provisions of Rules specifying the carrying of lights and shapes, these provisions shall be followed as closely as circumstances permit.

(b) The Rules concerning lights shall be complied with in all weathers from sunset to sunrise, and during such times no other lights shall be exhibited, except such lights as cannot be mistaken for the prescribed lights or do not impair their visibilty or distinctive character, or interfere with the keeping of a proper lookout. The lights prescribed by these Rules may also be exhibited from sunrise to sunset in restricted visibility and in all other circumstances when it is deemed necessary.

(c) In the following Rules, except where the context otherwise requires:

(i) the word "vessel" includes every description of water craft, other than a seaplane on the water, used or capable of being used as a means of transportation on water;

(ii) the word "seaplane" includes a flying boat and other aircraft designed to manoeuvre on the water;

(iii) the term "power-driven vessel" means any vessel propelled by machinery;

(iv) every power-driven vessel which is under sail and not under power is to be considered a sailing vessel, and every vessel under power, whether under sail or not, is to be considered a power-driven vessel;

(v) a vessel or seaplane on the water is "under way" when she is not at anchor, or made fast to the shore, or aground;

(vi) the term "height above the hull" means height above the uppermost continuous deck;

(vii) the length and breadth of a vessel shall be her length overall and largest breadth;

(viii) the length and span of a seaplane shall be its maximum length and span as shown in its certificate of airworthiness, or as determined by measurement in the absence of such certificate;

(ix) vessels shall be deemed to be in sight of one another only when one can be observed visually from the other;

(x) the word "visible," when applied to lights, means visible on a dark night with a clear atmosphere;

(xi) the term "short blast" means a blast of about one second's duration;

(xii) the term "prolonged blast" means a blast of from four to six seconds' duration;

(xiii) the word "whistle" means any appliance capable of producing the pre-scribed short and prolonged blasts;

(xiv) the term "engaged in fishing" means fishing with nets, lines or trawls but does not include fishing with trolling lines.

---

[1] Act of Sept. 24, 1963, 77 Stat. 194-210; 33 U.S.C. 1051-1053, 1061-1094; 49 U.S.C. 177(a), 560(a). Became effective 1 September 1965.

PART B. LIGHTS AND SHAPES

Rule 2

(a) A power-driven vessel when under way shall carry:

(i) On or in front of the foremast, or if a vessel without a foremast then in the forepart of the vessel, a white light so constructed as to show an unbroken light over an arc of the horizon of 225 degrees (20 points of the compass), so fixed as to show the light 112½ degrees (10 points) on each side of the vessel, that is, from right ahead to 22½ degrees (2 points) abaft the beam on either side, and of such a character as to be visible at a distance of at least 5 miles.

(ii) Either forward or abaft the white light prescribed in sub-section (i) a second white light similar in construction and character to that light. Vessels of less than 150 feet in length shall not be required to carry this second white light but may do so.

(iii) These two white lights shall be so placed in a line with and over the keel that one shall be at least 15 feet higher than the other and in such a position that the forward light shall always be shown lower than the after one. The horizontal distance between the two white lights shall be at least three times the vertical distance. The lower of these two white lights or, if only one is carried, then that light, shall be placed at a height above the hull of not less than 20 feet, and, if the breadth of the vessel exceeds 20 feet, then at a height above the hull not less than such breadth, so however that the light need not be placed at a greater height above the hull then 40 feet. In all circumstances the light or lights, as the case may be, shall be so placed as to be clear of and above all other lights and obstructing superstructures.

(iv) On the starboard side a green light so constructed as to show an unbroken light over an arc of the horizon of 112½ degrees (10 points of the compass), so fixed as to show the light from right ahead to 22½ degrees (2 points) abaft the beam on the starboard side, and of such a character as to be visible at a distance of at least 2 miles.

(v) On the port side a red light so constructed as to show an unbroken light over an arc of the horizon of 112½ degrees (10 points of the compass), so fixed as to show the light from right ahead to 22½ degrees (2 points) abaft the beam on the port side, and of such a character as to be visible at a distance of at least 2 miles.

(vi) The said green and red sidelights shall be fitted with inboard screens projecting at least 3 feet forward from the light, so as to prevent these lights from being seen across the bows.

(b) A seaplane under way on the water shall carry:

(i) In the forepart amidships where it can best be seen a white light, so constructed as to show an unbroken light over an arc of the horizon of 220 degrees of the compass, so fixed as to show the light 110 degrees on each side of the seaplane, namely, from right ahead to 20 degrees abaft the beam on either side, and of such a character as to be visible at a distance of at least 3 miles.

(ii) On the right or starboard wing tip a green light, so constructed as to show an unbroken light over an arc of the horizon of 110 degrees of the compass, so fixed as to show the light from right ahead to 20 degrees abaft the beam on the starboard side, and of such a character as to be visible at a distance of at least 2 miles.

(iii) On the left or port wing tip a red light, so constructed as to show an unbroken light over an arc of the horizon of 110 degrees of the compass, so fixed as to show the light from right ahead to 20 degrees abaft the beam on the port side, and of such a character as to be visible at a distance of at least 2 miles.

Rule 3

(a) A power-driven vessel when towing or pushing another vessel or seaplane shall, in addition to her sidelights, carry two white lights in a vertical line one over the other, not less than 6 feet apart, and when towing and the length of the tow, measuring from the stern of the towing vessel to the stern of the last vessel towed, exceeds 600 feet, shall carry three white lights in a vertical line one over the other, so that the upper and lower lights shall be the same distance from, and not less than 6 feet above or below, the middle light. Each of these lights shall be of the same construction and character and one of them shall be carried in the same position as the white light prescribed in Rule 2(a) (i). None of these lights shall be carried at a height of less than 14 feet above the hull. In a vessel with a single mast, such lights may be carried on the mast.

(b) The towing vessel shall also show either the stern light prescribed in Rule 10 or in lieu of that light a small white light abaft the funnel or aftermast for the tow to steer by, but such light shall not be visible forward of the beam.

(c) Between sunrise and sunset a power-driven vessel engaged in towing, if the length of tow exceeds 600 feet, shall carry, where it can best be seen, a black diamond shape at least 2 feet in diameter.

(d) A seaplane on the water, when towing one or more seaplanes or vessels, shall carry the lights prescribed in Rule 2(b)(i), (ii), and (iii); and, in addition, she shall carry a second white light of the same construction and character as the white light prescribed in Rule 2(b)(i), and in a vertical line at least 6 feet above or below such light.

Rule 4

(a) A vessel which is not under command shall carry, where they can best be seen, and, if a power-driven vessel in lieu of the lights prescribed in Rule 2(a) (i) and (ii), two red lights in a vertical line one over the other not less than 6 feet apart; and of such a character as to be visible all around the horizon at a distance of at least 2 miles. By day, she shall carry in a vertical line one over the other not less than 6 feet apart, where they can best be seen, two black balls or shapes each not less than 2 feet in diameter.

(b) A seaplane on the water which is not under command may carry, where they can best be seen, and in lieu of the light prescribed in Rule 2(b)(i), two red lights in a vertical line, one over the other, not less than 3 feet apart, and of such a character as to be visible all around the horizon at a distance of at least 2 miles, and may by day carry in a vertical line one over the other not less than 3 feet apart, where they can best be seen, two black balls or shapes, each not less than 2 feet in diameter.

(c) A vessel engaged in laying or in picking up a submarine cable or navigation mark, or a vessel engaged in surveying or underwater operations, or a vessel engaged in replenishment at sea, or in the launching or recovery of aircraft when from the nature of her work she is unable to get out of the way of approaching vessels, shall carry, in lieu of the lights prescribed in Rule 2(a)(i) and (ii), or Rule 7(a)(i), three lights in a vertical line one over the other so that the upper and lower lights shall be the same distance from, and not less than 6 feet above or below, the middle light. The highest and lowest of these lights shall be red, and the middle light shall be white, and they shall be of such a character as to be visible all round the horizon at a distance of at least 2 miles. By day, she shall carry in a vertical line one over the other not less than 6 feet apart, where they can best be seen, three shapes each not less than 2 feet in diameter, of which the highest and lowest shall be globular in shape and red in colour, and the middle one diamond shaped and white.

(d)(i) A vessel engaged in minesweeping operations shall carry at the fore truck a green light, and at the end or ends of the fore yard on the side or sides on which danger exists, another such light or lights. These lights shall be carried in addition to the light prescribed in Rule 2(a)(i) or Rule 7(a)(i) as appropriate, and shall be of such a character as to be visible all round the horizon at a distance of at least 2 miles. By day she shall carry black balls, not less than 2 feet in diameter, in the same position as the green lights.

(ii) The showing of these lights or balls indicates that it is dangerous for other vessels to approach closer than 3000 feet astern of the minesweeper or 1500 feet on the side or sides on which danger exists.

(e) The vessels and seaplanes referred to in this Rule, when not making way through the water, shall show neither the coloured side lights nor the stern lights, but when making way they shall show them.

(f) The lights and shapes prescribed in this Rule are to be taken by other vessels and seaplanes as signals that the vessel or seaplane showing them is not under command and cannot therefore get out of the way.

(g) These signals are not signals of vessels in distress and requiring assistance. Such signals are contained in Rule 31.

Rule 5

(a) A sailing vessel under way and any vessel or seaplane being towed shall carry the same lights as are prescribed in Rule 2 for a power-driven vessel or a seaplane under way, respectively, with the exception of the white lights prescribed therein, which they shall never carry. They shall also carry stern lights as prescribed in Rule 10, provided that vessels towed, except the last vessel of a tow, may carry, in lieu of such stern light, a small white light as prescribed in Rule 3(b).

(b) In addition to the lights prescribed in section (a), a sailing vessel may carry on the top of the foremast two lights in a vertical line one over the other, sufficiently separated so as to be clearly distinguished. The upper light shall be red and the lower light shall be green. Both lights shall be constructed and fixed as prescribed in Rule 2(a)(i) and shall be visible at a distance of at least 2 miles.

(c) A vessel being pushed ahead shall carry, at the forward end, on the starboard side a green light and on the port side a red light, which shall have the same characteristics as the lights prescribed in Rule 2(a)(iv) and (v) and shall be screened as provided in Rule 2(a)(vi), provided that any number of vessels pushed ahead in a group shall be lighted as one vessel.

(d) Between sunrise and sunset a vessel being towed, if the length of the tow exceeds 600 feet, shall carry where it can best be seen a black diamond shape at least 2 feet in diameter.

Rule 6

(a) When it is not possible on account of bad weather or other sufficient cause to fix the green and red sidelights, these lights shall be kept at hand lighted and ready for immediate use, and shall, on the approach of or to other vessels, be exhibited on their respective sides in sufficient time to prevent collision, in such manner as to make them most visible, and so that the green light shall not be seen on the port side nor the red light on the starboard side, nor, if practicable, more than 22½ degrees (2 points) abaft the beam on their respective sides.

(b) To make the use of these portable lights more certain and easy, the lanterns containing them shall each be painted outside with the colour of the lights they respectively contain, and shall be provided with proper screens.

Rule 7

Power-driven vessels of less than 65 feet in length, vessels under oars or sails of less than 40 feet in length, and rowing boats, when under way shall not be required to carry the lights prescribed in Rules 2, 3 and 5, but if they do not carry them they shall be provided with the following lights:

(a) Power-driven vessels of less than 65 feet in length except as provided in sections (b) and (3), shall carry:

(i) In the forepart of the vessel, where it can best be seen, and at a height above the gunwale of not less than 9 feet, a white light constructed and fixed as prescribed in Rule 2(a)(i) and of such a character as to be visible at a distance of at least 3 miles.

(ii) Green and red sidelights constructed and fixed as prescribed in Rule 2(a) (iv) and (v) and of such a character as to be visible at a distance of at least 1 mile, or a combined lantern showing a green light and a red light from right ahead to 22½ degrees (2 points) abaft the beam on their respective sides. Such lantern shall be carried not less than 3 feet below the white light.

(b) Power-driven vessels of less than 65 feet in length when towing or pushing another vessel shall carry:

(i) In addition to the side lights or the combined lantern prescribed in section (a)(ii) two white lights in a vertical line, one over the other not less than 4 feet apart. Each of these lights shall be of the same construction and character as the white light prescribed in section (a)(i) and one of them shall be carried in the same position. In a vessel with a single mast such lights may be carried on the mast.

(ii) Either a stern light as prescribed in Rule 10 or in lieu of that light a small white light abaft the funnel or aftermast for the tow to steer by, but such light shall not be visible forward of the beam.

(c) Power-driven vessels of less than 40 feet in length may carry the white light at a less height than 9 feet above the gunwale but it shall be carried not less than 3 feet above the sidelights or the combined lantern prescribed in section (a)(ii).

(d) Vessels of less than 40 feet in length, under oars or sails, except as provided in section (f), shall, if they do not carry the sidelights, carry, where it can best be seen, a lantern showing a green light on one side and a red light on the other, of such a character as to be visible at a distance of at least 1 mile, and so fixed that the green light shall not be seen on the port side, nor the red light on the starboard side. Where it is not possible to fix this light, it shall be kept ready for immediate use and shall be exhibited in sufficient time to prevent collision and so that the green light shall not be seen on the port side nor the red light on the starboard side.

(e) The vessels referred to in this Rule when being towed shall carry the side-lights or the combined lantern prescribed in sections (a) or (d) of this Rule, as appropriate, and a stern light as prescribed in Rule 10, or, except the last vessel of the tow, a small white light as prescribed in section (b)(ii). When being pushed ahead they shall carry at the forward end the sidelights or combined lantern prescribed in sections (a) or (d) of this Rule, as appropriate, provided that any number of vessels referred to in this Rule when pushed ahead in a group shall be lighted as one vessel under this Rule unless the overall length of the group exceeds 65 feet when the provisions of Rule 5(c) shall apply.

(f) Small rowing boats, whether under oars or sail, shall only be required to have ready at hand an electric torch or a lighted lantern, showing a white light, which shall be exhibited in sufficient time to prevent collision.

(g) The vessels and boats referred to in this Rule shall not be required to carry the lights or shapes prescribed in Rules 4(a) and 11(e) and the size of their day signal may be less than is prescribed in Rules 4(c) and 11(c).

Rule 8

(a) A power-driven pilot-vessel when engaged on pilotage duty and under way:

(i) Shall carry a white light at the masthead at a height of not less than 20 feet above the hull, visible all round the horizon at a distance of at least 3 miles and at a distance of 8 feet below it a red light similar in construction and character. If such a vessel is of less than 65 feet in length she may carry the white light at a height of not less than 9 feet above the gunwale and the red light at a distance of 4 feet below the white light.

(ii) Shall carry the sidelights or lanterns prescribed in Rule 2(a)(iv) and (v) or Rule 7(a)(ii) or (d), as appropriate, and the stern light prescribed in Rule 10.

(iii) Shall show one or more flare-up lights at intervals not exceeding 10 minutes. An intermittent white light visible all round the horizon may be used in lieu of flare-up lights.

(b) A sailing pilot-vessel when engaged on pilotage duty and underway:

(i) Shall carry a white light at the masthead visible all round the horizon at a distance of at least 3 miles.

(ii) Shall be provided with the sidelights or lantern prescribed in Rules 5(a) or 7(d), as appropriate, and shall, on the near approach of or to other vessels, have such lights ready for use, and shall show them at short intervals to indicate the direction in which she is heading, but the green light shall not be shown on the port side nor the red light on the starboard side. She shall also carry the stern light prescribed in Rule 10.

(iii) Shall show one or more flare-up lights at intervals not exceeding 10 minutes.

(c) A pilot-vessel when engaged on pilotage duty and not under way shall carry the lights and show the flares prescribed in sections (a)(i) and (iii) or (b)(i) and (iii), as appropriate, and if at anchor shall also carry the anchor lights prescribed in Rule 11.

(d) A pilot-vessel when not engaged on pilotage duty shall show the lights or shapes for a similar vessel of her length.

Rule 9

(a) Fishing vessels when not engaged in fishing shall show the lights or shapes for similar vessels of their length.

(b) Vessels engaged in fishing, when under way or at anchor, shall show only the lights and shapes prescribed in this Rule, which lights and shapes shall be visible at a distance of at least 2 miles.

(c)(i) Vessels when engaged in trawling, by which is meant the dragging of a dredge net or other apparatus through the water, shall carry two lights in a vertical line, one over the other, not less than 4 feet nor more than 12 feet apart. The upper of these lights shall be green and the lower light white and each shall be visible all round the horizon. The lower of these two lights shall be carried at a height above the side lights not less than twice the distance between the two vertical lights.

(ii) Such vessels may in addition carry a white light similar in construction to the white light prescribed in Rule 2(a)(i) but such light shall be carried lower than and abaft the all-round green and white lights.

(d) Vessels when engaged in fishing, except vessels engaged in trawling, shall carry the lights prescribed in section (c)(i) except that the upper of the two vertical lights shall be red. Such vessels if of less than 40 feet in length may carry the red light at a height of not less than 9 feet above the gunwale and the white light not less than 3 feet below the red light.

(e) Vessels referred to in sections (c) and (d), when making way through the water, shall carry the sidelights or lanterns prescribed in Rule 2 (a)(iv) and (v) or Rule 7(a)(ii) or (d), as appropriate, and the stern light prescribed in Rule 10. When not making way through the water they shall show neither the sidelights nor the stern light.

(f) Vessels referred to in section (d) with outlying gear extending more than 500 feet horizontally into the seaway shall carry an additional all-round white light at a horizontal distance of not less than 6 feet nor more than 20 feet away from the vertical lights in the direction of the outlying gear. This additional white light shall be placed at a height not exceeding that of the white light prescribed in section (c)(i) and not lower than the sidelights.

(g) In addition to the lights which they are required by this Rule to carry, vessels engaged in fishing may, if necessary in order to attract the attention of an approaching vessel, use a flare-up light, or may direct the beam of their searchlight in the direction of a danger threatening the approaching vessel, in such a way as not to embarrass other vessels. They may also use working lights but fishermen shall take into account that specially bright or insufficiently screened working lights may impair the visibility and distinctive character of the lights prescribed in this Rule.

(h) By day vessels when engaged in fishing shall indicate their occupation by displaying where it can best be seen a black shape consisting of two cones each not less than 2 feet in diameter with their points together one above the other. Such vessels if of less than 65 feet in length may substitute a basket for such black shape. If their outlying gear extends more than 500 feet horizontally into the seaway vessels engaged in fishing shall display in addition one black conical shape, point upwards, in the direction of the outlying gear.

Note.—Vessels fishing with trolling lines are not "engaged in fishing" as defined in Rule 1(c)(xiv).

Rule 10

(a) Except where otherwise provided in these Rules, a vessel when under way shall carry at her stern a white light, so constructed that it shall show an unbroken light over an arc of the horizon of 135 degrees (12 points of the compass), so fixed as to show the light $67\frac{1}{2}$ degrees (6 points) from right aft on each side of the vessel, and of such a character as to be visible at a distance of at least 2 miles.

(b) In a small vessel, if it is not possible on account of bad weather or other sufficient cause for this light to be fixed, an electric torch or a lighted lantern showing a white light shall be kept at hand ready for use and shall, on the approach of an overtaking vessel, be shown in sufficient time to prevent collision.

(c) A seaplane on the water when under way shall carry on her tail a white light, so constructed as to show an unbroken light over an arc of the horizon of 140 degrees of the compass, so fixed as to show the light 70 degrees from right aft on each side of the seaplane, and of such a character as to be visible at a distance of at least 2 miles.

Rule 11

(a) A vessel of less than 150 feet in length, when at anchor, shall carry in the forepart of the vessel, where it can best be seen, a white light visible all round the horizon at a distance of at least 2 miles. Such a vessel may also carry a second white light in the position prescribed in section (b) of this Rule but shall not be required to do so. The second white light, if carried, shall be visible at a distance of at least 2 miles and so placed as to be as far as possible visible all round the horizon.

(b) A vessel of 150 feet or more in length, when at anchor, shall carry near the stem of the vessel, at a height of not less than 20 feet above the hull, one such light, and at or near the stern of the vessel and at such a height that it shall be not less than 15 feet lower than the forward light, another such light. Both these lights shall be visible at a distance of at least 3 miles and so placed as to be as far as possible visible all round the horizon.

(c) Between sunrise and sunset every vessel when at anchor shall carry in the forepart of the vessel, where it can best be seen, one black ball not less than 2 feet in diameter.

(d) A vessel engaged in laying or in picking up a submarine cable or navigation mark, or a vessel engaged in surveying or underwater operations, when at anchor, shall carry the lights or shapes prescribed in Rule 4(c) in addition to those prescribed in the appropriate preceding sections of this Rule.

(e) A vessel aground shall carry the light or lights prescribed in sections (a) or (b) and the two red lights prescribed in Rule 4(a). By day she shall carry, where they can best be seen, three black balls, each not less than 2 feet in diameter, placed in a vertical line one over the other, not less than 6 feet apart.

(f) A seaplane on the water under 150 feet in length, when at anchor, shall carry, where it can best be seen, a white light, visible all round the horizon at a distance of at least 2 miles.

(g) A seaplane on the water 150 feet or upwards in length, when at anchor, shall carry, where they can best be seen, a white light forward and a white light aft, both lights visible all round the horizon at a distance of at least 3 miles; and, in addition, if the seaplane is more than 150 feet in span, a white light on each side to indicate the maximum span, and visible, so far as practicable, all round the horizon at a distance of 1 mile.

(h) A seaplane aground shall carry an anchor light or lights as prescribed in sections (f) and (g), and in addition may carry two red lights in a vertical line, at least 3 feet apart, so placed as to be visible all round the horizon.

Rule 12

Every vessel or seaplane on the water may, if necessary in order to attract attention, in addition to the lights which she is by these Rules required to carry, show a flare-up light or use a detonating or other efficient sound signal that cannot be mistaken for any signal, authorzed elsewhere under these Rules.

Rule 13

(a) Nothing in these Rules shall interfere with the operation of any special rules made by the Government of any nation with respect to additional station and signal lights for ships of war, for vessels sailing under convoy, for fishing vessels engaged in fishing as a fleet or for seaplanes on the water.

(b) Whenever the Government concerned shall have determined that a naval or other military vessel or waterborne seaplane of special construction or purpose cannot comply fully with the provisions of any of these Rules with respect to the number, position, range or arc of visibility of lights or shapes, without interfering with the military function of the vessel or seaplane, such vessel or seaplane shall comply with such other provisions in regard to the number, position, range or arc of visibility of lights or shapes as her Government shall have determined to be the closest possible compliance with these Rules in respect of that vessel or seaplane.

Rule 14

A vessel proceeding under sail, when also being propelled by machinery, shall carry in the daytime forward, where it can best be seen, one black conical shape, point downwards, not less than 2 feet in diameter at its base.

PART C. SOUND SIGNALS AND CONDUCT IN RESTRICTED VISIBILITY

(Preliminary)

1. The possession of information obtained from radar does not relieve any vessel of the obligation of conforming strictly with the Rules and, in particular, the obligations contained in Rules 15 and 16.

2. The Annex to the Rules contains recommendations intended to assist in the use of radar as an aid to avoiding collision in restricted visibility.

Rule 15

(a) A power-driven vessel of 40 feet or more in length shall be provided with an efficient whistle, sounded by steam or by some substitute for steam, so placed that the sound may not be intercepted by any obstruction, and with an efficient fog horn to be sounded by mechanical means, and also with an efficient bell. A sailing vessel of 40 feet or more in length shall be provided with a similar fog horn and bell.

(b) All signals prescribed in this Rule for vessels under way shall be given:

(i) by power-driven vessels on the whistle;

(ii) by sailing vessels on the fog-horn;

(iii) by vessels towed on the whistle or fog-horn.

(c) In fog, mist, falling snow, heavy rainstorms, or any other condition similarly restricting visibility, whether by day or night, the signals prescribed in this Rule shall be used as follows:

(i) A power-driven vessel making way through the water, shall sound at intervals of not more than 2 minutes a prolonged blast.

(ii) A power-driven vessel under way, but stopped and making no way through the water, shall sound at intervals of not more than 2 minutes two prolonged blasts, with an interval of about 1 second between them.

(iii) A sailing vessel under way shall sound, at intervals of not more than 1 minute, when on the starboard tack one blast, when on the port tack two blasts in succession, and when with the wind abaft the beam three blasts in succession.

(iv) A vessel when at anchor shall at intervals of not more than 1 minute ring the bell rapidly for about 5 seconds. In vessels of more than 350 feet in length the bell shall be sounded in the forepart of the vessel, and in addition there shall be sounded in the after part of the vessel, at intervals of not more than 1 minute for about 5 seconds, a gong or other instrument, the tone and sounding of which cannot be confused with that of the bell. Every vessel at anchor may in addition, in accordance with Rule 12, sound three blasts in succession, namely, one short, one prolonged, and one short blast, to give warning of her position and of the possibility of collision to an approaching vessel.

(v) A vessel when towing, a vessel engaged in laying or in picking up a submarine cable or navigation mark and a vessel under way which is unable to get out of the way of an approaching vessel through being not under command or unable to manoeuvre as required by these Rules shall, instead of the signals prescribed in subsections (i), (ii) and (iii) sound, at intervals of not more than 1 minute, three blasts in seccession, namely, one prolonged blast followed by two short blasts.

(vi) A vessel towed, or, if more than one vessel is towed, only the last vessel of the tow, if manned, shall, at intervals of not more than 1 minute, sound four blasts in succession, namely, one prolonged blast followed by three short blasts. When practicable, this signal shall be made immediately after the signal made by the towing vessel.

(vii) A vessel aground shall give the bell signal and, if required, the gong signal, prescribed in subsection (iv) and shall, in addition, give 3 separate and distinct strokes on the bell immediately before and after such rapid ringing of the bell.

(viii) A vessel engaged in fishing when under way or at anchor shall at intervals of not more than 1 minute sound the signal prescribed in sub-section (v). A vessel when fishing with trolling lines and under way shall sound the signals prescribed in sub-sections (i), (ii) or (iii) as may be appropriate.

(ix) A vessel of less than 40 feet in length, a rowing boat, or a seaplane on the water, shall not be obliged to give the above-mentioned signals but if she does not, she shall make some other efficient sound signal at intervals of not more than 1 minute.

(x) A power-driven pilot-vessel when engaged on pilotage duty may, in addition to the signals prescribed in sub-sections (i), (ii) and (iv), sound an identity signal consisting of 4 short blasts.

Rule 16

(a) Every vessel, or seaplane when taxi-ing on the water, shall, in fog, mist, falling snow, heavy rainstorms or any other condition similarly restricting visibility, go at a moderate speed, having careful regard to the existing circumstances and conditions.

(b) A power-driven vessel hearing, apparently forward of her beam, the fog-signal of a vessel the position of which is not ascertained, shall, so far as the circumstances of the case admit, stop her engines, and then navigate with caution until danger of collision is over.

(c) A power-driven vessel which detects the presence of another vessel forward of her beam before hearing her fog signal or sighting her visually may take early and substantial action to avoid a close quarters situation but, if this cannot be avoided, she shall, so far as the circumstances of the case admit, stop her engines in proper time to avoid collision and then navigate with caution until danger of collision is over.

PART D. STEERING AND SAILING RULES
(Preliminary)

1. In obeying and construing these Rules, any action taken should be positive, in ample time, and with due regard to the observance of good seamanship.

2. Risk of collision can, when circumstances permit, be ascertained by carefully watching the compass bearing of an approaching vessel. If the bearing does not appreciably change, such risk should be deemed to exist.

3. Mariners should bear in mind that seaplanes in the act of landing or taking off, or operating under adverse weather conditions, may be unable to change their intended action at the last moment.

4. Rules 17 to 24 apply only to vessels in sight of one another.

Rule 17

(a) When two sailing vessels are approaching one another, so as to involve risk of collision, one of them shall keep out of the way of the other as follows:

(i) When each has the wind on a different side, the vessel which has the wind on the port side shall keep out of the way of the other.

(ii) When both have the wind on the same side, the vessel which is to windward shall keep out of the way of the vessel which is to leeward.

(b) For the purposes of this Rule the windward side shall be deemed to be the side opposite to that on which the mainsail is carried or, in the case of a square-rigged vessel, the side opposite to that on which the largest fore-and-aft sail is carried.

Rule 18

(a) When two power-driven vessels are meeting end on, or nearly end on, so as to involve risk of collision, each shall alter her course to starboard, so that each may pass on the port side of the other. This Rule only applies to cases where vessels are meeting end on, or nearly end on, in such a manner as to involve risk of collision, and does not apply to two vessels which must, if both keep on their respective courses, pass clear of each other. The only cases to which it does apply are when each of two vessels is end on, or nearly end on, to the other, in other words, to cases in which, by day, each vessel sees the masts of the other in a line, or nearly in a line, with her own, and by night, to cases in which each vessel is in such a position as to see both the sidelights of the other. It does not apply, by day, to cases in which a vessel sees another ahead crossing her own course; or, by night, to cases where the red light of one vessel is opposed to the red light of the other or where the green light of one vessel is opposed to the green light of the other or where a red light without a green light or a green light without a red light is seen ahead, or where both green and red lights are seen anywhere but ahead.

(b) For the purposes of this Rule and Rules 19 to 29 inclusive, except Rule 20(c) and Rule 28, a seaplane on the water shall be deemed to be a vessel, and the expression "power-driven vessel" shall be construed accordingly.

Rule 19

When two power-driven vessels are crossing, so as to involve risk of collision, the vessel which has the other on her starboard side shall keep out of the way of the other.

Rule 20

(a) When a power-driven vessel and a sailing vessel are proceeding in such directions as to involve risk of collision, except as provided for in Rules 24 and 26, the power-driven vessel shall keep out of the way of the sailing vessel.

(b) This Rule shall not give to a sailing vessel the right to hamper, in a narrow channel, the safe passage of a power-driven vessel which can navigate only inside such channel.

(c) A seaplane on the water shall, in general, keep well clear of all vessels and avoid impeding their navigation. In circumstances, however, where risk of collision exists, she shall comply with these Rules.

Rule 21

Where by any of these Rules one of two vessels is to keep out of the way, the other shall keep her course and speed. When, from any cause, the latter vessel finds herself so close that collision cannot be avoided by the action of the giving-way vessel alone, she also shall take such action as will best aid to avert collision (see Rules 27 and 29).

Rule 22

Every vessel which is directed by these Rules to keep out of the way of another vessel shall, so far as possible, take positive early action to comply with this obligation, and shall, if the circumstances of the case admit, avoid crossing ahead of the other.

Rule 23

Every power-driven vessel which is directed by these Rules to keep out of the way of another vessel, shall on approaching her, if necessary, slacken her speed or stop or reverse.

Rule 24

(a) Notwithstanding anything contained in these Rules, every vessel overtaking any other shall keep out of the way of the overtaken vessel.

(b) Every vessel coming up with another vessel from any direction more than 22½ degrees (2 points) abaft her beam, i.e., in such a position, with reference to the vessel which she is overtaking, that at night she would be unable to see either of that vessel's sidelights, shall be deemed to be an overtaking vessel; and no subsequent alteration of the bearing between the two vessels shall make the overtaking vessel a crossing vessel within the meaning of these Rules, or relieve her of the duty of keeping clear of the overtaken vessel until she is finally past and clear.

(c) If the overtaking vessel cannot determine with certainty whether she is forward of or abaft this direction from the other vessel, she shall assume that she is an overtaking vessel and keep out of the way.

Rule 25

(a) In a narrow channel every power-driven vessel when proceeding along the course of the channel shall, when it is safe and practicable, keep to that side of the fairway or mid-channel which lies on the starboard side of such vessel.

(b) Whenever a power-driven vessel is nearing a bend in a channel where a vessel approaching from the other direction cannot be seen, such power-driven vessel, when she shall have arrived within one-half (½) mile of the bend, shall give a signal by one prolonged blast on her whistle which signal shall be answered by a similar blast given by any approaching power-driven vessel that may be within hearing around the bend. Regardless of whether an approaching vessel on the farther side of the bend is heard, such bend shall be rounded with alertness and caution.

(c) In a narrow channel a power-driven vessel of less than 65 feet in length shall not hamper the safe passage of a vessel which can navigate only inside such channel.

Rule 26

All vessels not engaged in fishing, except vessels to which the provisions of Rule 4 apply, shall, when under way, keep out of the way of vessels engaged in fishing. This Rule shall not give to any vessel engaged in fishing the right of obstructing a fairway used by vessels other than fishing vessels.

Rule 27

In obeying and construing these Rules due regard shall be had to all dangers of navigation and collision, and to any special circumstances, including the limitations of the craft involved, which may render a departure from the above Rules necessary in order to avoid immediate danger.

PART E. SOUND SIGNALS FOR VESSELS IN SIGHT OF ONE ANOTHER

Rule 28

(a) When vessels are in sight of one another, a power-driven vessel under way, in taking any course authorized or required by these Rules, shall indicate that course by the following signals on her whistle, namely:

One short blast to mean "I am altering my course to starboard."

Two short blasts to mean "I am altering my course to port."

Three short blasts to mean "My engines are going astern."

(b) Whenever a power-driven vessel which, under these Rules, is to keep her course and speed is in sight of another vessel and is in doubt whether sufficient action is being taken by the other vessel to avert collision, she may indicate such doubt by giving at least five short and rapid blasts on the whistle. The giving of such a signal shall not relieve a vessel of her obligations under Rules 27 and 29 or any other Rule, or of her duty to indicate any action taken under these Rules by giving the appropriate sound signals laid down in this Rule.

(c) Any whistle signal mentioned in this Rule may be further indicated by a visual signal consisting of a white light visible all round the horizon at a distance of at least 5 miles, and so devised that it will operate simultaneously and in conjunction with the whistle sounding mechanism and remain lighted and visible during the same period as the sound signal.

(d) Nothing in these Rules shall interfere with the operation of any special rules made by the Government of any nation with respect to the use of additional whistle signals between ships of war or vessels sailing under convoy.

PART F. MISCELLANEOUS

Rule 29

Nothing in these Rules shall exonerate any vessel, or the owner, master or crew thereof, from the consequences of any neglect to carry lights or signals, or of any neglect to keep a proper look-out, or of the neglect of any precaution which may be required by the ordinary practice of seamen, or by the special circumstances of the case.

Rule 30

Nothing in these Rules shall interfere with the operation of a special rule duly made by local authority relative to the navigation of any harbour, river, lake, or inland water, including a reserved seaplane area.

Rule 31

Distress Signals

(a) When a vessel or seaplane on the water is in distress and requires assistance from other vessels or from the shore, the following shall be the signals to be used or displayed by her, either together or separately, namely:

(i) A gun or other explosive signal fired at intervals of about a minute.

(ii) A continuous sounding with any fog-signalling apparatus.

(iii) Rockets or shells, throwing red stars fired one at a time at short intervals.

(iv) A signal made by radiotelegraphy or by any other signalling method consisting of the group · · · ----- · · · in the Morse Code.

(v) A signal sent by radiotelephony consisting of the spoken word "Mayday."

(vi) The International Code Signal of distress indicated by N.C.

(vii) A signal consisting of a square flag having above or below it a ball or anything resembling a ball.

(viii) Flames on the vessel (as from a burning tar barrel, oil barrel, etc.).

(ix) A rocket parachute flare or a hand flare showing a red light.

(x) A smoke signal giving off a volume of orange-coloured smoke.

(xi) Slowly and repeatedly raising and lowering arms outstretched to each side.

Note:—Vessels in distress may use the radiotelegraph alarm signal or the radio-telephone alarm signal to secure attention to distress calls and messages. The radiotelegraph alarm signal, which is designed to actuate the radiotelegraph auto alarms of vessels so fitted, consists of a series of twelve dashes, sent in 1 minute, the duration of each dash being 4 seconds, and the duration of the interval between 2 consecutive dashes being 1 second. The radiotelephone alarm signal consists of 2 tones transmitted alternately over periods of from 30 seconds to 1 minute.

(b) The use of any of the foregoing signals, except for the purpose of indicating that a vessel or seaplane is in distress, and the use of any signals which may be confused with any of the above signals, is prohibited.

ANNEX TO THE RULES

Recommendations on the use of radar information as an aid to avoiding collisions at sea.

(1) Assumptions made on scanty information may be dangerous and should be avoided.

(2) A vessel navigating with the aid of radar in restricted visibility must, in compliance with Rule 16(a), go at a moderate speed. Information obtained from the use of radar is one of the circumstances to be taken into account when determining moderate speed. In this regard it must be recognized that small vessels, small icebergs and similar floating objects may not be detected by radar. Radar indications of one or more vessels in the vicinity may mean that "moderate speed" should be slower than a mariner without radar might consider moderate in the circumstances.

(3) When navigating in restricted visibility the radar range and bearing alone do not constitute ascertainment of the position of the other vessel under Rule 16(b) sufficiently to relieve a vessel of the duty to stop her engines and navigate with caution when a fog signal is heard forward of the beam.

(4) When action has been taken under Rule 16(c) to avoid a close quarters situation, it is essential to make sure that such action is having the desired effect. Alterations of course or speed or both are matters as to which the mariner must be guided by the circumstances of the case.

(5) Alteration of course alone may be the most effective action to avoid close quarters provided that:

(a) There is sufficient sea room.

(b) It is made in good time.

(c) It is substantial. A succession of small alterations of course should be avoided.

(d) It does not result in a close quarters situation with other vessels.

(6) The direction of an alteration of course is a matter in which the mariner must be guided by the circumstances of the case. An alteration to starboard, particularly when vessels are approaching apparently on opposite or nearly opposite courses, is generally preferable to an alteration to port.

(7) An alteration of speed, either alone or in conjunction with an alteration of course, should be substantial. A number of small alterations of speed should be avoided.

(8) If a close quarters situation is imminent, the most prudent action may be to take all way off the vessel.

INLAND RULES[1]

I. ENACTING CLAUSE, SCOPE, AND PENALTY

Whereas the provisions of chapter eight hundred and two of the laws of eighteen hundred and ninety, and the amendments thereto, adopting regulations for preventing collisions at sea, apply to all waters of the United States connected with the high seas navigable by seagoing vessels, except so far as the navigation of any harbor, river, or inland waters is regulated by special rules duly made by local authority; and

Whereas it is desirable that the regulations relating to the navigation of all harbors, rivers, and inland waters of the United States, except the Great Lakes and their connecting and tributary waters as far east as Montreal and the Red River of the North and rivers emptying into the Gulf of Mexico and their tributaries, shall be stated in one act: Therefore,

Be it enacted by the Senate and House of Representatives of the United States of America in Congress assembled, That the following regulations for preventing collisions shall be followed by all vessels upon the harbors, rivers, and other inland waters of the United States, except the Great Lakes and their connecting and tributary waters as far east as Montreal, and the waters of the Mississippi River between its source and the Huey P. Long Bridge and all of its tributaries emptying thereinto and their tributaries, and that part of the Atchafalaya River above its junction with the Plaquemine-Morgan City alternate waterway, and the Red River of the North; and are hereby declared special rules duly made by local authority.

SEC. 2 (a) The Secretary of the Department in which the Coast Guard[2] is operating shall establish such rules to be observed, on the waters described in section 1 of this Act, by steam vessels in passing each other and as to the lights and day signals to be carried on such waters by ferryboats, by vessels and craft of all types when in tow of steam vessels or operating by hand power or horsepower or drifting with the current, and by any other vessels not otherwise provided for, not inconsistent with the provisions of this Act, as he from time to time may deem necessary for safety, which rules are hereby declared special rules duly made by local authority. A pamphlet containing such Act and regulations shall be furnished to all vessels and craft subject to this Act. On vessels and craft over sixty-five feet in length the pamphlet shall, where practicable, be kept on board and available for ready reference.

(b) Except in an emergency, before any rules or any alteration, amendment, or repeal thereof are established by the Secretary under the provisions of this section, the said Secretary shall publish the proposed rules, alterations, amendments, or repeals, and public hearings shall be held with respect thereto on such notice as the Secretary deems reasonable under the circumstances.

---

[1] 30 Stat. 96-103; 31 Stat. 30; 38 Stat. 381; 47 Stat. 415; 1417; 49 Stat. 669, 1367, 1380; 54 Stat. 150; 60 Stat. 1097; 61 Stat. 501; 62 Stat. 249; 63 Stat. 496, 561; 67 Stat. 497; 33 U. S. C. 154-159, 171-183, 191, 192, 201-222, 231, 232.

[2] By Reorganization Plan No. 26 of 1950, effective July 31, 1950 (15 F. R. 4935) the functions formerly vested in the Commandant, U. S. Coast Guard, were transferred to the Secretary of the Treasury with certain exceptions. The Secretary, however, by an order dated July 31, 1950 (15 F. R. 6521), delegated to the Commandant the functions formerly performed by him under Reorganization Plan No. 3 of 1946.

SEC. 3. Every licensed and unlicensed pilot, engineer, mate, or master of any vessel[3] who violates the provisions of this Act or the regulations established pursuant hereto shall be liable to a penalty of not exceeding $500, and for all dangers sustained by any passenger, in his person or baggage, as a result of such violation: Provided, That nothing herein shall relieve any vessel, owner, or corporation from any liability incurred by reason of such violation.

SEC. 4. Every vessel which is navigated in violation of any of the provisions of this Act or the regulations established pursuant hereto shall be liable to a penalty of $500, one-half to go to the informer, for which sum such vessel may be seized and proceeded against by action in any district court of the United States having jurisdiction of the offense.

Preliminary Definitions

In the following rules every steam vessel which is under sail and not under steam is to be considered a sailing vessel, and every vessel under steam, whether under sail or not, is to be considered a steam vessel.

The words "steam vessel" shall include any vessel propelled by machinery.

A vessel is "under way," within the meaning of these rules, when she is not at anchor, or made fast to the shore, or aground.

II. LIGHTS, AND SO FORTH

The word "visible" in these rules, when applied to light, shall mean visible on a dark night with a clear atmosphere.

ART. 1. The rules concerning lights shall be compiled with in all weathers from sunset to sunrise, and during such time no other lights which may be mistaken for the prescribed lights shall be exhibited.

Steam Vessels—Masthead Light

ART. 2.[4] A steam vessel when under way shall carry—(a) On or in the front of the foremast, or if a vessel without a foremast, then in the fore part of the vessel, a bright white light so constructed as to show an unbroken light over an arc of the horizon of twenty points of the compass, so fixed as to throw the light ten points on each side of the vessel, namely, from right ahead to two points abaft the beam on either side, and of such a character as to be visible at a distance of at least five miles.

Steam Vessels—Side Lights

(b) On the starboard side a green light so constructed as to show an unbroken light over an arc of the horizon of ten points of the compass, so fixed as to throw the light from right ahead to two points abaft the beam on the starboard side, and of such a character as to be visible at a distance of at least two miles.

(c) On the port side a red light so constructed as to show an unbroken light over an arc of the horizon of ten points of the compass, so fixed as to throw the light from right ahead to two points abaft the beam on the port side, and of such a character as to be visible at a distance of at least two miles.

(d) The said green and red side lights shall be fitted with inboard screens

[3] For a definition of the word "vessel," see Rule 1 (c)(i), International Rules.

[4] Article 2 is amended by an act of Congress approved April 25, 1940, describing lights required to be carried by every vessel propelled by machinery and not more than 65 feet in length except tugboats and towboats propelled by steam.

projecting at least three feet forward from the light, so as to prevent these lights from being seen across the bow.

Steam Vessels—Range Lights

(e) A seagoing steam vessel when under way may carry an additional white light similar in construction to the light mentioned in subdivision (a). These two lights shall be so placed in line with the keel that one shall be at least fifteen feet higher than the other, and in such a position with reference to each other that the lower light shall be forward of the upper one. The vertical distance between these lights shall be less than the horizontal distance.

(f) All steam vessels (except seagoing vessels and ferryboats), shall carry in addition to green and red lights required by article two (b), (c), and screens as required by article two (d), a central range of two white lights; the after light being carried at an elevation at least fifteen feet above the light at the head of the vessel. The headlight shall be so constructed as to show an unbroken light through twenty points of the compass, namely, from right ahead to two points abaft the beam on either side of the vessel, and the after light so as to show all around the horizon.

Steam Vessels—When Towing or Pushing

ART. 3. (a) A steam vessel when towing another vessel or vessels alongside or by pushing ahead shall, in addition to her side lights, carry two bright white lights in a vertical line, one over the other, not less than three feet apart, and when towing one or more vessels astern, regardless of the length of the tow, shall carry an additional bright white light three feet above or below such lights. Each of these lights shall be of the same construction and character, and shall be carried in the same position as the white light mentioned in article 2 (a) or the after range light mentioned in article 2 (f).

(b) A steam vessel carrying towing lights the same as the white light mentioned in article 2 (a), when pushing another vessel or vessels ahead, shall also carry at or near the stern two bright amber lights in a vertical line, one over the other, not less than three feet apart; each of these lights shall be so constructed as to show an unbroken light over an arc of the horizon of twelve points of the compass, so fixed as to show the light six points from right aft on each side of the vessel, and of such a character as to be visible at a distance of at least two miles. A steam vessel carrying towing lights the same as the white light mentioned in article 2 (a) may also carry, irrespective of the position of the tow, the after range light mentioned in article 2 (f); however, if the after range light is carried by such a vessel when pushing another vessel or vessels ahead, the amber lights shall be carried in a vertical line with and at least three feet lower than the after range light. A steam vessel carrying towing lights the same as the white light mentioned in article 2 (a), when towing one or more vessels astern, may also carry, in lieu of the stern light specified in article 10, a small white light abaft the funnel or aftermast for the tow to steer by, but such light shall not be visible forward of the beam.

Lights for Sailing Vessels and Vessels in Tow

ART. 5. A sailing vessel under way and any vessel being towed, except barges, canal boats, scows, and other vessels of nondescript type, when in tow of steam vessels, shall carry the same lights as are prescribed by article 2 for a steam vessel under way, with the exception of the white lights mentioned therein, which they shall never carry.

Lights for Small Vessels in Bad Weather

ART. 6. Whenever, as in the case of vessels of less than ten gross tons under way during bad weather, the green and red side lights cannot be fixed, these lights shall be kept at hand, lighted and ready for use; and shall, on the approach of or to other vessels, be exhibited on their respective sides in sufficient time to prevent collision, in such manner as to make them most visible, and so that the green light shall not be seen on the port side nor the red light on the starboard side, nor, if practicable, more than two points abaft the beam on their respective sides. To make the use of these portable lights more certain and easy the lanterns containing them shall each be painted outside with the color of the light they respectively contain, and shall be provided with proper screens.

Lights for Rowing Boats

ART. 7. Rowing boats, whether under oars or sail, shall have ready at hand a lantern showing a white light which shall be temporarily exhibited in sufficient time to prevent collision.

Lights for Pilot Vessels

ART. 8. Pilot vessels when engaged on their stations on pilotage duty shall not show the lights required for other vessels, but shall carry a white light at the masthead, visible all around the horizon, and shall also exhibit a flare-up light or flare-up lights at short intervals, which shall never exceed fifteen minutes.

On the near approach of or to other vessels they shall have their side lights lighted, ready for use, and shall flash or show them at short intervals, to indicate the direction in which they are heading, but the green light shall not be shown on the port side nor the red light on the starboard side.

A pilot vessel of such a class as to be obliged to go alongside of a vessel to put a pilot on board may show the white light instead of carrying it at the masthead, and may, instead of the colored lights above mentioned, have at hand, ready for use, a lantern with a green glass on one side and a red glass on the other, to be used as prescribed above.

Pilot vessels, when not engaged on their station on pilotage duty, shall carry lights similar to those of other vessels of their tonnage.

A steam pilot vessel, when engaged on her station on pilotage duty and in waters of the United States, and not at anchor, shall in addition to the lights required for all pilot boats, carry at a distance of eight feet below her white masthead light a red light, visible all around the hozizon and of such a character as to be visible on a dark night with a clear atmosphere at a distance of at least two miles, and also the colored side lights required to be carried by vessels when under way.

When engaged on her station on pilotage duty and in waters of the United States, and at anchor, she shall carry in addition to the lights required for all pilot boats the red light above mentioned, but not the colored side lights. When not engaged on her station on pilotage duty, she shall carry the same lights as other steam vessels.

Lights, Etc., of Fishing Vessels

ART. 9. (a) Fishing vessels of less than ten gross tons, when under way and when not having their nets, trawls, dredges, or lines in the water, shall not be obliged to carry the colored side lights; but every such vessel shall, in lieu thereof, have ready at hand a lantern with a green glass on one side and a red glass on the other side, and on approaching to or being approached by another vessel such lantern shall be exhibited in sufficient time to prevent collision, so that the green light shall not be seen on the port side nor the red light on the starboard side.

(b) All fishing vessels and fishing boats of ten gross tons or upward, when under way and when not having their nets, trawls, dredges, or lines in the water, shall carry and show the same lights as other vessels under way.

(c) All vessels, when trawling, dredging, or fishing with any kind of drag nets or lines, shall exhibit, from some part of the vessel where they can be best seen, two lights. One of these lights shall be red and the other shall be white. The red light shall be above the white light, and shall be at a vertical distance from it of not less than six feet and not more than twelve feet; and the horizontal distance between them, if any, shall not be more than ten feet. These two lights shall be of such a character and contained in lanterns of such construction as to be visible all around the horizon, the white light a distance of not less than three miles and the red light of not less than two miles.

Lights For Rafts or Other Craft Not Provided For

(d) Rafts, or other water craft not herein provided for, navigating by hand power, horse power, or by the current of the river, shall carry one or more good white lights, which shall be placed in such manner as shall be prescribed by the Commandant of the Coast Guard.

Lights for an Overtaken Vessel

ART. 10. (a) A vessel when underway, if not otherwise required by these rules to carry one or more lights visible from aft, shall carry at her stern a white light, so constructed that it shall show an unbroken light over an arc of the horizon of twelve points of the compass, so fixed as to show the light six points from right aft on each side of the vessel, and of such a character as to be visible at a distance of at least two miles. Such light shall be carried as nearly as practicable on the same level as the side lights.

(b) In a small vessel, if it is not possible on account of bad weather or other sufficient cause for this light to be fixed, an electric torch or a lighted lantern shall be kept at hand ready for use and shall, on the approach of an overtaking vessel, be shown in sufficient time to prevent collision.

Anchor Lights

ART. 11. A vessel under one hundred and fifty feet in length when at anchor shall carry forward, where it can best be seen, but at a height not exceeding twenty feet above the hull, a white light in a lantern so constructed as to show a clear, uniform, and unbroken light visible all around the horizon at a distance of at least one mile: Provided, That the Secretary of the Army may, after investigation, by rule, regulation, or order, designate such areas as he may deem proper as "special anchorage areas"; such special anchorage areas may from time to time be changed, or abolished, if after investigation the Secretary of the Army shall deem such change or abolition in the interest of navigation: Provided further, That vessels not more than sixty-five feet in length when at anchor in any such special anchorage area shall not be required to carry or exhibit the white light required by this article.

A vessel of one hundred and fifty feet or upward in length when at anchor, shall carry in the forward part of the vessel, at a height of not less than twenty and not exceeding forty feet above the hull, one such light, and at or near the stern of the vessel, and at such a height that it shall be not less than fifteen feet lower than the forward light, another such light.

The length of a vessel shall be deemed to be the length appearing in her certificate of registry.

Special Signals

ART. 12. Every vessel may, if necessary, in order to attract attention, in addition to the lights which she is by these rules required to carry, show a flare-up light or use any detonating signal that cannot be mistaken for a distress signal.

Naval Lights and Recognition Signals

ART. 13. Nothing in these rules shall interfere with the operation of any special rules made by the Government of any nation with respect to additional station and signal lights for two or more ships of war or for vessels sailing under convoy, or with the exhibition of recognition signals adopted by shipowners, which have been authorized by their respective Governments, and duly registered and published.

Steam Vessel Under Sail by Day

ART. 14. A steam vessel proceeding under sail only, but having her funnel up, may carry in daytime, forward, where it can best be seen, one black ball or shape two feet in diameter.

III. SOUND SIGNALS FOR FOG, AND SO FORTH

Preliminary

ART. 15. All signals prescribed by this article for vessels under way shall be given:

1. By "steam vessels" on the whistle or siren.
2. By "sailing vessels" and "vessels towed" on the fog horn.

The words "prolonged blast" used in this article shall mean a blast of from four to six seconds' duration.

A steam vessel shall be provided with an efficient whistle or siren, sounded by steam or by some substitute for steam, so placed that the sound may not be intercepted by any obstruction, and with an efficient fog horn; also with an efficient bell. A sailing vessel of twenty tons gross tonnage or upward shall be provided with a similar fog horn and bell.

In fog, mist, falling snow, or heavy rain storms, whether by day or night, the signals described in this article shall be used as follows, namely:

Steam Vessel Under Way

(a) A steam vessel under way shall sound, at intervals of not more than one minute, a prolonged blast.

Sailing Vessel Under Way

(c) A sailing vessel under way shall sound, at intervals of not more than one minute, when on the starboard tack, one blast; when on the port tack, two blasts in succession, and when with the wind abaft the beam, three blasts in succession.

Vessel at Anchor or Not Under Way

(d) A vessel when at anchor shall, at intervals of not more than one minute, ring the bell rapidly for about five seconds.

Vessels Towing or Towed

(e) A steam vessel when towing, shall, instead of the signals prescribed in sub-division (a) of this article, at intervals of not more than one minute, sound three blasts in succession, namely, one prolonged blast followed by two short blasts. A vessel towed may give this signal and she shall not give any other.

Rafts, or Other Craft Not Provided For

(f) All rafts or other water craft, not herein provided for, navigating by hand power, horse power, or by the current of the river, shall sound a blast of the fog horn, or equivalent signal, at intervals of not more than one minute.

Speed in Fog

ART. 16. Every vessel shall, in a fog, mist, falling snow, or heavy rain storms, go at a moderate speed, having careful regard to the existing circumstances and conditions.

A steam vessel hearing, apparently forward of her beam, the fog signal of a vessel the position of which is not ascertained shall, so far as the circumstances of the case admit, stop her engines, and then navigate with caution until danger of collision is over.

IV. STEERING AND SAILING RULES

Preliminary—Risk of Collision

Risk of collision can, when circumstances permit, be ascertained by carefully watching the compass bearing of an approaching vessel. If the bearing does not appreciably change, such risk should be deemed to exist.

Sailing Vessels

ART. 17. When two sailing vessels are approaching one another, so as to involve risk of collision, one of them shall keep out of the way of the other as follows, namely:

(a) A vessel which is running free shall keep out of the way of a vessel which is closehauled.

(b) A vessel which is closehauled on the port tack shall keep out of the way of a vessel which is closehauled on the starboard tack.

(c) When both are running free, with the wind on different sides, the vessel which has the wind on the port side shall keep out of the way of the other.

(d) When both are running free, with the wind on the same side, the vessel which is to the windward shall keep out of the way of the vessel which is to the leeward.

(e) A vessel which has the wind aft shall keep out of the way of the other vessel.

Approaching Steam Vessels

ART. 18. RULE I. When steam vessels are approaching each other head and head, that is, end on, or nearly so, it shall be the duty of each to pass on the port side of the other; and either vessel shall give, as a signal of her intention, one short and distinct blast of her whistle, which the other vessel shall answer promptly by a similar blast of her whistle, and thereupon such vessels shall pass on the port side of each other. But if the courses of such vessels are so far on the starboard of each other as not to be considered as meeting head and head, either vessel shall immediately give two short and distinct blasts of her whistle, which the other vessel shall answer promptly by two similar blasts of her whistle, and they shall pass on the starboard side of each other.

The foregoing only applies to cases where vessels are meeting end on, or nearly end on, in such a manner as to involve risk of collision; in other words, to cases in which, by day, each vessel sees the masts of the other in a line, or nearly in a line, with her own, and by night to cases in which each vessel is in such a position as to see both the side lights of the other.

It does not apply by day to cases in which a vessel sees another ahead crossing her own course, or by night to cases where the red light of one vessel is opposed to the red light of the other, or where the green light of one vessel is opposed to the green light of the other, or where a red light without a green light or a green light without a red light, is seen ahead, or where both green and red lights are seen anywhere but ahead.

RULE III. If, when steam vessels are approaching each other, either vessel fails to understand the course or intention of the other, from any cause, the vessel so in doubt shall immediately signify the same by giving several short and rapid blasts, not less than four, of the steam whistle.

RULE V. Whenever a steam vessel is nearing a short bend or curve in the channel, where, from the height of the banks or other cause, a steam vessel approaching from the opposite direction can not be seen for a distance of half a mile, such steam vessel, when she shall have arrived within half a mile of such curve or bend, shall give a signal by one long blast of the steam whistle, which signal shall be answered by a similar blast given by any approaching steam vessel that may be within hearing. Should such signal be so answered by a steam vessel upon the farther side of such bend, then the usual signals for meeting and passing shall immediately be given and answered; but, if the first alarm signal of such vessel be not answered, she is to consider the channel clear and govern herself accordingly.

When steam vessels are moved from their docks or berths, and other boats are liable to pass from any direction toward them, they shall give the same signal as in the case of vessels meeting at a bend, but immediately after clearing the berths so as to be fully in sight they shall be governed by the steering and sailing rules.

RULE VIII. When steam vessels are running in the same direction, and the vessel which is astern shall desire to pass on the right or starboard hand of the vessel ahead, she shall give one short blast of the steam whistle, as a signal of such desire, and if the vessel ahead answers with one blast, she shall direct her course to starboard; or if she shall desire to pass on the left or port side of the vessel ahead, she shall give two short blasts of the steam whistle as a signal of such desire, and if the vessel ahead answers with two blasts, shall direct her course to port; or if the vessel ahead does not think it safe for the vessel astern to attempt to pass at that point, she shall immediately signify the same by giving several short and rapid blasts of the steam whistle, not less than four, and under no circumstances shall the vessel astern attempt to pass the vessel ahead until such time as they have reached a point where it can be safely done, when said vessel ahead shall signify her willingness by blowing the proper signals. The vessel ahead shall in no case attempt to cross the bow or crowd upon the course of the passing vessel.

RULE IX. The whistle signals provided in the rules under this article for steam vessels meeting, passing, or overtaking, are never to be used except when steamers are in sight of each other, and the course and position of each can be determined in the day time by a sight of the vessel itself, or by night by seeing its signal lights. In fog, mist, falling snow or heavy rain storms, when vessels can not see each other, fog signals only must be given.

Two Steam Vessels Crossing

ART. 19. When two steam vessels are crossing, so as to involve risk of collision, the vessel which has the other on her starboard side shall keep out of the way of the other.

Steam Vessel Shall Keep Out of the Way of Sailing Vessel

ART. 20. When a steam vessel and a sailing vessel are proceeding in such directions as to involve risk of collision, the steam vessel shall keep out of the way of the sailing vessel.

Course and Speed

ART. 21. Where, by any of these rules, one of the two vessels is to keep out of the way, the other shall keep her course and speed.

[See articles 27 and 29.]

Crossing Ahead

ART. 22. Every vessel which is directed by these rules to keep out the way of another vessel shall, if the circumstances of the case admit, avoid crossing ahead of the other.

Steam Vessel Shall Slacken Speed or Stop

ART. 23. Every steam vessel which is directed by these rules to keep out of the way of another vessel shall, on approaching her, if necessary, slacken her speed, or stop, or reverse.

Overtaking Vessels

ART. 24. Notwithstanding anything contained in these rules every vessel, overtaking any other, shall keep out of the way of the overtaken vessel.

Every vessel coming up with another vessel from any direction more than two points abaft her beam, that is, in such a position, with reference to the vessel which she is overtaking that at night she would be unable to see either of that vessel's sidelights, shall be deemed to be an overtaking vessel; and no subsequent alteration of the bearing between the two vessels shall make the overtaking vessel a crossing vessel within the meaning of these rules, or relieve her of the duty of keeping clear of the overtaken vessel until she is finally past and clear.

As by day the overtaking vessel can not always know with certainty whether she is forward of or abaft this direction from the other vessels she should, if in doubt, assume that she is an overtaking vessel and keep out of the way.

Narrow Channels

ART. 25. In narrow channels every steam vessel shall, when it is safe and practicable, keep to that side of the fairway or midchannel which lies on the starboard side of such vessel.

Right of Way of Fishing Vessels

ART. 26. Sailing vessels under way shall keep out of the way of sailing vessels or boats fishing with nets, lines, or trawls. This rule shall not give to any vessel or boat engaged in fishing the right of obstructing a fairway used by vessels other than fishing vessels or boats.

General Prudential Rule

ART. 27. In obeying and construing these rules due regard shall be had to all dangers of navigation and collision, and to any special circumstances which may render a departure from the above rules necessary in order to avoid immediate danger.

Sound Signals for Passing Steamers

[See article 18.]

ART. 28. When vessels are in sight of one another a steam vessel under way whose engines are going at full speed astern shall indicate that fact by three short blasts on the whistle.

Precaution

ART. 29. Nothing in these rules shall exonerate any vessel, or the owner or master of crew thereof, from the consequences of any neglect to carry lights or signals, or of any neglect to keep a proper lookout, or of the neglect of any precaution which may be required by the ordinary practice of seamen, or by the special circumstances of the case.

Suspension of Lights on Naval and Coast Guard Vessels

ART. 30. The exhibition of any light on board of a vessel of war of the United States or a Coast Guard cutter may be suspended whenever, in the opinion of the Secretary of the Navy, the commander in chief of a squadron, or the commander of a vessel acting singly, the special character of the service may require it.

Distress Signals

ART. 31. When a vessel is in distress and requires assistance from other vessels or from the shore the following shall be the signal to be used or displayed by her, either together or separately, namely:

In the daytime—

A continuous sounding with any fog-signal apparatus, or firing a gun.

At night—

First. Flames on the vessel as from a burning tar barrel, oil barrel, and so forth.

Second. A continuous sounding with any fog-signal apparatus, or firing a gun.

Orders to Helmsmen

ART. 32. All orders to helmsmen shall be given as follows:

"Right Rudder" to mean "Direct the vessel's head to starboard."

"Left Rudder" to mean "Direct the vessel's head to port."

REGULATIONS[1]

TITLE 33—NAVIGATION AND NAVIGABLE WATERS

CHAPTER I—COAST GUARD, DEPARTMENT OF THE TREASURY

Subchapter D—Navigation Requirements for Certain Inland Waters

Part 80—Pilot Rules for Inland Waters

---

[1] The regulations in this part are reprinted from the Code of Federal Regulations of the United States of America, as amended.

General[2]

SEC. **80.01   General Instruction.** The regulations in this part apply to vessels navigating the harbors, rivers, and inland waters of the United States, except the Great Lakes and their connecting and tributary waters as far east as Montreal, the Red River of the North, the Mississippi River and its tributaries above Huey P. Long Bridge, and that part of the Atchafalaya River above its junction with the Plaquemine-Morgan City alternate waterway.[3]

SEC. **80.02   Definition of steam vessel and vessel under way; risk of collision.** In the rules in this part the words "steam vessel" shall include any vessel propelled by machinery. A vessel is under way, within the meaning of the rules in this part, when she is not at anchor, or made fast to the shore, or aground. Risk of collision can, when circumstances permit, be ascertained by carefully watching the compass bearing of an approaching vessel. If the bearing does not appreciably change, such risk should be deemed to exist.

Signals

SEC. **80.03   Signals.** The whistle signals provided in the rules in this part shall be sounded on an efficient whistle or siren sounded by stream or by some substitute for steam.

A short blast of the whistle shall mean a blast of about one second's duration.

A prolonged blast of the whistle shall mean a blast of from 4 to 6 seconds' duration.

One short blast of the whistle signifies intention to direct course to own starboard, except when two steam vessels are approaching each other at right angles or obliquely, when it signifies intention of steam vessel which is to starboard of the other to hold course and speed.

Two short blasts of the whistle signify intention to direct course to own port.

Three short blasts of the whistle shall mean, "My engines are going at full speed astern."

---

[2] Public Law 232, 83rd Congress, approved August 8, 1953, extended the applicability of the Inland Rules and the Pilot Rules published pursuant thereto to the Mobile River and its tributaries above Choctaw Point.

[3] §§ 80.01 to 80.33a issued under sec. 2, 30 Stat. 102, as amended, 33 U. S. C. 157. §§ 80.34 to 80.36 issued under R. S. 4405, as amended, 46 U. S. C. 375.

When vessels are in sight of one another a steam vessel under way whose engines are going at full speed astern shall indicate that fact by three short blasts on the whistle.

SEC. **80.1** **Danger signal.** If, when steam vessels are approaching each other, either vessel fails to understand the course or intention of the other, from any cause, the vessel so in doubt shall immediately signify the same by giving several short and rapid blasts, not less than four, of the steam whistle, the danger signal. (Former Pilot Rule I.)

SEC. **80.2** **Cross signals.** Steam vessels are forbidden to use what has become technically known among pilots as "cross signals," that is, answering one whistle with two, and answering two whistles with one. (Former Pilot Rule II.)

SEC. **80.3** **Vessels passing each other.** The signals for passing, by the blowing of the whistle, shall be given and answered by pilots, in compliance with the rules in this part, not only when meeting "head and head," or nearly so, but at all times when the steam vessels are in sight of each other, when passing or meeting at a distance within half a mile of each other, and whether passing to the starboard or port.

The whistle signals provided in the rules in this part for steam vessels meeting, passing, or overtaking are never to be used except when steam vessels are in sight of each other, and the course and position of each can be determined in the daytime by a sight of the vessel itself, or by night by seeing its signal lights. In fog, mist, falling snow, or heavy rainstorms, when vessels cannot so see each other, fog signals only must be given. (Former Pilot Rule III.)

Situations

SEC. **80.4** **Vessels approaching each other head and head, end on.** When steam vessels are approaching each other head and head, that is, end on, or nearly so, it shall be the duty of each to pass on the port side of the other; and either vessel shall give, as a signal of her intention one short and distinct blast of her whistle, which the other vessel shall answer promptly by a similar blast of her whistle, and thereupon such vessels shall pass on the port side of each other. But if the courses of such vessels are so far on the starboard of each other as not to be considered as meeting head and head, either vessel shall immediately give two short and distinct blasts of her whistle, which the other vessel shall answer promptly by two similar blasts of her whistle, and they shall pass on the starboard side of each other.

The foregoing only applies to cases where vessels are meeting end on or nearly end on, in such a manner as to involve risk of collision; in other words, to cases in which, by day, each vessel sees the masts of the other in a line, or nearly in a line, with her own, and by night to cases in which each vessel is in such a position as to see both the side lights of the other.

It does not apply by day to cases in which a vessel sees another ahead crossing her own course, or by night to cases where the red light of one vessel is opposed to the red light of the other, or where the green light of one vessel is opposed to the green light of the other, or where a red light without a green light or a green light without a red light is seen ahead, or where both green and red lights are seen anywhere but ahead. (Former Pilot Rule IV.)

SEC. **80.5** **Vessels nearing bend or curve in channel; moving from docks.** Whenever a steam vessel is nearing a short bend or curve in the channel, where, from the height of the banks or other cause, a steam vessel approaching from the opposite direction cannot be seen for a distance of half a mile, such steam vessel, when she shall have arrived within half a mile of such curve or bend, shall give a signal by one long blast of the steam whistle, which signal shall be answered by a similar blast, given by any approaching steam vessel that may be within hearing. Should such signal be so answered by a steam vessel upon the farther side of such bend, then the usual signals for meeting and passing shall immediately be given and answered; but, if the first alarm signal of such vessel be not answered, she is to consider the channel clear and govern herself accordingly.

When steam vessels are moved from their docks or berths, and other boats are liable to pass from any direction toward them, they shall give the same signal as in the case of vessels meeting at a bend, but immediately after clearing the berths so as to be fully in sight they shall be governed by the steering and sailing rules. (Former Pilot Rule V.)

SEC. 80.6 **Vessels running in same direction; overtaking vessel.** When steam vessels are running in the same direction, and the vessel which is astern shall desire to pass on the right or starboard hand of the vessel ahead, she shall give one short blast of the steam whistle, as a signal of such desire, and if the vessel ahead answers with one blast, she shall direct her course to starboard; or if she shall desire to pass on the left or port side of the vessel ahead, she shall give two short blasts of the steam whistle as a signal of such desire, and if the vessel ahead answers with two blasts, shall direct her course to port; or if the vessel ahead does not think it safe for the vessel astern to attempt to pass at that point, she shall immediately signify the same by giving several short and rapid blasts of the steam whistle, not less than four, and under no circumstances shall the vessel astern attempt to pass the vessel ahead until such time as they have reached a point where it can be safely done, when said vessel ahead shall signify her willingness by blowing the proper signals. The vessel ahead shall in no case attempt to cross the bow or crowd upon the course of the passing vessel.

Every vessel coming up with another vessel from any direction more than two points abaft her beam, that is, in such a position with reference to the vessel which she is overtaking that at night she would be unable to see either of that vessel's side lights, shall be deemed to be an overtaking vessel; and no subsequent alteration of the bearing between the two vessels shall make the overtaking vessel a crossing vessel within the meaning of the rules in this part, or relieve her of the duty of keeping clear of the overtaken vessel until she is finally past and clear.

As by day the overtaking vessel cannot always know with certainty whether she is forward of or abaft this direction from the other vessel she should, if in doubt, assume that she is an overtaking vessel and keep out of the way. (Former Pilot Rule VI.)

SEC. 80.7 **Vessels approaching each other at right angles or obliquely.** When two steam vessels are approaching each other at right angles or obliquely so as to involve risk of collision, other than when one steam vessel is overtaking another, the steam vessel which has the other on her own port side shall hold her course and speed; and the steam vessel which has the other on her own starboard side shall keep out of the way of the other by directing her course to starboard so as to cross the stern of the other steam vessel, or, if necessary to do so, slacken her speed or stop or reverse.

If from any cause the conditions covered by this situation are such as to prevent immediate compliance with each other's signals, the misunderstanding or objection shall be at once made apparent by blowing the danger signal, and both steam vessels shall be stopped and backed if necessary, until signals for passing with safety are made and understood. (Former Pilot Rule VII.)

Sec. **80.8** **Meeting of steam and sailing vessels; right of way.** When a steam vessel and a sailing vessel are proceeding in such directions as to involve risk of collision, the steam vessel shall keep out of the way of the sailing vessel. (Former Pilot Rule VIII.)

Sec. **80.9** **Avoidance of crossing ahead.** Every steam vessel which is directed by the rules in this part to keep out of the way of another vessel shall, if the circumstances of the case admit, avoid crossing ahead of the other. (Former Pilot Rule IX.)

Sec. **80.10** **Keeping to right in narrow channels.** In narrow channels every steam vessel shall, when it is safe and practicable, keep to that side of the fairway or mid-channel which lies on the starboard side of such vessel. (Former Pilot Rule X.)

Sec. **80.11** **Departure from rules.** In obeying and construing the rules in this part due regard shall be had to all dangers of navigation and collision, and to any special circumstances which may render a departure from said rules necessary in order to avoid immediate danger. (Former Pilot Rule XI.)

Sec. **80.12** **Fog signals.** In fog, mist, falling snow, or heavy rainstorms, whether by day or night, signals shall be given as follows:

A steam vessel under way, except when towing other vessels or being towed, shall sound, at intervals of not more than 1 minute, on the whistle or siren, a prolonged blast.

A steam vessel when towing other vessels shall sound, at intervals of not more than 1 minute, on the whistle or siren, three blasts in succession, namely, one prolonged blast followed by two short blasts.

A vessel towed may give, at intervals of not more than 1 minute, on the fog horn, a signal of three blasts in succession, namely, one prolonged blast followed by two short blasts, and she shall not give any other.

A vessel when at anchor shall, at intervals of not more than 1 minute, ring the bell rapidly for about 5 seconds. (Former Pilot Rule XII.)

Sec. **80.13** **Speed in fog; posting of rules; diagrams (a) Moderate speed in fog.** Every steam vessel shall, in a fog, mist, falling snow, or heavy rainstorms, go at a moderate speed, having careful regard to the existing circumstances and conditions.

A steam vessel hearing, apparently forward of her beam, the fog signal of a vessel the position of which is not ascertained shall, so far as the circumstances of the case admit, stop her engines and then navigate with caution until danger of collision is over.

(b) Posting of pilot rules. (1) On steam vessels of over 100 gross tons, two copies of the placard form of the rules (Form CG 803) in this part shall be kept posted up in conspicuous places in the vessel, one copy of which shall be kept posted up in the pilothouse.

(2) On steam vessels of over 25 gross tons and not over 100 gross tons, two copies of the placard form of the pilot rules shall be kept on board, one copy of which shall be kept posted up in the pilothouse.

(3) On steam vessels of 25 gross tons and under, and of more than 10 gross tons, two copies of the placard form of the pilot rules shall be kept on board, and, where practicable, one copy thereof shall be kept conspicuously posted up in the vessel.

(4) On steam vessels of not more than 10 gross tons, two copies of the pamphlet form of the pilot rules shall be kept on board, and, where practicable, one copy thereof shall be kept conspicuously posted up in the vessel.

(5) Nothing herein contained shall require copies of the pilot rules to be carried on board any motorboat as defined by section 1 of the act of April 25, 1940 (54 Stat. 163-167; 46 U. S. C. 526-526t).

(c) **Diagrams.** The following diagrams are intended to illustrate the working of the system of colored lights and pilot rules. (Former Pilot Rule XIII.)

First Situation

Here the two colored lights visible to each will indicate their direct approach "head and head" toward each other. In this situation it is a standing rule that both shall direct their courses to starboard and pass on the port side of each other, each having previously given one blast of the whistle.

Second Situation

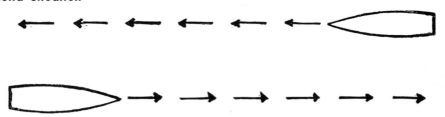

In this situation the red light only will be visible to each, the screens preventing the green light from being seen. Both vessels are evidently passing to port of each other, which is rulable in this situation, each pilot having previously signified his intention by one blast of the whistle.

Third Situation

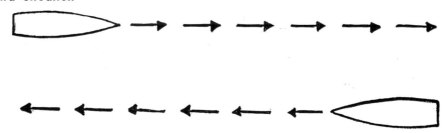

In this situation the green light only will be visible to each, the screens preventing the red light from being seen. They are therefore passing to starboard of each other, which is rulable in this situation, each pilot having previously signified his intention by two blasts of the whistle.

Fourth Situation

In this situation one steam vessel is overtaking another steam vessel from some point within the angle of two points abaft the beam of the overtaken steam vessel. The overtaking steam vessel may pass on the starboard or port side of the steam vessel ahead after the necessary signals for passing have been given with assent of the overtaken steam vessel, as prescribed in § 80.6.

Fifth Situation

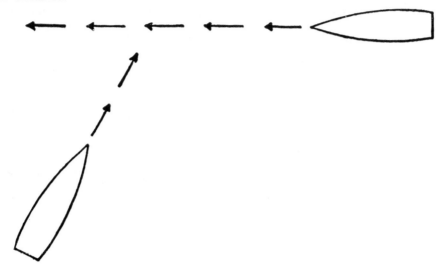

In this situation two steam vessels are approaching each other at right angles or obliquely in such manner as to involve risk of collision, other than where one steam vessel is overtaking another. The steam vessel which has the other on her own port side shall hold course and speed, and the other shall keep clear by crossing astern of the steam vessel that is holding course and speed, or, if necessary to do so, shall slacken her speed, stop, or reverse.

Lights for Certain Classes of Vessels[4]

SEC. **80.14** **Lights; time for.** The following rules in this part concerning lights shall be complied with in all weathers from sunset to sunrise.

SEC. **80.15** **Ferryboats.** (a) Ferryboats propelled by machinery and navigating the harbors, rivers, and other inland waters of the United States, except the Great Lakes and their connecting and tributary waters as far east as Montreal, the Red River of the North, the Mississippi River and its tributaries above Huey P. Long Bridge, and that part of the Atchafalaya River above its junction with the Plaquemine-Morgan City alternate waterway, shall carry the range lights and the colored side lights required by law to be carried on steam vessels navigating those waters, except that double-end ferryboats shall carry a central range of clear, bright, white lights, showing all around the horizon, placed at equal altitudes forward and aft, also on the starboard side a green light, and on the port side a red light, of such a character as to be visible on a dark night with a clear atmosphere at a distance of at least 2 miles, and so constructed as to show a uniform and un-

---

[4] See act of Congress approved April 25, 1940 (54 Stat. 164; 70 Stat. 228; 46 U. S. C. 526b), prescribing lights that shall be carried by certain classes of vessels of not more than 65 feet in length, amendatory of these rules. (See p. 445.)

broken light over an arc of the horizon of 10 points of the compass, and so fixed as to throw the light from right ahead to 2 points abaft the beam on their respective sides.

(b) The green and red lights shall be fitted with inboard screens projecting at least 3 feet forward from the lights, so as to prevent them from being seen across the bow.

(c) Officers in Charge, Marine Inspection,[5] in districts having ferryboats shall, whenever the safety of navigation may require, designate for each line of such boats a certain light, white or colored, which will show all around the horizon, to designate and distinguish such lines from each other, which light shall be carried on a flagstaff amidships, 15 feet above the white range lights.

SEC. 80.16 **Lights for barges, canal boats, scows and other nondescript vessels on certain inland waters on the Atlantic and Pacific Coasts.** (a) On the harbors, rivers, and other inland waters of the United States except the Great Lakes and their connecting and tributary waters as far east as Montreal, the Red River of the North, the Mississippi River and its tributaries above the Huey P. Long Bridge, and that part of the Atchafalaya River above its junction with the Plaquemine-Morgan City alternate waterway, and the waters described in §§ 80.16a and 80.17, barges, canal boats, scows, and other vessels of nondescript type not otherwise provided for, when being towed by steam vessels, shall carry lights as set forth in this section.

(b) Barges and canal boats towing astern of steam vessels, when towing singly, or what is known as tandem towing, shall each carry a green light on the starboard side and a red light on the port side, and a white light on the stern, except that the last vessel of such tow shall carry two lights on her stern, athwartship, horizontal to each other, not less than 5 feet apart, and not less than 4 feet above the deck house, and so placed as to show all around the horizon. A tow of one such vessel shall be lighted as the last vessel of a tow.

(c) When two or more boats are abreast, the colored lights shall be carried at the outer sides of the bows of the outside boats. East of the outside boats in last tier of a hawser tow shall carry a white light on her stern.

(d) The white light required to be carried on stern of a barge or canal boat carrying red and green side lights except the last vessel in a tow shall be carried in a lantern so constructed that it shall show an unbroken light over an arc of the horizon of 12 points of the compass, namely, for 6 points from right aft on each side of the vessel, and shall be of such a character as to be visible on a dark night with a clear atmosphere at a distance of at least 2 miles.

(e) Barges, canal boats or scows towing alongside a steam vessel shall, if the deck, deck houses, or cargo of the barge, canal boat or scow be so high above water as to obscure the side lights of the towing steamer when being towed on the starboard side of the steamer, carry a green light upon the starboard side; and when towed on the port side of the steamer, a red light on the port side of the barge, canal boat, or scow; and if there is more than one barge, canal boat or scow abreast, the colored lights shall be displayed from the outer side of the outside barges, canal boats or scows.

(f) Barges, canal boats or scows shall, when being propelled by pushing ahead of a steam vessel, display a red light on the port bow and a green light on the starboard bow of the head barge, canal boat or scow, carried at a height sufficiently above the superstructure of the barge, canal boat or scow as to permit

---

[5] For definition of an Officer in Charge, Marine Inspection, see 46 C. F. R. 70.10-33.

said side lights to be visible; and if there is more than one barge, canal boat or scow abreast, the colored lights shall be displayed from the outer side of the outside barges, canal boats or scows.

(g) The colored side lights referred to in this section shall be fitted with inboard screens so as to prevent them from being seen across the bow, and of such a character as to be visible on a dark night, with a clear atmosphere, at a distance of at least 2 miles, and so constructed as to show a uniform and unbroken light over an arc of the horizon of 10 points of the compass, and so fixed as to throw the light from right ahead to 2 points abaft the beam on either side. The minimum size of glass globes shall not be less than 6 inches in diameter and 5 inches high in the clear.

(h) Scows not otherwise provided for in this section on waters described in paragraph (a) of this section shall carry a white light at each end of each scow, except that when such scows are massed in tiers, two or more abreast, each of the outside scows shall carry a white light on its outer bow, and the outside scows in the last tier shall each carry, in addition, a white light on the outer part of the stern. The white light shall be carried not less than 8 feet above the surface of the water, and shall be so placed as to show an unbroken light all around the horizon, and shall be of such a character as to be visible on a dark night with a clear atmosphere at a distance of at least 5 miles.

(i) Other vessels of nondescript type not otherwise provided for in this section shall exhibit the same lights that are required to be exhibited by scows by this section.

NOTE: The regulations in §§ 80.16 to 80.17, inclusive, are not applicable to rafts. The requirements regarding lights for rafts are in § 80.32.

SEC. **80.16a** **Lights for barges, canal boats, scows and other nondescript vessels on certain inland waters on the Gulf Coast and the Gulf Intracoastal Waterway.** (a) On the Gulf Intracoastal Waterway and on other inland waters connected therewith or with the Gulf of Mexico from the Rio Grande, Texas, to Cape Sable (East Cape), Florida, barges, canal boats, scows, and other vessels of nondescript type not otherwise provided for, when being towed by steam vessels shall carry lights as set forth in this section.

(b) When one or more barges, canal boats, scows, or other vessels of nondescript type not otherwise provided for, are being towed by pushing ahead of a steam vessel, such tow shall be lighted by an amber light at the extreme forward end of the tow, so placed as to be as nearly as practicable on the centerline of the tow, a green light on the starboard side of the tow, so placed as to mark the maximum projection of the tow to starboard, and a red light on the port side of the tow, so placed as to mark the maximum projection of the tow to port.

(c) When one or more barges, canal boats, scows, or other vessels of nondescript type not otherwise provided for, are being towed alongside a steam vessel, there shall be displayed a white light at each outboard corner of the tow. If the deck, deck house, or cargo of such barge, etc., obscures the sidelight of the towing vessel, such barge, etc., shall also carry a green light upon the starboard side when being towed on the starboard side of a steam vessel or shall carry a red light on the port side of the barge, etc., when being towed on the port side of the steam vessel. If there is more than one such barge, etc., being towed abreast, the appropriate colored sidelight shall be displayed from the outer side of the outside barge.

(d) When one barge, canal boat, scow or other vessel of nondescript type not otherwise provided for, is being towed singly behind a steam vessel, such vessel shall carry four white lights, one on each corner or outermost projection of the bow and one on each corner or outermost projection of the stern.

(e) When two or more barges, canal boats, scows, or other vessels of nondescript type not otherwise provided for, are being towed behind a steam vessel in tandem, with an intermediate hawser, such vessels shall carry white lights as follows:

(1) The first vessel in the tow shall carry three white lights, one on each corner or outermost projection of the bow and a white light at the stern amidships.

(2) Each intermediate vessel shall carry two white lights, one at each end amidships.

(3) The last vessel in the tow shall carry three white lights, one on each corner or outermost projection of the stern and a white light at the bow amidships.

(f) When two or more barges, canal boats, scows, or other vessels of nondescript type not otherwise provided for, are being towed behind a steam vessel in tandem, close-up, such vessels shall carry white lights as follows:

(1) The first vessel in the tow shall carry three white lights, one on each corner or outermost projection of the bow and a white light at the stern amidships.

(2) Each intermediate vessel shall carry a white light at the stern amidships.

(3) The last vessel in the tow shall carry two white lights, one on each corner or outermost projection of the stern.

(g) When two or more barges, canal boats, scows, or other vessels of nondescript type not otherwise provided for, are being towed behind a steam vessel two or more abreast, in one or more tiers, each of the outside vessels in each tier shall carry a white light on the outboard corner of the bow, and each of the outside vessels in the last tier shall carry, in addition, a white light on the outboard corner of the stern.

(h) When one or more barges, canal boats, scows, or other vessels of nondescript type not otherwise provided for, are moored to the bank or dock in or near a fairway, such tow shall carry two white lights not less than four feet above the surface of the water, as follows:

(1) On a single moored barge, canal boat, scow, or other vessel of nondescript type not otherwise provided for, a light at each outboard or channelward corner.

(2) On barges, canal boats, scows, or other vessels of nondescript type not otherwise provided for, when moored in a group formation, a light on the upstream outboard or channelward corner of the outer upstream and a light on the downstream outboard or channelward corner of the outer downstream boat; and in addition, any boat projecting toward or into the channel from such group formation shall have two white lights similarly placed on its outboard or channelward corners.

(i) The colored side lights shall be so constructed as to show a uniform and unbroken light over an arc of the horizon of 10 points of the compass, so fixed as to show the light from right ahead to 2 points abaft the beam on their respective sides, and of such a character as to be visible at a distance of at least 2 miles, and shall be fitted with inboard screens so as to prevent either light from being seen more than half a point across the centerline of the tow.

(j) The amber light shall be so constructed as to show a uniform and unbroken light over an arc of the horizon of 20 points of the compass, so fixed as to show the light 10 points on each side of the tow, namely, from right ahead to two points abaft the beam on either side, and of such a character as to be visible at a distance of at least 2 miles.

(k) The white lights shall be so constructed and so fixed as to show a clear, uniform, and unbroken light all around the horizon, and of such a character as to be visible at a distance of at least 2 miles.

(l) All the lights shall be carried at approximately the same height above the surface of the water and, except as provided in paragraph (h) of this section, shall be so placed with respect thereto as to be clear of and above all obstructions which might tend to interfere with the prescribed arc or distance of visibility.

Sec. **80.16b** **Lights for barges, canal boats, scows, and other nondescript vessels temporarily operating on waters requiring different lights.** Nothing in §§ 80.16, 80.16a, or 80.17 shall be construed as compelling barges, canal boats, scows, or other vessels of nondescript type not otherwise provided for, being towed by steam vessels, when passing through any waters coming within the scope of any regulations where lights for such boats are different from those of the waters whereon such boats are usually employed, to change their lights from those required on the waters on which their trip begins or terminates; but should such boats engage in local employment on waters requiring different lights from those where they are customarily employed, they shall comply with the local rules where employed.

Sec. **80.17** **Lights for barges and canal boats in tow of steam vessels on the Hudson River and adjacent waters and Lake Champlain.** All nondescript vessels known as scows, car floats, lighters, and vessels of similar type, navigating the waters referred to in the following rules, shall carry the lights required to be carried by barges and canal boats in tow of steam vessels, as prescribed in such rules.

Barges and canal boats, when being towed by steam vessels on the waters of the Hudson River and its tributaries from Troy to the boundary lines of New York Harbor off Sandy Hook, as defined pursuant to section 2 of the act of Congress of February 19, 1895 (28 Stat. 672; 33 U. S. C. 151), the East River and Long Island Sound (and the waters entering thereon, and to the Atlantic Ocean), to and including Narragansett Bay, R. I., and tributaries, and Lake Champlain, shall carry lights as follows:

(a) Barges and canal boats being towed astern of steam vessels when towing singly shall carry a white light on the bow and a white light on the stern.

Singly

(b) When towing in tandem, "close up," each boat shall carry a white light on its stern and the first or hawser boat shall, in addition, carry a white light on its bow.

Tandem—Close Up

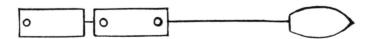

(c) When towing in tandem with intermediate hawser between the various boats in the tow, each boat shall carry a white light on the bow and a white light on the stern, except that the last vessel in the tow shall carry two white lights on her stern, athwartship, horizontal to each other, not less than 5 feet apart and not less than 4 feet above the deck house, and so placed as to show all around the horizon: Provided, That seagoing barges shall not be required to make any change in their seagoing lights (red and green) on waters coming within the scope of the rules of this section, except that the last vessel of the tow shall carry two white lights on her stern, athwartship, horizontal to each other, not less than 5 feet apart, and not less than 4 feet above the deck house, and so placed as to show all around the horizon.

Tandem—with Intermediate Hawser

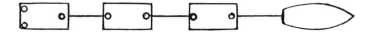

(d) Barges and canal boats when towed at a hawser, two or more abreast, when in one tier, shall each carry a white light on the stern and a white light on the bow of each of the outside boats.

Two or More Abreast in One Tier

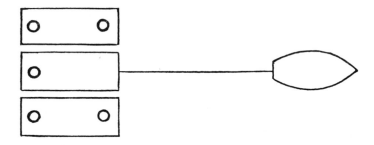

(e) When in more than one tier, each boat shall carry a white light on its stern and the outside boats in the hawser or head tier shall each carry, in addition, a white light on the bow.

Two or More Abreast and in More Than One Tier

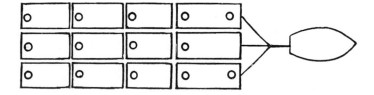

(f) The white bow lights for barges and canal boats referred to in the preceding rules shall be carried at least 10 feet and not more than 30 feet abaft the stem or extreme forward end of the vessel. On barges and canal boats required to carry a white bow light, the white light on bow and the white light on stern shall each be so placed above the hull or deck house as to show an unbroken light all around the horizon, and of such a character as to be visible on a dark night with a clear atmosphere at a distance of at least 2 miles.

(g) When nondescript vessels known as scows, car floats, lighters, barges or canal boats, and vessels of similar type, are towed alongside a steam vessel, there shall be displayed a white light at the outboard corners of the tow.

Towed Alongside—Various Positions

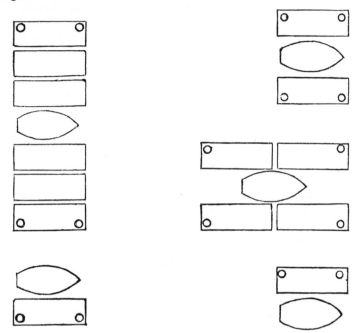

(h) When under way between the hours of sunset and sunrise there shall be displayed a red light on the port bow and a green light on the starboard bow of the head barge or barges, properly screened and so arranged that they may be visible through an arc of the horizon of 10 points of the compass; that is, from right ahead to 2 points abaft the beam on either side and visible on a dark night with a clear atmosphere at a distance of at least 2 miles, and be carried at a height sufficiently above the superstructure of the barge or barges pushed ahead as to permit said side lights to be visible.

Propulsion of Barge or Barges by Pushing

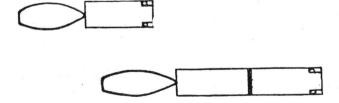

(i) Dump scows utilized for transportation and disposal of garbage, street sweepings, ashes, excavated material, dredging, etc., when navigating on the Hudson

River or East River or the waters tributary thereto between loading points on these waters and dumping grounds established by competent authority outside the line dividing the high seas from the inland waters of New York Harbor, shall, when towing in tandem, carry, instead of the white lights previously required, red and green side lights on the respective and appropriate sides of the scow in addition to the white light required to be shown by an overtaken vessel.

The red and green lights herein prescribed shall be carried at an elevation of not less than 8 feet above the highest deck house, upon substantial uprights, the lights properly screened and so arranged as to show through an arc of the horizon of 10 points of the compass, that is, from right ahead to 2 points abaft the beam on either side and visible on a dark night with a clear atmosphere a distance of at least 2 miles.

Provided, That nothing in the rules of this section shall be construed as compelling barges or canal boats in tow of steam vessels, passing through any waters coming within the scope of said rules where lights for barges or canal boats are different from those of the waters whereon such vessels are usually employed, to change their lights from those required on the waters from which their trip begins or terminates; but should such vessels engage in local employment on waters requiring different lights from those where they are customarily employed, they shall comply with the local rules where employed.

Lights and Day Signals for Vessels, Dredges of All Types, and Vessels Working on Wrecks and Obstructions, Etc.

Sec. 80.18   Signals to be displayed by a towing vessel when towing a submerged or partly submerged object upon a hawser when no signals can be displayed upon the object which is towed. (a) The vessel having the submerged object in tow shall display by day, where they can best be seen, two shapes, one above the other, not less than six feet apart, the lower shape to be carried not less than 10 feet above the deck house. The shapes shall be in the form of a double frustum of a cone, base to base, not less than two feet in diameter at the center nor less than eight inches at the ends of the cones, and to be not less than four feet lengthwise from end to end, the upper shape to be painted in alternate horizontal stripes of black and white, eight inches in width, and the lower shape to be painted a solid bright red.

(b) By night the towing vessel shall display the regular side lights but in lieu of the regular white towing lights shall display four lights in a vertical position not less than three feet nor more than six feet apart, the upper and lower of such lights to be white, and the two middle lights to be red, all of such lights to be of the same character as the regular towing lights.

Note: The regulations in §§ 80.18 to 80.31a, inclusive, are applicable on the harbors, rivers, and inland waters along the Atlantic and Pacific coasts and the coast of the Gulf of Mexico. Similar Department of the Army regulations are applicable on the Great Lakes and their connecting tributary waters as far as east as Montreal (Great Lakes) and Western Rivers and the Red River of the North and are contained in §§ 201.1 to 201.16, inclusive, of Title 33, Code of Federal Regulations.

Sec. 80.19   Steam vessels, derrick boats, lighters, or other types of vessels made fast alongside a wreck, or moored over a wreck which is on the bottom or partly submerged, or which may be drifting. (a) Steam vessels, derrick boats, lighters, or other types of vessels made fast alongside a wreck, or moored over a wreck which is on the bottom or partly submerged, or which may be drifting, shall display by day two shapes of the same character and dimensions and displayed in the same manner as required by § 80.18 (a), except that both shapes shall be painted a solid bright red, but where more than one vessel is working under the above conditions, the shapes need be displayed only from one vessel on each side of the wreck from which they can best be seen from all directions.

(b) By night this situation shall be indicated by the display of a white light from the bow and stern of each outside vessel or lighter not less than six feet above the deck, and in addition thereto there shall be displayed in a position where they can best be seen from all directions two red lights carried in a vertical line not less than three feet nor more than six feet apart, and not less than 15 feet above the deck.

SEC. 80.20 **Dredges held in stationary position by moorings or spuds.** (a) Dredges which are held in stationary position by moorings or spuds shall display by day two red balls not less than two feet in diameter and carried in a vertical line not less than three feet nor more than six feet apart, and at least 15 feet above the deck house and in such a position where they can best be seen from all directions.

(b) By night they shall display a white light at each corner, not less than six feet above the deck, and in addition thereto there shall be displayed in a position where they can best be seen from all directions two red lights carried in a vertical line not less then three feet nor more than six feet apart, and not less than 15 feet above the deck. When scows are moored alongside a dredge in the foregoing situation they shall display a white light on each outboard corner, not less than six feet above the deck.

SEC. 80.21 **Self-propelling suction dredges under way and engaged in dredging operations.** (a) Self-propelling suction dredges under way and engaged in dredging operations shall display by day two black balls not less than two feet in diameter and carried in a vertical line not less than 15 feet above the deck house, and where they can best be seen from all directions. The term "dredging operations" shall include maneuvering into or out of position at the dredging site but shall not include proceeding to or from the site.

(b) By night they shall carry, in addition to the regular running lights, two red lights of the same character as the white masthead light, and in the same vertical line beneath that light, the red lights to be not less than three feet nor more than six feet apart and the upper red light to be not less than four feet nor more than six feet below the masthead light, and on or near the stern two red lights in a vertical line not less than four feet nor more than six feet apart, to show through four points of the compass; that is, from right astern to two points on each quarter.

SEC. 80.22 **Vessels moored or anchored and engaged in laying cables or pipe, submarine construction, excavation, mat sinking, bank grading, dike construction, revetment, or other bank protection operations.** (a) Vessels which are moored or anchored and engaged in laying cables or pipe, submarine construction, excavation, mat sinking, bank grading, dike construction, revetment, or other bank protection operations, shall display by day, not less than 15 feet above the deck, where they can best be seen from all directions, two balls not less than two feet in diameter, in a vertical line not less than three feet nor more than six feet apart, the upper ball to be painted in alternate black and white vertical stripes six inches wide, and the lower ball to be painted a solid bright red.

(b) By night they shall display three red lights, carried in a vertical line not less than three feet nor more than six feet apart, in a position where they can best be seen from all directions, with the lowermost light not less than 15 feet above the deck.

(c) Where a stringout of moored vessels or barges is engaged in the operations, three red lights carried as prescribed in paragraph (b) of this section shall be displayed at the channelward end of the stringout. Where the stringout crosses the navigable channel and is to be opened for the passage of vessels, the three red lights shall be displayed at each side of the opening instead of at the outer end of the stringout. There shall also be displayed upon such stringout one horizontal how of amber lights not less than six feet about the deck, or above the deck house where the craft carries a deck house, in a position where they can best be seen from all directions, spaced not more than 50 feet apart so as to mark distinctly the entire length and course of the stringout.

SEC. 80.23 **Lights to be displayed on pipe lines.** Pipe lines attached to dredges, and either floating or supported on trestles, shall display by night one row of amber lights not less than eight feet nor more than 12 feet above the water, about equally spaced and in such number so as to mark distinctly the entire length and course of the line, the intervals between lights where the line crosses navigable channels to be not more than 30 feet. There shall also be displayed on the shore or discharge end of the line two red lights, three feet apart, in a vertical line with the lower light at least eight feet above the water, and if the line is to be opened at night for the passage of vessels, a similar arrangement of lights shall be displayed on each side of the opening.

SEC. 80.24 **Lights generally.** (a) All the lights required by §§ 80.18 to 80.23, inclusive, except as provided in §§ 80.18 (b) and 80.21 (b), shall be of such character as to be visible on a dark night with a clear atmosphere for a distance of at least two miles.

(b) The lights required by § 80.18 (b) to be of the same character as the regular towing lights and the lights required by § 80.21 (b) to be of the same character as the masthead light shall be of such character as to be visible on a dark night with a clear atmosphere for a distance of at least five miles.

(c) All floodlights or headlights which may interfere with the proper navigation of an approaching vessel shall be so shielded that the lights will not blind the pilot of such vessel.

SEC. 80.25 **Vessels moored or at anchor.** Vessels of more than 65 feet in length when moored or anchored in a fairway or channel shall display between sunrise and sunset on the forward part of the vessel where it can best be seen from other vessels one black ball not less than two feet in diameter.

Passing Floating Plant Working in Navigable Channels

SEC. 80.26 **Passing signals.** (a) Vessels intending to pass dredges or other types of floating plant working in navigable channels, when within a reasonable distance therefrom and not in any case over a mile, shall indicate such intention by one long blast of the whistle, and shall be directed to the proper side for passage by the sounding, by the dredge or other floating plant, of the signal prescribed in the local pilot rules for vessels under way and approaching each other from opposite directions, which shall be answered in the usual manner by the approaching vessel. If the channel is not clear, the floating plant shall sound the alarm or danger signal and the approaching vessel shall slow down or stop and await further signal from the plant.

(b) When the pipe line from a dredge crosses the channel in such a way that an approaching vessel cannot pass safely around the pipe line or dredge, there shall be sounded immediately from the dredge the alarm or danger signal and the approaching vessel shall slow down or stop and wait further signal from the dredge. The pipe line shall then be opened and the channel cleared as soon as practicable; when the channel is clear for passage the dredge shall so indicate by sounding the usual passing signal as prescribed in paragraph (a) of this section. The approaching vessel shall answer with a corresponding signal and pass promptly.

(c) When any pipe line or swinging dredge shall have given an approaching vessel or tow the signal that the channel is clear, the dredge shall straighten out within the cut for the passage of the vessel or tow.

NOTE: The term "floating plant" as used in §§ 80.26 to 80.31a, inclusive, includes dredges, derrick boats, snag boats, drill boats, pile drivers, maneuver boats, hydraulic graders, survey boats, working barges, and mat sinking plant.

SEC. 80.27 **Speed of vessels passing floating plant working in channels.** Vessels, with or without tows, passing floating plant working in channels, shall reduce their speed sufficiently to insure the safety of both the plant and themselves, and when passing within 200 feet of the plant their speed shall not exceed five miles per hour. While passing over lines of the plant, propelling machinery shall be stopped.

SEC. 80.28 **Light-draft vessels passing floating plant.** Vessels whose draft permits shall keep outside of the buoys marking the ends of mooring lines of floating plant working in channels.

SEC. 80.29 **Aids to navigation marking floating-plant moorings.** Breast, stern, and bow anchors of floating plant working in navigable channels shall be marked by barrel or other suitable buoys. By night approaching vessels shall be shown the location of adjacent buoys by throwing a suitable beam of light from the plant on the buoys until the approaching vessel has passed, or the buoys may be lighted by red lights, visible in all directions, of the same character as specified in § 80.24 (a): *Provided,* That the foregoing provisions of this section shall not apply to the following waters of New York Harbor and adjacent waters: the East River, the North River (Battery to Spuyten Duyvil), the Harlem River and the New York and New Jersey Channels (from the Upper Bay through Kill Van Kull, Newark Bay, Arthur Kill, and Raritan Bay to the Lower Bay).

SEC. 80.30 **Obstruction of channel by floating plant.** Channels shall not be obstructed unnecessarily by any dredge or other floating plant. While vessels are passing such plant, all line running therefrom across the channel on the passing side, which may interfere with or obstruct navigation, shall be slacked to the bottom of the channel.

SEC. 80.31 **Clearing of channels.** When special or temporary regulations have not been prescribed and action under the regulations contained in §§ 80.26 to 80.30, inclusive, will not afford clear passage, floating plant in narrow channels shall, upon notice move out of the way of vessels a sufficient distance to allow them a clear passage. Vessels desiring passage shall, however, give the master of the floating plant ample notice in advance of the time they expect to pass.

NOTE: If it is necessary to prohibit or limit the anchorage or movement of vessels within certain areas in order to facilitate the work of improvement, application should be made through official channels for establishment by the Secretary of the Army of special or temporary regulations for this purpose.

SEC. 80.31a **Protection of marks placed for the guidance of floating plant.** Vessels shall not run over anchor buoys, or buoys, stakes, or other marks placed for the guidance of floating plant working in channels; and shall not anchor on the ranges of buoys, stakes, or other marks placed for the guidance of such plant.

Lights for Rafts and other craft not provided for

Sec. 80.32 **Lights for rafts and other craft.** (a) Any vessel propelled by hand power, horse power, or by the current of the river, except rafts and rowboats, shall carry one white light forward not less than 8 feet above the surface of the water.

(b) Any raft while being propelled by hand power, by horse power, or by the current of the river, while being towed, or while anchored or moored in or near a channel or fairway, shall carry white lights as follows:

(1) A raft of one crib in width shall carry one white light at each end of the raft.

(2) A raft of more than one crib in width shall carry 4 white lights, one on each outside corner.

(3) An unstable log raft of one bag or boom in width shall carry at least 2 but not more than 4 white lights in a fore and aft line, one of which shall be at each end. The lights may be closely grouped clusters of not more than 3 white lights rather than single lights.

(4) An unstable log raft of more than one bag or boom in width shall carry 4 white lights, one on each outside corner. The lights may be closely grouped clusters of not more than 3 white lights rather than single lights.

(c) The white lights required by this section shall be carried from sunset to sunrise, in a lantern so fixed and constructed as to show a clear, uniform, and unbroken light, visible all around the horizon, and of such intensity as to be visible on a dark night with a clear atmosphere at a distance of at least one mile. The lights for rafts shall be suspended from poles of such height that the lights shall not be less than 8 feet above the surface of the water, except that the lights prescribed for unstable log rafts shall not be less than 4 feet above the water.

Special Day or Night Signals

Sec. 80.32a **Day marks for fishing vessels with gear out.** All vessels or boats fishing with nets or lines or trawls, when under way, shall in daytime indicate their occupation to an approaching vessel by displaying a basket where it can best be seen. If vessels or boats at anchor have their gear out, they shall, on the approach of other vessels, show the same signal in the direction from the anchor back towards the nets or gear.

Sec. 80.33 **Special signals for vessels employed in hydrographic surveying.** By day a surveying vessel of the Coast and Geodetic Survey, under way and employed in hydrographic surveying, may carry in a vertical line, one over the other not less than 6 feet apart where they can best be seen, three shapes not less than 2 feet in diameter of which the highest and lowest shall be globular in shape and green in color and the middle one diamond in shape and white.

(a) Vessels of the Coast and Geodetic Survey shall carry the above-prescribed marks while actually engaged in hydrographic surveying and under way, including drag work. Launches and other boats shall carry the prescribed marks when necessary.

(b) It must be distinctly understood that these special signals serve only to indicate the nature of the work upon which the vessel is engaged and in no way give the surveying vessel the right-of-way over other vessels or obviate the necessity for a strict observance of the rules for preventing collisions of vessels.

(c) By night a surveying vessel of the Coast and Geodetic Survey, under way and employed in hydrographic surveying, shall carry the regular lights prescribed by the rules of the road.

(d) A vessel of the Coast and Geodetic Survey, when at anchor in a fairway on surveying operation, shall display from the mast during the daytime two black balls in a vertical line and 6 feet apart. At night two red lights shall be displayed in the same manner. In the case of a small vessel the distance between the balls and between the lights may be reduced to 3 feet if necessary.

(e) Such vessels, when at anchor in a fairway on surveying operations, shall have at hand and show, if necessary, in order to attract attention, a flare-up light in addition to the lights which are, by this section, required to be carried.

Sec. **80.33a** **Warning signals for Coast Guard vessels while handling or servicings aids to navigation.** (a) Coast Guard vessels while engaged in handling or servicing an aid to navigation during the daytime may display from the yard two orange and white vertically striped balls in a vertical line not less than three feet nor more than six feet apart, and during the nighttime may display, in a position where they may best be seen, two red lights in a vertical line not less than three feet nor more than six feet apart.

(b) Vessels, with or without tows, passing Coast Guard vessels displaying this signal, shall reduce their speed sufficiently to insure the safety of both vessels, and when passing within 200 feet of the Coast Guard vessel displaying this signal, their speed shall not exceed 5 miles per hour.

Unauthorized Use of Lights; Unnecessary Whistling

Sec. **80.34** **Rule relating to the use of searchlights or other blinding lights.** Flashing the rays of a searchlight or other blinding light onto the bridge or into the pilothouse of any vessel under way is prohibited. Any person who shall flash or cause to be flashed the rays of a blinding light in violation of the above may be proceeded against in accordance with the provisions of R.S. 4450, as amended, looking to the revocation or suspension of his license or certificate.

Sec. **80.35** **Rule prohibiting unnecessary sounding of the whistle.** Unnecessary sounding the whistle is prohibited within any harbor limits of the United States. Whenever any licensed officer in charge of any vessel shall authorize or permit such unnecessary whistling, such officer may be proceeded against in accordance with the provisions of R.S. 4450, as amended, looking to a revocation or suspension of his license.

Sec. **80.36** **Rule prohibiting the carrying of unauthorized lights on vessels.** Any master, or pilot of any vessel who shall authorize or permit the carrying of any light, electric or otherwise, not required by law, that in any way will interfere with distinguishing the signal lights, may be proceeded against in accordance with the provisions of R.S. 4450, as amended, looking to a suspension or revocation of his lisense.

Part 84. Towing Barges

Sec. **84.1** **Tows of seagoing barges within inland waters.** Tows of seagoing barges navigating the inland waters of the United States are limited in length to five vessels, including the towing vessel or vessels.[6]

SEC. **84.2** **Hawser length; general.** With the exceptions noted below, hawsers are limited in length to 75 fathoms, measured from the stern of one vessel to the bow of the following vessel; and should in all cases be as much shorter as the weather or sea will permit.

SEC. **84.3** **Hawser length; exceptions.** In all cases where, in the opinion of the master of the towing vessel, it is dangerous or inadvisable, whether on account of the state of the weather, or sea, or otherwise, to shorten hawsers, hawsers need not be shortened to the prescribed length, except that hawsers must in any event be shortened to the prescribed length upon reaching the applicable locality named below:

(a) Tows from sea or Chesapeake Bay bound for Hampton Roads or beyond, before passing Thimble Light.

(b) Tows bounds up the Chesapeake to the northward of Baltimore Light.

(c) Tows bound up into New York from sea, at West Bank.

(d) Tows bound up the Delaware, between Fourteen Foot Bank and Cross Ledge Lighthouses.

(e) Tows from sea to Narragansett Bay, before reaching Rose Island.

(f) Hawsers may also be lengthened in the same places, under the same circumstances when tows are bound out.

SEC. **84.4** **Bunching of tows.** In all cases where tows can be bunched, it should be done.

(a) Tows navigating in the North and East Rivers of New York must be bunched above a line drawn between Robbins Reef Lighthouse and Owls Head, Brooklyn, but the quarantine anchorage and the north entrance to Ambrose Channel shall be avoided in the process of bunching tows. In the discretion of the master of the towing vessel, when tows are entering Long Island Sound from the westward, hawsers may be lengthened out after passing Fort Schuyler, and when entering Long Island Sound from the eastward, hawsers need not be shortened to the prescribed length until reaching Fort Schuyler.

(b) Tows must be bunched above the mouth of the Schuylkill River, Pa.

SEC. **84.5** **Reporting violations.** Any violation of the regulations in this part shall be reported in writing as soon as practicable to the Coast Guard District Commander most convenient to the officer or other person who may witness the violation.

---

[6] §§ 84.1 to 84.5, inclusive, issued under the authority contained in sec. 14, 35 Stat. 428; 33 U. S. C. 152.

MOTORBOAT ACT OF APRIL 25, 1940;[1]
EXCERPTS FROM

AN ACT TO AMEND LAWS FOR PREVENTING COLLISIONS OF VESSELS, TO REGULATE THE EQUIPMENT OF CERTAIN MOTORBOATS ON THE NAVIGABLE WATERS OF THE UNITED STATES, AND FOR OTHER PURPOSES

Motorboat Defined; Inspection

Be it enacted by the Senate and House of Representatives of the United States of America in Congress assembled, That the word "motorboat" where used in this Act shall include every vessel propelled by machinery and not more than sixty-five feet in length except tugboats and towboats propelled by steam. The length shall be measured from end to end over the deck, excluding sheer: Provided, That the engine, boiler or other operating machinery shall be subject to inspection by the Coast Guard, and to their approval of the design thereof, on all said motorboats, which are more than forty feet in length, and which are propelled by machinery driven by steam.

Classes of Motorboats

SEC. 2. Motorboats subject to the provisions of this Act shall be divided into four classes as follows:

Class A. Less than sixteen feet in length.

Class 1. Sixteen feet or over and less than twenty-six feet in length.

Class 2. Twenty-six feet or over and less than forty feet in length.

Class 3. Forty feet or over and not more than sixty-five feet in length.

Lights[2]

SEC. 3. Every motorboat in all weathers from sunset to sunrise shall carry and exhibit the following lights when under way, and during such time no other lights which may be mistaken for those prescribed shall be exhibited:

(a) Every motorboat of classes A and 1 shall carry the following lights:

First. A bright white light aft to show all around the horizon.

Second. A combined lantern in the fore part of the vessel and lower than the white light aft, showing green to starboard and red to port, so fixed as to throw the light from right ahead to two points abaft the beam on their respective sides.

(b) Every motorboat of classes 2 and 3 shall carry the following lights:

First. A bright white light in the fore part of the vessel as near the stem as practicable, so constructed as to show an unbroken light over an arc of the horizon

---

[1] As amended by Public Law 552, 84th Congress, approved June 4, 1956.

[2] Administrative interpretations of November 22, 1940:

Running Lights. These lights are running lights for motorboats in inland waters, the western rivers, and the Great Lakes and are to be carried in lieu of the running lights prescribed by the Inland, Western Rivers, and Great Lakes Rules. Motorboats when on the high seas must exhibit the lights prescribed by the International Rules.

Running lights not in conflict with other lights. These lights are not in conflict with lights, other than running lights, prescribed by Inland, Western Rivers, or Great Lakes Rules. Motorboats must carry such other lights as may be prescribed by applicable Inland, Western Rivers, or Great Lakes Rules.

of twenty points of the compass, so fixed as to throw the light ten points on each side of the vessel; namely, from right ahead to two points abaft the beam on either side.

Second. A bright white light aft to show all around the horizon and higher than the white light forward.

Third. On the starboard side a green light so constructed as to show an un-broken light over an arc of the horizon of ten points of the compass, so fixed as to throw the light from right ahead to two points abaft the beam on the starboard side. On the port side a red light so consructed as to show an unbroken light over an arc of the horizon of ten points of the compass, so fixed as to throw the light from right ahead to two points abaft the beam on the port side. The said side lights shall be fitted with inboard screens of sufficient height so set as to prevent these lights from being seen across the bow.

(c) Motorboats of Classes A and 1 when propelled by sail alone shall carry the combined lantern, but not the white light aft, prescribed by this section. Motor-boats of Classes 2 and 3, when so propelled, shall carry the colored side lights, suitably screened, but not the white lights, pescribed by this section. Motorboats of all classes, when so propelled, shall carry, ready at hand, a lantern or flashlight showing a white light which shall be exhibited in sufficient time to avert collision.

(d) Every white light prescribed by this section shall be of such character as to be visible at a distance of at least two miles. Every colored light prescribed by this section shall be of such character as to be visible at a distance of at least one mile. The word "visible" in this Act, when applied to lights, shall mean visible on a dark night with clear atmosphere.

(e) When propelled by sail and machinery any motorboat shall carry the lights required by this section for a motorboat propelled by machinery only.

(f) Any motorboat may carry and exhibit the lights required by the Regula· tions for Preventing Collisions at Sea, 1948, Act of October 11, 1951 (65 Stat. 406-420), as amended, in lieu of the lights required by this section.

NOTE: On motorboats of classes A and 1 the aft white all around light on the 12 point white stern light may be located off the centerline.

Whistles

SEC. 4. Every motorboat of class 1, 2, or 3, shall be provided with an efficient whistle or other sound-producing mechanical appliance.

Bells

SEC. 5. Every motorboat of class 2, or 3 shall be provided with an efficient bell.

*   *   *   *   *   *   *

Exemptions for Outboard Racing Motorboats

SEC. 9. The provisions of sections 4, 5, and 8 of this Act shall not apply to motorboats propelled by outboard motors while competing in any race previously arranged and announced or, if such boats be designed and intended solely for racing, while engaged in such navigation as is incidental to the tuning up of the boats and engines for the race.

*   *   *   *   *   *   *

Pilot Rules Not Required

SEC. 12. Motorboats shall not be required to carry on board copies of the pilot rules.

Negligent Operation

SEC. 13. No person shall operate any motorboat or any vessel in a reckless or negligent manner so as to endanger the life, limb, or property of any person.

Penalty for Negligent Operation

SEC. 14. Any person who shall operate any motorboat or any vessel in a reckless or negligent manner so as to endanger the life, limb, or property of any person shall be deemed guilty of a misdemeanor and on conviction thereof by any court of competent jurisdiction shall be punished by a fine not exceeding $2,000, or by imprisonment for a term of not exceeding one year, or by both such fine and imprisonment, at the discretion of the court.

Authority to Arrest for Negligent Operation

SEC. 15. Any officer of the United States authorized to enforce the navigation laws of the United States, shall have power and authority to swear out process and to arrest and take into custody, with or without process, any person who may commit any act or offense prohibited by section 13, or who may violate any provision of said section: Provided, That no person shall be arrested without process for any offense not committed in the presence of some one of the aforesaid officials: Provided further, That whenever an arrest is made under the provisions of this act, the person so arrested shall be brought forthwith before a commissioner, judge, or court of the United States for examination of the offense alleged against him, and such commissioner, judge, or court shall proceed in respect thereto as authorized by law in cases of crimes against the United States.

Penalty for Other Violations of Act

SEC. 16. If any motorboat or vessel subject to any of the provisions of this Act is operated or navigated in violation of this Act or any regulation issued thereunder, the owner or operator, either one or both of them, shall, in addition to any other penalty prescribed by law than that contained in section 14 of this Act, be liable to a penalty of $100: Provided, That in the case of motorboats or vessels subject to the provisions of this Act carrying passengers for hire, a penalty of $200 shall be imposed on the owner or operator, either one or both of them, thereof for any violation of section 6, 7, or 8 of this Act or any regulations pertaining thereto. For any penalty incurred under this section the motorboat or vessel shall be held liable and may be proceeded against by way of libel in the district in which said motorboat or vessel may be found.

Regulations; Enforcement

SEC. 17. The Commandant[3] of the Coast Guard shall establish all necessary regulations[4] required to carry out in the most effective manner all of the provisions of this Act, and such regulations shall have the force of law. The Com-

---

[3] By Reorganization Plan No. 26 of 1950, effective July 31, 1950 (15 F. R. 4935) the functions formerly vested in the Commandant, U. S. Coast Guard, were transferred to the Secretary of the Treasury with certain specified exceptions. The Secretary, however, by an order dated July 31, 1950 (15 F. R. 6521), delegated to the Commandant the functions formerly performed by him under Reorganization Plan No. 3 of 1946.

[4] Subchapter C of Chapter I, Title 46 (Shipping) of the Code of Federal Regulations of the United States of America, as amended.

mandant of the Coast Guard or any officer of the Coast Guard authorized by the Commandant may, upon application therefore, remit or mitigate any fine, penalty, or forfeiture incurred under this Act or any regulation thereunder relating to motorboats or vessels, except the penalties provided for in section 14 hereunder. The Commandant of the Coast Guard shall establish such regulations as may be necessary to secure the enforcement of the provisions of this Act by any officer of the United States authorized to enforce the navigation laws of the United States.

Exemptions

SEC. 18. The proviso contained in the last paragraph of section 2 of the Act of May 11, 1918 (40 Stat. 549) shall apply also with like force and effect to motorboats as defined in this Act.

Motorboats as defined in this Act are hereby exempted from the provisions of Revised Statutes 4399, as amended (48 Stat. 125).

*   *   *   *   *   *   *

Certificate of Award of Number; Exemptions

SEC. 21. The provisions of section 210 of title II of the Anti-Smuggling Act approved August 5, 1935 (49 Stat. 526; U. S. C., 1934 edition, Supp. IV, title 46, sec. 288), requiring a certificate of award of a number to be kept at all times on board of the vessel to which the number has been awarded shall not apply to any vessel not exceeding seventeen feet in length measured from end to end over the deck, excluding sheer, or to any vessel whose design of fittings are such that the carrying of a certificate of award of the number on such vessel would render such certificate imperfect, illegible, or would otherwise tend to destroy its usefulness as a means of ready identification.

INDEX

TRIMMED SIZE: 6¾ × 10¼
TYPE PAGE: 30 × 49 picas
TYPE FACE: Linotype Baskerville
TYPE SIZE: 11 point on 14
CHAPTER TITLE: 14 point Baskerville
PAPER: 50 lb. White Printone
CLOTH: Columbia Tanotex 320/2415 Skiver